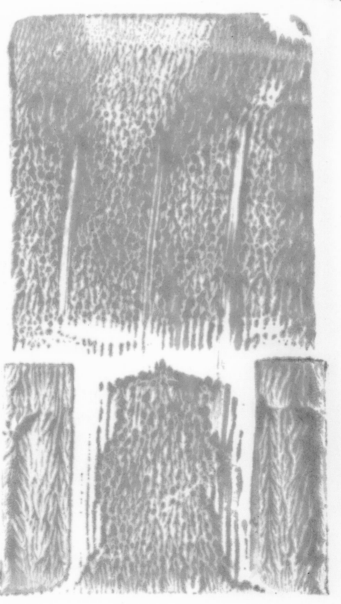

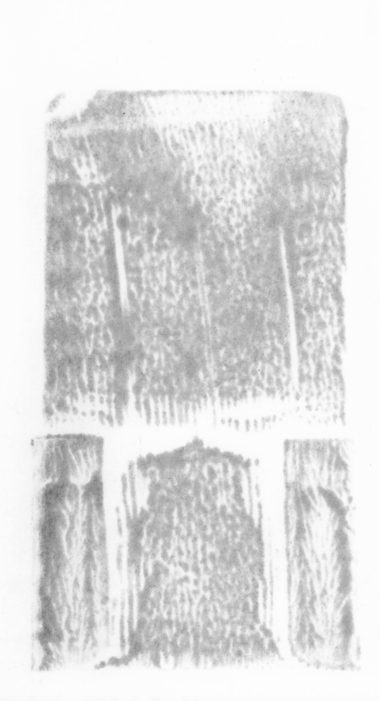

SERVOMECHANISM PRACTICE

McGRAW-HILL ELECTRICAL AND ELECTRONIC ENGINEERING SERIES

FREDERICK EMMONS TERMAN, *Consulting Editor*
W. W. HARMAN, HUBERT HEFFNER, AND
J. G. TRUXAL, *Associate Consulting Editors*

AHRENDT AND SAVANT · Servomechanism Practice
ANGELO · Electronic Circuits
ASELTINE · Transform Method in Linear System Analysis
ATWATER · Introduction to Microwave Theory
BAILEY AND GAULT · Alternating-current Machinery
BERANEK · Acoustics
BRENNER AND JAVID · Analysis of Electric Circuits
BROWN · Analysis of Linear Time-invariant Systems
BRUNS AND SAUNDERS · Analysis of Feedback Control Systems
CAGE · Theory and Application of Industrial Electronics
CAUER · Synthesis of Linear Communication Networks
CHEN · Linear Network Design and Synthesis
CHEN · The Analysis of Linear Systems
CHIRLIAN AND ZEMANIAN · Electronics
CLEMENT AND JOHNSON · Electrical Engineering Science
COTE AND OAKES · Linear Vacuum-tube and Transistor Circuits
CUCCIA · Harmonics, Sidebands, and Transients in Communication Engineering
CUNNINGHAM · Introduction to Nonlinear Analysis
EASTMAN · Fundamentals of Vacuum Tubes
EVANS · Control-system Dynamics
FEINSTEIN · Foundations of Information Theory
FITZGERALD AND HIGGINBOTHAM · Basic Electrical Engineering
FITZGERALD AND KINGSLEY · Electric Machinery
FRANK · Electrical Measurement Analysis
FRIEDLAND, WING, AND ASH · Principles of Linear Networks
GEPPERT · Basic Electron Tubes
GHOSE · Microwave Circuit Theory and Analysis
GREINER · Semiconductor Devices and Applications
HAMMOND · Electrical Engineering
HANCOCK · An Introduction to the Principles of Communication Theory
HAPPELL AND HESSELBERTH · Engineering Electronics
HARMAN · Fundamentals of Electronic Motion
HARMAN · Principles of the Statistical Theory of Communication
HARMAN AND LYTLE · Electrical and Mechanical Networks
HARRINGTON · Introduction to Electromagnetic Engineering
HARRINGTON · Time-harmonic Electromagnetic Fields
HAYT · Engineering Electromagnetics
HILL · Electronics in Engineering
HUELSMAN · Circuits, Matrices, and Linear Vector Spaces
JAVID AND BRENNER · Analysis, Transmission and Filtering of Signals
JAVID AND BROWN · Field Analysis and Electromagnetics
JOHNSON · Transmission Lines and Networks
KOENIG AND BLACKWELL · Electromechanical System Theory
KRAUS · Antennas

Servomechanism Practice

W. R. AHRENDT

Consultant and Lecturer
University of Maryland

C. J. SAVANT, Jr., Ph.D.

Director of Engineering
American Electronics, Inc.
and Visiting Associate Professor
University of Southern California

SECOND EDITION

McGRAW-HILL BOOK COMPANY, INC.

New York   Toronto   London

1960

SERVOMECHANISM PRACTICE

THE MAPLE PRESS COMPANY, YORK, PA.

00687

PREFACE

This book developed from a need to supplement the theory in college courses on servomechanisms with material on circuitry, electrical and mechanical components, and practical problems encountered in servo design and manufacture.

The field of servomechanisms, however, resembles the plight of a man on a treadmill who must "run as fast as he can just to stay even." With thousands of engineers developing servomechanism systems and components, a practical book of this type must be brought up to date at periodic intervals. This is the major objective in the second edition. All the sections on components have been rewritten to include the advances made since the first edition. Many tables of characteristics of typical components are presented. Since the data in these tables are representative and may have been changed, it is not advisable to use the information without checking the manufacturer's latest specifications. Also, some of the data are dependent upon operating conditions not specified in the tables. The nomenclature and symbolism used are as currently given by the ASME and the AIEE.

Included also are new chapters on accelerometers, gyroscopes, and pneumatic servos. The chapter on amplifiers has been enlarged to include transistor amplifiers. The order of the book has been rearranged for ease of presentation of the material.

We wish to express sincere thanks to the following companies:

Airborne Accessories Corp., Hillside, N.J.
Airpax Products Co., Baltimore, Md.
American Bosch Arma Corp., Garden City, N.Y., and Hempstead, N.Y.
American Electronics, Inc., Los Angeles, Calif.
Arnold Engineering Co., Marengo, Ill.
Barber-Coleman Co., Rockford, Ill.
Bowmar Instrument Corp., Fort Wayne, Ind.
Cadillac Gage Co., Detroit, Mich.
Computer Instruments Corp., Hempstead, N.Y.
Daystrom Pacific, Los Angeles, Calif.

Diehl Manufacturing Co., Somerville, N.J.
Donner Scientific Co., Concord, Calif.
Eclipse Pioneer Division, Bendix Aviation Corp., Teterboro, N.J.
Electric Indicator Co., Springdale, Conn.
Fairchild Controls Corp., Hicksville, N.Y.
Fellows Gear Shaper Co., Springfield, Vt.
Ford Instrument Co., Long Island City, N.Y.
Gamewell Co., Newton Upper Falls, Mass.
General Electric Co., Schenectady, N.Y., and Erie, Pa.
G. M. Giannini & Co., Inc., Pasadena, Calif.
G-M Laboratories, Inc., Chicago, Ill.
Greenleaf Mfg. Co., St. Louis, Mo.
Helipot Division, Beckman Instruments, Inc., Fullerton, Calif.
Humphrey, Inc., San Diego, Calif.
International Rectifier Corp., El Segundo, Calif.
Kearfott Company, Inc., Clifton, N.J.
Litton Industries (Ahrendt Instrument Co.), College Park, Md.
W. L. Maxson Corp., Long Island City, N.Y.
Minneapolis-Honeywell Regulator Co., Boston, Mass., and Minne-
    apolis, Minn.
Moog Valve Co., Inc., East Aurora, N.Y.
Muirhead Instruments, Inc., New York, N.Y.
Northern Ordnance, Inc., Boston, Mass.
Radio Corp. of America, Harrison, N.J.
Reeves Instrument Corp., New York, N.Y.
Schaevitz Engineering, Camden, N.J.
Servo Corp. of America, New Hyde Park, N.Y.
Servomechanisms, Inc., Hawthorne, Calif.
Servo-Tek Products Co., Hawthorne, N.J.
Statham Instruments, Inc., Los Angeles, Calif.
Sterling Precision Corp., Instrument Division, Flushing, N.Y.
Summers Gyroscope Co., Santa Monica, Calif.
Sunshine Scientific Inst., Philadelphia, Pa.
Technology Instrument Corp., Acton, Mass.
Texas Instruments, Inc., Dallas, Tex., and Houston, Tex.
Vickers, Inc., Detroit, Mich.
Western Gear, Inc., Lynwood, Calif.
Westinghouse Electric Corp., Pittsburgh, Pa.
Wiancko Engineering Co., Pasadena, Calif.

These companies kindly supplied glossy prints and technical data for
many of their products, and American Electronics, Inc., generously provided the typing and reproduction facilities for this second edition.   It is

with gratitude that assistance from associates in industry and the Federal government is acknowledged.   Of major aid in providing background material were contracts sponsored by the Bureau of Ordnance and the U.S. Navy Department.

WILLIAM R. AHRENDT
CLEMENT J. SAVANT, JR.

CONTENTS

Servomechanism Conversion Factors. Natural Trigonometric Functions.
Moment of Inertia Nomograph. Moment of Inertia Conversion Nomo-
graph. S Plane and Location of Roots. Percent Overshoot vs. ζ
for a Second-order System. Decibel Chart. Octave Chart. Amplitude
Deviation for the Quadratic Functions. Phase-shift Deviation from a
Straight-line Approximation for a Second-order System. Damping
Ratio ζ vs. Phase Margin φm. Damping Ratio ζ vs. Maximum $M(Mp)$.

CHAPTER 1

OPERATION OF A SIMPLE SERVOMECHANISM

1-1. Introduction. A *servomechanism* is a device that positions an object with respect to an arbitrarily varied signal capable of supplying only negligible power. Its operation depends upon the difference between the actual position of the object and the desired position. The servomechanism acts to reduce this difference to zero and hence render the actual position of the output equal to the desired position. The significant feature of closed-loop systems is that the system positions the output in accordance with the input position independent of variation of the components within the feedback loop. For example, if the gain changes in the amplifier of the servomechanism, the speed of response will vary, but the output will still follow the input and the system will tend to reduce the error between them to zero.

Servomechanisms, or servos for short, are part of a family of systems known as feedback control systems. Such systems are all fundamentally similar in that feedback is involved, and hence they operate on the difference between the actual state of a system and an arbitrarily varied desired state. These systems have wide military and industrial use, such as in the control of pressure, flow, liquid level, position, speed, acceleration, and temperature, and are finding increasing applications in such industries as oil refining and food processing and in steel-mill operations and the production of chemicals.

1-2. Applications of Servomechanisms. Servomechanisms represent the branch of the subject of feedback control that is concerned with positioning an object. Although this greatly narrows the scope of their application, there are many servomechanisms in both military and civilian use. The military applications include the automatic position-ing of guns, radar antennas, and other such apparatus in gunfire control, the positioning of rudders and steering controls on ships, the control of the altitude and direction of an airplane by means of an automatic pilot, the repeating of positional information to various remote points, and the countless numbers of servomechanisms found in computing devices. Civilian applications of servomechanisms include remote positioning of valves, remote indication of information, the control of machine tools such as contour followers and diesinking machines, steering boosters, and similar uses.

While all automatic feedback control systems are based on a common body of theory, the application of this theory to servomechanism—its circuitry, mechanical design, operation, and experimental techniques—differs enough from other branches of the subject to make separate treatment desirable. It is the purpose of this book to present such a treatment, to enable those familiar only with the theory of the subject to learn how this theory is actually applied. It will also aid those who are unacquainted with the subject to acquire a knowledge of its fundamentals and, particularly, of its physical manifestations. Those who are interested in reviewing some of the theoretical aspects of the subject may refer to the Appendix, either as a background to this book or for the review of principles as various subjects are discussed or terms are introduced. Those who wish to pursue the theory yet further are referred to a number of books listed in the Bibliography* in which this topic is adequately treated.

Many applications of servomechanisms can be drawn with respect to the human body. For example, consider a person driving an automobile along the highway. The driver maintains his car on the road by observing the error with respect to the white line down the center of the road. In this case, the eye is the error detector; that is, it senses the difference in position with respect to the white line. This signal is operated on in the brain and amplified. The prime mover is actuated by means of this amplified signal, and the arms correct the error. Notice that three distinct operations take place. These can be described as (1) error detection, (2) amplification, and (3) prime-mover action. These same functions are found in all servomechanisms.

1-3. Components of a Position Servomechanism. The physical explanation of how an extremely simple servomechanism operates is presented first. A servomechanism is shown schematically in Fig. 1-1. Figure 1-2 shows an electrical diagram of this device, and Fig. 1-3 shows its block diagram. The letter symbols used for each of the signals are identified in Fig. 1-3. If interest centers on the principle involved in any servo or in the dynamic aspects of its operation, it is usual to draw the block diagram in which is eliminated the command, the reference-input elements, the feedback elements, and the primary feedback and to place the error-detector transfer-function block in position to receive the actuating signal. A simplification of the servo of Fig. 1-1 results in the block diagram of Fig. 1-4.

Suppose that it is the function of this servomechanism to reproduce the angular position of a shaft at some remote location. The position r of

* See Refs. 1, 10, 11, 17, 26, 34, 38, and 48.

the command shaft can be arbitrarily varied, and its value at any instant is given by the dial reading. The controlled shaft must reproduce accurately the position of the command shaft. To accomplish this, the position of the command shaft is converted to a voltage proportional

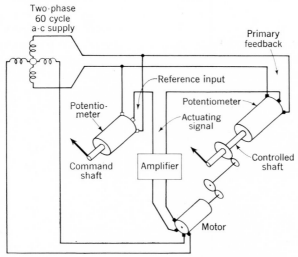

FIG. 1-1. Schematic diagram of a servomechanism.

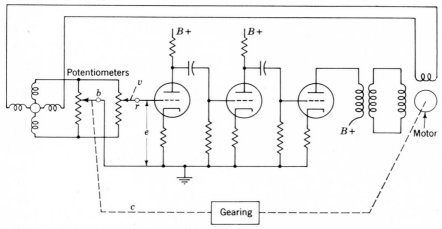

FIG. 1-2. Electrical diagram of the servomechanism of Fig. 1-1.

to its position by means of a potentiometer and is designated as the reference input to the servomechanism. Similarly, the position c of the controlled shaft is converted to a proportional voltage by means of another potentiometer fed from the same voltage source as the first potentiometer. The primary-feedback signal b in this servomechanism is this potentiometer output voltage. The difference $e(= r - b)$ between these two voltages is known as the *actuating signal* and is a measure of the lack of correspondence between the command shaft and the controlled shaft. The actuating signal is not an exact measure of the error, partly because of the inaccuracies in the error detector.

This difference voltage is fed into the amplifier. The resulting signal is amplified until it is of sufficient power to drive the control winding of a two-phase* motor whose other winding is connected to a constant voltage that has a phase angle of 90° with respect to the amplifier output. The shaft of the motor is geared down to the shaft of the controlled shaft and is connected in such a direction as to reduce the voltage input to the

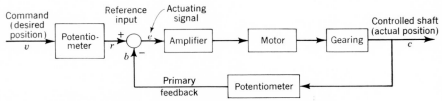

FIG. 1-3. Block diagram of the servomechanism of Fig. 1-1.

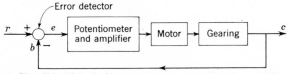

FIG. 1-4. Simplified block diagram for servomechanism of Fig. 1-1.

amplifier. Therefore, if any voltage exists at the input to the amplifier, the motor rotates until that voltage is zero.

As is typical of all servomechanisms, this example has three essential components. First, it has a means for detecting the error between the actual position of the controlled shaft and its desired value, as given by the command shaft. In this application the error detector is a pair of potentiometers. Second, there is a means of amplifying the error voltage signal to a value large enough to control a source of power. The electronic amplifier performs this function. The third requisite for a servomechanism is the source of power, a prime mover, which is used to bring about corrective action. In this case an a-c motor is used; and, in conjunction with the gearing, it serves to drive the controlled shaft.

Each of the potentiometers converts its shaft position to an alternating voltage that is a measure of the shaft position. The difference between these voltages is, therefore, a measure of the lack of correspondence

* Two-phase servomotors are discussed in Chap. 7.

between the controlled-shaft and the command-shaft positions.   Polarity
is determined by the equation $e = r - b$.

Figure 1-5 shows the voltage waveforms at the output of each potentiometer for various positions of the shaft.   Assume that each of the
potentiometers has 360° of windings and that 36 volts rms is applied
across each.   This means that each degree of shaft rotation of the potentiometers results in $\frac{1}{10}$ volt output.   A command-shaft position of 10°,
therefore, results in 1 volt output from this potentiometer.   Suppose
that the position of the command shaft is at 10° and the instantaneous
position of the controlled shaft is 9°.   The condition of voltages existing

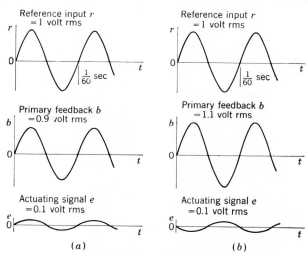

FIG. 1-5. Instantaneous potentiometer voltages.

on each of the brushes of the potentiometer and also their difference
voltage, which is fed to the amplifier, are illustrated in Fig. 1-5a.

On the other hand, suppose that the command remains at 10° but the
controlled shaft instantaneously has the position of 11°.   The voltages
existing under these conditions are shown in Fig. 1-5b.   Because of the
simple voltage subtraction, both the magnitude and direction of the
actuating signal are indicated.   If the difference between the two shaft
positions is 2° instead of 1°, as in the previous example, the actuating
signal is twice as large.   Note, too, that the polarity of the actuating
signal is a measure of the direction of the "error" in the system.   A
polarity in one direction, as in Fig. 1-5a, indicates an "error" of one
direction.   The opposite polarity for the actuating signal, as shown in
Fig. 1-5b, indicates an "error" in the opposite direction.

It is essential that all error detectors indicate this difference in direction
of the actuating signal, since the source of servo power must know in

which direction to drive to reduce the actuating signal. It is not essential
that the error detector indicate the magnitude of the actuating signal as
well; but in all continuous servomechanisms, such as those considered in
this book, this proportionality is likewise a requirement. A continuous
servomechanism develops a correc-
tion signal proportional to the magnitude of the error signal. Another
type of servo, known as an "on-off"
or "bang-bang" system, applies
maximum correction voltage for an
error. A servo of this type is shown
in Fig. 1-6. No proportional amplifier is used; instead a relay applies a

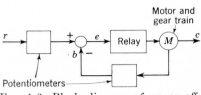

Fig. 1-6. Block diagram of an on-off
servomechanism.

maximum correction signal to the motor. The direction of this signal is
dependent upon the sign of the error signal.

In a continuous servo that employs a-c power, the amplifier increases
the small error signal to one large enough to drive the motor. A conventional a-c amplifier that has adequate response to the a-c signals
introduced is suitable. That is to say, a typical audioamplifier having a
good frequency response at low frequencies would be satisfactory.

The motor used in this servomechanism is an a-c motor. It is a two-
phase motor, which means that the motor rotates if two a-c voltages
separated 90° in phase are applied to its terminals. If the polarity of one
of the voltages reverses, the motor rotates in the opposite direction. In
this application, a voltage 90° out of phase with the potentiometer voltage
is applied to two terminals of the motor. This voltage is constant in
magnitude. The voltage from the amplifier that is applied to the other
two terminals of the two-phase servomotor is known as the *control
voltage*. It can vary from zero, when the actuating signal is zero, to a
maximum value that represents the maximum output of the amplifier.
A characteristic of such a motor is that the output torque is approximately
proportional to the magnitude of the control voltage. Assuming no
restraining forces, the motor is therefore free to rotate in a direction
determined by the polarity of the control voltage and hence by the
polarity of the actuating signal. It will be accelerated by a torque
proportional to the magnitude of the control voltage, which in turn is
proportional to the magnitude of the actuating signal. Since the motor
is a fairly high speed device and since the controlled shaft may encounter
some load such as friction, the motor shaft is geared down to a lower speed
and the output of the gearing is connected to the potentiometer attached
to the controlled shaft.

1-4. Dynamic Response of the Servomechanism. The servomechanism must be so connected electrically and mechanically that the motor

torque produced as a result of the actuating signal tends to reduce this signal. By reversing the leads on either of the potentiometers or on either of the voltages applied to the motor, or anywhere within the amplifier, or by changing the gearing so that the direction of rotation of the controlled shaft is reversed for a given direction of motor-shaft rotation, the servo will be connected backward and the motor will produce a torque proportional to the actuating signal but in a direction to increase the actuating signal rather than to reduce it. This condition can easily be corrected by a reversal of the leads or a change in gearing. This tendency to increase the actuating signal rather than reduce it is one form of instability that is easily corrected. After such a servomechanism is properly connected, however, it may be unstable and oscillate with no motion of the command. Instability such as this is a problem in servomechanism design and construction. The theoretical aspects of servo instability are considered in the Appendix, and the design considerations obviating it are treated in Chap. 2.

Suppose that the servomechanism has been properly connected and that it is stable in operation, i.e., that the controlled shaft does not have sustained oscillations for any position of the command shaft. To learn something of its dynamic characteristics, its operation is observed for various test command variations, assuming the servo is initially at rest. Let the command shaft be suddenly moved to a new value, say 1° from its original position. If the dials are all initially at zero, typical plots of the motion of the command shaft (the command v), the controlled shaft (the controlled variable c), and the actuating signal (e) are as shown in Fig. 1-7. These angular positions can be obtained with sufficient accuracy from recordings of the potentiometer voltages. If

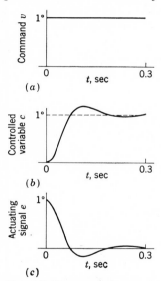

FIG. 1-7. Response of servo to step-function position command.

the command is moved instantaneously to its new value, assuming that all the shafts are originally at a dial reading of zero, the position of the command as a function of time is known as a *step-function* change in position.

Because of the inertia of the servomotor and any additional inertia that may be attached to the controlled shaft, the controlled shaft does not instantaneously go to its final position. When the command is moved 1°, the actuating signal is instantaneously 0.1 volt. This 0.1 volt applied to the terminals of the amplifier results in a large voltage applied to the motor. The motor accelerates and gradually rotates the controlled shaft to a position approaching that of the command shaft. When they are in correspondence, the actuating voltage is zero. The momentum of the controlled shaft and the motor rotor, however, usually causes the position of the controlled shaft to overshoot its desired value. When it has done so, the voltage from the potentiometers, the actuating signal, reverses its polarity and causes a torque in the opposite direction to come to bear on the controlled shaft. The motor slows down, reverses, and again reaches a point of zero actuating signal. At this point a small momentum still exists, and the system overshoots; after this reversal of the control torque, the controlled shaft finally settles to its ultimate position and the actuating signal is zero. In a typical servomechanism, this entire operation may be completed in a few tenths of a second.

Another typical test command is shown in Fig. 1-8. The command shaft, initially at rest at a position of zero degrees, is suddenly rotated at a constant angular velocity—in this case, 30°/sec. This is known as a step-function change in reference-input velocity, since its velocity suddenly changes from zero to some constant value. Again, the controlled shaft, in attempting to follow the position of the command, is not able to do so instantaneously because of the motor inertia and any other inertia connected to the controlled shaft. The actuating signal becomes larger, and the control voltage causes the motor to exert torque on the controlled shaft, which after a few moments is being rotated at a velocity exceeding that of the command shaft. The actuating signal, however, is still of the direction to drive the controlled shaft faster. It does this until the controlled shaft has overtaken the command shaft. The actuating signal at this instant is zero, the controlled shaft overshoots, and the motor torque reverses, thus slowing down the motor and swiftly reducing the speed of the controlled shaft. After another overshoot, the controlled shaft is rotating at the same speed as the command shaft, but there is a steady-state error. This error is caused by the dragging effect of viscous friction, such as that from the oil in the bearings or gearing, and by eddy currents in the motor, which produce an effect like viscous friction. The explanation for the presence of a steady-state error

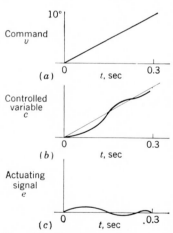

FIG. 1-8. Response of servo to step-function velocity command.

is that, in order to rotate the controlled shaft at a constant velocity, a torque must be exerted on it. The motor can exert a torque only when a control voltage is applied to it. This con-
dition exists only when an actuating signal is fed to the input of the amplifier. An actuating signal must therefore persist in the steady state, and it is proportional to the velocity of the reference input. If the inaccuracy of the error detector is small, the servo error is proportional to the actuating signal.

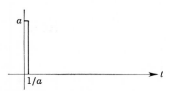

Fig. 1-9. Definition of an impulse function:

$$\delta(t) = \lim_{a \to \infty} a \left[u(t) - u(t - 1/a) \right]$$

where $u(t)$ designates a unit step-function input.

Another input often used for theoretical purposes is shown in Fig. 1-9. In the limit as a approaches infinity, the function becomes large in amplitude but narrow in width. The area remains constant according to the equation

$$\int_0^\infty \delta(t) \, dt = 1 \tag{1-1}$$

The function applies a sudden shock to the system, similar to the impulse applied to a nail when hit with a hammer. From a position at zero degrees, the command shaft is suddenly rotated to a maximum and then quickly returned to zero. This action is known as an *impulse com-mand*. Since the input shaft is at zero after the first instant, the ac-tuating signal is the negative of the controlled-variable signal. The im-pulse imparts a momentum to the system that causes the controlled variable to respond as is shown in Fig. 1-10. The system responds to the application of the impulse with a damped sinusoid.

Fig. 1-10. Response of servo to an impulse position command.

This type of input is used for determining the transfer functions of systems or components, since the Laplace transform of the impulse response is the transfer function.*

1-5. Effect of Varying Parameters. It is interesting to see the effect on the responses depicted in Figs. 1-7 and 1-8 of varying the parameters of this servomechanism. If the inertia is increased, for instance, and no other changes are made, the system becomes more oscillatory—i.e.,

---

* See the Appendix and Refs. 13, 19, and 38 for more information concerning Laplace transforms and transfer functions.

the response of the controlled shaft, and consequently of the actuating signal, has a larger overshoot, and there are more overshoots before the oscillations die down. The oscillations are also at a lower frequency. If the damping is increased with the original value of inertia left fixed, the system response becomes more highly damped; i.e., there are fewer overshoots. The response to a constant-velocity command such as is shown in Fig. 1-8 would indicate a more highly damped system, but the steady-state following error would be greater. If the damping is doubled, the steady-state error will be doubled. If the amplifier gain of the system is increased, leaving all other parameters at their original values, the system will become more oscillatory; i.e., the overshoots will be larger and more numerous, but the frequency of the overshoots will be higher. The steady-state following error, however, is made smaller. The same effect is obtained by increasing the sensitivity of the motor, i.e., by increasing the torque output for a given voltage input. If the gear ratio between the motor and the controlled shaft is decreased, assuming that the controlled shaft is inertialess and frictionless, the system becomes more oscillatory. The torque sensitivity of the controlled shaft—i.e., the restoring torque per unit of actuating signal—is reduced; hence it is less capable of resisting load torques such as friction. The steady-state following error is decreased. Increasing the excitation of the potentiometers produces the same dynamic effect as increasing the sensitivity of the motor or increasing the amplifier gain.

Another interesting experiment is to change the various parameters, such as inertia and damping, and the amplifier gain simultaneously, so that the same number of overshoots occur in response to a step-function change of command position. If this is done—say, by decreasing the inertia and the amplifier gain until the number of overshoots is about the same—the system will have a lower torque sensitivity and a larger steady-state following error. If, for example, the damping and then the amplifier gain are increased so that the system has the same number of overshoots in response to a step-function command as it did originally, the system then will have a higher frequency of response; i.e., the transient is finished in a shorter period of time, and the steady-state following error is reduced. The torque sensitivity of the system is higher as well, since the amplifier gain is increased. Qualitatively, it would then seem that, to have a system that responds very rapidly and has a small steady-state following error, the damping should be increased and the amplifier gain increased in proportion. While this is true from the standpoint of response, there are disadvantages, such as expense in terms of equipment and power expended. Other methods of improving the response of the servomechanism are generally preferred. These methods are discussed in Chap. 2 and elsewhere in this book.

1-6. Effect of Nonlinearities : Saturation and Backlash. The responses shown in Figs. 1-7, 1-8, and 1-10 are correct only if the servomechanism does not saturate, a phenomenon that takes place if further increase of actuating signal does not result in an increase in restoring torque. All servos saturate. The servomechanism of Fig. 1-2 saturates because the torque output of the motor is limited through magnetic saturation; once the control voltage has achieved a certain value (at approximately the rated voltage of the motor), further increase in control voltage does not produce any additional torque. The amplifier also saturates; i.e., its output voltage is limited and will not increase beyond its limiting value no matter how large the actuating signal. When either the amplifier or the motor is saturated, the motor torque achieves its maximum value and, if allowed to remain thus, causes the motor to rotate at its maximum speed for the given conditions of load and internal damping.

If a step-function command is introduced to the servo and is large enough so that the actuating signal initially saturates the servo, full motor torque is applied. If the angle is very large, the motor achieves its full speed and the controlled shaft rotates at maximum velocity. When the controlled shaft approaches the position of the command, the response is very much like the latter portion of Fig. 1-7 but is somewhat more oscillatory because of the momentum of the controlled shaft. Saturation produces no change in the servo response to a step-function velocity command except that the controlled-shaft velocity is limited to a maximum value dependent upon the maximum speed of the motor and the gear ratio. The servo will not be able to follow command velocities that are larger than this maximum.

In actual operation, the servo is usually not subjected to such pure shapes of commands as are shown in Figs. 1-7, 1-8, and 1-9. A typical command might appear to be almost random in its motion. The controlled shaft tends to follow this random motion, and the error under these conditions is small if the servo is properly performing its functions. The servo will then be operating in its linear, or unsaturated, region. Other influences, such as load torques on the controlled shaft, may increase the size of the errors. Such disturbances may be the result of uneven friction in the gearing or, in the case of an automatic machine-tool servo, variations in the amount of metal being cut, or if the servo is being used to drive a radar antenna, variations in wind loading on the antenna.

Another nonlinear effect that is present in almost all servomechanisms is backlash. The effect is produced in gear trains. Because of eccentricity, two gears will not mesh uniformly around the circumference. One gear can move with respect to the other. Many techniques are used to avoid this problem (e.g., spring-loaded and nylon gears); however, it is often present and causes inferior performance of the system. Backlash has a destabilizing effect on the system, especially about the null. When the system is operating in one direction, as when subjected to a ramp function (Fig. 1-8a), the teeth of the gears are held to each other by the force transmitted through them. When the output shaft is oscillating (e.g., the response to a step function, as shown in Fig. 1-7) about the null, the direction is changing. Each time the output changes direction, the output shaft loses correspondence to the drive shaft for a short period. For large amounts of backlash, the system tends to "hunt" (i.e., to evidence small quivering about the null position) between the limits of the backlash.

1-7. Servomechanism Components. Although such a servo as discussed in this chapter contains all the basic elements of any servomechanism, there are a great many ways of performing each of the required functions. It is of interest to point out what types of devices are used in servomechanisms as the basic elements—the error detector, the means to control a source of power, and the prime mover, or source of power. Some means must be provided to achieve the desired stability and accuracy of performance.

The purpose of the error detector is to measure the difference between the command and the controlled variable and to convert this difference to some usable form. The form frequently found of greatest value is an electrical voltage. Linear wire-wound potentiometers are often used as error detectors, connected in the manner shown in Fig. 1-1. If they are excited by a direct voltage, the actuating signal is a direct voltage of varying magnitude. If the potentiometers are excited by an alternating voltage, the magnitude of the actuating signal is the envelope of the difference voltage.

Another type of error detector relies upon magnetic coupling of its parts. Into this class of device fall differential transformers, E transformers, and synchros. They operate on the principle that the a-c magnetic coupling between two or more coils can be varied by varying their relative positions. In these devices, the actuating signal is obtained either by the subtraction of two voltages, each proportional to a shaft position, or by the subtraction of magnetic fields corresponding to shaft position and the induction of a voltage proportional to this difference. Like potentiometers, these devices are commercially available, and their usage is not complicated.

Differential gears can be used to measure the angular difference between the command and controlled shafts. The output shaft of the differential can then be used to rotate a potentiometer if a proportional voltage is desired for the actuating signal or to position a valve if a flow is desired.

The means used to control the source of power involves amplification of some sort. This amplification can be electrical, mechanical, hydraulic, or a combination of these. Electrical amplifiers are d-c or, more commonly, a-c and have merely the function of converting the small signal output of the error detector to a power great enough to actuate the prime mover. The amplifiers may be electronic, using either vacuum or gas-filled tubes or transistors, or magnetic and for large powers may consist of motor-generator sets of special design. Amplification means the control of some source of power; if the source of power is oil under high pressure, a valve that controls the flow of this oil to a hydraulic motor or cylinder is an amplifier. In order to operate the valve, it may be necessary to convert an electric actuating signal to position by means of a motor. Associated with the process of amplification, the apparatus may also convert an electric actuating signal to a more usable form, as by demodulating, modulating, or filtering.

The prime mover, or source of the servo motivating power, may be an a-c motor in the smaller power applications or a d-c motor for the larger power necessary for operation from thyratrons or motor-generator amplifiers. On the other hand, if the servo is hydraulic, a ram and cylinder for translational motions or a variable-displacement pump and motor for rotary motions may be employed for obtaining very large power output.

To achieve the desired margin of stability, viscous damping or even the eddy-current damping of the motor itself may be used. Networks of various sorts are also utilized to modify dynamically the actuating signal and thereby increase stability and improve accuracy. Feedback from small generators coupled to the controlled shaft is also commonly employed to introduce stabilizing rate signals.

In numerous applications the three requisites take on quite different form. For example, in many airborne applications it is necessary to record the position of the body in space. For this application, inertia components such as accelerometers and gyroscopes must be included in the system. Although more complex in transfer function, these elements can be used in the block diagrams of the servomechanism.

This book describes the many ways in which these essential functions of servomechanism components can be accomplished. No book is an adequate substitute for experimentation with the apparatus itself, but some of the pitfalls of its use can be pointed out. The design of a servomechanism is considered in the following chapter. Various types of error detectors are discussed, followed by a discussion of the electrical portions of typical servomechanisms such as modulators, demodulators, networks, and amplifiers. Next, such electromechanical components as servomotors and rate generators are considered. This is followed by chapters on accelerometers and gyroscopes. After a discussion of hydraulic and pneumatic systems, notes on the manufacture, adjustment, and tests of servomechanisms are given. Finally, a typical servo and its operation are discussed.

PROBLEMS

1-1. Show the relationship of operation, positioning control, feedback control, and temperature control, using Euler's circles or some other method of graphing logic.

1-2. Explain how a servomechanism can be used to steer a ship automatically in accordance with a compass heading.

1-3. Draw a block diagram describing a servomechanism that can be used in a machine tool to reproduce cams.

1-4. Draw a block diagram of a man steering an automobile and label each of the blocks and the signals according to servomechanism nomenclature.

1-5. Draw a block diagram describing how a servomechanism with an accelerometer input can control the acceleration of a vibration table.

1-6. Explain the operation of a servomechanism in which the error detector indicates only the direction of the error and not the magnitude. (The magnitude of the signal output of the error detector is constant, no matter how small the error.)

1-7. Sketch the controlled variable and actuating signal for the servomechanism of Fig. 1-1 when the reference input is a sinusoidal signal with the following form:

$$r(t) = A_o \sin 2\pi t$$

where A_o is the peak amplitude and is $10°$.

1-8. Explain the function of each of the components of servomechanisms: error detector, amplifier, prime mover, and gearing.

1-9. Is the reversal of amplifier leads in the signal channel of the amplifier equivalent to adding an idler gear to change the direction of gear rotation without changing its gear ratio?

1-10. Explain the effect on the transient responses of a servomechanism that is considered first to be linear and then to saturate on a finite actuating signal of increase in (a) system damping, (b) inertia, (c) gear ratio from motor to load, (d) motor torque sensitivity, and (e) error-detector sensitivity.

1-11. What is the effect of reduction of mass in each of the systems of Fig. 1-11?

CHAPTER 2

DESIGN OF SERVOMECHANISMS

2-1. Introduction. Just as there is no unique solution to the servomechanism-design problem, there is no unique method of obtaining a solution. The method of design that is presented in this chapter is one logical way to go about the problem of designing a servomechanism for a given application but is by no means the only way. Furthermore, two designers using this same method may well achieve performance within a specified tolerance but with widely different systems.

While the method set forth should be adequate for most problems encountered, the customer may impose additional specifications not touched upon here; or the problem may involve another branch of science, such as aerodynamics. For cases more complicated than the ones discussed in this chapter, the contents here present a starting point for the design and serve to orient the thinking of those not familiar with the design problem.

2-2. Design Procedure. The suggested design procedure comprises the following steps:

1. Study the problem.
2. Lay out a block diagram.
3. Perform a steady-state analysis.
4. Perform a preliminary stability analysis.
5. Optimize the system.
6. Select the prime mover.
7. Select the gear ratio.
8. Select the apparatus between the signal source and the prime mover.
9. Perform preliminary tests.
10. Finalize the design and the system.
11. Perform final tests.

A study of the problem provides the background material that is necessary before any of the other steps can be taken. This includes studying the specifications and gathering information concerning the application of the servomechanism. Laying out a block diagram is like plotting out a route on a road map before a vacation. This step places the entire problem on one sheet of paper to ease comprehension. A brief steady-state analysis is made with approximate transfer functions. This step guarantees that the servo is capable of satisfying the static requirements of the specification. A preliminary stability analysis is made to determine that the chosen system is capable of satisfying, with realizable stabilizing networks, the dynamic requirements of the specification. Should the system prove difficult to stabilize, an alternate system should be sought and steps 1 through 4 repeated. The system block diagram is next optimized to reduce the system to its simplest form. Tentative specifications for the components in the system are written.

Selection of the prime mover is a major step in the design of the servo-mechanism, for much of the design, both mechanical and electrical, is dependent upon this choice. Various types are available, and a wise choice at this point will save much trouble at a later date. The selection of the gear ratio between the prime mover and the controlled-shaft load is a problem that often receives only arbitrary and cursory attention from the designer. Since the performance of the servomechanism, both under dynamic conditions and in the steady state, is dependent to a large extent upon the gear ratio chosen, some logical method of choice, such as is set forth in this chapter, should be utilized. The selection of apparatus between the signal source and the prime mover depends largely on the general form of the servomechanism, the amount of amplification required, and the choice of the circuits involved. While the amount of amplification is dependent upon the performance require-ments, its form depends upon the form of the prime mover selected.

At this stage, a reexamination of the selection of prime mover may be in order—i.e., further developments in the design may prove that the prime mover originally chosen is inadequate or undesirable. Preliminary tests, which take place after the selection of apparatus between the signal source and the prime mover, determine the dynamic response of certain parameters of the system as an aid to refinement of the design. Some of these tests may have taken place at earlier stages, but it is at this point that the system stability and steady-state performance are verified. The dynamic performance is optimized experimentally during this stage. As a result of the preliminary tests, the design is firmed up and the system is finalized. The final tests are then necessary to see whether or not the finalized design meets all the requirements of the specification or the application.

As the servomechanism progresses from the breadboard stage to the prototype, to the final production model, to the final quantity production, tests may be in order to see that the requirements of specification and application are still being met and to note the effect of component sub-stitutions, parameter variations resulting from commercial tolerances and environmental changes, and design modifications made desirable by such other considerations as economics.

2-3. The Study of the Problem. The first logical step in the design procedure is to study the problem. There are a variety of ways in which the problem can be set forth. The problem may be stated in such general terms as a request to design "a system that will be satisfactory" for a certain application. On the other hand, very complete and detailed performance specifications may be given. Presumably, the customer has determined that if the servo meets these specifications, it will be satisfactory for the application intended. Because the design problem may be presented to the engineer in a variety of ways, the information necessary to specify a servomechanism completely must be analyzed.

In the design of servomechanisms, as in the design of any piece of apparatus, there are certain general requirements that are concerned indirectly and directly with the performance of the servomechanism. These include life, serviceability, reliability, workmanship, restrictions on material, and economic considerations. Other factors that affect the performance in some measure are weight, size, resistance to shock, vibration, the power to be supplied and its voltage and frequency variations, the ambient temperature range of the servo, and its duty cycle. The latter groups largely restrict the choice of components that can be used— not in type, but in the actual physical form, such as the substitution of a ruggedized tube in place of the ordinary vacuum tube. The power supply, however, has a considerable effect on the over-all design, the selection of the prime mover, and the methods of achieving system dynamics. Additional design constraints may be imposed by procurement problems or the necessity of using components specified or supplied by the customer. It is important that all these factors be known and taken into account.

The performance requirements of a servomechanism can be expressed in a variety of ways. The diagram of Fig. 2-1 shows, in successively greater detail, the information that constitutes the complete performance specifications of a servo, starting from the application of the system in which the servo is to be used. While this chart has been devised for the problem of a servo whose load consists entirely of inertia, viscous friction, and a more or less constant torque such as coulomb friction, the designer can extend this chart to more complicated systems including dynamic load torques.

Between each pair of dotted lines is enough information to specify the performance of the servo. The most general method of giving this information is contained in the first line of this chart, which is that the servo must be satisfactory in the application intended. From this, enough information must be extracted to design the servo. The required information appears in lower levels of the chart.   With a thorough knowledge of the application, he can decide the limitations on noise transmission, the margin of stability required of the servo, the allowable error, the load, and information about the position, velocity, and acceleration of the reference input.   From this level of information, he can extract more detailed requirements of the servomechanism; and ultimately he can attain complete design specifications by setting forth what the loop transfer function and the steady-state requirements must be in order that this servo satisfactorily meet the requirements of the application.

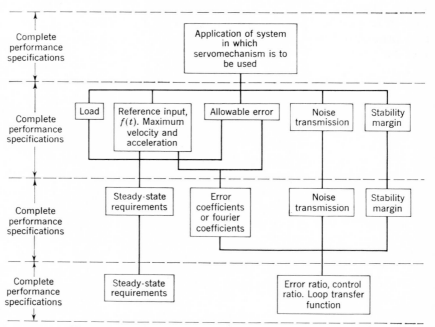

FIG. 2-1. Derivation of servo performance specifications.

Sometimes the designer does not even know the general application of the system and must be content with information contained in the lower levels of the diagram.   In any event, if the requirements as set forth in the lower levels have not been defined completely, the designer must be given enough information from the upper levels from which to derive the necessary information.

The specifications encountered in servo design can usually be divided into two types: (1) specifications stated in terms of frequency and (2) specifications stated in terms of time response.

Frequency-domain Specifications.   A servo specification is commonly written in the same sense as one for an electronic amplifier or a filter.

"Hi-fi" enthusiasts will recall that their amplifiers are specified and compared on the basis of their bandwidths, i.e., flat from 30 to 15,000 cps. Most filters—i.e., bandpass, low-pass, band-reject, etc.—are specified in terms of the amplitude response vs. frequency. The *bandwidth*, which is shown in Fig. 2-2, is defined in this text as the frequency range over which the amplitude response does not drop 3 db (0.707 amplitude ratio) below the amplitude at the center of the passband. Decibel (db) is defined as $20 \log_{10} A_2/A_1$, where A_2/A_1 is an amplitude ratio. The bandwidth is an index of the ability of the system to reproduce the shape of the input signal. For example, if a square pulse is applied to the input of a low-pass filter that has a bandwidth limit at a finite cutoff frequency ω_c,* the output will not be a square pulse but might be distorted as shown in Fig. 2-3.

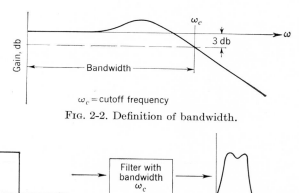

FIG. 2-2. Definition of bandwidth.

FIG. 2-3. Effect of bandwidth on pulse shape.

A variety of other frequency-domain specifications may be encountered in practical control-system design. For example, if a control system is used in an aircraft that has a resonance due to the structure or to aerodynamics at a particular frequency, it may be necessary to design a system that blocks the transmission of signals in this band of frequencies but passes both higher and lower frequencies. If noise that is limited to a particular band is present, a special bandpass characteristic must be specified to block these undesirable frequencies.

Time-domain Specifications. Often the desired characteristics of the system performance are specified in terms of time-domain quantities, that is, by the response to a step function or a ramp function. A complete transient solution is required to satisfy exactly the time-domain

---

* The *cutoff frequency* is the frequency that delimits the passband. It is the frequency at which the amplitude is down 3 db, as shown in Fig. 2-2.

requirements. It is, however, impossible to find the transient solution until most of the design has been completed. As an aid in bridging the gap between specifications given in the time domain and useful design quantities (such as damping ratio ζ and natural resonant frequency ω_n), the second-order solution* may prove useful. Care must be exercised in more complex systems, since the extension of the second-order system to these can be misleading. At least, however, the second-order system provides a starting point.

The more important time-domain specifications are best defined by reference to the transient response of a second-order system, shown in Fig. 2-4. The following three quantities conveniently describe this curve:

The *overshoot*, expressed in per cent of the final value, measures the amount the output overshoots the steady-state response value for a unit step input. For Fig. 2-4, the overshoot is $(A_1/1)$ per cent.

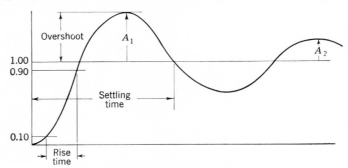

FIG. 2-4. Time-domain specifications.

The *rise time* is defined as the time required for the response to a unit step function to rise from 10 per cent to 90 per cent of the final value. An alternate definition is sometimes used: the rise time is defined as equal to the reciprocal of the slope of the response at the instant the response is half the final value. The first definition seems preferable.

The *settling time* is defined as the time required for the error response to a unit step function to arrive first at less than a specified absolute percentage of its final value and thereafter to stay within that value. Often it is essentially equal to the time required for the response to cross unit amplitude again after overshooting the first time.

2-4. Laying Out the Block Diagram. Once the background of the problem is understood and the requirements have been established, a layout of the method of achieving the desired result must be established. This effort should culminate in a system block diagram. The process of obtaining such a block diagram is usually one of trial and error. The

* See the example in Appendix A.

engineer conceives of one or more methods of performing the job. It is usually safer if more than one system is conceived. In this manner the engineer is in a position to choose the best of several systems. Advantages and disadvantages of each system are listed in a more or less formal fashion. Although a complete decision cannot be reached at this stage, since questions of stability and steady-state errors must be evaluated, the most likely system is chosen. A mathematical block diagram should be drawn and reduced to its simplest form.*

Approximate transfer functions for the various components—for example, motors, gear train, and amplifier—should be determined. Since exact numerical values for all time constants and other constants are not available at this stage, reasonable estimates are to be made for purposes of further analysis.

2-5. Steady-state Analysis. The steady-state requirements are the static error, the limitations on the velocity and acceleration of the servo controlled shaft, and the load conditions. These are principally caused by the nonlinearities of the servo. If the servo were completely linear, it would have unlimited velocity and acceleration and the static error caused by coulomb friction would be zero. The static error represents one portion of the total allowable error; the sum of the static error and the dynamic error equals the total allowable error. Unless the static error is independently specified, a wise choice of the relative magnitude of the two must be made in order that neither component of error be unduly restricted at the expense of the other. The static error of the servomechanism is the error that exists when the servo is at rest. It is the result of a combination of the error in the measuring means, such as in the potentiometers or synchros, and the effect of internal or external load torques on the servo.

These load torques may be specified in terms of the coulomb friction of the load and the additional torque required to rotate the controlled shaft at certain velocities; or they can be derived from a knowledge of the application, as in the case of the wind torque on a radar dish. The weight and geometry of the external load must be known, so that the inertia and the coulomb and viscous friction can be estimated if they are not given. So that the controlled shaft of the servo will never be pushed out of synchronism, the maximum torque output for the servo must exceed the greatest load that can be applied. The limitation on static error, however, covers this requirement.

The limitations on velocity of the controlled shaft are derived in part from the general application of the system and in part from the command or reference-input variations, which of course also ultimately come from

* See Ref. 38, pp. 18–21, for a discussion of block-diagram algebra and the method of block-diagram reduction.

the general application. The controlled shaft must be capable of traveling at least as swiftly as the maximum rate of change of the command. In addition, the application may dictate that the slew velocity of the controlled shaft be considerably higher than the maximum expected rate of change of command, in order to reduce the time for the controlled shaft to travel from one position to another, as, for example, in switching inputs. In addition to the fast-velocity requirements, there may be a minimum velocity that the servo is required to track smoothly. Some servomechanisms have a tendency to operate with jitter about the desired position when rotating at a very low velocity. This can be caused by backlash in the gearing, irregular coulomb friction, or irregular control torques. If jitter is an important consideration, the magnitude of these excursions about the desired position of the controlled shaft can be restricted. Even though these excursions are within the allowable static error of the servomechanism, their abruptness of motion may be deleterious to the operation of the system for the particular application in question.

The controlled shaft of the servomechanism must also be able to accelerate at least as fast as the command it is required to follow. In some cases, to reduce the total slewing time, the servo is required to accelerate as rapidly as possible. On the other hand, there may be upper limits on the amount of acceleration that the servo is permitted to undergo. These limits are set by considerations of the wear and tear on the apparatus or the safety or comfort of personnel who may be moving with the controlled shaft.

This group of steady-state requirements therefore represents one of the two major portions of the information that a servo designer must have in order to proceed with his design. Although the dynamic requirements of a servomechanism may be given in terms of the open-loop transfer function of the servomechanism and the transfer functions from disturbances or loads to the controlled shaft, the theory of linear servomechanisms, which is included in the Appendix and in Refs. 11, 38, and 48, treats this problem. It is then an additional requirement that the servo be linear over the range of commands to be encountered. A steady-state requirement which ensures that saturation will not take place within the operating range of the servomechanism is the specification of the maximum velocity and acceleration that will be encountered. While it may be impossible to discover what every combination of acceleration and velocity will be, the velocity when the acceleration is a maximum can be determined. (At worst, in lieu of any other information, it can be assumed that the maximum load velocity and the maximum load acceleration occur simultaneously.) A piece of information which yields the same results but which is not as easily determined is the limiting magnitude of sinusoidal command at each frequency component of command. Again, some indication of which components will exist simultaneously must be had.

2-6. Error Coefficients. The loop transfer function is completely defined by a specification on the control or error ratio. Alternatively, information on the error coefficients can be given in addition to the stability information of the servo. The error coefficients provide a method of establishing the steady-state error conditions. For a system that has unity feedback ($H = 1$), the error coefficients are defined as

$$\text{Positional error constant} = K_p = \lim_{s \to 0} G(s) \qquad (2\text{-}1)$$

$$\text{Velocity error constant} = K_v = \lim_{s \to 0} sG(s) \qquad (2\text{-}2)$$

$$\text{Acceleration error constant} = K_a = \lim_{s \to 0} s^2 G(s) \qquad (2\text{-}3)$$

where $G(s)$ is the forward-loop transfer function. For $H = 1$, unity feedback, the actuating signal $E(s)$ is the transform of the error ($= R - C$). The error $e(t)$ results from the application of various types of inputs and is based upon linear theory. It does not include errors due to such conditions as coulomb friction and backlash. This analysis forms the basis for determining the least error that is possible with the given servo.

To gain insight into the magnitude of the steady-state error in a linear system, servomechanisms are classified according to type. Transformation of the differential equation relating error to R gives the expression

$$E = \frac{R}{1 + G} \qquad (2\text{-}4)$$

for $H = 1$. In general, the product G, which is found by multiplying the transfer-function operators of all elements cascaded around the open loop of the system, is expressed by the following typical form of transfer function:

$$G(s) = \frac{K(s + 1/\tau_1)(s + 1/\tau_3)}{s^n(s + 1/\tau_2)(s + 1/\tau_4)} \qquad (2\text{-}5)$$

The values of s that make the denominator of G zero are called "poles" of $G(s)$. The values of s that make the numerator zero are called "zeros" of $G(s)$. Thus, $s = -1/\tau_1$, $-1/\tau_3$ are first-order zeros and $s = -1/\tau_2$, $-1/\tau_4$ are first-order poles. Finally, the term s^n in the denominator comprises a pole of order n of the open-loop transfer function at the origin of the s plane.

Because of the form of this transfer function, the system has a definite steady-state response to various types of inputs of magnitude depending upon the value of n. Hence the steady-state error is specified by knowing the value of n, which is defined as the type of the system:

Type 0 *system:* one for which $n = 0$, in Eq. (2-5).

Type 1 *system:* one for which $n = 1$, in Eq. (2-5), etc.

A summary of the error coefficients and the corresponding steady-state errors is included in Table 2-1 for three types of system. From a consideration of Table 2-1, it might appear, without further investigation, that the higher the type of the system, the better the servo. For systems of type 2, zero error occurs for either a unit step in position or a unit step in velocity and only a finite error for a unit step in acceleration. However, with stability of servo systems under consideration, those having a second- or higher-order pole at the origin, corresponding to type 2 and higher, are increasingly more difficult to stabilize. Systems with a zero or first-order pole at the origin are more easily stabilized. As with most other engineering problems, the design of feedback control systems is usually effected by compromising between the steady-state error that results in a system and the degree of stability (i.e., the magnitudes of the damping constants) that may be obtained with a particular type of system. Although all systems with good steady-state behavior are not necessarily hard to stabilize, often this is true.

TABLE 2-1. STEADY-STATE ERRORS

n	K_p	ϵ_p	K_v	ϵ_v	K_a	ϵ_a
0	Finite constant	$\dfrac{1}{1 + K_p}$	0	∞	0	∞
1	∞	0	Finite constant	$\dfrac{1}{K_v}$	0	∞
2	∞	0	∞	0	Finite constant	$\dfrac{1}{K_a}$

The error coefficients can also be determined from a knowledge of the maximum allowable error and the reference input as a function of time. Servo error comprises the sum of the static error and the dynamic error. If the relative magnitudes of the static error and the dynamic error are completely under the jurisdiction of the designer, a choice must be made on the basis of the static error expected from the error detector and the error due to load. If there is no appreciable load, by far the major component of the static error is caused by the error detector. Additional constraints on the problem may include the form in which the command signal is received, such as shaft rotation, synchro voltages, or magnitudes of direct or alternating voltages. On the other hand, the choice of the error detector may be in the hands of the engineer, and he may be able to ease his dynamic problem by the use of a more accurate error detector.

After the expected maximum static error has been subtracted from the total allowable error, the portion remaining is the allowable dynamic error. A trial-and-error process again ensues for the purpose of choosing the error coefficients such that the dynamic error does not exceed the permissible value for a given reference input vs. time.

The reference input vs. time may be in the form of an equation, such as an inverse tangent function, or in the form of a graph. If it is in the form of an equation, the problem is quite simple, for the various derivatives of the reference input can be determined analytically.* The components of the dynamic error are then obtained by multiplying these derivatives by appropriate coefficients according to the equation

$$e(t) = K_0 r(t) + K_1 \frac{dr(t)}{dt} + K_2 \frac{d^2 r(t)}{dt^2} + \cdots \qquad (2\text{-}6)$$

This expression consists of a sum of terms, each of which is composed of one of the derivatives of the reference-input motion and a constant whose values depend upon the characteristics of the servomechanism. Various constants, different for each different servomechanism, can be computed. This is shown in the Appendix and in Table 2-2.†

If the reference input vs. time is in the form of a graph, the derivatives must be obtained graphically. Although the information thus obtained may be so fragmentary as to require corroboration by actual tests of the servomechanism in its final application, at least the first approximation can be obtained. For example, the total error is assumed to be all velocity error; and by finding the point of maximum velocity the velocity-error coefficient K can be chosen to keep the velocity error somewhat less than the total allowable error. The second derivative may also be obtained if the reference input is a smooth curve. One technique of doing this is to approximate the reference input by an analytical expression and differentiate that expression.

If the reference input as a function of time is not specified by the customer, the designer must obtain it from geometrical considerations of the application. One example of this is the case of radar tracking an airplane. If the motion of the aircraft with respect to the radar is assumed or known for a given tactical situation, the geometry of the problem determines the reference input vs. time. Knowledge of the limitations of the velocities and accelerations of the target is an aid in choosing the worst possible case.

2-7. Preliminary Stability Analysis. The other major portion of the design is the dynamic requirements. When the servo designer has enough information to establish the loop transfer function of a servo-

---

* See Ref. 49, pp. 80–87, for a more complete analysis of error coefficients.
† Calculation of the elements of Table 2-2 is accomplished in the Appendix.

TABLE 2-2. SERVO ERROR COEFFICIENTS

$$\left[e = K_0 r + K_1 \frac{dr}{dt} + K_2 \frac{d^2r}{dt^2} + K_3 \frac{d^3r}{dt^3} + \cdots \quad (K_0 = 0 \text{ for all servos in table}) \right]^*$$

Locus identification	Transfer function G	K_1	K_2	K_3
6-12	$\dfrac{\omega_0\omega_1}{s(s+\omega_1)}$	$\dfrac{1}{\omega_0}$	$\dfrac{\omega_0 - \omega_1}{\omega_0^2\omega_1}$	$\dfrac{\omega_1 - 2\omega_0}{\omega_0^3\omega_1}$
6-12-18	$\dfrac{\omega_0\omega_1\omega_2}{s(s+\omega_1)(s+\omega_2)}$	$\dfrac{1}{\omega_0}$	$\dfrac{\omega_0\omega_1 + \omega_0\omega_2 - \omega_2\omega_1}{\omega_0^2\omega_1\omega_2}$	$\dfrac{\omega_0^2 - 2\omega_0\omega_1 - 2\omega_0\omega_2 + \omega_1\omega_2}{\omega_0^3\omega_1\omega_2}$
6-12-6-12	$\dfrac{\omega_0\omega_1(s+\omega_2)}{s(s+\omega_1)(s+\omega_3)}$	$\dfrac{\omega_3}{\omega_0\omega_2}$	$\dfrac{\omega_0\omega_2(\omega_1 + \omega_3) - \omega_1\omega_3(\omega_0 + \omega_3)}{\omega_0^2\omega_2^2\omega_1}$	$\dfrac{\omega_0\omega_2(\omega_0\omega_2 - 2\omega_3^2 - 2\omega_1\omega_3 - \omega_0\omega_3 - \omega_0\omega_1) + \omega_1\omega_3(\omega_0 + \omega_3)^2}{\omega_0^3\omega_2^3\omega_1}$
6-12-6-12	$\dfrac{\omega_0\omega_1\dfrac{\omega_2}{\omega_3}(s+\omega_3)}{s(s+\omega_1)(s+\omega_2)}$	$\dfrac{1}{\omega_0}$	$\dfrac{\omega_0\omega_3(\omega_1 + \omega_2) - \omega_1\omega_2(\omega_0 + \omega_3)}{\omega_0^2\omega_1\omega_2\omega_3}$	$\dfrac{\omega_0\omega_3(\omega_0\omega_3 - 2\omega_2\omega_3 - 2\omega_1\omega_3 - \omega_0\omega_2 - \omega_0\omega_1) + \omega_1\omega_2(\omega_0 + \omega_3)^2}{\omega_0^3\omega_3^3\omega_1}$
12-6-12	$\dfrac{\omega_0(s+\omega_1)}{s^2(s+\omega_2)}$	0	$\dfrac{\omega_2}{\omega_0\omega_1}$	$\dfrac{\omega_1 - \omega_2}{\omega_0\omega_1^2}$

* K_n is given by the expression

$$K_n = \frac{1}{n!}\lim_{s\to 0}\frac{d^n}{ds^n}\left(\frac{1}{1+G}\right)$$

26

mechanism and the transfer functions from disturbances or loads to the controlled shaft, he has completely specified the dynamic requirements. The combination of the dynamic requirements and the steady-state requirements constitutes the complete performance specification and permits the next stage of design to be undertaken. A loop transfer function that specifies the dynamic performance of the servomechanism can be expressed analytically or graphically. The designer may be working under the additional constraint that the loop transfer function is derived not only from the application of the system in which the servo is to be used but also from independently specified control or error ratios. If this is so, naturally the more restrictive loop transfer function is chosen unless the specifications are in conflict and this discrepancy can be pointed out to the customer. (These additional constraints, however, are possible for any stage of the information shown in Fig. 2-1; and the customer may specify some of the requirements in the various blocks independent of the requirements as derived from the application.)

Several methods of servomechanism synthesis are available, for example, the root-locus and frequency-response methods (Nyquist). These are described in the Appendix and in Refs. 17, 38, and 49. A combination of the various methods seems most desirable. The frequency-response methods can be utilized to find analytical approximations for the transfer functions of certain components. These components, whose transfer functions are difficult to determine, can usually be tested by applying sinusoidal inputs and measuring amplitude and phase response of the output when loaded, as in the actual application. When analytic expressions for all transfer functions have been determined, either analytically or experimentally with frequency-response techniques, the root-locus method is suited to perform the stability analysis. When verifying the design or in final testing, frequency-response methods are again used. As indicated in Sec. 2-3, the dynamic specifications can be specified in terms of either frequency- or time-domain quantities. Regardless of the method by which the dynamic requirements are specified it is possible to convert, at least approximately, between them. The Appendix contains several charts that permit approximate conversion between frequency- and time-domain specifications. Phase margin, maximum magnitude (M_p), and per cent overshoot are related to the damping ratio of the least-damped roots.

Normally it is desirable to have a large margin of stability, so that the servo response to any command is highly damped. This is also desirable in order to prevent shifts in the servo component characteristics from causing the performance to deteriorate markedly. In addition, servomechanisms are often used in applications that are followed by other servos or other devices using the controlled-shaft position as their inputs, and a servo which is quite oscillatory will introduce spurious signals which introduce noise into the other devices.

The stability margin can be more or less completely specified by the phase or gain margin of the loop transfer function. On the other hand, the stability margin can be expressed as the maximum allowable peak magnitude of the error ratio or the control ratio (M criterion). For most applications of servomechanisms, a safe stability margin is considered to be that which will permit the control ratio to have a peak value of less than 2, usually 1.5, and in some cases as small as 1.3. This commonly yields a phase margin on the order of 45 to 50°.

Still another method of giving the stability margin is statement of the transient response of the servo to a step-function command. The number of overshoots to a step-function command of a magnitude less than that which saturates the servo can be specified. Often the dynamic requirements are specified directly in terms of the damping ratio and natural frequency of the least-damped roots. These can be plotted on the s plane, as shown in Fig. 2-5, for direct application of the root-locus method.

Because of nonlinearities, such as backlash and saturation in servo systems, the actual performance will deviate somewhat from that deter-mined by the theoretical analysis.

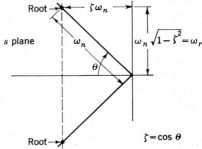

FIG. 2-5. Roots located by knowledge of damping ratio and natural frequency.

When final tests are made, the stability margin must be checked at all positions of operation.

The system can be equalized in at least three ways: (1) cascade, (2) feedback, and (3) load stabilization.

In order to achieve proper system dynamics by the use of the first of these methods, an a-c or d-c network is cascaded into the servoamplifier. The characteristics of this network are so chosen that the combination of the actual loop dynamics before equalization and the cascaded network achieves the desired loop dynamics. An approximation of the required network transfer function can be obtained either graphically or analyt-ically by means of division. Combinations of simple lead and lag net-works can be used. On the other hand, the network having a given transfer function with a minimum of components can be synthesized.*

The second method, the use of feedback, refers to the vast variety of stabilizing means employing feedback of signals. These signals can be obtained from rate generators or potentiometers geared to some inter-

* Network synthesis is discussed in Chap. 5.

mediate shaft of hydraulic or pneumatic servos, from accelerometers, by simple voltage feedback within the amplifier or by feedback of voltage from the motor terminals, from networks, or from some other point in the system where a voltage can be obtained. Feedback of voltage within the amplifier to achieve certain dynamic results can be equivalent to the use of a cascading network. The use of a rate-generator voltage affects not only the loop dynamics but the steady-state error as well.

The third method utilizes the dynamic characteristics of a load, such as a friction damper.* This method frequently introduces large steady-state errors.

In any particular problem it may be possible to use any of these methods, or combinations of them, as a means of achieving the proper dynamic response of the system. Care must be exercised, however, to avoid nullifying the effect of one method with another, as in feeding back signals around a cascaded network and thus minimizing its effectiveness. Then too, the loop transfer function does not have to be synthesized exactly. It is necessary only that the loop transfer function have a given form over a range of frequencies. Thus, if it is desirable that the optimum loop transfer function at low frequencies be inversely proportional to the third power of the frequency and the equation therefore implies the necessity of three integrations, or two in addition to the normal integrating characteristics of a servomotor, the same dynamic effect for a given range of frequencies can be achieved by cascading two lag networks in series to the motor.

Table 2-2 is presented to aid in the synthesis problem. This table gives the loop transfer function, the error coefficients, and the loop transfer locus identification for various common types of servomechanism.

2-8. Optimize the System. The system should now be reviewed from the point of view of both steady-state error and stability. Other requirements in the specification should also be considered, for example, the transmission of noise through the proposed system.

If the command does not contain spurious signals, the designer has no restriction on noise transmission. There are cases, however, in which noise at the command masks the true desired position of the controlled shaft. Sometimes these noise components are well above the frequency response of the servomechanism; and the noise-transmission requirements can be easily set forth by specifying the passband of the servomechanism, i.e., by specifying the magnitude of the control ratio vs. frequency. If the noise frequencies are all at frequencies that the servomechanism is required to pass, it is impossible for linear servomechanisms to distinguish between the noise and the true signals. There is a borderline case, however, in which some of the noise frequencies are as low as some of the

* Section 7-8 presents a discussion of friction dampers.

frequencies contained in the true command; and when these signals overlap, it may be desirable to limit the passband of the servo so that the servo ignores a portion of the noise.   If this is done, however, the servo will also fail to pass some of the true signals and a compromise must be effected.   This compromise is reached by evaluating the effect on performance of successively reducing bandwidth.

The amount of noise (undesirable components of the command) transmitted by a servo of loop transfer function G is dependent upon the frequency spectrum.   The rms noise appearing at the controlled shaft (i.e., the undesirable components of its motion caused by noise in the command) is proportional to the square of the magnitude of the control ratio.   If the noise transmission is to be small, the control ratio must cut off at low frequencies; consequently the noise-transmission characteristics of the servo can be expressed directly in terms of the control ratio. With an appreciable noise problem, the servo must usually have the narrowest possible bandwidth that will permit it to meet the accuracy requirements.   If such a servo still has too high a noise transmission for these applications, the accuracy requirements must be compromised. In the absence of any specification on noise, the passband of the servo should be made as small as possible without compromising the other requirements.

Before the optimum system can be achieved, many other requirements should be considered, such as package size, reliability, and power supply.

2-9. Selection of the Prime Mover.   Prime movers for servomechanisms are usually a-c induction motors, d-c motors, hydraulic or pneumatic systems, or clutches.   The type selected is determined by the power requirements of the load, the power sources available, physical and economic limitations of the equipment, and the dynamic characteristics.   A prime mover* having the most desirable dynamic characteristics should be chosen; however, the power requirements of the prime mover are considered here.   The other limitations may be imposed by the application of the system in which the servo is to be used.

Although prime movers are generally characterized by an output torque independent of speed or by a torque that falls off more or less linearly with speed, the methods discussed are independent of the shape of the torque-speed curves.   Hydraulic motors and some d-c motors fall within the first category, whereas the second contains a-c induction motors, such as those designed for instrument servomechanism use.

The power requirements of the servomechanism and the gear train required are best learned from the application of a few fundamental formulas to the steady-state requirements discussed earlier.   The total power absorbed by the load, both in rotating at constant velocity in

* Various prime movers are discussed in Chap. 7.

opposition to a load torque and in accelerating the load and motor inertia, is given by

$$p_t = vq + av(J + k^2 J_m) \qquad (2\text{-}7)$$

where p_t = total power required by load

v = load velocity required

q = load torque (assumed constant, including any internal loading of the servo such as its gearing)

a = load acceleration required

J = load moment of inertia, including that of the gearing (which may be ignored as a first approximation)

J_m = motor moment of inertia

k = gear ratio

The prime mover must be capable of supplying this amount of power in order that the servo controlled shaft will rotate with the specified velocity and acceleration. Since the inertia of the motor is included in the total power required, it influences the power requirement of the servomechanism. In order to obtain the first approximation of the power required, some intelligent guess at the servo inertia and gear ratio must be chosen; as a first approximation, the reflected inertia of the motor $k^2 J_m$ can be assumed equal to that of the load J and the total power thus determined. Preliminary calculations can be made on the assumption of negligible gear inertia; later, when the gearing has been established, the error resulting from such an assumption can be computed.

An actual motor can then be chosen whose maximum power output approximately equals this figure, and the motor inertia can be obtained from a catalogue or by measurement. With the inertia of the chosen motor as J_m of Eq. (2-8), the equation is plotted as a function of gear ratio k. A typical curve appears in Fig. 2-6. It is a graph of the total power required by the load (including the motor inertia) if the worst combination of acceleration and velocity should occur simultaneously with a constant-load torque. This curve is a function of gear ratio between the motor

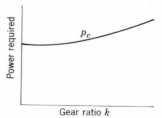

FIG. 2-6. Servo power requirements.

and the load only because part of the power is used to accelerate the motor itself. The power-output capabilities of the motor must also be considered.

To determine whether the motor is capable of supplying this power and, as an incidental result, to learn the proper gear ratio to choose, an additional curve must be superposed on that of Fig. 2-6. This curve is a plot of motor power produced if the output of the gearing assumed attached to the motor (i.e., the controlled shaft) is rotating at the required velocity v, as a function of the gear ratio of the assumed gearing. A typical curve is given in Fig. 2-7. This curve bears no relation to the power requirements of the servo and is a function only of the torque-speed or power-speed curve of the motor.

The curve of Fig. 2-7 is obtained by assuming a gear ratio k and applying a braking load at the output of the gear train such as to cause the output shaft to rotate at the velocity v used in Eq. (2-8) and Fig. 2-6. The motor produces a certain amount of power p_m for this gear ratio k, which point is plotted on the graph. The data for Fig. 2-7, however, are actually calculated thus: from the motor power-speed curve (which can be derived from the torque-speed curve), as given in the catalogue, a power is chosen, and the motor speed read from the curve. The gear ratio k is then calculated as the ratio of the motor speed to the required velocity v. This process is repeated until the plot of Fig. 2-7 is obtained.

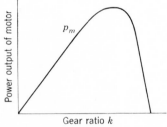

FIG. 2-7. Motor power capability.

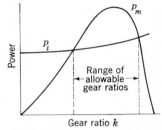

FIG. 2-8. Combination of power required and power capability.

The curves of Figs. 2-6 and 2-7 are superposed in Fig. 2-8 and show, as a function of gear ratio, the power absorbed by the system and the power-output capabilities of the motor. If the two curves intersect, the motor has sufficient power to satisfy the requirements of the specifications; and if any safety factor is deemed advisable, its magnitude is clearly shown. If the motor chosen is too small or if it is believed that a smaller motor can be used, a new motor is chosen and the process repeated. The points of intersection represent the range of gear ratios which can be selected and which still enables the motor to meet the requirements. Which gear ratio should be chosen is discussed below.

It is sometimes more convenient, however, to work with torque-speed curves rather than power-speed curves in selecting the range of allowable gear ratios and to check on whether the motor is capable of driving the load at the required velocity and acceleration. After a motor of the assumed proper power rating has been chosen, graphs similar to Fig. 2-8 can be plotted on the basis of torque rather than power. This method has the advantage that the motor curve can be derived directly from the torque-speed curve without the necessity of computing power. Also, the relative magnitudes of the friction of the load and acceleration torques are more easily visualized when put in this form. The torque can be referred either to the controlled shaft or to the motor shaft.

For example, if the torque is referred to the controlled shaft, the total required torque is given by the equation

$$q_t = q + a(J + k^2 J_m) \tag{2-8}$$

where q_t is the total torque required by the load. As before, this equation is plotted as a function of gear ratio k. The motor curve is plotted by determining what braking torque is necessary to cause the shaft on the output of the gearing to rotate at the required velocity v as a function of

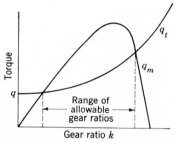

FIG. 2-9. Combination of torque required and torque available (referred to controlled shaft).

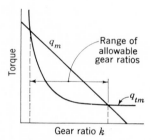

FIG. 2-10. Combination of torque required and torque available (referred to motor shaft).

the gear ratio k. A typical pair of curves is shown in Fig. 2-9, in which the intersections of the curves yield the range of gear ratios.

Similarly, the method can be extended to express the equation in terms of the torque referred to the motor shaft. The resulting expression is

$$q_{tm} = \frac{q}{k} + ak\left(\frac{J}{k^2} + J_m\right) \tag{2-9}$$

Typical curves are shown in Fig. 2-10.

As an example of this method, consider the problem of selecting the optimum gear ratio for the motor with the assumed linear speed-torque curve of Fig. 2-11. The load-speed and torque conditions for maximum power demand are known. When the speed is known, the torque is given by the expression

$$L = \frac{1.356P \times 10^3}{N} \tag{2-10}$$

TABLE 2-3. COMPUTATION OF OPTIMUM GEAR RATIO

Assumed gear ratio	Motor speed, rpm	Motor torque, oz-in.
10	1,000	2.17
20	2,000	1.08
30	3,000	0.724
40	4,000	0.543
50	5,000	0.434

where P = mechanical power, watts
L = torque, oz-in.
N = speed, rpm
For the case $N = 100$ rpm

$$L = \frac{(1.356)(10^3)(1.6)}{100} = 21.7 \text{ oz-in.}$$

Various possible gear ratios between motor and load are arbitrarily assumed. Based on each assumption, the motor speed and motor torque are calculated and arranged in tabular form. Table 2-3 shows the calcu-

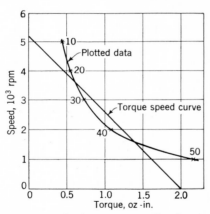

FIG. 2-11. Optimum gear ratio chosen from speed-torque curve.

lation of a series of assumed gear ratios and motor conditions. Each gear ratio results in motor-speed and motor-torque points that are plotted directly on the motor speed-torque curve. Each assumed gear ratio yields a point on the curve. These are connected to yield a curve that is plotted on the motor speed-torque curve shown in Fig. 2-11.

All portions of the gear-ratio curve that lie beneath the motor speed-torque curve represent satisfactory gear ratios. All gear ratios above the normal motor speed-torque curve are unusable and will not yield the required load performance. If the whole gear-ratio curve lies outside the motor speed-torque curve, the motor has insufficient power and will not do the job.

With the over-all gear ratio chosen, the best ratio for each gear mesh can now be selected. This is accomplished with the nomogram* of

* This nomogram is taken from Reeves catalogue RICO-10; the derivation is available from Reeves or also in Sec. 13-13 of Ref. 49.

Fig. 2-12, which determines the individual stage ratios that will reflect a minimum gear-train inertia for any given over-all ratio and any assumed number of stages. Although the minimum reflected inertia results only for an infinite number of meshes, the nomogram gives the best mesh ratios while keeping the reflected inertia to a minimum.

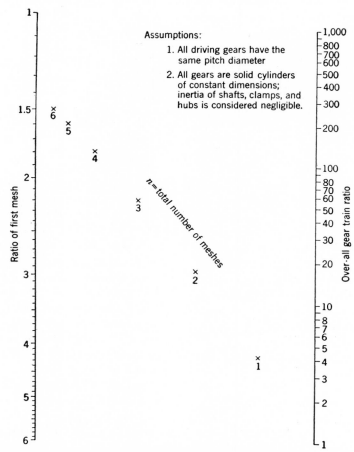

Assumptions:
1. All driving gears have the same pitch diameter
2. All gears are solid cylinders of constant dimensions; inertia of shafts, clamps, and hubs is considered negligible.

FIG. 2-12. Nomogram for approximating the optimum ratio for each gear mesh. (*Reeves Instrument Corp., New York.*)

Suppose a gear ratio of 75 is desired in four meshes. Referring to the nomogram, place a straight edge through the point that corresponds to the over-all gear ratio on the right-hand scale (75:1). From the left-hand scale the gear ratio of the first stages is read as 1.72. Round this off to 1.75 and determine the remaining gear ratio, 75/1.75 equals about 43. To determine the second-stage ratio repeat this process using 43 as

the over-all ratio and 3 as the number of stages.   The subsequent stage
ratios are found in a similar fashion.

Although the example given shows a motor whose torque drops linearly
with speed, these methods apply equally well to the type of motor in
which the torque is approximately independent of speed.

2-10. Selection of the Gear Ratio.   The methods given above yield
the range of possible gear ratios that can be used for the given motor.
The factors that determine what the values should be within the range are
now discussed.

Normally, if the motor power exceeds that of the bare requirements of
the servo load, so that there are two points of intersection rather than a
single one, a choice of any gear ratio between the two points of intersection
results in a higher maximum velocity than that required.   If this required
velocity is the servo slew speed or even the maximum velocity at which
the reference input travels, nothing is lost by exceeding the maximum
velocity required as long as any required additional weight and cost are
not important considerations.

There may be a number of reasons for choosing a gear ratio somewhere
near the lower limit of allowable ratio.   For example, if the friction load
is not a large percentage of the total load, the gear train can be made as
simple and economical as possible.   This also results in the reduction of
the gain of the servoamplifier for a given phase margin.   The economical
advantage of reducing the number of meshes and thus saving on the complexity of the mechanical portion of the servomechanism and reducing
the required gain of the amplifier may be significant.

There may be good reason why the gear ratio chosen should be as large
as possible.   For example, the servo may be used to track extremely low
velocities in addition to being able to achieve the required velocity v.
The choice of as large a gear ratio between the motor and load as possible
minimizes any irregularity in the torque output of the motor.   In
addition, the largest possible torque sensitivity at the controlled shaft is
obtained, which causes it to resist the effect of any load torques with the
least static error.

An alternate guide must be provided for cases in which there exists an
absence of data that allows the gear ratios to be determined in accordance
with the previous analysis.   It may be that the load torque is negligible,
as in the case of an instrument servomechanism used to position a dial.
The gear ratio can be chosen such that the reflected inertia of the motor
is equal to that of the load, as in the equation

$$k = \sqrt{\frac{J}{J_m}}$$

This choice of gear ratio maximizes the acceleration of the controlled
shaft.

On the other hand, if a gear ratio is chosen such that the motor is operating at its maximum power output when the controlled shaft is rotating at the required slew speed, this gear ratio (k = motor speed for maximum power output/v) permits the greatest friction load to be applied to the controlled shaft. If the acceleration and load requirements are not known precisely, such a gear ratio is often a wise choice since it permits the servo to resist the maximum friction load and still achieve the maximum velocity required.

It is desirable at this point to discuss the effect on the torque sensitivity K when gearing is involved. Figure 2-13 shows a block diagram of a typical single-loop servomechanism, which will illustrate the point. The actuating signal E is fed into a potentiometer that has a transfer function of K_p. The output of this is fed into an amplifier having a simple gain of K_a, and this in turn is fed into a motor having a transfer function $K_m/(Js^2 + Bs)$, where K_m is the torque per unit volt of the

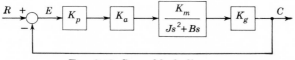

FIG. 2-13. Servo block diagram.

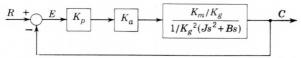

FIG. 2-14. Servo block diagram (constants referred to controlled shaft).

motor. The transfer function of the gear ratio from motor-shaft position to controlled-shaft position is K_g (equal to $1/k$). The loop transfer function, derived by multiplying together all the transfer functions, is

$$G = \frac{K_p K_a K_m K_g}{Js^2 + Bs} = \frac{K}{s^2 + (B/J)s} \qquad (2\text{-}11)$$

The K obtained in this equation is the torque sensitivity divided by the moment of inertia J and is referred to the motor shaft, since J and B are the moment of inertia and damping constant referred to the motor shaft. A small gear ratio results in the largest torque sensitivity at the motor shaft, which is desirable if the friction load occurs at the motor shaft rather than the controlled shaft.

To obtain the torque sensitivity referred to the controlled shaft, the block diagram can be redrawn to reflect the moment of inertia J, damping constant B, and the torque constant K_m of the motor to the controlled shaft, yielding the block diagram shown in Fig. 2-14. Again, the product of the individual blocks is made to obtain the loop transfer function G

as follows:

$$G(s) = \frac{K_p K_a K_m / K_g}{J/K_g^2 s^2 + B/K_g^2 s} \qquad (2\text{-}12)$$

In this case, the torque sensitivity, now referred to the controlled shaft, is the numerator of the expression. A large gear ratio yields the highest torque sensitivity at the controlled shaft and hence provides the highest resistance, for a given error, to torque loads on that shaft. (Note that K_g is normally a number less than 1, so that, if the gear ratio k is 100, $K_g = \frac{1}{100}$).

It is possible to obtain this same result by physical reasoning, rather than by multiplying transfer functions. If the torque sensitivity referred to the controlled shaft is desired, mentally rotate the controlled shaft 1 radian, assuming linearity, and find the restoring torque. A displacement of the controlled shaft by 1 radian results in an output voltage of the potentiometer of K_p, of the amplifier $K_p K_a$, and the torque of the motor $K_p K_a K_m$. This expression divided by K_g (or multiplied by k) yields the torque output at the controlled shaft per radian of displacement from correspondence. (The transfer function of gearing from position input to position output is the exact inverse of the transfer function of gearing from torque input to torque output.)

On the other hand, if the torque sensitivity referred to the motor shaft is desired, rotate the motor shaft 1 radian. This results in a rotation of the controlled shaft of K_g radians and a torque applied to the motor shaft of $K_g K_p K_a K_m$. The torque sensitivity referred to the motor shaft is therefore equal to this expression.

2-11. Selection of Apparatus between Signal Source and Prime Mover. After selecting the prime mover and the gear ratio, the next step in the design process is the selection of the apparatus between the signal source and the prime mover. In the initial consideration, little regard is given to the dynamics of the over-all loop. Principal interest is in the form of the servomechanism, the amount of amplification required, and the selection of the circuits. The block diagram of the servomechanism is utilized. Within the blocks, which indicate the function to be performed by each element of the system, an approximate transfer function of the element is written. If the approximate transfer function is not known, such words as amplifier, prime mover, and modulator can be written in the blocks.

From the preliminary stability and steady-state-error analysis an order of magnitude of desired gain is obtained. Any amplifier gain calculated at this point will be only approximate; so it is necessary that the amplifier, at least in its breadboard form, be constructed to have some means of varying the amount of amplification. The proper range of amplification is based on the preliminary calculations, and thus the approximate form of the amplifier is known.

The amount of gain required by the servo can be obtained from a knowledge of the allowable errors, the gear ratio, and the static characteristics of the prime mover. The gain must be at least enough so that the allowable static error will generate sufficient torque to overcome the load. If, for instance, the allowable static error of the servomechanism is 0.3° and the error detector uses up 0.2°, the reference input is 0.1°. If the torque load is 10 oz-in. and the gear ratio is 50:1, the torque load of the motor shaft is 0.2 oz-in. If the error detector has a sensitivity of 1 volt/deg, an actuating signal corresponding to 0.1° produces 0.1 volt output from the synchros. If the motor requires 4 volts to produce the required amount of torque (0.2 oz-in.), the lower limit on amplification, in order that the friction be overcome, is therefore 40. The upper limit on the amount of amplification required can be determined from the amount necessary to saturate the prime mover and hence deliver maximum torque for the maximum error of the servo. In the previous example, if the motor saturates with 100 volts, the upper limit on gain is 100/0.1 = 1,000.

Another method of computing the approximate amplification required is based on the velocity error of the servo when tracking the maximum reference-input velocity. Calculation can be made of the voltage required to cause the prime mover to rotate at this maximum tracking velocity. The allowable error at this maximum tracking velocity, when amplified, must produce the voltage required by the prime mover. Although the examples are given in electrical terms, the prime mover need not be electrical and the foregoing can be expressed in terms of other variables.

After determining the amount of amplification, a choice must be made as to how this amplification is to be obtained. The answer to this question depends largely upon whether the servo is to be electrical, electrohydraulic, pneumatic, or some combination. Circuits must be chosen for modulation, demodulation, or any of the other special functions dictated by the block diagram. A logical adjunct to the schematic circuit diagram is a schematic mechanical diagram, showing the various gear ratios, limit stops, differentials, dials, rotating components, electrical limit switches, hand cranks, and other such equipment as required by the specifications or for the manufacturer's convenience.

2-12. Preliminary Test. The next stage of the design is the preliminary test, in which the dynamic response of certain fixed parameters of the system is determined. For this purpose it may be desirable to set up portions of the servomechanism in experimental form. Principally the prime mover is connected to a dummy load and to the output stage

FIG. 2-15. Breadboard components.   (*Helipat Corp., Fullerton, Calif.*)

FIG. 2-16. Mechanical breadboard of instrument servo.   (*Reeves Instrument Corp., New York.*)

of the amplifier as a means of driving the prime mover. Such experimentation is often facilitated by the use of breadboard mechanical arrangements, as well as breadboard electrical amplifiers. A portion of the servomechanism can be breadboarded by using slotted plates, so that a variety of shaft hangers, synchros, and servomotors can be quickly assembled. Figure 2-15 shows the types of components that can be used for instrument servo breadboards.

Tests of the amplifier itself, the amplifier in conjunction with the prime mover, modulation and demodulation circuits, the rate generators, or any component of the over-all block diagram that affects the dynamic performance of the system can be made. It may be that some of the components which have been chosen have dynamic characteristics which are well known because of previous tests or manufacturers' catalogue data. The primary purpose of these tests is to determine what must be added to the dynamic response of the system in order that the final servomechanism meet the loop transfer functions as set up in the study phase.

TABLE 2-4. CHECK LIST OF FACTORS IMPORTANT IN OVER-ALL SERVO DESIGN
AND PERFORMANCE

Environmental problems:
  Supply variations, voltage, and
    frequency
  Type of supplies available
  Input-power requirements
  Ambient temperature
  Humidity
  Pressure
  Shock and vibration
  Degree of enclosure
  Corrosive atmosphere
  Operating position

Signal problems:
  Noise
  Phase shifts
  Quadrature
  Harmonics
  Impedance levels
  Alignment and zeroing
  Grounding
  Shielding
  Distributed capacitance and
    inductance
  Pickup, hum, and ripple
  Coupling through power supplies
  Leakage

Mechanical problems:
  Accuracy of parts
  Friction
  Backlash and looseness
  Lubrication

Over-all size and weight:
  Workmanship
  Strength

Component and materials problems:
  Contact materials
  Fungus
  Aging
  Tolerances
  Size and weight
  Availability
  Reliability
  Temperature rise
  Voltage and current ratings
  Audible noise
  Electromagnetic radiation
  Difference between manufacturers
  Spare parts
  Life
  Insulating properties
  Corrosion resistance
  Machinability
  Component characteristics

General problems:
  Cost
  Cost of maintenance (accessibility,
    test points, component replacement)
  Standardization
  Safety (to personnel and equipment)
  Instructions (operation, maintenance,
    and test)
  Interconnection with other equipment
  Performance (see Fig. 2-1)

Figure 2-16 shows a mechanical breadboard ready for electrical connections and subsequent test.

An analog computer is often used for cases where the components are not available or where certain components cannot readily be set up in a breadboard form, for example, when portions of the servomechanism require aerodynamic or hydraulic loading. The computer can be used to simulate portions of the system working together with the actual components. Alternately, the entire system can be set up on a computer* and optimized by varying the system parameters.

2-13. Finalizing the Design. With the system set up in either breadboard form or on a computer, the engineer is in a position to check all points in the specification and firm up the design. With the prime mover, gear train, and amplifiers specified, the method of achieving system dynamics can be verified. This includes a consideration of both loop dynamics and the transfer path from load disturbances to the controlled shaft. The particular form of the equalizer is chosen, and final component values of the network are established.

Since at this stage the design is finalized, the complete block diagram, circuit and wiring diagrams, component specifications, mechanical-component design, test specifications, etc., must be engineered for fabrication of the unit.

2-14. Final Test. The purpose of the final test is to determine whether or not the design is within the requirements of the specifications and the margin of safety available for manufacturing tolerances. The method of making environmental and other tests incidental to dynamic performance is not discussed. A check list of factors that are important to over-all servo design and performance is shown in Table 2-4. At this point in the project, reference to Chap. 14, which presents a discussion of performance testing, is suggested.

PROBLEMS

2-1. Using the diagram of Fig. 2-1, give various combinations of information that would completely specify the performance of a servomechanism.

2-2. How would the chart of Fig. 2-1 be extended to take into account the effect of dynamic-load torques?

2-3. What circumstances might alter how detailed the information is that the customer gives the designer on the performance requirements of a servomechanism?

2-4. How is the cost of the servomechanism affected by the requirements on (a) noise transmission, (b) stability margin, (c) static accuracy, (d) dynamic accuracy?

2-5. Find position, velocity, and acceleration coefficients for the following forward-loop transfer functions ($H = 1$ for all systems):

(a) $G = \dfrac{K}{(s + 10)(s + 100)}$

(b) $G = \dfrac{K}{s(s + 10)(s + 100)}$

* See Ref. 46 for a discussion of analog computers.

(c) $G = \dfrac{K}{s^2(s^2 + 2\zeta\omega_n s + \omega_n{}^2)}$

(d) $G = \dfrac{Ks}{(s + 1)(s + 10)(s + 100)}$

(e) $G = \dfrac{100}{s^2 + 2\zeta\omega_n s + \omega_n{}^2}$

(f) $G = \dfrac{100(s + 10)(s + 50)}{s^3(s^2 - 2\zeta\omega_n s + \omega_n{}^2)}$

2-6. A target airplane at an elevation of 3,000 yd and 4,000 yd minimum slant range flies at 400 mph in a passing course by a tracking director. For a 6–12 servomechanism having a 45° phase margin and corner frequency of 8 cycles, sketch the time components of train and elevation errors vs. time.

2-7. A servomechanism has a maximum velocity requirement of 100°/sec, an acceleration requirement of 400°/sec², and a constant-load torque of 150 oz-in. Show how the application of the methods of this chapter will obtain the acceptable gear ratios for motors whose torque-speed characteristics are assumed linear. Sketch appropriate graphs, using the power relationships and the torque relationships referred both to the controlled shaft and to the motor shaft.

2-8. Prove that a gear ratio chosen so that the motor is operating at its maximum power output when the control shaft is rotating at the required slew speed permits the servo to resist the maximum load friction.

2-9. Compare the advantages and disadvantages of the three methods available to improve the dynamic performance of a servomechanism.

CHAPTER 3

POSITION-MEASURING INSTRUMENTS

3-1. Potentiometer Applications.   Chapter 1 shows an application of potentiometers in servomechanisms in which a pair of potentiometers act as an error detector.   They measure the difference between the command shaft and the controlled shaft and convert this angular difference into a voltage whose magnitude and polarity indicate the magnitude

FIG. 3-1. A 2-in. diameter precision potentiometer.   (*Technology Instrument Corp., Acton, Mass.*)

and direction of the actuating signal.   Figure 3-1 shows a typical potentiometer used for this purpose.   If the command shaft is close to and in line with the controlled shaft, a single potentiometer can be used as an error detector by coupling the potentiometer shaft to the command shaft and the potentiometer case to the controlled shaft.   The voltage excitation is so arranged with a center tap that the output voltage is zero when the shafts are in correspondence.   The occasions when this scheme can be used are rare.

44

In addition to the application shown in Chap. 1, there exist other uses of potentiometers involving computers. The most straightforward of these is the conversion of mechanical position to voltage. By applying a constant potential to a linear potentiometer, the output voltage at the brush can be made proportional to the angle of shaft rotation.

A potentiometer, comprising a slider that moves along a resistance element, is shown in Fig. 3-2a. A more useful schematic, with excitation v_1 and output voltage v_2 included, is shown in Fig. 3-2b. The transfer function of a potentiometer is determined from the voltage gradient (volts/radian or volts/in.) along the potentiometer. The potentiometer of Fig. 3-2b has a voltage v_1 applied across a total angle of θ_{max} in degrees. The transfer function is

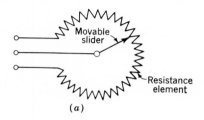

(a)

$$\frac{v_2}{\theta} = \frac{v_1}{\theta_{max}} \qquad (3-1)$$

The most common potentiometer, utilizing a linear resistance element, finds wide use in computers and for position comparison in feedback control systems. Single-turn potentiometers (Fig. 3-1) usually have a usable rotation of less than 360°. The remaining angle is available for

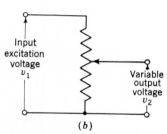

(b)

Fig. 3-2. Schematic diagram of a potentiometer.

conducting overtravels (10 to 15° arcs at each end of the resistance element). One typical unit is shown in the photograph of Fig. 3-1 and in the outline drawing of Fig. 3-3. The accuracy is proportional to the diameter of the potentiometer and to the mechanical precision. Careful design, precision machining, and choice of optimum materials result in an accurate instrument.

Some potentiometers are deliberately wound so that they do not give a linear voltage output for a shaft input; i.e., the resistance of these potentiometers is not a linear function of shaft angle. These potentiometers can be wound to reproduce sine or cosine functions, ballistic data, and other such functions. If these potentiometers are excited with a constant voltage, the output voltage is a function, for example, of the sine or cosine of the input angle, instead of the angle itself. Of course, sine and cosine functions and ballistic data can also be obtained from linear potentiometers by using nonlinear cams or linkage to drive the shafts and hence perform the computation.

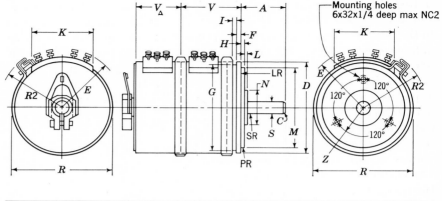

K E Y	A	C	D	E	F	G	H	I	K	L	M	N	R	R2	S	V	V_Δ	Z
Servo and tapped hole	$\frac{15}{16}$	$\frac{1}{32} \times 45°$	2.000	$1\frac{3}{8}$	0.093	1.870	0.062	0.078	$1\frac{3}{4}$	0.061	1.8750	0.750	$2\frac{7}{64}$	$1\frac{19}{64}$	0.250	1.412	0.974	0.625
Tolerance	$+\frac{1}{32}$ $-\frac{1}{32}$		±0.005	max	±0.005	±0.005	±0.005	±0.005	max	±0.005	+0.0000 -0.0005	+0.0000 -0.0005	max	max	+0.0000 -0.0005	max	max	±0.005

PR (pilot runout) 0.001″ max   SR (shaft runout) 0.001″ max   LR (lateral runout) 0.001″/in. radius (max)

FIG. 3-3. Outline drawing of the potentiometer shown in Fig. 3-1. (*Technology Instrument Corp., Acton, Mass.*)

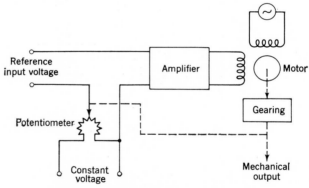

FIG. 3-4. Conversion of voltage to position.

The reverse of the above operation is also used in analog computation. This involves the conversion of voltage to a mechanical position proportional to that voltage.

This is accomplished as shown in Fig. 3-4. The reference input in this case is the voltage that is to be converted to a shaft rotation. A linear potentiometer excited by a constant voltage from the same a-c source is also used. The difference between the reference-input voltage and the voltage at the potentiometer arm is fed into an amplifier and motor, whose constant-voltage winding is excited from the same a-c source but shifted 90° in phase and whose output is used to position the potentiometer arm. If the voltage at the output of the potentiometer is not equal to the reference-input voltage, the servomechanism operates to make this difference equal to zero despite any variations of the input voltage. The output of the system is the position of the potentiometer arm.

If it is desired to multiply two quantities together, one of the quantities is put in the form of voltage. This voltage is used to excite a linear potentiometer. The other quantity is put in the form of the potentiometer shaft rotation, which can be derived from a voltage in the manner explained above. The output voltage is the product of these two quantities. This connection is shown in Fig. 3-5. Through appropriate use of scale factors, any magnitude of voltage can represent any number of any physical

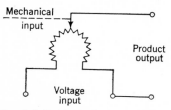

FIG. 3-5. Product of two variables.

quantity, and any shaft angle can similarly represent any number of physical quantity.

It is sometimes desired to take the reciprocal of a function. This can be done by the servo shown in Fig. 3-6. The circuit is similar to that

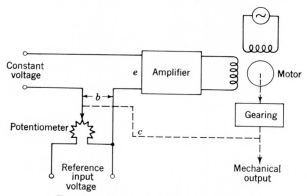

FIG. 3-6. Computation of a reciprocal.

shown in Fig. 3-4, except that the variable voltage whose reciprocal is desired is applied to a linear potentiometer as the reference input r and c is nulled against a constant voltage of unity magnitude by feeding the difference e into a servoamplifier. The servo tends to make these two voltages equal by rotation of the potentiometer through an angle c. If they are equal, the shaft position must equal the reciprocal of the reference-input voltage since their product is always equal to 1. In equation form,

$$1 - rc = e = 0 \qquad (3\text{-}2)$$

and therefore $$c = \frac{1}{r} \hspace{4cm} (3\text{-}3)$$

In actual practice, as in gunfire-control computers, this computation takes place continuously with varying reference inputs.

3-2. Potentiometer Construction. The diameter of potentiometers used for servomechanism or computing applications is generally 1 to 5 in., and the units are usually wire-wound.   Where resolution or high-temperature operation is important, potentiometers utilize conducting plastic

Fig. 3-7. Internal construction of a potentiometer.   (*Technology Instrument Corp., Acton, Mass.*)

or conducting films deposited on glass.   Both linear-motion and angular-motion potentiometers are manufactured.   Potentiometers can be excited with alternating or direct current.   As shown in Fig. 3-7, they generally consist of the following parts: (1) a shaft of about $\frac{1}{4}$ in. diameter; (2) a case either of metal or, more frequently, of molded plastic; (3) bearings, either bronze or ball bearings; (4) a rotor, consisting of a casting, stamping, or fabricated parts; (5) a winding, usually consisting of many turns of wire wrapped around a plastic or soft copper mandrel, insulated with formex or some other enamel; (6) a sliding contact assembly, consisting of a slider, a contact (often made of pure silver), springs, and a guide to cause the contact to come against the windings; (7) terminals, to which external connections can be made to the winding; and (8) the sliding contact.   In some cases, slip rings and contacts are also used to complete the circuit from the case to the sliding contact.   Often provisions are made for ganging the potentiometers so that a single shaft will rotate several brush assemblies, as shown in Fig. 3-8.

The physical form of a potentiometer varies with the manufacturer. Figure 3-9 shows a cutaway view of a multiturn unit. This unit has a $\frac{7}{8}$-in. diameter, 1.587-in. body length, and is available with a 0.25 per cent linearity tolerance. The winding is in the form of a helix, and, to make contact with the winding, the contact assembly is such that the brush travels in a helix. Potentiometers are limited in angular travel from slightly under 1 revolution to 2, 3, 10, 40, and even 50 revolutions before hitting internal limit stops (sometimes omitted on single-turn potentiometers).

Fig. 3-8. Ganged potentiometers. (*Fairchild Controls Corp., Hicksville, N.Y.*)

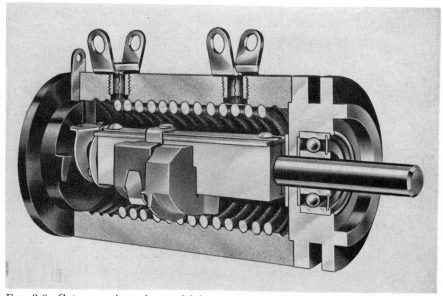

Fig. 3-9. Cutaway view of a multiple-turn potentiometer. (*Helipot Corp., South Pasadena, Calif.*)

In computer applications it is necessary to "gang" or assemble several potentiometers on a single shaft. The unit shown in Fig. 3-8 permits the ganging of up to 20 units on a single shaft. The individual cups are held together with circular clamps. When circuit elements require change, the potentiometers are easily removed and rephased. One manufacturer has produced a "plug-in potentiometer," which is shown in Fig. 3-10. A modified terminal board has small, pin-type plugs in place of conventional terminals. Each potentiometer is quickly removed and replaced without disconnecting wires or soldering.

FIG. 3-10. Plug-in potentiometers provide rapid removal and replacement. (*Fairchild Controls Corp., Hicksville, N.Y.*)

Figure 3-11 illustrates a view of a linear-motion potentiometer, which receives a linear (translational) actuation motion rather than a rotational shaft motion. Stroke lengths are available from $2\frac{1}{2}$ to 15 in. Up to three separate resistance elements can be installed within a single unit, with individual voltage takeoffs actuated by the common shaft. An accuracy of ± 1 per cent is possible for both linear and nonlinear resistance functions.

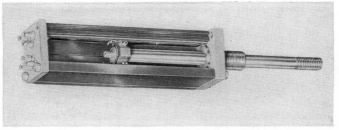

FIG. 3-11. Linear-motion potentiometer. (*Technology Instrument Corp., Acton, Mass.*)

Figure 3-12 shows carbon-film elements for various precision potentiometers. This type of potentiometer overcomes such undesirable characteristics as finite resolution, large inductive and capacitive effects at high frequencies, and relatively large size. A wiper, traversing the carbon film, produces a continuously varying stepless voltage. The smooth, unbroken surface of the element permits high-speed operation and assures long life (1 million cycles at rotational speeds up to 1,000 rpm). Film-application techniques have been applied to a large variety of base shapes for specific requirements. They are especially applicable where the potentiometer must be built into the associated mechanical component because of space or available mechanical power limitations. Typical of these are sensing elements in gyros, altitude controllers, and accelerometers for autopilots. The carbon film is bonded to an insulating base which has a temperature expansion coefficient which equals that of the carbon film. These units can be operated at 150° with a 0.01 per cent linearity and with an infinite resolution. The construction details of a typical dual carbon-film potentiometer are shown in Fig. 3-13.

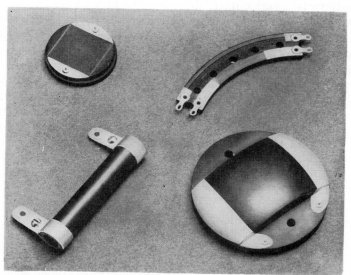

FIG. 3-12. Special-purpose carbon-film elements. Upper left: sine-cosine card. Element produces, simultaneously, sine and cosine of angle of rotation. Upper right: dual linear card. Lower left: linear card on round mandrel. Lower right: linear card on spherical surface. (*Computer Instruments Corp., Hempstead, N.Y.*)

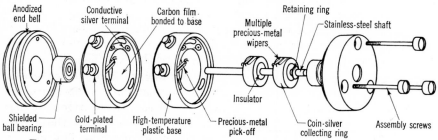

FIG. 3-13. Construction details of typical, dual, carbon-film potentiometer.

3-3. Potentiometer Characteristics. Typical precision potentiometers have about 150 to 800 turns of wire per inch of mandrel. The torque necessary to rotate the shaft varies from 1 to 10 oz-in.; approximately 2 oz-in. is standard. Miniature potentiometers are built with an input torque as low as 0.003 oz-in. An exploded view of such a potentiometer, whose outside diameter is 1 in., is shown in Fig. 3-14. Such a potentiom-

eter is used when the command can furnish only a very small amount of
torque without impairing the accuracy of the source of the command
signal.

Although the bearings can cause a significant contribution, the principal
source of friction is the brush riding on the winding.   The total resistance
of potentiometers varies from about 25 ohms up to 1 megohm and for
most servo applications is usually on the order of a few thousand ohms.
The power ratings vary from about 1 to 10 watts, and they are generally
rated conservatively with a dissipation of less than $\frac{1}{2}$ watt/in.^{2} of
winding area.   Any variation of resistance with current due to heating
would change the linearity of the potentiometer.   This fact limits the
voltage that can be applied to the potentiometer and hence limits the
obtainable gradient, i.e., the number of volts per degree of shaft displacement.   The voltage applied to potentiometers used in servo applications
is on the order of 4 to 20 volts, and the gradient therefore becomes about

FIG. 3-14. Construction of a low-torque potentiometer.   (*G. M. Giannini and Co.,
Inc., Pasadena, Calif.*)

0.01 to 0.05 volt/deg.   A higher-gain amplifier is therefore required than
if synchros were used for the error detector since synchros have approximately 100 times as high a voltage gradient.

A high voltage, and consequently a high voltage gradient from the
potentiometer, requires a high resistance.   A high-resistance potentiometer is more susceptible to pickup and tends to be loaded by other

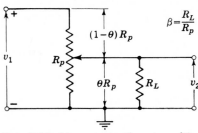

$$\beta = \frac{R_L}{R_p}$$

FIG. 3-15. Linear potentiometer with
shunt-load resistance.

circuits following it and hence reduces
the voltage gradient.   It does not,
however, affect the linearity if the load
resistance appears between the brushes
of the input and output potentiometers
since under conditions of zero actuating signal the voltage across the
brushes is zero.

If a load resistance is placed between the brush and one end of a
linear potentiometer, as shown in Fig.
3-15, the potentiometer will no longer be linear.   As current is drawn
through the slider a so-called "loading error" results.   The loading error

varies with slider position. The output voltage is given by the expression

$$\frac{v_2}{v_1} = \frac{\theta}{1 + (\theta/\beta)(1 - \theta)} \tag{3-4}$$

where β is the ratio of load resistance R_L to potentiometer resistance R_p; θ is the setting of the potentiometer, expressed as a fraction of the total resistance; v_1 is the applied input voltage; and v_2 is the output voltage.

The deviation or error from the straight-line curve is given by the expression

$$\frac{v_2}{v_1} = \frac{(\theta^2/\beta)(1 - \theta)}{1 + (\theta/\beta)(1 - \theta)} \tag{3-5}$$

The loading error, as plotted in Fig. 3-16, varies with slider position. The error is zero at both ends of the coil and has a maximum value at approximately two-thirds rotation. The error varies with load resistance. A load resistance 10 times that of the potentiometer resistance produces a maximum error of 1.5 per cent of the applied voltage. An error of 0.15 per cent results when the load resistance is 100 times the potentiometer resistance. The effect of loading can be reduced by (1) winding on the potentiometer a slight nonlinear function, which compensates for the loading; or (2) locating a tap at the $\frac{2}{3}$ point on the potentiometer. An appropriate resistor connected between the tap and the 100 per cent point compensates for the loading.

The loading error of potentiometers, as shown in Fig. 3-16, is normally considered detrimental. The loading curves can become useful, since an appropriately loaded potentiometer can be utilized to obtain many nonlinear functions with the linear nontapped potentiometer.

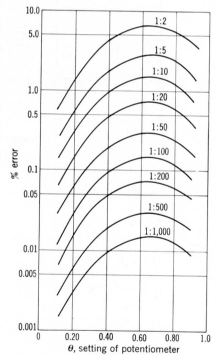

FIG. 3-16. Potentiometer loading error curve.

Equation (3-4) produces the nonlinear curves of Fig. 3-17 for β in the range 0.01 to 1.0. When the potentiometer is loaded on the top, as

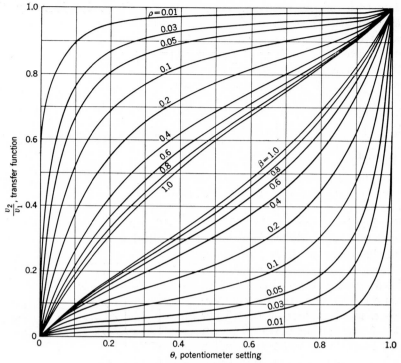

FIG. 3-17. Potentiometer loading curves.

shown in Fig. 3-18, the potentiometer transfer function is given by

$$\frac{v_2}{v_1} = \frac{(1 - \theta) + \rho}{(1 - \theta) + (\rho/\theta)} \tag{3-6}$$

Equation (3-6) plots into the curves of Fig. 3-17 when ρ is in the range 0.01 to 1.0.

Other types of nonlinear functions can be obtained by either of the

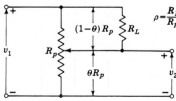

FIG. 3-18. Equivalent circuit for a loaded potentiometer.

following methods: (1) a standard linear potentiometer with voltage taps and resistance loading or (2) a nonlinear winding that depends upon a variation of resistance as θ varies.

3-4. Potentiometer Linearity and Conformity. In general, the same characteristics are inherent in the precision nonlinear potentiometer as in precision linear units (i.e., resolution, loading error, etc.). The deviation of the output voltage from the prescribed function is called conformity rather than linearity.

The transfer function of Eq. (3-1) represents a straight-line input-output relationship. The deviation of the potentiometer from this straight line is a measure of the linearity accuracy. Two definitions of linearity are in common use: (1) *independent linearity* (used in connection with precision potentiometers) and (2) *zero-based linearity* (used in connection with a rheostat or variable resistance).

Independent linearity tolerance is the maximum allowable deviation from the best straight line that can be drawn through a plot of the actual points of voltage on the voltage vs. rotation curve. The tolerance is expressed as a per cent of the maximum voltage output. This is shown in Fig. 3-19a, where the straight line has been oriented to best fit the actual output curve. In the absence of any qualifying statement, this is the linearity that is generally meant when applied to a potentiometer.

Linearity specifications are usually expressed as a percentage variation of voltage from the correct value at any angle of shaft rotation. Linearity figures can be applied to either the deviation of resistance or output voltage for a given shaft angle or the deviation of shaft angle for a given resistance or output voltage, when the winding is unloaded.

If the potentiometer has a tolerance of 0.1 per cent and a winding of about 350°, the error spread will be 0.7°. The maximum error in position of the shaft from a straight-line approximation of the resistance vs. angle curve of the potentiometer is 0.35°. This straight-line approximation is chosen so as to make the error spread as small as possible, and there are points of intersection between this line and the linearity curve of the potentiometer that have zero error. The user does not generally know where these points are and might define the position of zero error of the servo at some other more convenient point. If two such potentiometers are used in a servomechanism and any point, for example, the center of each potentiometer's winding, is defined as zero error, the maximum error possible between the two shaft angles with the servo at null is 1.4°. This is a most unusual case, however, since it requires that one of the two potentiometers have its maximum positive error at the point chosen as the zero-error position and that the other potentiometer have its maximum negative error at the same position. It further requires that the maximum negative error of the first potentiometer occur at the same angular position as the maximum positive error of the second. The actual error that might be expected from such a system is less than half this value.

For some applications, it is necessary that the resistance between the brush and the bottom point of the winding of the potentiometer be zero when the angle is zero. Potentiometers used in computers often have this requirement. This is known as *zero-based linearity* and is shown in Fig. 3-19b. In this case, the straight-line approximation must go

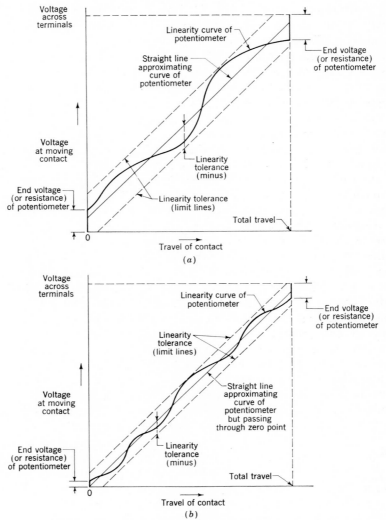

FIG. 3-19. (a) Independent linearity; (b) zero-based linearity.

through zero. In neither of these two cases is the absolute resistance, i.e., the total resistance of the potentiometer, a factor in determining the linearity of the potentiometer.

An even more stringent type of linearity is absolute ohmic linearity, which requires that the total resistance be as closely correct as the linearity of resistance with brush travel. In measuring this type of linearity, a line is drawn on a scale of resistance vs. shaft angle. This line goes through the zero point and the point of maximum resistance and

total shaft angle. The deviation of actual resistance from the theoretically perfect straight line, expressed as a percentage of the total
resistance, must be less than the tolerance.

Precision linear potentiometers have a tolerance of linearity on the
order of 1 per cent. Standard units are available with linearity tolerances down to 0.1 and even 0.01 per cent. The accuracy of such a potentiometer is dependent upon the uniformity of wire resistance, the shape
and surface of the mandrel upon which it is wound, the uniformity of
spacing of the winding, the shape and width of the brush, the eccentricity
of the shaft and mandrel, and the backlash between the brush and
the shaft. Some manufacturers compensate for many of the errors
and variations of the wire and mandrel by special controls on their winding machines. These controls automatically vary the spacing between
individual turns of wire in order to maintain a linear relationship between
the resistance and length of winding on the mandrel. Nonlinearities
of potentiometers can also be corrected
by the use of adjustable cams, sometimes built right into the potentiometer
case, in which the motion of the brush
is advanced or retarded as necessary to
cause the potentiometer to be more
linear. Potentiometer errors must be
kept to a minimum since these errors

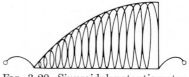

FIG. 3-20. Sinusoidal potentiometer
winding.

add directly to the servo error. The highest-accuracy potentiometers
are normally obtained by selection.

Nonlinear potentiometers are generally made by either winding on a
mandrel that has the shape of the slope of the function, like the sinusoidally shaped winding in Fig. 3-20, or
by the use of taps on a linear winding.
Fastening taps to the winding without
interfering too greatly with the spacing
between turns constitutes a difficult
mechanical problem. Sections of winding between the taps can be loaded with
various external resistors to vary the resistance between one end of the winding
and the output brush of the potentiometer. Some manufacturers even use this
scheme as a means of making a poten-

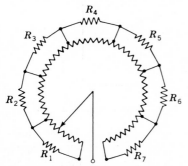

FIG. 3-21. Tapped potentiometer.

tiometer more linear. This is accomplished by measuring the actual
resistance at the brush before adding these loading resistors and by
calculating the proper loading resistor to make the potentiometer linear.

Figure 3-21 shows a circuit from which calculations can be made of the number of taps required, their positions, and the values of load resistance required. For example, to correct a winding that originally has a linearity of 1 per cent to one having a linearity of 0.1 per cent,

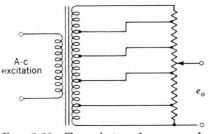

about 4 to 10 taps are normally required. The expense of adding these taps, together with the problem of maintaining the tolerance of the original winding despite the mechanical insertion of taps, largely restricts the use of tapped windings to the generation of nonlinear functions. One company uses a separate winding for the load resistors, and their values are obtained by adjusta-

FIG. 3-22. Tapped transformer used with a tapped potentiometer.

ble taps on this auxiliary winding connected with fixed taps on the primary winding.

Transformer tapping used in connection with a tapped potentiometer, as shown in Fig. 3-22, provides a convenient method of (1) linearizing a

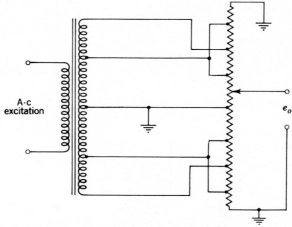

FIG. 3-23. Sinusoidal function generated with tapped transformer and tapped potentiometer.

potentiometer, (2) reducing the loading error, and (3) providing a method of generating nonmonotonic functions. As an example, a ± 3 per cent sinusoidal function is obtained with seven taps and a tapped transformer as shown in Fig. 3-23. The resulting function is comprised of straight lines and closely approximates the actual sinusoidal function as is shown in Fig. 3-24. Sine-cosine potentiometers can also be made by moving a contact in a circle on the surface of a flat rectangular card around which evenly spaced windings have been placed. Such a potentiometer is shown in Fig. 3-25.

3-5. Potentiometer Resolution. The resolution of a potentiometer is the minimum change of resistance output (obtained by rotating the shaft) expressed as a percentage of the total resistance of the potentiometer. It is dependent upon the number of turns of wire per inch on the winding and upon the diameter of the arc upon which the brush travels.

Since the potentiometer slider does

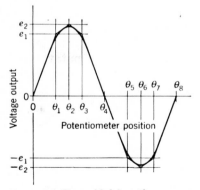

Fig. 3-24. Sinusoidal function generated by tapped potentiometer.

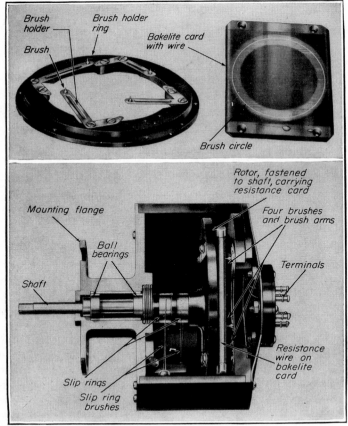

Fig. 3-25. Sine-cosine potentiometer.   (*The Gamewell Co., Newton Upper Falls, Mass.*)

not move along a continuous wire, the transfer function is not a continuous curve but a succession of steps. As the slider moves from turn to turn, the voltage increases in a stepwise fashion, as shown in Fig. 3-26. This stepwise output voltage ΔE is the total voltage E divided by the number of turns of resistance wire n. For a wiper that touches only one wire at a time, the resolution is given by the following definition:

$$\text{Resolution} = \frac{\Delta E}{E} = \frac{E/n}{E} = \frac{1}{\substack{\text{number of turns on} \\ \text{the potentiometer}}} \qquad (3\text{-}7)$$

It is usually somewhat smaller than this because of the interpolation effect of the brush wiper.

It is desirable to have good resolution, since high-gain servomechanisms may have a tendency to "hunt" between turns of wire on the potentiometer, seeking a voltage that does not exist on that surface. One way of

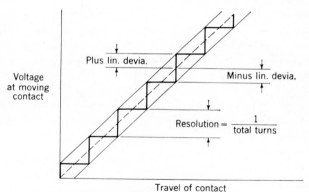

Fig. 3-26. Resolution in wire-wound potentiometers.

increasing the resolution of the common type of potentiometer is to increase the diameter of its winding. Another method is to use a multiple-turn potentiometer in which the slide wire is coiled into a helix. For a given length of winding, this method results in a smaller unit. A still further way of increasing the resolution is to use finer wire for the winding. There is a limit, however, because of the wear of fine wire.

The resolution of the potentiometer places an upper limit on the accuracy that can be obtained. For example, if the resolution is 0.1 per cent, the best possible accuracy that can be obtained from such a potentiometer is 0.05 per cent, and it would normally be worse than this. A potentiometer that has virtually zero resolution is the stepless potentiometer, in which the winding consists of a single high-resistance wire. The brush rides on this wire, which forms its own mandrel. While the resistance of such a device is limited by the resistivity of the wire, potentiometers can be obtained with nominal resistances on the order of 1,500 ohms and an accuracy of ± 0.03 per cent in models capable of 30 turns of rotation.

Use of the deposited-carbon-film potentiometer of Fig. 3-13 also eliminates the steplike transfer function and provides a continuous output curve.

3-6. Potentiometer Life. The life of most precision potentiometers is on the order of 1 million cycles, during which none of the mechanical or electrical specifications exceeds its tolerance by more than 50 per cent. Some conducting plastic potentiometers have been tested to 20 million cycles of operation.

At one extreme, life may be defined in terms of shaft revolutions before the slider contact wears through or the shaft seizes. At the other, it might be defined as ending when any operating characteristic fails to meet initial specification.

Therefore, two definitions are used: *physical life*, which ends when some part wears out; and *useful life*, which ends when the potentiometer no longer functions properly in a given application. The following operating characteristics of a precision potentiometer can be expected to change during use: (1) total resistance, (2) linearity, (3) noise, (4) torque, and (5) shaft play. In general, wear has the greatest effect on each of these characteristics. The environmental conditions to which a potentiometer is subjected during use may also cause changes. Contact wear increases with increasing contact force and increasing temperature. It can be minimized by proper engineering of the coil-and-contact system, which takes into consideration (1) wire alloy, (2) wire size, (3) winding pitch, (4) resistance-element length, (5) contact alloy, and (6) contact-spring design. In any potentiometer, the contact should be soft enough to prevent undue wear of the resistance element but not so soft as to abrade and contribute noise-producing particles or so soft as to limit the potentiometer's life. For the same wire alloy and size, the contact alloy may change for different resistance-element lengths. For example, in a multiturn potentiometer with an element 400 in. long, the contact should be harder and more wear-resistant than in a single-turn unit with an element only 4 in. long.

Wear of a sliding-contact carrying current is not due to mechanical abrasion alone. The sliding contact of a potentiometer shorts two or more turns of wire on the resistance element. A large portion of the coil current flows into the contact and back into the coil. This current is continually interrupted as the contact moves along the element, resulting in electrical or arc erosion of the contact. It is the coil current, rather than the load current, that is responsible for this effect. To minimize loading error, the load current in a potentiometer is usually held to no more than 1 per cent of the coil current.

Externally excited vibrations may produce wear by causing contact movement at right angles to the resistance element as well as along the element. The amplitude of this movement is small; but, if continued for appreciable time at moderate frequencies, the total travel is great.

3-7. Potentiometer Noise. Noise in a potentiometer shows the presence of spurious, unwanted voltages. There are several types of such voltage that exist in the output of potentiometers used in servo-mechanism applications. If a typical wire-wound potentiometer is excited with direct voltage, for example, the fact that the potentiometer has a finite resolution causes a ripple voltage to appear at the brush as the shaft is rotated. This discontinuity of voltage output might cause harm if, for example, a lead network were used for stabilization, since such a network tends to pass noise voltages with less attenuation than true signals. A similar noise effect due to resolution exists if the potentiometer is excited with alternating voltage. Such noise is minimized in the single-wire potentiometer or in the plastic or film type. Noise of a similar character is caused by brush jump, brush vibration, wire irregularity, or variation of contact resistance as from pressure or such surface conditions as dirt or oxide film. Another cause of noise output in the potentiometer is stray capacitance or pickup, which can be minimized by grounding the center tap of the potentiometer.

When used with a servomechanism as an error detector, the voltage applied to a pair of potentiometers excited with alternating voltage must be of exactly the same phase lest a quadrature noise voltage be produced. Even lead resistance must be carefully taken into account. For example, a 1° phase difference on a pair of potentiometers excited with 15 volts will produce up to $\frac{1}{4}$ volt quadrature voltage. Assuming that the potentiometers are single-turn, the sensitivity of these potentiometers is 0.05 volt/deg of error. It is thus seen that the error must be over 5° before the error voltage exceeds the quadrature voltage.

The presence of quadrature voltage in the actuating signal is a fault common to all error detectors, and its effect on servomechanisms is the same, regardless of source. This quadrature voltage produces no useful torque in the servomotor and results only in excessive heating of its windings. If the quadrature voltage is large enough, it can saturate the amplifier, thus preventing it from functioning properly. Furthermore, if a two-phase motor is used as a prime mover and if the fixed voltage is not exactly of the proper phase, the presence of a quadrature component of voltage in the control voltage can cause the servo to drive to a null position slightly different from the correct null position. This is caused by the fact that the servomotor drives to minimize the control voltage at right angles to the fixed voltage. This can only be a minimum if a finite actuating-signal voltage combines with the quadrature-voltage output of the error detector.

3-8. Mechanical Considerations in Potentiometers. Mechanical tolerances of potentiometers are important in servo applications. They must be manufactured with accurate external surfaces in order to allow interchangeable manufacture and to permit accurate, low-backlash, and free-running gear trains. Typically, the diameter of the shaft and pilot mounting bushings are held to tolerances of $+0$ and -0.0002 to -0.0005 in. The squareness between the shaft and the mounting surface is held

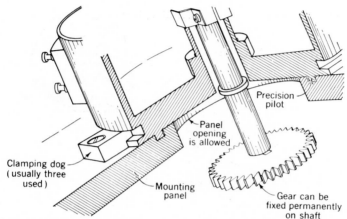

Fig. 3-27. Servo mount for clamping potentiometer to panel surface.

to about 0.001 in./in., the shaft play to about 0.001 in., and the concentricity of shaft to pilot bushing to about 0.001 in. total indicator reading (TIR).

Because of these accurate mechanical tolerances, the mounting of a precision potentiometer is an important consideration. At least three methods are utilized. The *servo mount*, shown in Fig. 3-27, is commonly used to secure potentiometers on a mounting plate or casting, such as may form a part of a gear box or a gimbal. A pilot, in the form of a raised hub on the mounting surface of the potentiometer base, engages a mating part and thus precisely positions the axis of potentiometer shaft rotation. Mounting dogs, or clamps, engage a groove on the circumference of the potentiometer base and are screwed down to the mounting plate to hold the potentiometer firmly in place. Loosening these clamps allows the potentiometer to be rotated for external adjustment. Since the pilot and mounting structure are at the outer edge of the mounting surfaces, a hole can be cut in the mounting panel to allow insertion of a gear, which is permanently fixed on the shaft.

The tapped-hole mount, shown in Fig. 3-28, can be used with panels, brackets, and mounting plates that allow access to screws extending through the mounting structure and into tapped holes in the potentiometer base. Small potentiometers usually have two tapped holes; large potentiometers, three. A hub or pilot is required for precise positioning of the potentiometer. Indexing adjustment must be made through the shaft connection, since the potentiometer base cannot be rotated.

In the *flange mount* the potentiometer mounting face has a flange surface extending radially beyond the body. The flange may have holes for receiving mounting screws, and these holes are usually slotted to allow

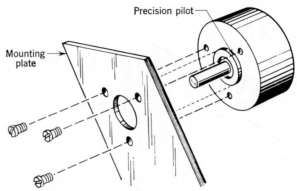

Fig. 3-28. Tapped-hole mounting with precision pilot for exact centering on panel.

a few degrees of case rotation for indexing adjustment. Mounting dogs, such as those used with the servo mount, can also be employed to secure the flange in place. A precision pilot is required for accurate centering of the potentiometer.

A large variety of taps, resistance, shaft extensions, stops, and tapped continuous-rotation units give a wide latitude to potentiometer applications. The factors to be considered in potentiometer selection can be summarized as follows:*

Electrical Suitability

1. Linearity as required by the application
2. Tolerance on total resistance and shaft angle
3. Resolution error and its effect on servo stability and wear
4. Sufficient electrical insulation strength
5. Freedom from stray capacitive and inductive effects
6. Generation of undesirable radio interference

Mechanical Suitability

1. Adequate life to meet anticipated performance cycle
2. Adaptability to environmental conditions such as temperature and humidity

* This summary has been taken, in part, from Ref. 16.

3. Ability to withstand vibration without excessive contact bounce
4. Precision of mounting surface and shaft extension
5. Precision mounting for easy zeroing and calibration
6. Acceptable starting friction

Table 3-1, page 66, gives typical electrical and mechanical characteristics of commercially available potentiometers.

3-9. Theory and Application of E-type Transformers. Although potentiometers are widely used as error detectors in servomechanisms, they suffer such inherent disadvantages as brush and wire wear, finite resolution, low voltage sensitivity, and limited angular rotation. Another method of measuring the difference between the command-shaft angle and the controlled-shaft angle and converting this difference into an electrical actuating-signal voltage relies upon magnetic coupling. Devices that employ this principle are known variously as synchros, pickoffs, linear transformers, differential transformers, and E transformers, depending upon their form.

A schematic diagram of the E transformer is shown in Fig. 3-29. It consists of two magnetic structures, one of which is in the shape of an I and the other in the shape of an E. An alternating carrier voltage is applied to the center coil of the E, and if the shunting bar is in its central position, equal voltages v_1 and v_2 are introduced in the two legs. These two voltages are subtracted to give the difference voltage, which is the output of the E transformer. When the shunting coil is in a position other than its central one, more flux is carried in the arm having the least reluctance. If the shunting bar, for example, is slightly above the position shown in Fig. 3-29, v_1 exceeds v_2 because of the higher reluctance of

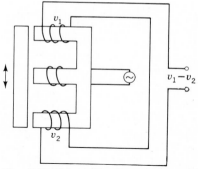

Fig. 3-29. Schematic diagram of an E transformer.

the bottom magnetic path. The voltage $v_1 - v_2$ is of a certain magnitude and polarity. If the shunting bar is placed an equal distance below the central position, v_2 exceeds v_1. The difference voltage is equal to that of the first case but of opposite polarity. A linear variable differential transformer has a magnetic circuit very much like that of an E transformer. The output voltage and phase vs. core position of such a unit are shown in Fig. 3-30.

The difference voltage is roughly proportional to the deviation of the shunting bar from its central position and of a polarity such as to indicate the direction of displacement from the central position. This device

TABLE 3-1. TYPICAL POTENTIOMETERS

No. of turns	Manufacturer	Type	Diameter, in.	Depth, in.	Mounting	Resistance range, ohms to kilohms	Resistance tolerance, %	Linearity, %	Resolution, %	Torque, oz-in.
1	Fairchild	751	0.875	0.686	Servo mount	200–50	± 5	0.3 to 0.5	0.1	0.10–0.25
1	Fairchild	756	1.75	0.80	Tapped-holes and servo mount	800–50	± 5	0.25	0.05	1.5
10	Litton Industries	MA20	2.0	2.06	Servo or panel	1,000–150	± 1	0.02 to 0.01	0.014–0.0048	0.5
10	Litton Industries	MA30	3.0	2.9	Servo or panel	2,000–300	± 1	0.01 to 0.005	0.0068–0.0024	1.0
10	Helipot	A	1.8	2.0	Bushing	10–300	± 5	± 0.05–0.5	0.043–0.007	1.5
1	Helipot	J	2.0	1.03	Flange-servo	50–50	± 5	± 0.15–0.5	0.017–0.0057	0.5
1	Helipot	T	0.875	0.78	Flange-servo	100–100	± 5	± 0.25–0.5	0.017–0.0065	0.5
3	Helipot	CN	1.8	1.09	Flange-servo	30–75	± 5	± 0.25–0.5	0.03–0.006	0.9
40	Helipot	E	3.3	6.0	Bushing	200–1,000	± 5	± 0.5		3.75
1	Galetronics	3RE	1.25	1.0	Servo	350 kilohms max	± 1 to ± 5	0.1–0.5	0.03	0.02
1	Gamewell	RL272	5.0	0.625	Panel	460–500	± 10	± 0.1	0.01–0.05	1.0
1	Gamewell	RL	1.25	0.625	Panel	80–64	± 10	± 0.3	0.05–0.25	0.5
1–20	Giannini	85171A	1.75	1.61	Servo or panel	50–250	± 5	± 0.01–± 0.1	0	0.6
1	Giannini	85181	1.125	1.16	Servo or panel	500–100	± 5	± 0.5	0.2–0.06	0.1
1	Giannini	85184	0.87	0.78	Servo mount	500–100	± 5	± 0.5	0.2–0.06	0.01
1	Technology Instrument Corp.	ST09	0.087	0.635	Servo mount	100–20	± 1	± 0.3–1	0.1–0.3	0.1
1	Technology Instrument Corp.	RVP-3	3.00	1.223	Servo or tapped-holes	100–200	± 1 to ± 5	± 0.1–± 0.5	0.04–0.15	1.0
10	Technology Instrument Corp.	M10T19	1.84	2.06	Servo or tapped-holes	1,000–200	± 1 to ± 5	± 0.025 to ± 0.05	0.002–0.016	1.0
1	Electro-Mec Lab.	9	0.75	0.81	Servo mount	90 kilohms max	± 5	0.2 to 0.5	0.06	0.02
1	DeJur-Amsco Corp.	C-078	0.875	0.50	Servo mount	25 kilohms max	± 5	± 1.0	0.1	1.0

66

can therefore be used to measure the difference in position of two objects. If one of these is the command shaft and the other is the controlled shaft, the device can be used as an error detector in a servomechanism.

One application of the E transformer is in the error detector of a ship's gyrocompass. In this application, the E portion of the transformer is fastened to a large ring that is positioned by the gyroscope and is capable of rotation through 360° in a horizontal plane. The shunting bar is placed on a ring that travels in the same plane as that of the E transformer, and a servomotor is geared to the ring. The amplifier feeding the servomotor is connected to the output of the E transformer.

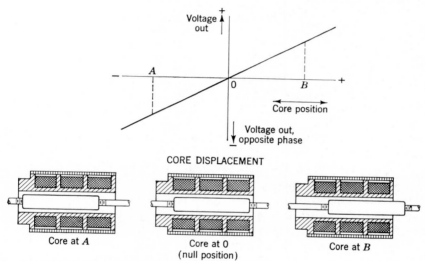

Fig. 3-30. LVDT output voltage and phase as function of core position. (*Schaevitz Engineering, Camden, N.J.*)

The apparatus is initially set so that the shunting bar is opposite the E bars. Under operating conditions, the servo tends to drive the outer ring until the output voltage of the error detector is zero and the shunting-bar ring follows the motion of the E transformer, thus measuring the output position of the gyrocompass. Other apparatus to be rotated in accordance with the ship's direction can be fastened to the outer ring, which is capable of exerting considerably more force than can the gyrocompass.

Another application of the E transformer is in a gunsight in which an E transformer measures the displacement of a rate gyro. In this application, the voltage output from the E transformer in the sight is used to null against a voltage of a remotely placed E transformer. Thus, if the two E transformers have almost identical characteristics, it is possible to get a remote indication of the displacement of the gyro inside the case of the sight.

3-10. Construction of E-type Transformers. The physical construction of a linear variable differential transformer* is shown in Fig. 3-31. Electrically, the LVDT is a symmetrically proportioned hollow coil structure with one primary winding located between two equal secondary windings. When the secondary windings are connected in series opposing, the net voltage output is the difference between the voltages induced in the individual windings. This depends on the axial position of the magnetic core which moves in the space inside the coil

FIG. 3-31. Typical linear-variable differential transformer (core in front). (*Schaevitz Engineering, Camden, N.J.*)

structure. This core is a completely separate part that the user attaches or assembles to the source of motion.

The length of the core of the LVDT is generally designed for maximum linear range of operation at the specified excitation frequency. However, a different length of core produces an increase in sensitivity at the expense of a reduction in maximum range.

The coil forms of many LVDT types are designed for enclosure in an insulating tubular cover or case of ceramic or molded phenolic material. In some other designs the coil form is protected by a tubular case of aluminum alloy with a full-length slot to prevent "shorted-turn" losses. The aluminum case of an LVDT should be electrically connected to the circuit ground, or "common," to provide electrostatic shielding between the transformer coils and any adjacent electrical wiring or parts. However, such an aluminum case has little shielding effect on the magnetic field produced by the primary winding or on any disturbing magnetic field that may be produced by external sources. The performance of the LVDT is tested and proved under the conditions of the completed transformer assembly, including any metal case or parts in the design. When an external electrically conductive and/or magnetic object is placed in the immediate magnetic field of the transformer, the effect is to modify or distort the field. Depending on exact conditions, the linear response in such a case may deteriorate, the null voltage may become high, and the phase angle may vary in some manner. Special

* The linear variable differential transformer, LVDT, is manufactured by Schaevitz Engineering, Camden, N.J.

units can be obtained with high-permeability iron or alloy cases, which aid in reducing the effects of external magnetic fields.

3-11. Characteristics of E-type Transformers. For the E transformer to be used as an error detector, as shown in Fig. 3-29, it is necessary that the number of turns in the coils producing v_1 and v_2 be exactly equal, that their resistance be equal, and that the shunting bar be properly oriented with respect to the E bars. If the two coils producing v_1 and v_2 are not the same, phase shifts can result between v_1 and v_2, thus preventing an exact voltage null from ever existing. At some position of the shunting bar, the voltage $v_1 - v_2$ will be a minimum, but the fundamental voltage remaining will be in phase quadrature to the desired phase.

The significance of these statements is perhaps most easily seen by means of the phasor diagram* of Fig. 3-32. If the E transformer were perfect and the shunting bar at its center position, the phasors representing v_1 and v_2 would be 180° apart and of the same magnitude. Each of the voltages and their difference would be in phase with (or 180° out of phase with) some reference, say v_1. The phase of this reference voltage can be obtained either by measur-

Fig. 3-32. Phasor diagram of component voltages of the E transformer.

ing v_1 directly or by measuring $v_1 - v_2$ for a position of the shunting bar that causes v_1 to be much larger than v_2. It is this reference phase which is then used to adjust the phases of the rest of the system, such as the voltage applied to the fixed voltage winding of a two-phase servomotor.

Motion of the shunting bar causes one of the phasors to increase in magnitude and the other to decrease, but they remain 180° apart. With a physical E transformer, the phasors are not 180° apart. Their lengths and their phase angle change with the position of the shunting bar. Although v_1 increases and v_2 decreases as the shunting bar is raised and v_1 decreases and v_2 increases as the shunting bar is lowered, their relative phase angles also vary through small angles. If the reference phase is again chosen as that of v_1, the null condition exists for a position of the shunting bar that causes the component of v_2 in phase with v_1 to be equal to v_1. The component of v_2 at right angles to v_1 is quadrature voltage.

These phase relationships are illustrated in Fig. 3-33. The phasor OP represents the input (primary) voltage. OS_1 and OS_2 represent the output voltage of the two opposite ends of the linear range. OS_0 represents the minimum output voltage, which occurs at the "null" point. The other solid-line phasors represent the output voltage for intermediate

* A phasor diagram represents the time relation among several sinusoidal functions of time.

displacements.   The magnitude of the minimum voltage OS_0 is greatly exaggerated in the figure for purposes of illustration.   The dotted line represents the output of a perfectly balanced LVDT having zero minimum voltage.   The phasors OT_1 and OT_2 are the output voltages at the ends of the linear range.   The line passes through zero, and the phase changes abruptly by 180° at that point.

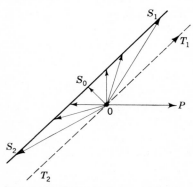

FIG. 3-33. Output phase angles for various core positions (amplitude of null voltage exaggerated for clarity).

For a certain range of motion, the output voltage of an LVDT is a linear function of core displacement.   Within this range a graph of output voltage vs. core displacement (as in Fig. 3-30) is essentially a straight line.   Beyond this range the graph deviates from a straight line.

The linear range of any LVDT varies in some degree with frequency. However, it is convenient practice to identify each type of LVDT with a figure corresponding to a single nominal linear-displacement range measured plus or minus from null core position.   When the transformer is used with the correct core provided for the specified frequency, the actual linear-displacement range will always equal or exceed the nominal range. In some applications where precise linearity is not essential the useful range may extend well beyond the actual linear range.

The term "linear range" normally refers to the linear-displacement range from null core position (plus or minus).   However, the LVDT user should remember that the total linear travel is always double the linear-displacement range.   In many applications, as in null balance systems, this total linear travel can be utilized.

The degree of linearity within the linear range is defined as the maximum deviation of the output curve from the "best-fit" straight line passing through the origin, expressed as a percentage of the output at nominal range.   For example, if the output is 1.25 volts when the core is displaced from null to the limit of the nominal range, or 0.250 in., and the maximum deviation of the output curve from the straight line through the origin that best fits the curve is ±0.005 volt, the linearity is

$$\pm\ \frac{0.005}{1.25}\qquad\text{or}\qquad\pm0.4\%$$

The linearity and linear range of an LVDT are most commonly specified for a 0.5-megohm load, since most grid-input amplifiers and vacuum-tube voltmeters have input resistances of 0.5 megohm or higher. The LVDT may be connected to a wide variety of load impedances, from infinity down to an impedance of the same order as the differential secondary impedance of the LVDT. In many applications the load may be given any value in this range with only small effect on linearity or linear range. This is shown graphically in Fig. 3-34 for a typical unit.

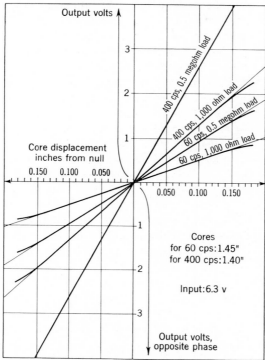

Fig. 3-34. Linear voltage output of LVDT into different resistance loads.

The rated sensitivity is usually stated in terms of millivolts (or volts) output per 0.001 in. core displacement per volts input (commonly written mv out per 0.001 in. per volts in). In a particular application the input voltage may have a constant specified value so that sensitivity is often simply described in millivolts (or volts) output per 0.001 in. core displacement. Since the voltage sensitivity varies with frequency, the frequency should be stated when specifying sensitivity. The motion of the core and the surface of the faces of the core across which flux passes must be such that the voltage sensitivity is about the same for either direction of travel of the shunting bar.

One of the difficulties of this type of error detector, common to all those using magnetic coupling, is the presence of harmonic voltages.

These harmonic voltages are caused by the nonlinearity of the iron. Their flux path is slightly different from that of the fundamental fluxes, so that, even for the position of the shunt at which the fundamental inphase components of v_1 and v_2 are equal, the harmonic voltages do not cancel. This means that the voltage output of the device contains harmonics at all positions, including null. These harmonics tend to heat the motor, in some cases produce torques on the motor, and may be of large enough magnitude to saturate or partially saturate the amplifier, thus rendering it less effective.

In applications requiring the matching of two E transformers, the problems are magnified because the characteristics of each of the two E transformers must be as nearly identical as possible. For instance, the same displacement of the shunting bar from its neutral position in each of the transformers must produce identical output voltages.

The E-type transformer usually demonstrates little or no disturbing sensitivity to small displacements of the core in any direction perpendicular to the transformer axis providing the core remains parallel to the axis. Hence, the core does not ordinarily need to be accurately centered within the transformer but should be accurately restrained from incidentally tilting or assuming an angular position when the core is actuated. This small transverse sensitivity depends on transformer proportions and on the displacement of the core axis from alignment with the transformer axis. In different designs the sensitivity to transverse motion may vary in value from above 1 per cent to less than 0.1 per cent of the useful sensitivity measured parallel to the axis.

The E-type transformer finds its widest use as an integral part of various instruments such as accelerometers and pressure transducers. Several methods of mounting the movable core are shown in Fig. 3-35.

3-12. The Microsyn. Although the E transformer can be used for measuring either linear displacement or angular displacement (if the shunting bar and E portion are axially aligned), the device is not widely used for measuring angular motion. Another device, operating on much the same principle, is the microsyn, which is shown schematically in Fig. 3-36. The microsyn consists of a laminated stator and rotor. The stator has four poles, upon each of which are a primary and a secondary winding. The rotor has no windings but serves to change the reluctance of the flux paths between the stator poles. Since the rotor has no windings, no brushes or slip rings are necessary. All the primary windings are in series and, when excited with an alternating voltage, are connected in the sense that flux tends to flow from pole 2 to 4 and from pole 3 to 1. The secondary windings are also in series but so connected that voltages induced in the windings on poles 2 and 4 oppose those in the windings on poles 3 and 1.

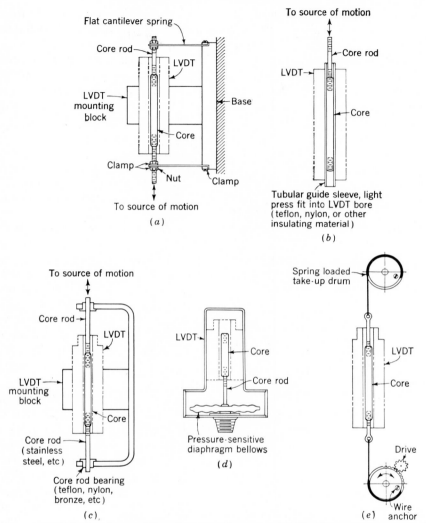

FIG. 3-35. Methods of assembling the movable core. (a) Cantilever spring support (no friction); (b) core guide, or bearing; (c) core rod bearings; (d) integral core rod extension from moving element; (e) cable suspension. (*Schaevitz Engineering, Camden, N.J.*)

The rotor is of such a symmetrical shape that the voltage output of the secondary is zero if the rotor is in its neutral position, as shown in Fig. 3-36. Any deviation of the rotor results in a proportional voltage output. The normal sensitivity of the microsyn is about 0.5 volt/deg.

The microsyn can be made to have a very accurate voltage vs. angle characteristic and can be constructed so as to be closely linear or to yield

any one of a great variety of functional forms.   It can also be obtained
as a torque transmitter, producing a torque proportional to the product
of two currents.

3-13. Synchro Applications.   Probably the most widely used error
detector in servomechanisms is a pair of synchros.   A typical servomechanism showing a pair of synchros used as error detectors is given in
Fig. 3-37.   The command shaft is geared or coupled to the shaft of the

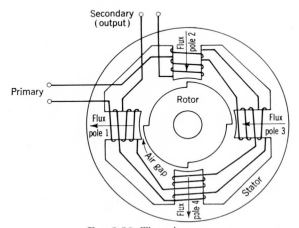

FIG. 3-36. The microsyn.

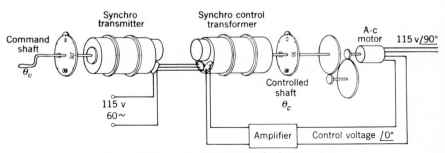

FIG. 3-37. Servomechanism employing synchros.

synchro transmitter.   The synchro transmitter is excited with an alternating voltage, in this case 115 volts, 60 cycles—although it could be
115 volts, 400 cycles; 26 volts, 400 cycles; or some other voltage and frequency, depending upon the rating of the synchro.   Three wires coming
from the synchro transmitter are connected to the synchro control transformer, which might be at a point remote from that of the transmitter.
The shaft of the synchro control transformer is geared or coupled to the
controlled shaft, and two wires from the synchro control transformer are
fed into the servoamplifier.   This voltage input is the actuating signal

and is a measure of the servo error. Just as in the case of the use of potentiometers for an error detector, actuating-signal voltage is amplified and applied to the servomotor. The servomotor shaft is geared down to a speed and torque capable of driving a load attached to the controlled shaft. The rated speed (1,500 rpm) and life (100 million rotations) are much greater than for potentiometers.

A number of different applications and types of synchros are discussed in this book. Some of these are described briefly in Table 3-2. When excited by an alternating voltage, a synchro transmitter applies to the three output leads voltages whose relative magnitudes and polarities uniquely define the angular position of the shaft with respect to its stator. It can be used either in a remote-indicating system in conjunction with

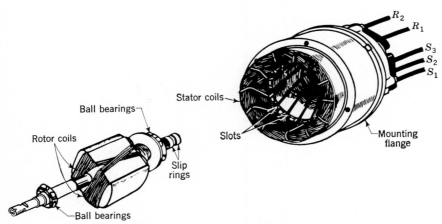

FIG. 3-38. The rotor and stator of a synchro transmitter.

repeaters or in a servomechanism, as shown in Fig. 3-37, used with a synchro control transformer. The function of the synchro control transformer is to convert the three output voltages of the transmitter into a single voltage that is proportional to the sine of the angular difference of the two rotor shafts:

$$v_{R_1 R_2} = K_s \sin (\theta_r - \theta_c) \qquad (3\text{-}8)$$

where θ_r is the reference-shaft angle and θ_c is the controlled-shaft angle. For small angular differences, the voltage is proportional to the angular difference itself:

$$v_{R_1 R_2} = K_s (\theta_r - \theta_c) \qquad (3\text{-}9)$$

This output voltage is the actuating signal of the servomechanism.

3-14. Theory of Synchro Operation. The rotor and stator of a synchro transmitter are shown in Fig. 3-38. The rotor is a salient-pole dumbbell-

TABLE 3-2. SYNCHRO TYPES

Name	Symbol	Schematic diagram	Function	Application
1. Transmitter	G or TX	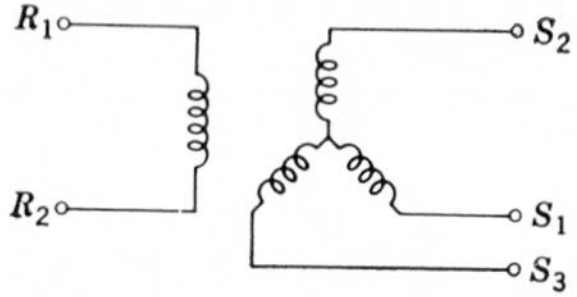	When its two input leads are excited by an alternating voltage, it applies to its three output leads voltages whose relative magnitudes and polarities uniquely define the angular position of its shaft with respect to its stator	Servomechanism (when used with a control transformer) or remote-indicating system (when used with a receiver)
2. Control transmitter	CG or CX	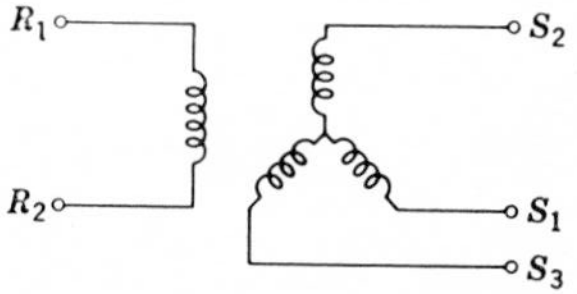	When its two input leads are excited by an alternating voltage, it applies to its three output leads voltages whose relative magnitudes and polarities uniquely define the angular position of its shaft with respect to its stator	Servomechanism
3. Control transformer	CT	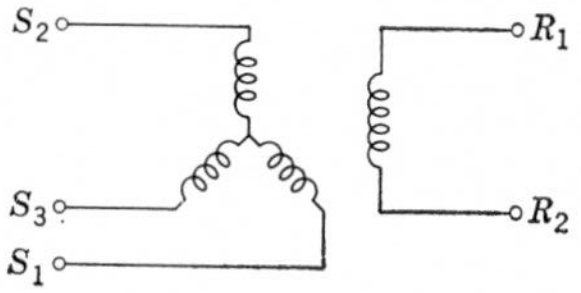	When its three input leads are excited by voltages which define an angle, it applies to its two output leads a voltage which is proportional to the sine of the difference between this angle and the angular position of its shaft with respect to its stator	Servomechanism
4. Differential transmitter	DG or TDX	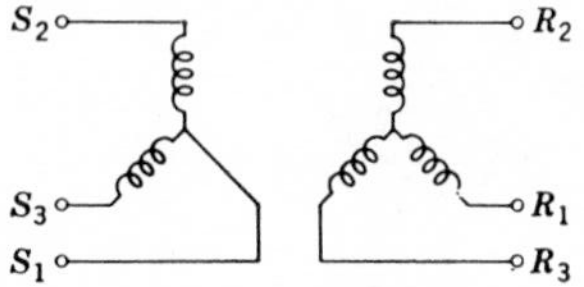	When its three input leads are excited by voltages which define an angle, it applies to its three output leads voltages whose relative magnitudes and polarities uniquely define a second angle which is the sum of the first angle and the angular position of its shaft with respect to its stator	Servomechanism (when used with a control transformer) or remote-indicating system (when used with a receiver)

76

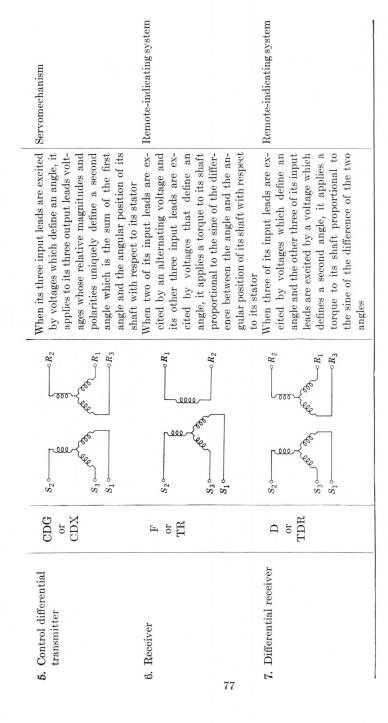

5. Control differential transmitter	CDG or CDX		When its three input leads are excited by voltages which define an angle, it applies to its three output leads voltages whose relative magnitudes and polarities uniquely define a second angle which is the sum of the first angle and the angular position of its shaft with respect to its stator	Servomechanism
6. Receiver	F or TR		When two of its input leads are excited by an alternating voltage and its other three input leads are excited by voltages that define an angle, it applies a torque to its shaft proportional to the sine of the difference between the angle and the angular position of its shaft with respect to its stator	Remote-indicating system
7. Differential receiver	D or TDR		When three of its input leads are excited by voltages which define an angle and the other three of its input leads are excited by a voltage which defines a second angle, it applies a torque to its shaft proportional to the sine of the difference of the two angles	Remote-indicating system

77

shaped magnetic structure having the primary windings of the transmitter. Voltage is applied to these windings by means of the slip
rings and brushes mounted on the stator housing. The stator has
the secondary coils wound in its skewed slots distributed around its
periphery. Although the stator windings are distributed, they act as if
they were oriented 120° apart, as shown in Fig. 3-39. Despite the fact
that the windings are shown 120° apart, thus resembling schematic
diagrams of three-phase machines, only single-phase voltage appears
across any of the windings. The flux links each of the various coils
depending upon the angular position of the rotor. In the position shown
in Fig. 3-39, the maximum voltage appears across S_2 and the neutral,
and a voltage of opposite polarity but equal to one-half this voltage in
magnitude appears across the windings S_3 to neutral and S_1 to neutral.

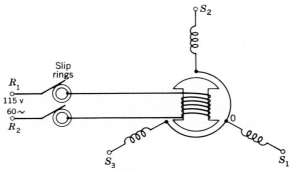

FIG. 3-39. Winding orientation of a synchro transmitter.

If the shaft of the synchro transmitter is rotated, the voltage from S_2
to neutral decreases and is zero when the rotor is at 90° from the position
shown in Fig. 3-39. The magnitudes of the voltages from S_2 to neutral,
S_1 to neutral, and S_3 to neutral also vary as the cosine of the angular
displacement of the rotor from its maximum.

Since the neutral is not brought out in a synchro transmitter, the only
voltages that can be measured are the voltages appearing at the terminals
S_1, S_2, and S_3. At the position of electrical zero, the voltage S_3S_1 is
zero. As the shaft is rotated in a counterclockwise direction, the voltage
$v_{s_2s_1}$ becomes a maximum at 90° to this position. Since for small angles
the sine is equal to the angle, a synchro transmitter can be used to provide
a voltage proportional to shaft angle for some computer applications in
which the small angular range is no limitation and in which large current
capacity or perfect resolution is required. The voltages induced across
each of the terminals are shown in Fig. 3-40 as functions of counterclockwise angle of shaft rotation. The voltages are shown as negative if their
polarity is opposite to the polarity of the voltage applied to R_1R_2. It is

evident that, for each angular position of the rotor shaft, a unique set of voltages appears at the terminals of the transmitter. These voltages uniquely establish the angular position of the transmitter shaft.

In a typical servomechanism, these voltages are applied to the leads of the synchro control transformer. This unit is similar in appearance to that of a synchro transmitter except that its rotor is circular in cross section and has distributed rotor windings. The fact that the rotor is of circular cross section minimizes the change of input impedance with angular rotation of the shaft. The primary windings of the synchro control transformer are in the stator. The secondary windings are on the rotor and, although distributed, behave

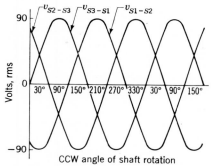

FIG. 3-40. Terminal voltages vs. shaft position.

exactly as if they were wound on a dumbbell-shaped rotor. A schematic diagram showing a synchro control transformer is given in Fig. 3-41.

The synchro control transformer usually has higher-impedance windings than those of the synchro transmitter, so that several synchro control

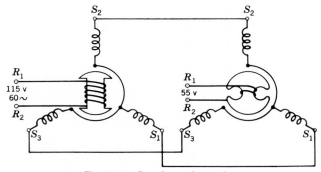

FIG. 3-41. Synchro schematics.

transformers can be connected electrically to the same transmitter. Some loss of accuracy (and even voltage gradient, if the number of control transformers is large) can be expected. The voltages applied to S_1, S_2, and S_3 of the control transformer produce in its magnetic structure exactly the same flux distribution that is produced in the synchro transmitter by the voltage excitation that is applied to its rotor. This is true because of the essentially identical magnetic construction of the two machines and because of the very nature of flux and voltage. If a voltage applied to R_1R_2 of a transmitter produces a flux that causes certain magnitudes of voltages to appear across the S windings, then, with losses neglected, these same voltages applied to the S windings produce the same flux in the transmitter and even induce the original voltage across R_1R_2. Similarly, the voltages appearing at the transmitter stator leads, when applied to the control-transformer stator, produce the same flux pattern in the control transformer that produced the voltages in the transmitter.

A control-transformer rotor can be likened to a search coil that indicates the direction of flux of the synchro transmitter. Thus, in the position shown in Fig. 3-41, the flux produced in the synchro transmitter is vertical and that produced by the voltages S_1, S_2, and S_3 in the synchro control transformer is also vertical. This means that the rotor voltage appearing across R_1 and R_2 is a maximum. If the synchro transmitter shaft is held fixed and the rotor of the control transformer is rotated to a position 90° from that shown, the voltage appearing across R_1 becomes zero.

The magnitude of the voltage output of the synchro control transformer is a sinusoidal-function output. The envelope of the output voltage of the control transformer vs. its shaft angular position, with a fixed angular position of the transmitter, is shown in Fig. 3-42. This graph shows the magnitude of the control-transformer rotor voltage.

The polarity information is obtained by comparison with the reference. When the envelope is a positive quantity, as in Fig. 3-42,

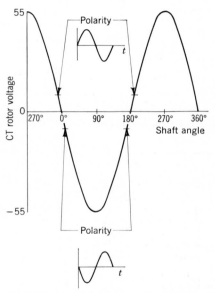

FIG. 3-42. Control-transformer voltage vs. shaft position.

the output is in phase with the reference applied (i.e., 115-volt 60-cps signal applied to $R_1 - R_2$). When the envelope is negative, the output signal is 180° out of phase with the reference input.

If the synchro transmitter is placed at an angle, there are two positions of the control-transformer shaft that yield zero output voltage from its rotor windings. A servo must be able to distinguish between these two positions, which are 180° of shaft rotation apart. If, when in one of the two null positions, the control-transformer rotor is rotated counterclockwise a small angle, its rotor voltage has a certain polarity. If it is rotated in the opposite direction, the polarity is opposite. If, however, the synchro control transformer is at the other null position, rotor rotation yields polarities opposite from those produced when it is in the first rotor position. A two-phase servomotor rotates in opposite directions for opposite polarities of voltage applied to the control winding.

Often, for servo applications, a synchro control transmitter is used in place of the synchro transmitter. This has virtually the same construction as a synchro transmitter, except that the impedance of its windings is slightly higher and somewhat more care is taken with respect to its accuracy since its sole application is in servo devices.

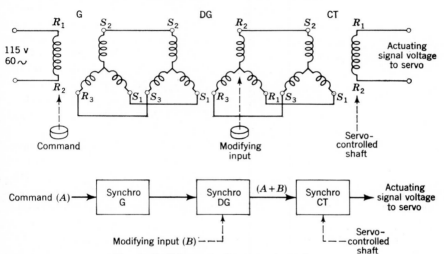

Fig. 3-43. Schematic diagram of synchros.

If it is desired to position the controlled shaft of a servomechanism to a shaft position that is the sum or difference of two shaft angles, a synchro differential transmitter can be used. This device is similar in appearance to a synchro transmitter except that its rotor has a distributed three-phase winding. As shown schematically in Fig. 3-43, the synchro differential transmitter has rotor windings that act as if they were 120° apart. The stator windings also appear as if they were 120° apart. The stator leads, when connected to the output leads of a synchro transmitter, produce a flux in the differential transmitter that is in the same orientation as the flux in the transmitter. This takes place in the same manner as the transmitter flux is reproduced in the control transformer. Since the rotor of the differential transmitter has the same 120° orientation of its windings as does the stator of the transmitter, a given flux in the differential transmitter produces the same three output voltages across its $R_1R_2R_3$ leads as would be produced across the $S_1S_2S_3$ leads of the transmitter if the R coils were aligned with the S coils.

The differential transmitter thus modifies the voltage from the transmitter so that the angular position of the flux in the control transformer is the sum of the angular positions of the transmitter and the differential transmitter. A synchro differential control transmitter is a similar device used exclusively in connection with servomechanisms. The differential transmitter has many applications, particularly in gunfire control when it is desired to add angles, such as lead angles or parallax angles, or in computers when various angles must be added to or subtracted from each other.

In each of these applications of synchros, the effect on the servomechanism of reversing such leads as R_1 and R_2 and S_1 and S_2 can easily be determined. By means of such reversals, the shaft rotation can be changed or the servo can be made to null at various 120° positions. In the case of the differential transmitter, the servo can be driven to the difference between the two angles rather than their sum.

3-15. Synchro* Construction. Synchros are manufactured in various sizes, and a tabulation of some of the physical characteristics of standard military synchros is given in Table 3-3. Since the rotor inertia is of dynamic importance for dynamic response, these values are included in the table. The larger-sized transmitters are capable of supplying many more control transformers than the smaller (and in the case of indicating synchros can transmit to many more receivers). At one time the larger units could be made more accurately than the smaller units, but this is no longer the case.

Sizes 1, 3, and 5 are the most popular synchros in present use. The outline drawings and photographs of typical units are shown in Fig. 3-44. The internal construction of these units is similar. Figure 3-45 shows the construction of a Telesyn† receiver. This unit is fabricated with a specially constructed damper that not only prevents oscillation when synchronizing but will positively overcome any tendency to "spin." This damper is also effective in minimizing roughness.

The 400-cycle control units, as with any transformer, can be made smaller than corresponding 60-cycle units, which is the principal reason for their existence. In addition, the dynamic errors are reduced usually by a factor of 7. The use of 400-cps synchros allows the advantage of weight and space savings to be taken in the rest of the servo.

Besides the wide variety of standard synchros that are manufactured,

---

* Selsyn, a trade name of the General Electric Co., is frequently used synonymously with synchro.

† Telesyn is the trade name for the line of synchros manufactured by Ford Instrument Co., Long Island City, N.Y.

TABLE 3-3. SPECIFICATIONS AND PERFORMANCE DATA*
Transmitters and Receivers

Unit type	Weight, lb	Rotor inertia oz-in.^{2}	Maximum error, minutes	Minimum torque gradient, oz-in./deg
1HG	1.2	0.34	18	0.07
1HG400	1.2	0.34	18	0.06
3HG	2.4	1.5	18	0.25
5HG	4.2	2.96	18	0.40
5HG400	4.2	2.96	18	0.48
1F	1.3	0.55	90	0.07
1F400	1.3	0.55	90	0.06
3F	2.6	3.28	36	0.25
5F	4.7	7.80	36	0.40
5F400	4.7	7.80	36	0.48

Differential Transmitter and Receiver

Unit type	Weight, lb	Rotor inertia, oz-in.^{2}	Maximum error, minutes	Minimum torque, oz-in./deg
1HDG	1.2	0.34	18	0.04
3HDG	2.8	1.50	18	0.15
5HDG	4.8	4.12	18	0.30
5HDG400	4.8	4.12	18	0.30
5D	5.3	8.96	54	0.30

Control Transformers

Unit type	Weight, lb	Rotor inertia, oz-in.^{2}	Maximum error, minutes	Maximum secondary impedance, ohms
1HCT	1.2	0.34	18	900
1HCT400	1.2	0.34	18	830
3HCT	2.6	1.5	18	400

* Ford Instrument Co., Long Island City, N.Y.

many special configurations are produced. One example of a special design adaptation is the Autosyn* synchro with external slip rings. A photograph of some typical units is shown in Fig. 3-46. These units are used in applications where it is found desirable to rotate the Autosyn

* Autosyn is the registered trademark of Eclipse-Pioneer Division, Bendix Aviation Corp., Teterboro, N.J.

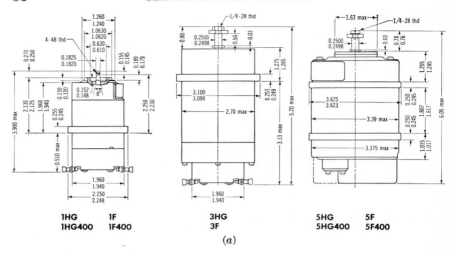

| 1HG | 1F | 3HG | 5HG | 5F |
| 1HG400 | 1F400 | 3F | 5HG400 | 5F400 |

(a)

(b)

FIG. 3-44. Outline drawing and photograph of sizes 1, 3, and 5 synchros. (*Ford Instrument Co., Long Island City, N.Y.*)

stator in addition to or instead of rotating the rotor. The external slip rings furnish a convenient means of electrical contact with the rotor and stator elements of the synchro as contrasted to the usual fixed leads or terminals.

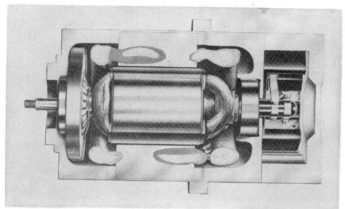

Fig. 3-45. Internal construction of a synchro receiver. (*Ford Instrument Co., Long Island City, N.Y.*)

Fig. 3-46. External slip-ring synchros. (*Eclipse-Pioneer Div., Bendix Aviation Corp., Teterboro, N.J.*)

3-16. Indicating Synchros. Synchros are utilized in servomechanisms as shown in Fig. 3-37. In this application the synchros do not in themselves position shafts but rather are positioned by the command to the servo and the servo controlled shaft. There is a class of synchros that are used for remote positioning and indication that do not require servomechanisms to position the shafts. For applications in which transmission is accomplished directly between the synchros, the units are connected as shown in Fig. 3-47. For this application, it is usually necessary to utilize larger units. Typical of these elements are the Magslips,* one of which is shown in Fig. 3-48. The 2-in. Magslip operates with a torque gradient of 0.14 oz-in./deg.

A synchro receiver resembles a synchro transmitter and is in fact electrically identical to it. It has, however, a mechanical damper attached to its shaft as shown in the cutaway view of Fig. 3-45. This is usually inside the case, so that externally it has the same appearance. The synchro receiver has applied to its rotor a constant voltage, and the stator leads are connected to the synchro transmitter. If the shaft of the synchro transmitter is held fixed, the shaft of the synchro receiver

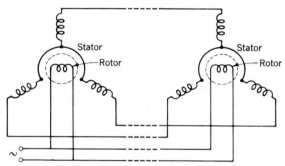

FIG. 3-47. Basic synchro transmission system.

rapidly rotates until it is at the same angle as the transmitter. If the shaft of the transmitter is moved, the receiver follows that position.

Such a pair of synchros is used in cases where it is desired to indicate remotely the position of a shaft. The receivers, however, can exert only a small amount of torque against any load and are consequently used only for indicating a shaft position on a dial. If two synchros are connected together and used for the transmission of mechanical power, the torque produced by the receiver must be supplied mechanically to turn the transmitter. The torque demanded will cause a proportional displacement of the receiver from the true transmitter angle. Accuracy and torque may thus be regarded as alternatives—if torque is demanded, accuracy is sacrificed. Accuracy may, however, be regained in a measure but at the expense of another characteristic, namely self-alignment. This is achieved by the use of mechanical gearing between the object being controlled and the receivers.

This is best illustrated by an example: Suppose a rotating beacon must

* Magslip is the trade name of the synchros and related devices produced by Muirhead and Co., Ltd., Beckenham, England.

Fig. 3-48. Cutaway view and external appearance of a large synchro utilized for direct synchro transmission. 3-in. Magslip. Over-all length, 6¼ in. (15.9 cm); over-all diameter, 3⅜ in. (8.55 cm); end-cover (mounting) diameter, 2⅞ in. (7.3 cm); spindle diameter, 5⁄16 in. (0.8 cm); weight, 4 lb (1.8 kg). (*Muirhead and Co., Ltd., Beckenham, England.*)

be controlled to an accuracy of ¼°. The torque on the shaft of the beacon to overcome friction, acceleration forces, and windage is, say, 10 lb-in. and the speed of operation 3 rpm maximum. If the maximum synchro speed is 300 rpm, the gear ratio required is 100:1; assuming 50 per cent efficiency of gearing, the torque on the synchro shaft is $(10 \times 16)/50 = 3.2$ oz-in.

A 2-in. Magslip operates with a torque gradient of 0.14 oz-in./deg.; hence this element will handle the load with a torque lag of

$$\left(\frac{3.2}{0.14}\right)^{\circ} = 23^{\circ}$$

The accuracy of the drive is obtained by dividing the torque-lag angle by the gear ratio, i.e., $23°/100 = 0.23°$.

The inaccuracies of indicating synchros often make them undesirable, and a servomechanism, which of course is more complex in structure, must sometimes be substituted. Another disadvantage is their poor dynamic response. If the shaft of a transmitter is oscillated sinusoidally at a certain critical frequency, the shaft motion of the receiver can amplify this as much as 10 times. This type of synchro system is often quite oscillatory and cannot be made as highly damped as can the response of a servo. Furthermore, dynamic inaccuracies on the part of the receiver or static errors caused by loads or sticky bearings change the magnitudes of the voltages on the stator leads supplying it. Thus, if any other receiver is connected to the same leads, its stator voltages and hence its rotor position will be in error because of the error of the first receiver.

3-17. Synchro Static and Dynamic Errors. As is the case with most components, synchros are not so perfect as is intimated in the explanation of the fundamentals of their operation. They suffer two major faults—inaccuracy and residual voltages. The servo can be no more accurate than its error detector. If the error detector does not accurately indicate the difference between two shaft angles, the servo will be in error by at least this inaccuracy. The servoamplifier and motor drive the servo to a voltage null. If this voltage null does not occur when the command shaft has precisely the same angle as the controlled shaft, the servo will be in error and there is nothing to indicate to the amplifier and motor that such an error exists.

Although synchros can be built with a static error of but a few minutes, the typical error of a transmitter–control transformer combination is on the order of 18 minutes maximum and is a function of rotor position. One way of determining the error of a synchro pair is to affix accurate dials to the shaft of the transmitter and the control transformer. Suppose that the shafts are brought into correspondence so that the voltage output is a null at electrical zero. If the shaft of the transmitter is rotated 10°, in general the shaft of the control transformer must be rotated at an angle other than 10° to achieve a null once more. The difference between the angle to which the control transformer must be rotated and 10° is the error of the synchro pair. If this experiment is repeated throughout 360°, a typical graph of the error as a function of shaft angle is obtained as is illustrated in Fig. 3-49.

If it is desired to find the error merely of the synchro transmitter, this can be done by defining zero error as, say, electrical zero, affixing a very accurate dial to the shaft and measuring the stator voltages induced for any angular position of the shaft. Because these stator voltages define an angle, the angle corresponding to the measured voltages can be calculated. If this calculated angle differs from the measured angle, the difference is the error. Similarly, voltages having the exact proper relative magnitudes for a given angle can be fed to a synchro control transformer and the shaft angle necessary to cause a null measured. If this shaft angle differs from the angle corresponding to the applied voltages, an error exists and is equal to this difference.

Provided that the synchro has been properly designed, the cause of synchro errors is generally the result of manufacturing difficulties. For example, errors can result if the stator coils of a transmitter are not identical. These differences in coils can be caused by different numbers of turns on the coils or, more subtly, by different wire resistance caused by using wire from different manufacturers or even from the same manufacturer but from different spools. For salient-pole machines, the

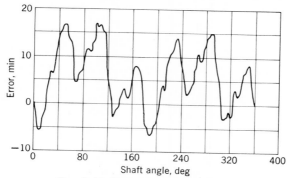

Fig. 3-49. Error of a synchro pair.

length and shape of the pole are important. In machines with non-salient-pole rotors, both the rotor and the stator must be ground to be exactly round. Ellipsing of either the stator or the rotor can cause errors. For example, ellipsing of either the rotor or the stator by such an amount that the difference between the major and minor axes of the ellipse is as small as 1/10,000 in. results in a spread of about 4 minutes error in a typical small synchro.

The rotor must be placed exactly in the center of the bore of the stator, and the laminations must be of uniform magnetic property, so that even the direction of rolling of the sheet must be taken into account. For this reason, the laminations are skewed when stacked. The slots are also skewed so that the reluctance of the slots is evenly distributed lengthwise over the magnetic path. The angle of skew is carefully designed. The length of the rotor laminations compared with the stator laminations is also important. To control this factor, the laminations are cemented together to eliminate the flare that might exist if they were merely stacked and bound mechanically.

The static error of synchros can be resolved into various space harmonics. The largest error is usually the second harmonic; i.e., the error goes through two complete cycles in 360° of shaft rotation. This is caused mainly by ellipsing of the stator. If the rotor is ellipsed, a fundamental component of error, i.e., the error goes through one cycle in 360°, can exist. Another common space harmonic is the sixth harmonic, caused by the "three-phase" winding distribution—unequal impedances of the windings and the leads connecting the synchros. Another harmonic present is equal to the number of slots in the rotor or stator or is double that number of slots and is caused by the nonsinusoidal flux distribution as a result of the reluctance of the slots or of varying resistance or reluctance of the coils themselves.

The accuracy of synchros is, therefore, fundamentally a problem of how accurately the parts can be manufactured. As in the case of potentiometers, the mounting surfaces and the shaft must be held to close concentricity and size to permit interchangeable manufacture in the servomechanism itself.

Although the static error is the error of principal concern, there is also a dynamic error present in synchros. This is caused by magnetic fluxes existing in synchros being cut by the wire of the rotor coils. If a synchro transmitter and control transformer are coupled at null position and the synchro transmitter is excited from a source of alternating voltage in the usual manner, the output of the control transformer is zero if there is no static error or residual voltage present in the units. This is true for any angular position of the coupled shafts. If, however, they are rotated at a constant velocity and their stators held fixed, a voltage appears across the rotor of the control transformer. At about 300 rpm rotation of the shaft for typical 60-cycle units, the voltage is about 1 volt. If the shafts are displaced by 1° so that when they are standing still there is about 1 volt output from the control transformer and the shaft is again rotated at 300 rpm, the voltage output would be zero. Thus, servos using synchros have an additional error when the shafts are rotating at high speed; this error is roughly proportional to the speed of shaft rotation. The phase of this voltage also shifts slightly from the phase of the synchro output voltage when the shafts are stationary. The direction of the dynamic synchro error for constant shaft velocity is in the direction to increase the steady-state error of a servomechanism when following a constant-velocity command.

The voltage that is generated when the synchro shafts are rotating at constant velocity is also generated whenever the synchro shafts are moving and thus can add to the dynamic errors of the system. This effect is usually small, though it can be appreciable for servos that are required to follow rapidly moving signals. The effect can be shown by a comparison of the voltage obtained from a pair of synchros under conditions of slow sinusoidal oscillation and then under increased oscillating frequency. If the shaft of the synchro transmitter is held fixed and the control-transformer shaft is oscillated sinusoidally for small angles, the voltage appearing at the output as a function of time is as shown in Fig. 3-50. This is representative of the voltage appearing on an oscilloscope whose sweep frequency is the same as the mechanical oscillating frequency of the control transformer. If, however, the frequency of the oscillation of the control-transformer shaft is made very high, the voltage appearing at its terminal will be as shown in Fig. 3-51. A clean null

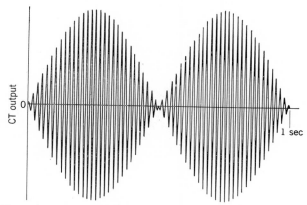

FIG. 3-50. Synchro signal for low-frequency shaft oscillation.

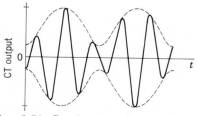

FIG. 3-51. Synchro signal for high-frequency shaft oscillation.

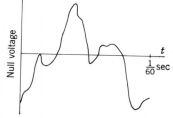

FIG. 3-52. Voltage output of a control transformer at null.

no longer appears. A similar picture is obtained if both the control-transformer shaft and the transmitter shaft are oscillated sinusoidally, as is the case when a servomechanism is being subjected to sinusoidal oscillations.

3-18. Synchro Residual Voltages and Phase Shift. Another defect of synchros is the presence of residual voltages and the presence of a phase shift between the excitation voltage and the output voltage of the control transformer. When the shafts are in correspondence, the voltage output of the control transformer is at null. Figure 3-52 is a typical output-voltage waveform of the pair of synchros at null. The magnitude of the output is not zero but 0.05 volt rms.   This residual voltage consists of two parts: harmonics of the fundamental excitation frequency and quadrature voltage.   Harmonic voltages exist for the same reason as they do in the E transformer—the nonlinearity of the iron.   Their distribution throughout the magnetic structure is somewhat different from the fundamental flux, and therefore they do not null when the fundamental flux is nulled.

A plot of the harmonic voltages as a function of angular shaft position for a typical transmitter–control transformer pair of synchros having a sensitivity of 1 volt/deg is shown in Fig. 3-53.   The presence of harmonic voltages in the excitation voltage applied to the synchros adds somewhat to the harmonic-voltage output of the control transformer, although even a pure voltage source will not eliminate the harmonic voltages produced

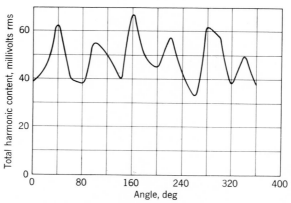

FIG. 3-53. Harmonic-voltage output of a synchro pair at null.

within the synchros.   The effect on the servo of harmonic voltages is the same as described for the E transformer.   Since these harmonic voltages are particularly undesirable in using a-c equalizing networks, filters are often used to attenuate these harmonics.

Quadrature voltage also exists in the output of a control transformer. The minimum voltage of fundamental frequency that is obtained at null is the quadrature voltage for the transmitter and control-transformer pair at a particular angular position of the transmitter and the correspondence position for the control transformer.   The position of minimum fundamental output is the correspondence position; the voltage of fundamental frequency is the quadrature voltage.   The phase of this quadrature voltage is at right angles to the voltage output of the control transformer when the shafts are nowhere near correspondence and the control-transformer output voltage is consequently large.   Many of the reasons given for the presence of synchro errors as the result of the manufacturing process can also be given as the cause of quadrature voltage. A plot of the quadrature voltage of a pair of synchros as a function of shaft angle of the null position is shown in Fig. 3-54.

Another problem in connection with the application of synchros is the presence of a phase shift between the excitation voltage and the output voltage of the control transformer, even if the residual voltages are zero. This phase shift is caused by the resistance and inductance of the synchro winding and is in such a direction that the control-transformer voltage leads the excitation voltage to the transmitter. It must be taken into account in adjusting the phase of the voltage applied to the fixed field of the two-phase motor and also the reference voltage of the phase-sensitive detector. This phase shift varies between 10 and 50°, depending upon the size of the synchro.

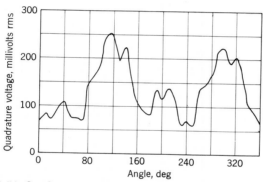

FIG. 3-54. Quadrature-voltage output of a synchro pair at null.

Sometimes synchro capacitors are used in conjunction with synchros. A capacitor across each of the stator leads of a control transformer tends to reduce the phase shift between the transmitter excitation and the control-transformer output; but, more important, it also reduces the exciting current that the control transformer draws from the transmitter. This permits more control transformers to be supplied by a given transmitter. For similar reasons, capacitors are also used across the primary leads of differential units. The fundamental limitation on the number of control transformers that can be excited from a single generator, however, is usually the resulting inaccuracy, particularly if all the control transformers are not in synchronism.

3-19. Induction Potentiometers. A synchro transmitter can also be used as a potentiometer for small angles within the linear range, where a high sensitivity and infinite resolution are desired. As a matter of fact, special units called induction potentiometers are designed for this purpose and are linear over a range of ± 45 to $\pm 60°$. These units, of course, can be excited only by alternating current.

A resolver, which is discussed later in this chapter, can also be used as an induction potentiometer and trimmed to a linearity of about a quarter per cent over a $\pm 45°$ range. This is done by shorting one pair of the stator leads and putting about 1,000 ohms in series with the other, which is the input to the device. One of the rotor windings is loaded with the proper resistance, and the output appears across the other rotor winding.

3-20. Error Reduction with Double-speed Synchronizing Networks. Synchros suffer from two basic limitations: inaccuracy and the presence of noise voltages at null. The first of these problems can be greatly helped by the use of double-speed transmission. Such a scheme also reduces the effect of noise voltages. The use of double-speed* transmission, however, introduces another problem requiring the use of the synchronizing network.

The basic problem is that of improving the accuracy of synchros.

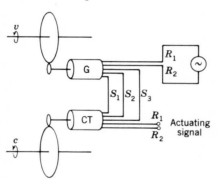

FIG. 3-55. Synchros geared 5:1 to the command and controlled shafts.

With the previously described application of synchros coupled directly to the command shaft and the controlled shaft, any inaccuracy of the synchros becomes directly an inaccuracy of the servomechanism. Suppose that, instead of direct coupling, the synchro transmitter and the synchro control transformer are each geared to their respective shafts by a ratio of 5:1, as is illustrated in Fig. 3-55. Assume that the angles v and c are made equal to zero and the synchros are adjusted by positioning the stator of the control transformer so that its voltage output is made equal to zero.

Suppose that the command shaft is moved through 10°. This means that, if the gearing is accurate, the transmitter shaft rotates 50°. Shaft c is then rotated by hand until a null voltage exists at the output of the control transformer. With perfect synchros, this angle is precisely 10° and the control transformer must be rotated through 50°. Suppose, however, the synchro pair has an error of 10 minutes at this point. This means that the shaft of the control transformer must be rotated through 10 minutes to effect a null. This is accomplished by rotating the angle c

* This is a confusing but conventional term which means that the position of a shaft is transmitted electrically, usually by synchros that rotate at two different speeds. Only one shaft rotates at the same speed as the command shaft.

through only 2 minutes. The error, therefore, is cut by a factor of 5, which is equal to the gear ratio between the command shaft and the synchro transmitter.

If the voltage from the control transformer is fed to a servoamplifier, which in turn feeds a servomotor geared to the controlled shaft, the error introduced by the synchro transmission system will be cut by a factor of 5 since the servo operates to make the actuating signal equal to zero. In a similar manner, a gear ratio of, say, 25:1, or almost any other gear ratio, can be used. Since the synchro rotates at a higher speed for a given controlled-shaft speed, the synchro dynamic error at the synchro shaft is increased by a factor of the gear ratio; but, when it is divided by the gear ratio, the synchro dynamic error referred to the controlled shaft remains unchanged. The inertia of the synchro reflected to the servomotor, however, is increased under the use of geared-up synchros.

Notice that the voltage sensitivity of the synchro system is increased by the factor of the gear ratio. A motion of 1° of the command shaft, for example, causes a voltage of 5 volts to appear at the control-transformer output leads for a 5:1 gear train and for synchros with a sensitivity of 1 volt/deg. This means that the servoamplifier used would have one-fifth the gain that would be necessary if a one-speed transmission were used.

A difficulty, however, is introduced by the use of the scheme shown in Fig. 3-55. Suppose the command shaft is clamped so that it cannot move and the controlled shaft is moved through an angle of 72°, or one-fifth revolution. The synchro control transformer is then rotated through a complete revolution, and a null voltage again appears in the output of the control transformer. The shafts v and c, however, are now 72° apart. If the system shown in Fig. 3-55 is used in a servomechanism, the servo will drive to the nearest of the five null positions, only one of which brings shafts v and c into correspondence. It is necessary, there-

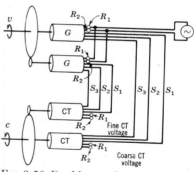

FIG. 3-56. Double-speed synchro transmission system.

fore, that additional information be fed to the servomechanism to tell it which of the five possible null positions is the correct one.

3-21. Basic Double-speed System.

This system can be set up according to the scheme shown in Fig. 3-56. Double-speed synchro transmission requires a pair of synchro transmitters and a pair of control transformers. As before, the transmitter and control transformer are geared

5:1 with the command shaft and controlled shaft, respectively; but in addition, a transmitter and control transformer are coupled directly to the two shafts.

The hour and minute hands of a clock constitute a form of double-speed system. The hour hand tells the approximate time, and the minute hand affords an even more accurate indication. The minute hand alone does not give sufficient information unless the hour is known.

It is instructive to look at the voltages that are developed in the various synchros. Suppose that the shaft v is in an arbitrary position and that shaft c is rotated until they are in correspondence. If shaft v is held fixed and shaft c rotated, the magnitude of the output voltages of each of the control transformers will be as shown in Fig. 3-57 for one complete revolution of shaft c. In one revolution of shaft c, the fine control-transformer voltage has a null of the proper polarity five times, but the

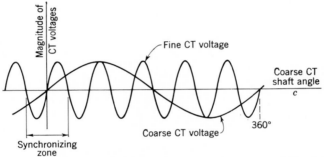

FIG. 3-57. Control-transformer voltages for the system of Fig. 3-56.

null of the coarse control-transformer voltage has only one null of the proper polarity. When a servomechanism is used to operate with the synchro transmission system of Fig. 3-56, a circuit that causes the servo-amplifier to be fed from the coarse control-transformer voltage when the actuating signal is large and from the fine control-transformer voltage when the actuating signal is small is necessary.

The simplest imaginable device that will do this is a relay whose coil is fed from the coarse control-transformer voltage. If the coarse control-transformer voltage is large, the relay closes and its contacts feed the coarse control-transformer voltage into the servoamplifier. When the coarse control-transformer voltage becomes smaller, indicating that the servo has rotated the controlled shaft close to its correspondence position, the relay drops out and the contacts feed the fine control-transformer voltage to the servoamplifier. The servo-controlled shaft is then positioned only by the voltage output of the fine control transformer, and the accuracy of the transmission system is improved by the factor of the gear ratio. When used in this application, the relay is known as a synchronizing network and is one of many types of devices that can be employed.

In the example given, the gain of the synchro system changes by a factor of 5, and therefore it would seem that the torque sensitivity would also change by a factor of 5 when the relay switches from fine to coarse. No difficulty exists, however, since the servoamplifier is usually saturated by a very small actuating signal. Once the amplifier has saturated, its output voltage is approximately constant, independent of the magnitude of its input signal. At the point of transfer from the fine control-transformer voltage to the coarse control-transformer voltage, the amplifier is usually saturated by either signal, and hence no change of torque or loop gain occurs. The servo is therefore designed for fine synchro gain, since it will normally be operating with the fine control transformer supplying the actuating signal.

There are two positions (see Fig. 3-57) at which the coarse control-transformer voltage is close to zero, indicating that the relay drops out and feeds fine control-transformer voltage to the servoamplifier. One position of c is 180° away from its proper position. Although the relay drops out and feeds fine control-transformer voltage to the servo at the 180° position, the polarity of the fine control-transformer voltage and the servomotor tends to drive the controlled shaft away from this point toward correspondence, so that no false null is introduced.

During normal application of a servomechanism employing a double-speed synchro transmission, the servo is always operating on the fine actuating signal whenever the controlled shaft is expected to follow the command shaft closely. The only time it is not expected to follow closely is when the servo is deenergized or when the command shaft is moved so swiftly that the controlled shaft cannot follow, i.e., when the command shaft is rotated at a velocity faster than the controlled shaft can rotate even with the motor traveling at full speed.

For example, if the servo has been deenergized and the shafts put out of correspondence by rotation of the command shaft, when the servo is reenergized, the synchronizing network then causes coarse actuating-signal voltage to be fed to the servoamplifier until the controlled shaft is almost in correspondence with the command shaft. At this time, the synchronizing network operates to cause the fine voltage to be fed into the servoamplifier. Similarly, if the command shaft is slewed (moved rapidly) to a new position, the synchronizing network causes the coarse voltage to be fed to the servoamplifier until the servo shafts are again in close correspondence, at which point the synchronizing network causes the fine voltage to feed into the servoamplifier.

Gear ratios commonly used between fine and coarse synchros are 16:1,

20:1, 25:1, and 36:1.   As long as the gear ratio is odd, no additional problem is introduced.   The case of even gear ratios is discussed later in this chapter.

The zone in which transfer from coarse to fine must take place is always equal to one revolution of the fine control transformer.   If 1- and 75-speed transmissions are used rather than 1- and 5-, the total width of this zone is $\frac{1}{75}$ revolution, or 4.8°.   For synchros having a sensitivity of 1 volt/deg and having the relay synchronizing circuit described, the relay must transfer from coarse to fine at a coarse synchro voltage less than 2.4 volts as the servo error decreases.   If the servo error is increasing, the relay must also transfer from fine to coarse at a coarse synchro voltage less than 2.4 volts.   The practical problem of selecting the voltage at which the transfer takes place must be considered.   Actually, the transfer can occur at any place within the synchronizing zone, which is illustrated in Fig. 3-58.   Practical circuit problems, however, place some restrictions on the transfer point normally chosen.   For example, the transfer point could be at a position very slightly to the left of the position labeled A in Fig. 3-58, where the position of A in degrees of rotation of the coarse control-transformer shaft is given by

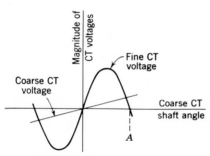

FIG. 3-58. Synchronizing zone.

$$\frac{1}{2}\frac{360°}{N}$$

where N is the gear ratio between the coarse and fine control transformers. This means that, when the servo is coming into synchronism, the voltage being fed to the servoamplifier switches from coarse to fine voltage slightly to the left of point A.   The servo then operates on fine voltage and drives to the zero position.   At the instant of transfer, the actuating-signal voltage drops to a low value and, although it still drives the servo to the proper null position, it may show some hesitation in so doing.

Another difficulty is that a slight shift in parameters, a shift in circuit values, or a shift in the relay characteristics may cause the point of transfer to shift to the right of A.   This may result in oscillation of the servo and the relay.   For these reasons, a safe value of the transfer point is about 90° away from the zero of the fine synchro.   The fine synchro voltage is a maximum at this point.   A 1- and 75-speed system would therefore transfer at a coarse control-transformer voltage of 1.2 volts. Hence, the possibility of a shift in parameters, causing the servo to oscillate, is minimized; yet the transfer point is not so close to the null position that the coarse voltage will not normally saturate the amplifier for most designs.

To have some margin of safety for relay differential and relay adjustment, the synchronizing zone cannot be too small. For example, if the coarse synchro error in a 1- and 75-speed system is 1.5° at some angular position of v and the relay is adjusted to transfer from fine to coarse at 1.2 volts, the relay will improperly transfer the amplifier input from fine to coarse even though the servo is exactly in correspondence. The relay could again cause the servo to oscillate. It must be remembered in these explanations that the actuating-signal voltage from the control transformers will be zero for any angle from 0 to 360° of the command and controlled shafts as long as they are at the same angle.

3-22. Practical Circuitry for Double-speed Synchronizing Networks. Although the relay synchronizing circuit described above presents a simple method of explaining the basic principles of a synchronizing network, it is not a practical circuit to use because the relay must be of a very high sensitivity to operate on the low voltages involved and must have an impedance on the order of 10,000 ohms so as not to load the control transformers. It is difficult to make such a relay rugged and reliable with a sufficiently small differential between drop-out and pickup voltages and with positive snap action. These problems can be overcome by the use of an amplifier in the relay circuit, so that a practical synchronizing circuit results from the coarse control-transformer voltage being fed to the amplifier, which in turn operates the relay.

A circuit that accomplishes this is shown in Fig. 3-59. The coarse control-transformer voltage is rectified and applied to the grid of a tube having proper cathode bias. The relay is closed as long as the coarse

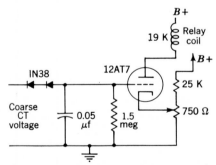

FIG. 3-59. Relay synchronizing network.

control-transformer voltage is small. When the control-transformer voltage, and hence the grid-voltage bias, exceeds a certain value, the tube current falls below the 4 ma necessary to keep the relay closed, and the contacts are so arranged that coarse control-transformer voltage is then fed to the amplifier. A similar circuit is shown in Fig. 3-60. Here a relay is operated by a thyratron. Under normal operation of the servo the actuating signal is small. If the 1-speed signal is small, the relay is energized and the fine control-transformer voltage is fed to the servo-amplifier. The voltage fed from the single-speed control transformer, when rectified, supplies a small negative potential to the grid of the thyratron. Since the circuit is designed so that the ionization voltage of the thyratron is exceeded despite the small negative grid potential, the alternating voltage applied to the plates of the thyratron causes the tube to fire and the relay coil is energized. Although the thyratron fires only on the positive half cycles of the a-c supply, the relay can be chosen so that it does not drop out on the negative half cycle when no current is being supplied to its coils. The contacts are so arranged that the high-speed signal is fed to the servoamplifier under these conditions. If, however, the low-speed signal exceeds a certain value, the rectified control-transformer voltage causes the grid voltage of the thyratron to be quite negative and the critical voltage of the thyratron is no longer

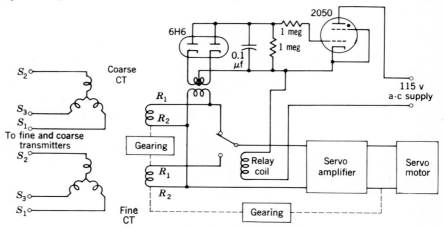

FIG. 3-60. Servo using relay synchronizing network.

exceeded. The thyratron therefore does not fire, and the relay drops to the other position. The contacts then allow the coarse synchro signal to go to the servoamplifier.

Most synchronizing networks do not employ relays; for example, the circuit shown in Fig. 3-61 utilizes diodes. In this circuit, the fine control-transformer voltage is virtually short-circuited when it exceeds a certain value, and the voltage fed to the servoamplifier is the sum of the coarse control-transformer voltage and the limited fine control-transformer voltage. Figure 3-62c shows the voltage fed to the servoamplifier using this circuit for a 1- and 5-speed synchro system and obtained from adding the coarse control-transformer voltage of part b. For actuating signals close to zero, the rectifier has no effect, and the sum of the coarse and fine control-transformer voltages is fed to the servoamplifier. (In applications where the gear ratio between the fine and coarse control transformers is quite large, the coarse control-transformer actuating-signal voltage is

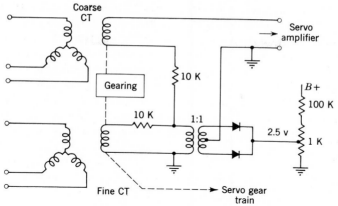

FIG. 3-61. Diode synchronizing network.

small compared with that obtained from the fine control transformer and therefore the coarse control transformer has little effect on the actuating signal.) When the controlled shaft and the command shaft are not in close correspondence, the servo has no ambiguity of position, as seen in Fig. 3-62. The limiting voltage must be of such a value that the sum of the coarse and fine voltages can never equal zero between the points of zero and 180° of the angle $v - c$. In a safe design, the fine-voltage maximum should be limited to half the value of the coarse voltage at point A in Fig. 3-58.

The disadvantage of this circuit is that the residual voltages of the one-speed control transformer are being fed to the servoamplifier when the actuating signal is close to zero, the same as they are when the actuating signal is not close to zero. This means that, under normal operation of the servo when both

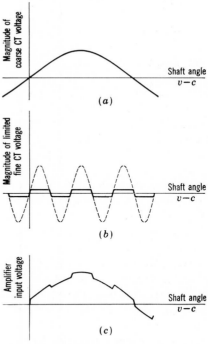

FIG. 3-62. Voltages in the network of Fig. 3-61.

control-transformer voltages are close to zero, the residual voltages from both control transformers are being fed to the servoamplifier.

A circuit that does not have this basic limitation is shown in Fig. 3-63. It employs two sets of selenium rectifiers used back to back. Their resistance is small when the voltage across them is large, and conversely, when the voltage across them is small, their resistance is large. The circuit operates in the following manner: when the output voltage of both control transformers is small and the resistance of the rectifier circuits is large, the voltage to the servoamplifier will consist largely of that coming from the fine transmitter. When the shafts are considerably out of correspondence, however, the voltages from both control transformers are large and the resistance of both rectifier circuits is small. The fine control-transformer voltage, therefore, is virtually short-circuited, and almost the full output voltage of the coarse control transformer is introduced to the servoamplifier.

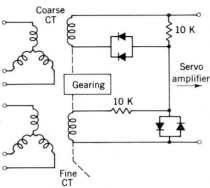

FIG. 3-63. Synchronizing circuit employing selenium rectifiers.

This circuit, however, suffers the difficulty that it attenuates the actuating signal by a factor of about 20, because of selenium-rectifier imperfections. There will also be phase shifts in the signal voltage resulting from the selenium rectifiers acting as capacitors as well as rectifiers. Since this capacitance is in parallel with the rectifier resistance, the phase shift varies with the drop across the rectifiers.

A difficulty exists in the use of synchronizing networks and double-speed transmission when an even gear ratio is used between the coarse and fine control transformer. Most military applications employ even gear ratios, and a common synchro transmission system uses 1- and 36-speed synchros. This is done in part so that shaft angles can be read accurately with the use of two dials. A dial fastened to the coarse control-transformer shaft tells the angle quite closely. Another dial, fastened to the fine control-transformer shaft so that one revolution of the fine control transformer equals 10° of the coarse control transformer, can be used to read the shaft position of the controlled shaft with 36 times the accuracy. The problem that arises can be seen from observing Fig. 3-64, and it occurs at the 180° point of the coarse control transformer. The polarity of the voltage output of both the fine control transformer and the coarse control transformer in the vicinity of zero degrees is seen to be the proper polarity to drive the servo to null at zero degrees. At the point 180° away from correspondence, while the coarse control transformer is of the proper polarity to drive the servo to the proper null at zero degrees, the polarity of the fine control-transformer voltage is such as to drive the servo toward 180°.

The problem results from all the synchronizing networks discussed causing the fine control-transformer voltage to be fed into the servo-amplifier whenever the coarse control-transformer voltage is small. The coarse control-transformer voltage is small both at 0 and 180°.

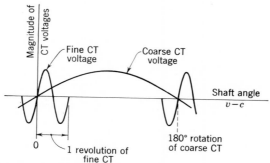

Fig. 3-64. Synchro voltages for even gear ratio between coarse and fine synchros.

Therefore, if the servo should happen to be 180° away from its proper correspondence position (say, when the servo was deenergized and happened to be rotated to this position and then reenergized), the fine control-transformer voltage would be fed to the servoamplifier and would drive the servo toward the false null, 180° away from the proper null.

The solution to this problem consists in adding a voltage called a *stick-off* to the coarse control-transformer voltage. As shown in Fig. 3-65, this voltage is added immediately at the output of the control transformer. Adding voltage of the proper magnitude from the

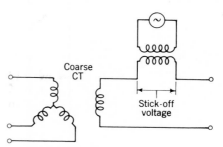

Fig. 3-65. Method of adding stick-off voltage.

same a-c source and in phase with the coarse control-transformer voltage causes the voltages to be as shown in Fig. 3-66. The addition of stick-off voltage causes the null of the coarse control transformer to be shifted 90° from the fine shaft angle at both the 0 and 180° positions of the coarse control transformer. For a 1- and 36-speed synchro transmission system using synchros that have a sensitivity of 1 volt/deg, the voltage added is 2.5 volts. With this voltage added, the coarse control transformer is zeroed; i.e., its stator is shifted by an angle corresponding to a quarter

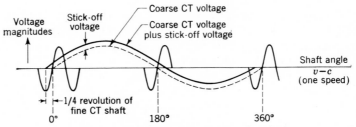

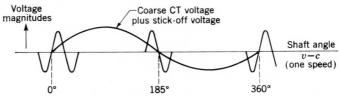

FIG. 3-66. Plot of addition of stick-off voltage.

FIG. 3-67. Voltages after shift of coarse control-transformer stator.

of a revolution of the fine control transformer. For the synchros used in the previous example, this angular shift of the stator is 2.5°. The voltage output of the two control transformers, including the stick-off voltage, is then as given in Fig. 3-67.

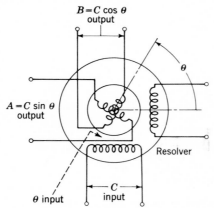

FIG. 3-68. Schematic diagram of a resolver.

In the vicinity of correspondence, i.e., at the zero position, all conditions of actuating-signal voltage are the same as before. The other zero-output-voltage position of the sum of the coarse control transformer and the stick-off voltage, however, occurs not at 180° but at an angle corresponding to a half revolution of the fine control transformer away from that point. For the previous example, this angle is 185°. To eliminate the problem of false nulls with any of the synchronizing networks shown, therefore, a stick-off voltage should be added to the coarse synchro signal.

3-23. Resolver* Applications. The schematic diagram of an electrical resolver that is widely used in computing servomechanisms is shown in Fig. 3-68. The resolver outwardly resembles a synchro. It has a round

* The authors are indebted to the Reeves Instrument Corp., which permitted the use of their very excellent "Resolver Handbook" for much of the material of the next three sections.

rotor on which two isolated windings are wound at right angles to one another. Two windings on the stator are also placed 90° apart.

Solving unknowns in a right triangle, such as is given in Fig. 3-69, proves to be the widest application of resolvers. If θ is available as a shaft angle and C is available as a voltage, A and B can be determined directly from a resolver by applying the voltage C as an input to the stator, positioning the rotor by an angle θ, and reading A and B as the outputs.

Suppose, however, that the sides C and A are known as voltages and it is desired to find the angles θ and B. Figure 3-70 illustrates how a servo may be used to accomplish this solution. A voltage proportional to C is introduced to the resolver. The servomechanism is satisfied only when the resolver angle is equal to θ, which occurs when the input to the amplifier is null. The output of one of the resolver windings is then $B = C \cos \theta$. (Instead of obtaining the voltage for the constantly excited windings of the motor from a two-phase source, the single-phase power can be shifted 90° by means of a phasing capacitor in series with this winding.)

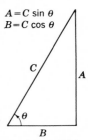

$A = C \sin \theta$
$B = C \cos \theta$

FIG. 3-69. Right triangle which is solved with a resolver.

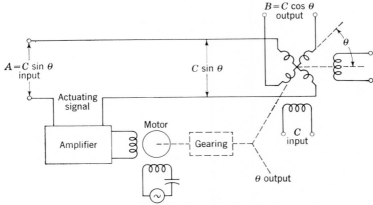

FIG. 3-70. Servo to solve for θ and B.

Figure 3-71 illustrates the case in which θ and C can be solved if A and B are known. The output of one of the rotor windings is fed to the servoamplifier. The servo drives to cause this voltage to be null, which is possible only when the angle of the rotor shaft is θ. This vector addition solves the equations

$$C = \sqrt{A^2 + B^2} \quad \text{and} \quad \theta = \tan^{-1}\frac{A}{B} \qquad (3\text{-}10)$$

These solutions are made continuously, even though the sides of the triangle are constantly changing. They can be used to solve very complicated problems involving many resolvers and many simultaneous equations.

Resolvers also find wide application in the rotation of rectangular coordinates. In this application, both stators and rotors are used. With rectangular coordinates x and y as inputs to a resolver, as in Fig. 3-72, the outputs are also rectangular coordinates of the same point referenced

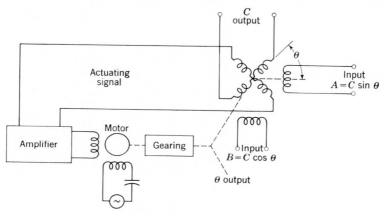

FIG. 3-71. Servo to solve for θ and C.

to a new set of axes rotated with respect to the first. The resolver equations, as obtained from the phasor diagram of Fig. 3-72, are summarized as

$$E_{R3} = E_{S2} \cos \theta - E_{S1} \sin \theta \qquad (3\text{-}11)$$
$$E_{R2} = E_{S1} \cos \theta + E_{S2} \sin \theta \qquad (3\text{-}12)$$

The actual operation can best be understood by separating it into two steps. The xy coordinates impressed on the two stators form a flux vector in the resolver. This vector is independent of rotor position. Its angular position is the arctan of y/x. Each of the rotor windings develops a voltage proportional to the sine or cosine of its angular position with respect to the flux vector (not with respect to zero). If the reference is made with respect to zero, the outputs follow Eqs. (3-11) and (3-12). The rotor voltages are the $x'y'$ components of the flux vector. The angle between the $x'y'$ coordinate reference and the xy coordinate reference of the inputs is the same as the rotor angular position.

Resolvers may be used to perform reciprocal operations, as shown in Fig. 3-73. The voltage from one rotor is fed back to the amplifier input. Since the gain in the feedback loop varies as cosine θ, the closed-loop gain of the system varies as the reciprocal of cosine θ, which is the secant θ. The other output becomes tangent θ. Cosecants may be similarly obtained. In operation, the limits of θ must be such that only negative feedback is obtained. A further practical problem is encountered with

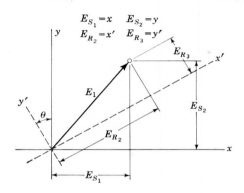

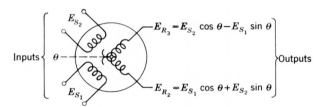

FIG. 3-72. Coordinate rotation.

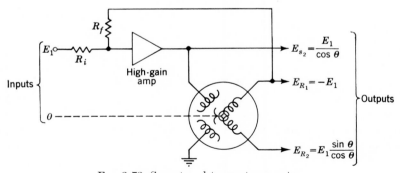

FIG. 3-73. Secant and tangent computer.

the amplifier since it must be stable over a wide range of values of loop gain. Even with these difficulties, arrangements of this type are quite practical and will in many instances eliminate the need for a servo system for performing division.

The resolver also finds application as a phase shifter. Figure 3-74a to c shows several arrangements. When the arrangement of Fig. 3-74a is excited with two voltages 90° apart in phase and of equal amplitude, the output voltages remain constant in magnitude but variable in phase, depending upon the rotor position. The two rotor voltages are shifted 90° apart.

A system that is somewhat easier to adjust is shown in Fig. 3-74b. This method requires only one input, and since the resolver rotors are well balanced in amplitude and phase, only the resistor need be adjusted to obtain proper operation. The amplifier and feedback resistor R_2 in

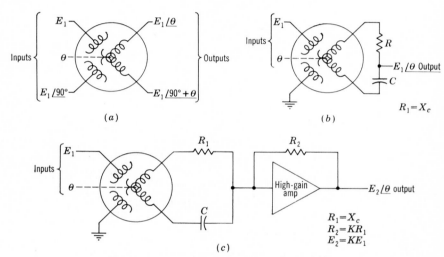

Fig. 3-74. Use of a resolver as a phase shifter.

the circuit of Fig. 3-74c may be used when a low impedance output is required.

In these latter two circuits, the loading of the resolver must be considered when calculating the precision of the unit being used as a phase shifter. If a resistance of 1 megohm is used in 60-cycle applications, the loading effect is negligible. Where isolation amplifiers are used to eliminate the loading, a precision of approximately 2 minutes is obtainable from production units.

Resolvers are used for precision data transmission, as in Fig. 3-75. The application is similar to that of three-wire synchros. The rotors are connected together because of their better electrical balance. In practice, it is desirable to use capacitors across the rotor windings for power-factor correction. Typical single-speed data-transmission systems have an accuracy of better than 1 mil or 3.5 minutes. This is equivalent to one part in over 6,000 or 0.016 per cent. To obtain this precision with conventional three-wire synchros, it is necessary to use a two-speed system.

3-24. Resolver Construction. Resolvers suffer the same difficulties of residual voltage and errors that other synchros do, and for the same reasons. They are generally manufactured to even higher accuracy tolerances. The exploded view of an electrical resolver in Fig. 3-76 gives some idea of the workmanship involved. A cutaway view of a resolver is shown in Fig. 3-77. Typical characteristics of resolvers are

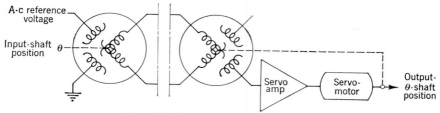

FIG. 3-75. Data transmission system.

FIG. 3-76. Electrical resolver. (*Reeves Instrument Corp., New York.*)

summarized in Table 3-4, and photographs of typical units are shown in Figs. 3-78 and 3-79.

Compared to alternate devices for the solution of trigonometric problems, these induction units are unusually compact. For example, in the problem of vector composition and coordinate rotation, the induction resolver is equivalent to two separate card-type sine-cosine generators, each with two outputs. In addition to being more accurate, however, resolvers afford signal isolation not available with potentiometers.

The resolver shown schematically in Fig. 3-72 is the basic electromagnetic unit and requires compensation and standardization by means

TABLE 3-4. CHARACTERISTICS OF TYPICAL RESOLVERS

Manufacturer	Type	Frequency, cps	Transformation ratio	Phase shift	Weight, lb	Angular error, minutes	Null voltage, mv(rms)/volt input	Input voltage
American Electronics	IR23	400	0.975 ± 0.020	1.0° ± 0.5'	1.0	± 3	1.0	100
American Electronics	IR15	400	0.980 ± 0.020	3.5° ± 1.0'	0.6	± 7.0	1.0	60
American Electronics	IR11	400	0.960 ± 0.020	6.0° ± 1.5'	0.35	± 7.0	1.0	60
Arma	1P	400	0.98 ± 0.02	75' ± 20'	1.75	± 3.5	1	0.5-16
Arma	03NN400	400	0.955 ± 0.015	4°30' ± 30'	0.35	± 7.0	1	0.5-16
Arma	03JJ400	400	1.000 ± 0.0025	0°0' ± 3.5'	0.35	± 7.0	1	0.5-16
Reeves	R600Mod101	60	0.9750 ± 0.020	8.5° ± 2.00°	1	± 3	1.0	0.5-20
Reeves	R600Mod102	400	1.000 ± 0.005	1.2° ± 0.40°	1	± 3	1.0	1-100
Bendix	AY-220S-25	400	0.454 ± 0.012	6.3° ± 1°	0.31	±15	0.7	0.5-26
Ford Instrument	76-165	400	1.02 ± 0.0020	90°	0.35	± 1.5	1.0	1-24
Ford Instrument	31	400	1.000 ± 0.0006	0°	2.8	± 1.5	1.0	0.25-12

110

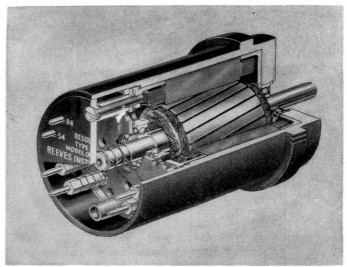

FIG. 3-77. Cutaway view of an electrical resolver. (*Reeves Instrument Corp., New York.*)

FIG. 3-78. An electrical resolver. (*Arma Division, American Bosch Arma Corp., New York.*)

FIG. 3-79. Size 15 resolver. (*American Electronics, Inc., Los Angeles.*)

of trimming networks and booster amplifiers (these can either be designed by the user or purchased directly with the resolver as a complete combination). Figure 3-80 shows a booster resolver of the network-compensated type, available as shown from the manufacturer. The over-all transformation ratio of 1.000 is attained by setting amplifier gain. Temperature-sensitive resistors bring the phase to zero over the entire temperature range. For maximum interchangeability, all trimmer resistors are in the head of the resolver.

High precision is obtained in electrical resolvers by use of the most advanced techniques in machine-shop practices. Many tolerances are held to within two ten-thousandths of an inch. Angular precision in the laminations is obtained by using dies manufactured to close tolerances and by close control of the lamination heat-treating process. By using top-quality nickel-alloy lamination material and special techniques in applying interlamination insulation, harmonic distortion and null voltages are held to less than 0.1 per cent. Aluminum finishes are

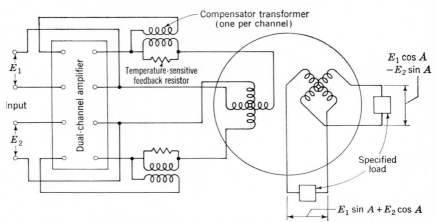

FIG. 3-80. Elementary diagram of fully compensated resolver. (*Arma Division, American Bosch Arma Corp., New York.*)

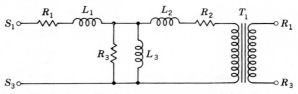

FIG. 3-81. Equivalent circuit for noncompensator winding resolver.

anodized, machined steel parts are made from noncorrosive materials, and brass parts are suitably plated. The plastics used must be selected for low moisture absorption and antifungus properties. Only the finest-grade ball bearings are used, and the negligible radial play found in these is eliminated by use of spring loading. Slip rings and brushes are of special alloys selected for this particular application.

3-25. Resolver Characteristics. For any given rotor position, resolvers perform in a manner similar to transformers with low core loss and high leakage inductance. The equivalent circuit for a noncompensator winding-type resolver is shown in Fig. 3-81. The constants for various elements may be determined by open- and short-circuit measurements on the resolver. The schematic is shown for one pair of windings at maximum coupling; however, as a result of the rectangular and sinusoidal relationship between the windings, the input and output impedances remain essentially constant for various rotor positions. The leakage inductance varies about ± 3 per cent for different rotor positions and may differ by ± 10 per cent from a mean value for the two rotor-stator pairs in a given resolver. These variations may be disregarded unless the units are operated into low-impedance loads. In such cases they should be taken into consideration. The effect can be calculated readily from the equivalent schematic.

When one resolver stator is excited and the other is shorted, the rotor voltages vary sinusoidally with rotor angular position. Any deviations from a true sinusoid constitute an angular error or an equivalent amplitude error. For a constant percentage amplitude error the angular error will vary with angle. Thus, an error of 0.1 per cent of maximum

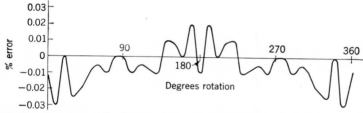

Fig. 3-82. Functional error for Reeves resolver Type R600.   (*Reeves Instrument Corp., New York.*)

output voltage at a point near zero, is equivalent to an angular error of 1 mil or 3.5 minutes. At 60°, a similar amplitude error is equivalent to 2 mils or 7 minutes. The angular accuracy of resolvers is usually defined in terms of the equivalent amplitude error. This is consistent with accuracy specifications on other computing devices, such as potentiometers. Maximum errors of 0.05 per cent are often obtainable. This is equivalent to an angular error of 0.5 mil or 1.75 minutes, in the vicinity of zero of a sine wave. Actual errors frequently are less than half this figure. A typical error curve is shown in Fig. 3-82.

In order to define more completely the accuracy of each type resolver, the maximum interaxis error is often specified. This error is defined as the deviation from 90° of the two rotor-stator pairs. It is held to less than 3 minutes of angle in many standard production types. Angular tolerances for the standard units are given in the resolver specification sheets.

The specifications for resolvers are generally based on operation of the resolver into an infinite impedance load. When this is not the case, the effect of loading the resolver can be determined by reference to the equivalent schematic for the unit and a few calculations. For most calculations the shunt inductance and the iron loss may be neglected. The output impedance for the unit consists primarily of the leakage reactance and the stator and rotor copper loss, which is essentially the same as the d-c value.

Consideration must be given to the variation of the copper loss with temperature, approximately 0.4 per cent per degree centigrade, and to the variation of the leakage reactance with rotor position, which amounts to about ±3 per cent. Unless both stators are operated from essentially zero impedances, the source impedances must also be considered. If only one stator is operated from a low-output-impedance amplifier, the other should be short-circuited. Resistive loading causes the output voltage to drop and the phase to lag. For both cases, the variation in loading effect with temperature and with rotor angular position is easily calculated.

Capacitive loading also effects the high-frequency response of the circuit. The capacity resonates with the leakage reactance, resulting in a lower natural frequency. For units intended for wide-band operation with irregular waveshapes, capacitive loading can be a major problem.

For the compensator-winding type of resolver, the relation between the compensator and rotor outputs is usually of primary interest. In making calculations for these units, the impedance common to both rotor and compensator may be neglected. This includes the stator copper loss and a portion of the leakage reactance.

Except for those variations resulting from the change in copper loss with temperature, precision resolvers are virtually free of amplitude and phase variations as a function of temperature. With compensated-type resolvers, the effects of copper loss are very nearly canceled since they appear equally in both the compensator and rotor outputs. Actual tests at both 60 and 400 cps show that under a no-load condition the phase variation between the rotor and compensator output voltages is only about 1 to 2 minutes for a temperature variation of −55 to + 85°C. Under the same conditions, the variation in transformation ratio between the rotor and compensator is about ±0.05 per cent, or only about seven parts per million per degree centigrade. When used with a suitable amplifier, the phase and amplitude variations with temperature between the amplifier input and the resolver output may be maintained at a similar precision. The results of a temperature test performed on a Reeves resolver Type R151, Model 102 selected at random from a production run are shown in Fig. 3-83.

For the most exacting applications, resolvers must be temperature-compensated. Since the source impedance of the unit varies with angular position of the rotor, the input impedance of the resolver should be infinite and only infinite impedance loads should be used. Also, the source impedance should be low. These conditions can be approached only by the use of a booster amplifier, which is a unity-gain amplifier having high input impedance and low output impedance. A circuit diagram of a booster amplifier, used with an Arma resolver, is shown in Fig. 3-84.

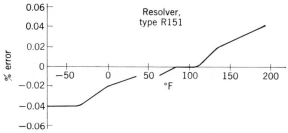

Fig. 3-83. Variation in transformation ratio with temperature.

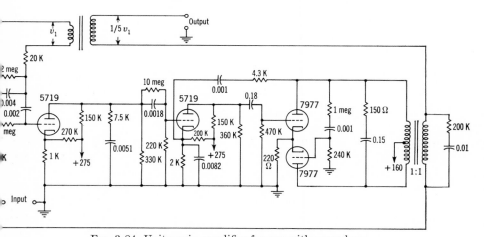

Fig. 3-84. Unity-gain amplifier for use with a resolver.

When the rotor of a resolver is positioned for minimum coupling to the stator, there is usually a residual output voltage. This voltage is proportional to the input voltage and results from eddy currents and core saturation in the stator and rotor. It is chiefly third-harmonic and amounts to about 0.1 per cent or less of the input voltage for resolvers. It is held to this small value by insulating each lamination prior to stacking.

The high stator impedance of most types of resolvers makes them especially suitable for operation in the plate circuit of vacuum tubes. Tests indicate that direct current has negligible effect on the performance

of the resolvers if the peak stator-current rating is not exceeded.   Use of
direct current in the winding reduces the peak a-c voltage that may be
applied, but this does not represent a serious difficulty.   Voltage levels
as large as 50 volts rms may still be used on many types even with direct
current in the winding.   Use of direct current in the resolver also results
in the generation of some second-harmonic distortion, but it generally
does not exceed 0.1 per cent for the rated operating voltage.   A nominal
d-c level is 8 to 10 ma for the 400-cps units and 15 ma for the 60-cps
units.   A supply voltage of 150 volts is usually sufficient.

One difficulty with resolvers is shown in the application of Fig. 3-70.
Since the output voltage of the resolver is proportional to the sine of the
angle θ, the sensitivity of the resolver, i.e., the number of volts generated
per degree of displacement from a given position, varies with the sine of
the angular position.   This means that the sensitivity of the servo varies
with the sine of the angular position, and the loop gain changes with the

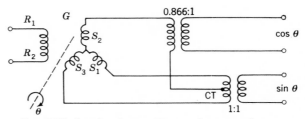

Fig. 3-85. Synchro transmitter used as a resolver.

angle θ.   Such a condition tends to make the servo more oscillatory at
angles close to $\theta = 0$ and very sluggish at angles of θ approaching 90°,
and at angles very close to 90°, the resolver cannot be used at all because
of the complete loss of sensitivity.

If this change of sensitivity is a problem, a potentiometer or variable
attenuator coupled to the resolver shaft can be used to change the sensitivity of the amplifier with the shaft angle in an inverse relationship to
the change in sensitivity of the resolver itself.   This attenuator can be
calibrated so that the product of the sensitivity of the resolver and of
the attenuator will be approximately constant.   Another method of
accomplishing the same result is through the use of a variable-gain
vacuum tube in which the gain is varied with the voltage output of the
resolver.   Thus, this stage of amplification can be caused to have a low
gain when the voltage output of the resolver is close to zero and θ is near
zero degrees and a high gain when the voltage output of the resolver is
close to a maximum and θ is near 90°.

To obtain highest accuracy from resolvers, all secondary windings
must be terminated in the proper impedance, with dummy loads used for

those windings not being employed. If a primary winding is unused, it should be short-circuited. All windings should be grounded.

A synchro transmitter can be used in some applications in place of a resolver by yielding a voltage proportional to the sine and cosine of its shaft angle. Figure 3-85 shows a Scott-T transformer connected to the output of a transmitter to provide these signals. One advantage of this system is its low output impedance, which can be made almost as low as desired by choosing a large enough synchro. A disadvantage is the inaccuracy of the synchro and, to some extent, the added error introduced by the imperfections of the transformers, although with some increase of impedance they can be standardized with trimming resistors to have the precise voltage ratio required.

PROBLEMS

3-1. Explain how two signals can be multiplied together if (a) they exist as shaft angles; (b) they exist as direct voltages. Explain how they can be divided.

3-2. Name the advantages and disadvantages of multiturn potentiometers.

3-3. What considerations enter into the size of the following components of potentiometers: (a) the wire from which the winding is made, (b) the diameter of the mandrel, (c) the shaft diameter, (d) the potentiometer diameter, (e) the brush pressure, and (f) the type of bearings?

3-4. What determines the total resistance of the potentiometer?

3-5. What is the formula for voltage sensitivity of a pair of potentiometers used in a servomechanism in terms of the voltage applied to the potentiometer pair and the angle of active winding?

3-6. What is the effect of exciting each of the two potentiometers used as an error detector in a servomechanism with a different magnitude of voltage?

3-7. Derive the formula for the effect of load resistance from the brush to one of the potentiometer terminals on an otherwise linear potentiometer. See Eq. (3-4).

3-8. What is the maximum departure from linearity caused by the loading of a 1,000-ohm potentiometer with a 10,000-ohm load if the potentiometer is otherwise linear?

3-9. In what applications are each of the various types of linearity important?

3-10. For what applications would the total resistance of the potentiometer be important?

3-11. Explain why a pair of potentiometers having a linearity tolerance of 0.1 per cent and a winding angle of 350° could yield an error of 1.4°.

3-12. Explain how backlash between brush and shaft, uniformity of wire resistance, and the shape of the mandrel affect the accuracy of the potentiometer.

3-13. Assume that a potentiometer is completely linear and that the slide wire is caused to be slightly elliptic in form rather than in its original round shape. Derive the approximate relationship of the error from linearity caused by a slight ellipsing of the slide wire.

3-14. A linear potentiometer has a number of taps for the purpose of generating nonlinear functions by shunting resistors across the taps. Prove that the curve of voltage output vs. shaft rotation consists of straight-line segments.

3-15. A potentiometer is originally linear and has four taps in addition to its two end terminals. To what accuracy can the function $R = K\theta^2$ be generated with shunting resistors?

3-16. How many taps would a linear potentiometer need to be able to generate a sine function to a conformity of 1 per cent?

3-17. For the circuit of Fig. P3-17, determine the loading error as a function of potentiometer setting for the following values of θ: 0.2, 0.4, 0.6, 0.8, and 1.00.

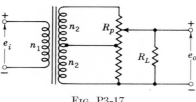

FIG. P3-17

3-18. Repeat Prob. 3-17 for three taps. As a result, generalize the problem to one tap and determine the effect of taps on potentiometer loading.

3-19. What is the theoretical limit of linearity of a 3-in.-diameter potentiometer using wire with a diameter of 0.001 in.?

3-20. What is the quadrature voltage for any relative shaft positions of a pair of single-turn potentiometers used as error detectors if they are excited with 10 volts and the phase difference between the two voltages is 2°?

3-21. Explain how quadrature voltage in the actuating signal can cause an error in the servomechanism.

3-22. There are arrangements for the use of a single E transformer as an error detector and also for the use of two E transformers. Sketch the electrical and mechanical arrangement involved, and note the advantages and limitations of each method.

3-23. Sketch the mechanical and electrical arrangement of a single synchro used as an error detector.

3-24. A synchro transmitter and synchro control transformer are correctly connected electrically and are used in a servomechanism. What would be the effect of (a) reversing R_1 and R_2 of the transmitter, (b) reversing R_1 and R_2 of the control transformer, (c) reversing S_1 and S_3 leads, (d) reversing S_2 and S_3 leads?

3-25. Explain how a cam could be used to compensate for synchro errors.

3-26. The stator voltages of a synchro transmitter are measured when the shaft angle is 30°. The smaller of the two voltages is found to be 1 per cent higher than a zero-error synchro would be. What is the error of the synchro at this point?

3-27. Explain how ellipsing of the rotor or stator of a synchro causes errors. Show whether each causes fundamental or second-harmonic space errors.

3-28. Compare the advantages and disadvantages for various applications of a pair of synchros and a pair of potentiometers as error detectors.

3-29. Show how a two-speed system employing potentiometers could be built. Is this a practical application of potentiometers?

3-30. Explain the importance of gearing accuracy with various arrangements of single-speed and double-speed synchro transmission.

3-31. When transmitting at 1- and 55-speed, what is the synchro error if it is 18 minutes for single-speed transmission?

3-32. What is the effect of a synchronizing network on the relative margin of stability of a servo?

3-33. A servo employs a relay-type synchronizing network. Explain how improper connection of the synchros may cause the servo and the synchronizing network to oscillate.

3-34. Derive an expression for the fine to coarse transfer points of a double-speed synchro system employing a synchronizing network.

3-35. Compare the advantages and disadvantages of a relay-type synchronizing network with a selenium-rectifier type.

3-36. What is the effect of harmonic voltages in the stick-off voltage?

3-37. What is the effect of variation of supply voltage in a servo where stick-off voltage is used?

3-38. Derive an expression for the range of size of stick-off voltage when a relay synchronizing network is used.

3-39. Compare the relative advantages and disadvantages of a double-speed synchro transmission system which uses an odd gear ratio with one which uses an even gear ratio and stick-off voltage.

3-40. State the advantages and disadvantages of the various types of synchronizing networks shown in the figures of Chap. 3.

3-41. Derive Eqs. (3-11) and (3-12).

3-42. Show how a resolver can be used to transform from polar to rectangular coordinates.

3-43. What is the effect of temperature variation upon the performance of a precision resolver?

3-44. How can the variation of sensitivity with angular displacement be compensated?

CHAPTER 4

DEMODULATORS AND MODULATORS

4-1. Discussion of Demodulators and Modulators. It is often neces-sary to convert alternating-voltage signals existing in the servomechanism to direct voltages. An instance in which this is necessary occurs when the actuating-signal voltage exists as the envelope of an alternating carrier voltage and it is desirable to use low-pass networks to equalize this signal. Another application occurs in the rectification of an alternating-voltage signal from an a-c tachometer generator in order to use d-c networks to modify the signal.

Conversely, it may be necessary to reconvert direct voltages to alter-nating voltages in order to drive a-c motors. An example of this applica-tion occurs when the actuating-signal voltage is in the form of a direct voltage and it is desired to use an a-c amplifier. Similarly, a d-c tachom-eter may be used in conjunction with an a-c amplifier and therefore would require its output to be modulated to an alternating voltage. Demodu-lators and modulators are extensively used in servo circuits.

Many types of modulation exist. In servomechanism applications, amplitude modulation, which is the process by which the amplitude of a carrier signal is varied by an intelligence signal, is most common. Two basic forms of amplitude modulation exist: (1) carrier-present modulation and (2) carrier-suppressed modulation. Carrier-present modulation is defined by the following equation:

$$e(t) = [1 + mf(t)] \sin \omega_c t \tag{4-1}$$

where $f(t)$ is the intelligence signal and $\sin \omega_c t$ represents the carrier. The modulated carrier is $e(t)$ and m is the modulation constant. This type of amplitude modulation is utilized in most small AM radio receivers. Carrier-suppressed modulation is expressed by the following equation:

$$e(t) = f(t) \sin \omega_c t \tag{4-2}$$

The modulated carrier $e(t)$ in this case is the product of the intelligence signal and the carrier. The form of the signal information in a servo-mechanism is often electrical, and if it is an alternating voltage, the direc-tion of the signal is determined from the instantaneous polarity of the voltage with respect to some reference. The magnitude of the envelope is a measure of the size of the signal. If the signal is also sinusoidal, the form of the intelligence signal is

$$f(t) = \sin \omega_c t \qquad (4\text{-}3)$$

and the modulated signal voltage is

$$e(t) = \sin \omega_s t \sin \omega_c t \qquad (4\text{-}4)$$

where ω_s is the angular frequency of oscillation of the signal and ω_c is the carrier frequency. If a potentiometer winding is excited with an alternating supply and its shaft oscillated sinusoidally about the position of zero output voltage, a modulated wave of the form of Eq. (4-4) is obtained. The frequency of supply is the carrier frequency and the signal frequency is the frequency of shaft oscillation. The form of the voltage is shown in Fig. 4-1 for a single value of ω_s and ω_c.

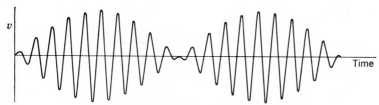

FIG. 4-1. Suppressed-carrier voltage.

The product of the two sine terms of Eq. (4-4) can be written as the sum

$$e(t) = \tfrac{1}{2} \cos\left[(\omega_c - \omega_s)t\right] - \tfrac{1}{2} \cos\left[(\omega_c + \omega_s)t\right] \qquad (4\text{-}5)$$

The voltage $e(t)$ is equal to the algebraic sum of two sinusoidal voltages, neither of which has the frequency ω_c of the supply and neither of which has the frequency ω_s of the signal. It is called a *suppressed carrier voltage*, since the carrier frequency is not present. Because of the widespread use of carrier-suppressed modulation in servo systems, this book emphasizes this type of modulation.

Demodulation is the reverse process to modulation. In this process the intelligence signal is recovered from the modulated carrier. Demodulators depend for their operation upon a time-varying circuit element, such as a synchronous converter or vibrating reed; a time-varying parameter, such as a transistor in which the conductance is varied as a function of time; or a nonlinear element, such as a diode. Filter networks, which are discussed in Chap. 5, are usually required for modulation and demodulation systems.

The basic elements of a modulator and demodulator are shown in Fig. 4-2. For the modulator of Fig. 4-2a the two inputs are the intelligence $f(t)$ and the carrier $\sin \omega_c t$. The time-varying element or parameter contained within the multiplier can be controlled by either the carrier or the intelligence. The multiplier, which is denoted by $g(t)$, yields two possible outputs, as shown in Fig. 4-2. This signal is passed through a filter that yields the desired modulated signal. A bandpass filter with ω_c as a center frequency is often used with the modulator.

The operation of a demodulator, which is shown in Fig. 4-2b, is similar to the modulator. The two inputs are now the modulated signal $f(t) \sin \omega_c t$ and the reference signal $\sin \omega_c t$. The multiplier output is smoothed in a filter (often a low-pass filter) yielding the intelligence $f(t)$ at the output.

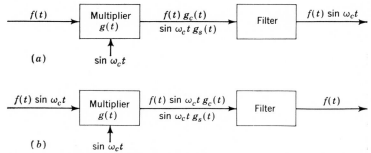

FIG. 4-2. Block diagrams of (a) modulator and (b) demodulator.

Close examination of Fig. 4-2 indicates an important fact. Except for the filter, there is no fundamental difference between a modulator and demodulator. Hence, theoretically, any modulator without its filter can be used to demodulate a signal of the same form as its original output. Practical considerations require that the circuit be designed for the application (either modulator or demodulator).

4-2. Theory of Operation.* For purposes of analysis, a modulator can be represented by the simple circuit of Fig. 4-3. This system comprises a key (switch), which is controlled by the carrier signal, and a series resistor. The intelligence signal is applied to the input. Suppose the key is closed during the positive portion of the carrier signal (assumed to be a sinusoidal function) and open during the negative half. The switching accomplished by the multiplier is included in Fig. 4-4.

To obtain an analytic expression for the output, let the input be composed of two different input frequencies:

$$v(t) = \sin \omega_s t + \sin \Omega_s t \qquad (4\text{-}6)$$

* See Ref. 32 for an excellent discussion of modulators and demodulators.

The multiplier function $g(t)$ is expanded in a Fourier series as follows:

$$g(t) = \left[\frac{1}{2} + \frac{2}{\pi}\left(\sin \omega_c t + \frac{1}{3}\sin 3\omega_c t + \cdots\right)\right] \quad (4\text{-}7)$$

The output function is given by the product of Eqs. (4-6) and (4-7), which yields the result

$$e(t) = (\sin \omega_s t + \sin \Omega_s t)\left[\frac{1}{2} + \frac{2}{\pi}\left(\sin \omega_c t + \frac{1}{3}3\omega_c t + \cdots\right)\right] \quad (4\text{-}8)$$

Equation (4-8) is multiplied and simplified by converting products into sums as follows:

$$\begin{aligned}
e(t) &= \frac{1}{2}\sin \omega_s t + \frac{1}{2}\sin \Omega_s t + \frac{2}{\pi}(\sin \omega_s t \sin \omega_c t + \sin \Omega_s t \sin \omega_c t) \\
&\quad + \frac{2}{3\pi}(\sin \omega_s t \sin 3\omega_c t + \sin \Omega_s t \sin 3\omega_c t) + \cdots \\
&= \frac{1}{2}(\sin \omega_s t + \sin \Omega_s t + \frac{1}{\pi}[\cos(\omega_c - \omega_s)t - \cos(\omega_c + \omega_s)t \\
&\quad + \cos(\omega_c - \Omega_s)t - \cos(\omega_c + \Omega_s)t] + \frac{1}{3\pi}[\cos(3\omega_c - \omega_s)t \\
&\quad - \cos(3\omega_c + \omega_s)t + \cos(3\omega_c - \Omega_s)t - \cos(3\omega_c + \Omega_s)t] + \cdots
\end{aligned}$$
$$(4\text{-}9)$$

Equation (4-9) can also be obtained by adding the outputs of the modulator when $\sin \omega_s t$ and $\sin \Omega_s t$ are inserted separately—hence the

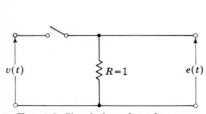

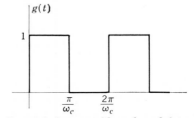

FIG. 4-3. Simple keyed modu ator.   FIG. 4-4. Output of keyed modulator.

output of this type of modulator is linear. No intermodulation distortion [terms of the form $\cos(\omega_s + \Omega_s)t$] exists. A bandpass filter is chosen to eliminate signal-frequency components, such as ω_s and Ω_s, and higher harmonic components, such as $(3\omega_c + \omega_s)$. The bandwidth of this filter is largely dependent upon the largest value of ω_s (or Ω_s) that is contained in the intelligence frequency. The limit is $\omega_c/2$. If $\omega_s > \omega_c/2$, the component corresponding to ω_s will be at a higher frequency than the component corresponding to $\omega_c - \omega_s$. The maximum passband of the filter is limited at the lower end to $\omega_c/2$, and hence ω_s must be less than $\omega_c/2$.

Figure 4-5 illustrates the action of a phase-sensitive demodulator.*
Figure 4-5a shows the magnitude and direction of the servo-error transient response to a step-function command. Figure 4-5b shows the
actuating signal, the output of the synchro or other a-c error-detecting
device such as a pair of potentiometers or E coils. It is the product of
Fig. 4-5a and a sine wave, Fig. 4-5c. Figure 4-5d shows the rectified
actuating signal, the idealized output of a full-wave phase-sensitive
detector. With a half-wave phase-sensitive detector, only half as many

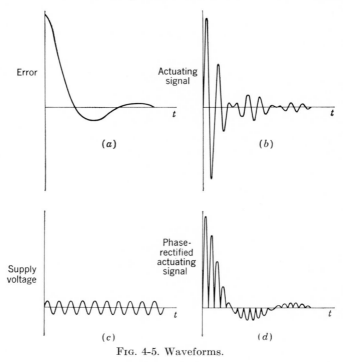

Fig. 4-5. Waveforms.

signal pulses exist. The output of a phase-sensitive detector is not so
smooth as the output of a d-c error detector. A d-c error detector, such
as a pair of potentiometers excited with a direct voltage, however, may
not be suitable.

4-3. Types of Demodulators. The choice of the type of modulation
depends largely on the application. In the case of amplitude modulation,
the carrier-suppressed form is most common in servo applications because

---

* Demodulators used in servomechanism circuits are normally called *phase-sensitive
detectors*, or *phase-sensitive rectifiers*. The output of a phase-sensitive detector gives
a direct voltage that is proportional to the amplitude of the alternating voltage. The
polarity depends upon the polarity of the alternating voltage.

many of the components used in a-c servomechanisms, such as synchros, variable-differential transformers, E pickoffs, etc., utilize carrier-suppressed signals. Also, the poor null characteristics of carrier-present modulation preclude its use in null-seeking systems (servomechanisms).

The type of demodulator or modulator, whether it utilizes a vibrator, a vacuum tube, or a transistor, depends upon such factors as the end use of the item, the cost, and the performance. Various types are considered in the next three sections. Since modulators and demodulators are similar, emphasis is placed upon the demodulators.

The Vibrator as a Demodulator. A schematic of perhaps the simplest type of phase-sensitive detector is shown in Fig. 4-6. It employs a vibrator, or chopper. The moving arm of the vibrator oscillates in synchronism with the supply voltage. Units are designed for either 60 or 400 cycles depending upon the frequency of the signal to be rectified.

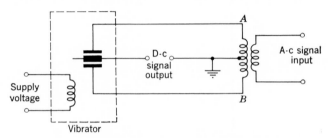

Fig. 4-6. Vibrator as a phase-sensitive detector.

As is true for all phase-sensitive detectors, the supply voltage must come from the same source as the error-detector supply.

If the signal input is zero, the d-c output is zero. The vibrator continues to be oscillated between the two outer contacts. If the a-c signal is not zero and is of such a polarity that, during the half cycles when the vibrator is resting on the top contact, point A is positive and, during the half cycles when the vibrator contact is resting on the bottom contact, the polarity of the voltage appearing at B is positive, the d-c signal will be positive with respect to ground. If, however, the a-c signal is reversed in polarity so that the moving contact rests on the top contact when A is at the negative polarity and rests on the bottom contact when B is negative, the signal output will be negative with respect to ground. Thus, this circuit is a phase-sensitive detector. The output voltage is proportional to the input voltage and of a polarity depending upon the polarity of the input signal.

Phase-sensitive detectors have a property that is quite incidental to their primary function but is often a desirable by-product of their operation. This property is the ability to discriminate against quadrature voltage, which might be an undesirable component of the output of a control transformer. Although this property is common to all phase-sensitive detectors, for simplicity it is explained with reference to the chopper.

Figure 4-7a is one cycle of supply frequency. Assume that the moving contact of Fig. 4-6 rests on the upper contact during interval 1 and on the lower contact during interval 2. Figure 4-7b shows the waveform of any quadrature voltage in the a-c signal. During interval 1, the net direct-voltage appearing at A is zero, and therefore the d-c signal output contributed by the quadrature voltage is zero. Similarly, the net direct voltage appearing at point B, and hence at the output, is zero during interval 2. A voltage at phase quadrature with the supply voltage, therefore, produces no d-c output from the phase-sensitive detector. Due care must be exercised in adjusting the phase of the supply voltage so that the contact oscillation is in phase with the a-c input signal. If necessary, any ripple voltage that is produced can be filtered.

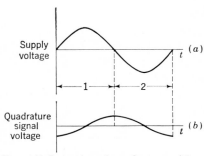

Fig. 4-7. Rejection of quadrature with a phase-sensitive demodulator.

The above discussion suggests another application of the phase-sensitive detector. In some servomechanisms, the actuating signal is of approximately constant magnitude but has a signal voltage whose phase with respect to the supply voltage is a measure of the servo error. If this type of signal is the input to the network, the d-c output is zero whenever the phase of the signal is 90° with respect to the supply and is roughly proportional to the phase-angle difference between the signal and the supply. Thus, the servo drives this error detector to make the input to the network have a phase of 90° and thus effect a null.

It can also be shown in a diagram similar to Fig. 4-7 that the phase-sensitive network can be used to discriminate against third-harmonic signal voltages provided that the signal voltages have the proper "phase" relationship with the supply.

Commercially available choppers can interrupt up to 100 volts and 25 ma and operate over a temperature range of -65 to $+85°C$ with case vibration of 0.06 in. travel for 10 to 55 cycles. Above $-10°C$, the phase shift between the center of the contact on-time and the supply voltage is $65 \pm 15°$. The internal construction of such a vibrator is shown in Fig. 4-8. One type of chopper has a noise level of a few microvolts for circuits of about 1 megohm impedance, which is a lower level than can be obtained with the other circuits described in this chapter. Such a chopper should be used if the voltage levels are this low.

Usually the chopper is excited by an alternating drive current that acts through a drive coil and associated magnetic circuit to set an armature in vibration. The armature carries a contact that is alternately closed to each of two fixed contacts. In the presence of external mechanical vibration, the armature tends to be driven by mechanical motion as

Fig. 4-8. Internal construction of vibrator. (*Airpax Products Co., Cambridge, Md.*)

Fig. 4-9. Sketch of internal construction of balanced armature chopper. (*Airpax Products Co., Cambridge, Md.*)

well as by the magnetic field of the drive coil. The result can be erratic switching action of the chopper.

In some types of choppers the armature is supported on a pivot at its center and is accurately balanced about this pivot. A typical sample is shown in Fig. 4-9. External mechanical vibration imparts only translation to the armature—the same as it does to the fixed contacts. The balanced structure effectively isolates the armature from extraneous torques that could interfere with its desired motion. The drive coil and polarized magnetic circuit couple to the balanced armature at one end. The moving contact is mounted at the opposite end and is well removed from the magnetic driving field to minimize stray pickup.

The curve of Fig. 4-10 shows contact derangement as a function of frequency for vibrations of constant 15 g in the plane that is most sensitive to vibration. Contact derangement is the aggregate fluctuation in make or break due to bounce, chatter, and phase modulation and dissymmetry due to vibration. It is measured in electrical degrees.

Choppers suffer certain limitations. They may be unusable in circuits where the phase of the contact oscillation must be invariant. This is particularly true since the phase of contact motion relative to the supply voltage shifts markedly with the supply frequency. Chopper life is generally limited to about 1,000 hours, thus comparing unfavorably with

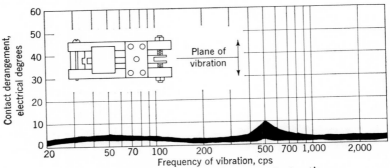

FIG. 4-10. Effect of 15 g vibration on contact action.

selenium-rectifier circuits. Because of the travel of the center contact, the on-time is between 115 and 165°, instead of a full 180°. On the other hand, the center contact of some choppers short-circuits the outer contacts for a portion of the cycle and must be internally adjusted to prevent this if the application so demands. In critical circuits, variation of this time can cause faulty operation of the servo. This is sometimes caused by contact bounce but more often by the variation of contact resistance with time. With certain units, the contact material tends to flake and wear, thus making erratic contact at the beginning and end of the contact period. However, in circuits where noise levels, cleanness of signal, and simplicity of circuitry are important, choppers are probably the best type of demodulator (or modulator) to use.

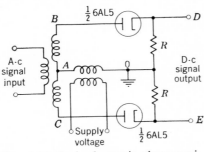

FIG. 4-11. Basic electronic phase-sensitive detector.

Basic Electronic Phase-sensitive Detector. A simple phase-sensitive detector employing no mechanical moving parts is shown in Fig. 4-11.

As with all the rectifiers shown in this chapter, the rectifiers may be tubes, crystals, or dry-disk rectifiers.   This half-wave demodulator operates in the following manner: A supply voltage, say 60 cycles, is applied to the transformer and appears across AO.   The alternating signal that is to be rectified is applied to the input of the network.   When the input signal is zero, the output of the circuit should also be zero. During the positive half cycle, the voltage at A is positive with respect to O, and the voltages at B and C are equal to the voltage at A.   The voltage BO and the voltage CO are equal and positive during this half cycle, and equal currents flow through rectifying tubes and produce equal voltage drops across the resistors R.   The output voltages from D to O and from E to O are equal, and consequently the d-c output, which is the voltage DE, is equal to zero.   During the negative half cycle, the tubes do not conduct; therefore no voltage appears across DO and EO, and consequently the voltage DE remains zero.

Suppose, however, that a signal voltage is applied to the input of the network.   If the voltages are properly phased, the signal voltage will either be exactly in phase with or exactly out of phase with the supply voltage.   Assume first that the signal voltage is in phase with the voltage appearing across AO. Reference to Fig. 4-12a and b will aid in the discussion.   The voltages v_{OA} and v_{AB} under these conditions are in phase so that the voltage v_{OB} is the sum of the two. The voltages v_{OA} and v_{AC} are 180° out of phase.   Since the voltage v_{OC} is the algebraic sum of the two, the magnitude is the difference between the two magnitudes.   The voltage v_{OB} applied across the rectifier and resistor combination results in a large current through the resistor and a large voltage v_{DO}.   At the same time, the voltage v_{OC} applied to the rectifier and resistor results in a smaller current and consequently in a smaller voltage v_{EO}.   If the rectifier drop is negligible, the voltage output during this half cycle is the difference between v_{OB} and v_{OC}.   Since point D is more positive with respect to point E, a signal voltage of the polarity originally chosen results in D being positive.   During the negative half cycle, neither tube conducts, and the circuit gives no output.   If, however, the signal voltage is of opposite polarity, a voltage output results in which D is negative with respect to E.

The output voltage in each case is proportional to the signal voltage and is independent of the magnitude of the reference voltage provided

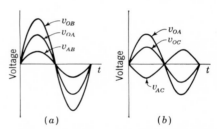

FIG. 4-12. Voltages in the circuit of Fig. 4-11.

the signal voltage is smaller than the reference voltage. A filter is required since the output of all phase-sensitive detectors is rectified a-c. This filter is commonly a capacitor in parallel with a resistor R. For better smoothing, however, a full-wave phase-sensitive rectifier is often used, also with a filter capacitor.

Triode Demodulator. Figure 4-13 shows another version of the half-wave phase-sensitive detector. This unit has the advantage of requiring no transformers. Typical circuit values are also given. The voltage applied to the grids of the tubes can come directly from the alternating voltage of the line or from the output of the power-supply transformer. During the positive half cycle of the grid voltage, the combination of tubes conducts in either direction and acts like a short circuit for either positive or negative voltage applied to point A. During the negative half cycle, however, the tubes are completely cut off, and no current flows through them. If the voltage input is of the same polarity as the voltage

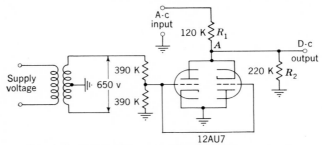

Fig. 4-13. Triode phase-sensitive demodulator circuit.

applied to the grids of the tubes and is thus positive when the grid voltages are positive, point A is short-circuited to ground and the voltage at point A is zero. During the negative half cycle, both the input voltage and the voltage applied to the grids reverse phase. Since point A is no longer short-circuited to ground, it becomes negative with respect to ground; and the output voltage is equal to the input voltage reduced by the potentiometer effect of resistors R_1 and R_2.

If, however, the input voltage is of the opposite polarity, it is negative during the half cycle when the grids are positive. Point A is short-circuited, and the output voltage is zero during the half cycle. During the other half cycle, the grid voltages are negative; and the input voltage is positive. The output voltage is positive during this half cycle and is equal to the input voltage times the factor $R_2/(R_1 + R_2)$. The output voltage is therefore a half-wave rectified voltage proportional to the input and of a polarity depending upon the polarity of the input voltage. Figure 4-14 presents experimental results obtained with the use of this circuit.

Another example of a half-wave phase-sensitive detector, in this case employing triodes, is shown in Fig. 4-15. With this circuit, the output voltage is proportional to the amplified magnitude of the input voltage. The polarity is determined by that of the signal voltage. A capacitor is added to smooth the ripple voltage.

In both the circuits of Fig. 4-11 or 4-15, the voltage from D to E is proportional to the input signal during one half cycle and zero during

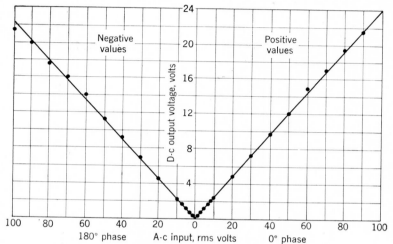

Fig. 4-14. Experimental results of the circuit of Fig. 4-13.

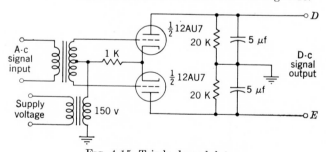

Fig. 4-15. Triode demodulator.

the other half cycle. The voltages from D to O and from E to O are both large during the first half cycle even with no input signal applied. If the voltage v_{DE} is fed to the input of a push-pull amplifier, the ripple voltage appearing at the grid at D and at the grid at E can be appreciable. If, however, point E is grounded and point D fed to the input of a d-c amplifier, the input voltage has much less ripple. The drift problems are normally so great with single-ended d-c amplifiers that despite this disadvantage the voltage v_{DE} is normally applied to a push-pull d-c amplifier.

Full-wave Phase-sensitive Detector. Figure 4-16 shows a full-wave phase-sensitive detector. This circuit is the full-wave version of Fig. 4-11. Typical component values are given as an illustration of the filtering commonly required for 60 cps.

Ring Demodulator. Figure 4-17 shows a device known as a ring demodulator. It is a full-wave circuit and operates as follows: The supply voltage applied to the tubes causes the upper tubes to conduct

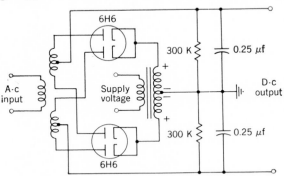

Fig. 4-16. Full-wave phase-sensitive detector.

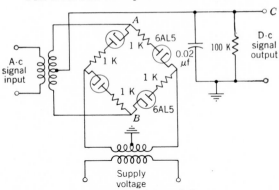

Fig. 4-17. Ring demodulator.

in the first half cycle and the lower tubes to conduct in the second half cycle. Each half cycle, then, is characterized by either the upper two tubes conducting or the lower two tubes conducting. When the tubes are conducting, the points between the two tubes are placed at ground potential, on the assumption that the drops across the tubes and resistors in each half of the circuit are equal. This results in putting the point *A* or *B* at ground potential on alternate half cycles.

If the polarity of the a-c signal input is such that during the first half cycle point *A* is positive with respect to *B* and during this half cycle point *B* is put at ground potential by the supply voltage, point *C* is positive with respect to ground and for the entire half cycle is equal to exactly half the voltage appearing across AB. During the next half cycle, point A is placed at ground potential by the tubes firing; and since the a-c input signal also reverses polarity, point B is positive with respect to point A, and the voltage appearing at C is half the voltage appearing across AB. The voltage at C, therefore, is a full-wave rectified voltage of positive polarity. If the a-c signal input reverses its polarity, the voltage at point C will be negative and equal to half the voltage v_{AB}.

4-4. Types of Modulators. As indicated in Sec. 4-1 no significant difference exists between a demodulator and a modulator. Most demodulator circuits can be reversed and used as modulators. Modulator circuits used in servomechanism circuits must also be phase-sensitive; i.e., they must have an output a-c signal voltage proportional to the input d-c signal voltage in magnitude and a polarity dependent upon the polarity of the direct voltage.

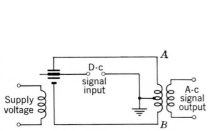

FIG. 4-18. Vibrator as a modulator.

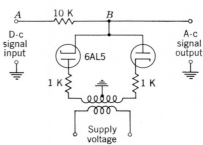

FIG. 4-19. Modulator circuit.

The Vibrator as a Modulator. The simplest example of a modulator is the vibrator shown in Fig. 4-18. The contacts of the vibrator are oscillated in synchronism with the supply voltage. If the polarity of the d-c signal appearing at the center contact is plus, point A will be plus on the first half cycle and point B will be plus on the second half cycle. But if the d-c signal is negative, point A is negative on the first half cycle. The output is an alternating voltage with the same frequency as the supply voltage but of opposite polarity to that of the first case. The output voltage of the vibrator circuit is essentially a square wave, as is the output voltage of the other modulators that are discussed.

Electronic-modulator Circuits. Tube circuits can be analyzed, again assuming that the voltage drop across the tube is virtually zero. In each case, selenium rectifiers, crystals, or other types of rectifier can be used in place of vacuum-tube rectifiers. In the circuit of Fig. 4-19, assume that current flows in the diodes during the first half cycle, thus putting point B at ground potential if there are equal drops across the load resistors and tubes. On the second half cycle, the tubes are open circuits, and point B is not affected. The voltage at B oscillates from a ground potential to the potential of point A in synchronism with the supply voltage. If point A is of negative polarity, point B is alternately minus and zero. If point A is of positive polarity, point B is alternately plus and zero.

Figure 4-20 shows another modulator circuit. During the half cycle of the reference voltage when the tubes are conducting, point B is at the same potential as point A, assuming equal drops across the tubes and resistors. On the negative half cycle, point B is at ground potential. Therefore, point B alternates between the voltage at point A and ground. If point A is a direct voltage of positive polarity, point B is alternately plus and ground. If point A is negative, point B is alternately minus and ground. The output therefore has a magnitude equal to the input

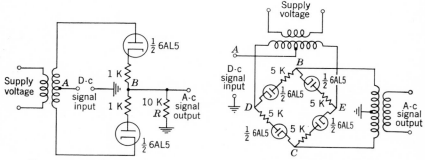

FIG. 4-20. Modulator circuit.   FIG. 4-21. Ring modulator.

voltage and a polarity depending upon the polarity of the d-c input signal.

Figure 4-21 shows the ring modulator. On alternate half cycles the supply voltage places the potential of point A at points B and C by causing alternate pairs of tubes to conduct. For example, when the supply voltage is such that point D is plus with respect to E, the lower tubes conduct and point C is placed at the potential of point A if the drops of the tubes and resistors are equal in each half of the circuit. On the other half cycle, the upper tubes are conducting and point B is placed at the potential of A. The a-c output, therefore, is proportional in magnitude to the d-c input and of a polarity depending upon the polarity of the input voltage.

Figure 4-22 is the modulator version of Fig. 4-13. Again, no transformer is necessary. On the half cycles when the grid is positive, point A is at ground potential. When the tubes are negative, they act as open circuits and, for equal resistors in the circuit, point A is half the input potential. Its polarity is again determined by the polarity of the d-c input signal. Figure 4-23 shows the experimental results from this circuit. The a-c output with zero-input voltage is 0.2 volt.

Figure 4-24 is a modulator that employs amplification. Graphs that show the experimental performance characteristics of this circuit are given in Figs. 4-25a and 4-25b. Figure 4-25a indicates the linearity and the sensitivity of the circuit. Figure 4-25b shows the change in phase shift of the output signal with magnitude of the input signal.

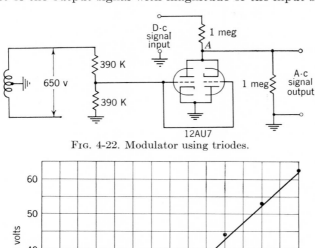

Fig. 4-22. Modulator using triodes.

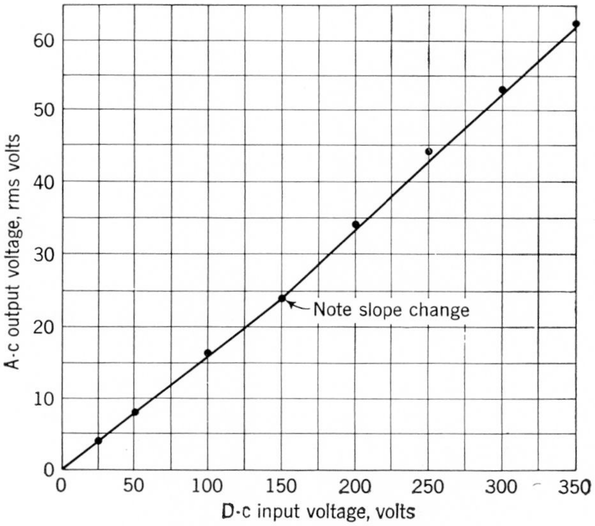

Fig. 4-23. Experimental results of the circuit of Fig. 4-22.

As in all modulators, it is desired that the change in phase shift be invariant with signal level. Provided the phase shift remains constant, it can be any value and is often deliberately made 90°. In the use of the chopper, for instance, the supply-voltage phase is often shifted so that the contacts are closed with a phase of 90° with respect to the line voltage. By phasing the actuating signal at right angles to the line, a two-phase servomotor can have constant excitation supplied directly

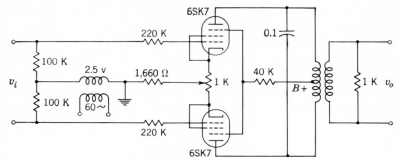

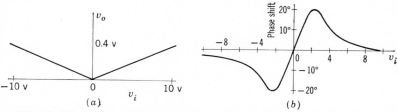

FIG. 4-24. Modulator employing pentodes.

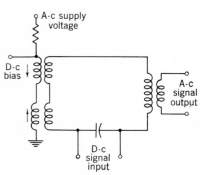

FIG. 4-25. (a) Alternating-voltage output vs. direct-voltage input for the circuit of Fig. 4-24; (b) phase shift vs. direct-voltage input for the circiut of Fig. 4-24.

from the line. If the d-c signal that is being modulated is a rectified alternating current and the signal cannot be sufficiently filtered, erratic operation of the servo may result, particularly if equalizing networks are used. In such cases, it is better to obtain the 90° phase shift elsewhere.

Magnetic Modulators. Magnetic amplifiers can also be used as modulators. Since they are discussed in Chap. 6, they are not considered here. The principle of saturation, however, is employed in the magnetic modulator of Fig. 4-26. The supply voltage is applied to two opposing coils, which are wound on separate cores. The d-c signal-input current during one half cycle aids the flux of one of the two coils and subtracts from the flux in the other of the two coils. In the core where the fluxes are opposed, the impedance of the primary coil is higher; consequently the voltage drop across it is higher, and the induced voltage in the secondary coil is higher. In the other half cycle, the direct current is in the same direction, but the direction of the supply-voltage fluxes is changed. Consequently, the impedance in the

FIG. 4-26. Magnetic modulator.

other coil is increased, and the voltage drop induced in the secondary is of the opposite polarity. A capacitor C is used to present a low impedance for the alternating voltage since the signal input is usually fed from a high impedance source.

These units are commercially available with a signal-winding impedance of about 700 to 4,000 ohms and require an a-c excitation of a few hundred milliamperes. When they are operated with a d-c bias in addition to the reference voltage, the output voltage is principally fundamental. When they are operated without a bias, which is the most stable operation for the magnetic modulator, the output voltage is principally second-harmonic.

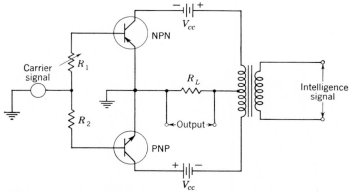

Fig. 4-27. Carrier-suppressed modulator (or demodulator) employing complementary symmetry.

4-5. Transistor Modulators and Demodulators. As with many other applications, transistors can be used for modulator and demodulator circuits with good advantage. Because of the variation of parameter values from unit to unit, special care must be exercised to maintain a balanced output in the design of transistor modulators and demodulators. In many cases, no amount of compensation either on the input or on the output can completely eliminate unbalanced output. Special techniques are necessary since in every case two transistors are required.

The complementary symmetry circuit of Fig. 4-27 utilizes one n-p-n and one p-n-p* for a modulator. In this example the grounded-emitter connection is used, and the switching is controlled with the modulating signal. The operation of this circuit can be understood by considering one transistor at a time. The intelligence signal determines which transistor conducts. When the intelligence signal is positive, the p-type transistor allows collector current to flow. The n-type transistor permits collector current to flow when the intelligence signal is negative.

* See Sec. 6-7 for an analysis of transistors and a definition of the parameters.

When the intelligence voltage is negative, the n-type transistor is controlling the output. The characteristic curves and corresponding load line are shown in Fig. 4-28. The carrier voltage appearing across each half of the center-tapped transformer winding is maintained at a constant peak-to-peak value of 2 V_{cc} volts so that the output of each transistor reaches ground potential. The carrier voltage v_s causes the load line to move parallel to itself an amount corresponding to $\pm V_{cc}$ volts on the voltage axis. It can be seen from Fig. 4-28 that the maximum excursion of the collector current is proportional to the base current. The linear relationship is based upon the uniform spacing of the constant-base-current curves. The operation of the p-type transistor, i.e., with

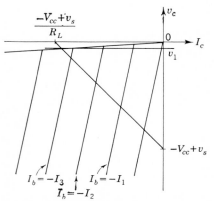

Fig. 4-28. Linearized constant base-current characteristics.

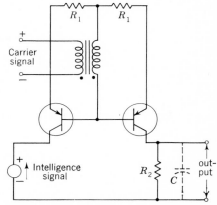

Fig. 4-29. Transistor modulator (or demodulator).

positive base current, is the same as that of the n-type except for a reversal of the sign of all the quantities.

In this application, collector current exists during a large portion of the carrier cycle. The collector current is unsaturated during the time required for the load line to be moved from point v_1 in Fig. 4-28 to the origin and back. Collector current flows during the balance of the cycle.

The modulator shown in Fig. 4-27 can easily be made to operate as a phase-sensitive detector. In this application, the carrier-suppressed signal is applied at the terminals marked intelligence signal, and a low-pass filter is used at the output. The operation of the circuit remains unchanged.

Figure 4-29 shows another circuit that can be used either as a modulator or a demodulator. The operation of the circuit as a modulator is described. No emitter current is permitted to flow in either transistor when the carrier signal is negative. When it is positive, the intelligence voltage is faced with the forward resistance of the first collector diode, two base resistances, and the back resistance of the second collector diode, the last of which is quite large. Hence, little current can flow through R_c. When the intelligence voltage is reversed, the action of the two transistors is reversed, but still no appreciable output results.

When the carrier voltage is positive, emitter current flows and, hence, negative collector current is allowed to flow in either transistor. Collector current flows whether the sign of the intelligence voltage is positive or negative. The circuit behaves much the same as a switch that is turned on and off by the carrier voltage.

The circuit of Fig. 4-29 will also operate as a demodulator. In this case the carrier-suppressed voltage is applied at the intelligence-signal input. For use in a demodulator, a capacitor is used as a filter (shown in dashed lines on the figure).

4-6. Practical Aspects of Demodulator and Modulator Circuits. The ordinary ripple voltage across DE of Fig. 4-11 is attenuated by use of a condenser from D to ground and from E to ground. A typical circuit value for the resistor R is about $\frac{1}{2}$ megohm, and 0.05-μf condensers are often used in 60-cycle circuits. The time constant of such a filter is about 0.02 sec, so that the transfer function of the phase-sensitive detector is

$$\frac{K}{1 + \tau s}$$

where τ is about 0.02 sec. Since one of the purposes of phase-sensitive detectors is to rectify the actuating-signal voltage in order to use d-c equalizing networks, it is often necessary to use a more sophisticated filter than the simple condenser. This is caused by the fact that some equalizing networks present higher gains to ripple voltages than to the fundamental signal frequencies. These more complex filters are discussed in the following chapter.

The filter problem is, of course, greatly aided by an increase in carrier frequency. 400-cycle phase-sensitive detectors have less ripple-voltage output than the 60-cycle phase-sensitive detectors for a given time constant in the transfer function. If the circuit is to operate with a broadband servo, the highest signal frequency to which the servo responds will be on the same order of magnitude as the carrier frequency; then the filter problem becomes a more serious one.

The result of experiments performed on the circuit of Fig. 4-16 (the supply voltage from cathodes to ground is 45 volts) is shown in Fig. 4-30. The output is almost linear with respect to the input voltage, and the circuit is relatively insensitive to quadrature voltage. An increase in supply voltage causes the circuit to be somewhat more sensitive because the gain is somewhat higher. The circuit must be balanced to eliminate the effect of any unequal outputs of the transformer half windings, unequal impedances of the diodes or transformers, or unequal load resistors. Any of these will produce an output voltage under zero-input-voltage conditions. A null adjustment is easily provided by putting a potentiometer between the two resistors and adjusting it so that under zero-input-signal conditions the output voltage is also zero.

The proper behavior of detector circuits requires that the relative magnitude of the supply voltage and the signal voltage be considered. The waveforms of Fig. 4-31 are drawn to show the effect of saturation. In this illustration v_s is the fixed supply voltage, v_i is the input voltage, and v_o is the output voltage of the circuit of Fig. 4-20.

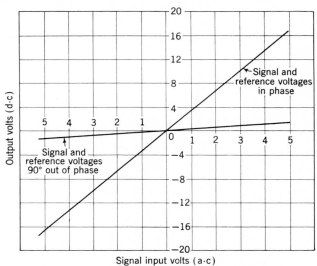

Fig. 4-30. Experimental results from the circuit of Fig. 4-16.

The tube resistance is neglected. It is important to recognize the fact that current can flow through the resistor R if the combination of signal-input and transformer voltages makes the plate of the upper diode positive with respect to its cathode or the cathode of the lower diode negative with respect to its plate. Figure 4-31a shows that, if the input voltage is small compared with the reference voltage, the output voltage is approximately a square wave. As the input voltage becomes progressively a greater percentage of the reference voltage, the waveform changes. Finally, in Fig. 4-31c, saturation is reached. Further increase in the input voltage, as shown in Fig. 4-31d, results in no increase in output of the network. This effect is observed in all the modulator circuits shown, and these waveforms are obtained experimentally. The circuit of Fig. 4-22 is somewhat different from the others in that it does not saturate for positive signal voltage, and for very large negative signal voltages the output reduces to zero.

A measured curve of voltage output vs. voltage input for the circuit of Fig. 4-20 is shown in Fig. 4-32, and the effect of saturation is clearly

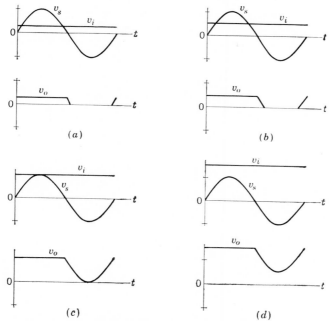

FIG. 4-31. Waveforms showing saturation of the circuit of Fig. 4-20.

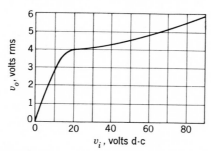

FIG. 4-32. Experimental a-c output vs. d-c input for the circuit of Fig. 4-20.

indicated. Before saturation takes place, the curve shows that the output is linear with input voltage. Exact linearity in servo circuits is not usually a requirement since servomechanisms seek a null voltage and the signals being modulated are normally either the actuating signal or feedback signals, neither of which has critical linearity requirements.

In all these circuits no output voltage when the signal voltage is zero is desirable. The amount of noise voltage present in the output is a function of the magnitude of the supply voltage, the impedance level of the circuits, and unbalances in the tube and circuit characteristics. Any increase in the reference voltage increases the maximum possible output voltage, i.e., increases the size of the input signal that can be applied before obtaining saturation. Unfortunately, however, it also increases the noise voltage by accentuating any unbalance in the circuits.

For the circuit of Fig. 4-24, the ratio of maximum output voltage to noise voltage is about 400:1. Variations among tubes cut this ratio in half. For the circuit of Fig. 4-20, the maximum signal-to-noise ratio was obtained in an experiment in which $R = 200,000$ ohms; the signal-to-noise ratio was then measured as 800:1. To obtain this ratio requires great care in shielding and grounding the 6H6's that were used in place of the 6AL5's.

When matched crystals, copper-oxide rectifiers, or selenium rectifiers are used in place of tubes, the greater variation in the resistance of such devices in the reverse direction causes the unbalance to be much worse than in tube circuits and consequently causes a higher noise output. For example, the noise output of the circuit of Fig. 4-20 when matched 1N34's were used was 40 times as high as when diodes were used. With diodes used in these circuits, the noise can be reduced somewhat by standard methods of reducing hum, such as by placing the heaters at either a positive or a negative potential with respect to the cathodes. Under conditions where the noise level of the circuit is critically important, the mechanical modulator should be used. Some vibrators have noise outputs of a few microvolts even for load resistors of 1 megohm.

It is important also that there be no unwanted components of output voltage, not only when the output signal is zero but at all other times. The output voltage of the mechanical modulator is almost a square wave and differs from it only because of the finite time for the vibrating reed to travel from one contact to the other. The harmonic content of typical electronic-modulator circuits shows about 40 per cent second, 15 per cent fourth, and 10 to 20 per cent odd harmonics.

4-7. Rectifier-circuit Analysis. Circuits involving rectifiers for either modulation or demodulation are admittedly nonlinear. It is possible, however, to use linear-circuit theory to analyze them. The values of the parameters are linear but undergo discontinuous changes. The analysis is therefore also discontinuous. It is accomplished by assuming that certain conditions of voltage magnitude exist in the circuit, drawing the applicable circuit diagram for these conditions, and solving for the unknown currents or voltages. If an incorrect assumption is made, inconsistent results are obtained in the circuit. For a consistent solu-

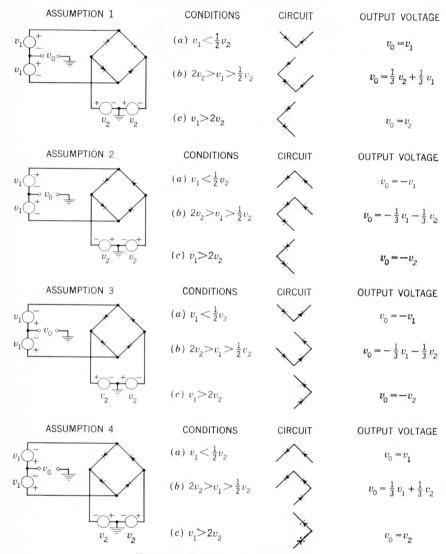

FIG. 4-33. Rectifier-circuit analysis.

tion, the currents must be flowing in the proper directions through the rectifiers. If an inconsistent result is obtained, a different circuit must be drawn until the resulting currents and voltages are consistent with the conditions and the actual circuit diagram.

For example, the ring demodulator of Fig. 4-17 can be analyzed in this manner. Figure 4-33 is a tabulation that presents the results of a complete analysis of this circuit.   In column 1 are circuit diagrams for each of the four assumed polarities of voltages, both signal and reference. To simplify the analysis, it is assumed that the rectifiers have equal and finite resistance in one direction and infinite resistance in the other.   The analysis can be carried out in exactly the same manner without this assumption, although somewhat more difficult circuits and equations result.

To start the analysis, assume that v_1 is small compared with v_2.   The rectifier circuit then must be as shown in column 3 of Fig. 4-33 and the output voltage is equal to v_1, as given in column 4.   This circuit and equation are both correct as long as v_1 is very small.   When the magnitude of v_1 is increased to half of v_2 or more, inconsistent results are obtained, so that the limit of the conditions of voltage under which this circuit can be used is given in column 1; i.e., v_1 must be less than half of v_2.   Similar analysis reveals the other limits on the conditions and the circuit results in an equation for the output voltage in each case.   This is the desired result of the analysis.

The tabulated results are useful, for example, to determine the waveform of the output voltage of this network for any magnitude or phase of input voltage and reference voltage.   The reference voltage and the input voltage are plotted, the various regions are marked off, and the conditions prevailing for each region are noted.   The output voltage is found in each region and plotted.

The swiftest results, however, are obtained by experimenting on the actual circuits and using this analysis to learn the effect of transformer impedances or other characteristics not easily varied experimentally. The analysis can also be used to show the direction in which the variable should be adjusted in order to approach optimum performance.

PROBLEMS

4-1. Show how a chopper used as a phase-sensitive detector can discriminate against third-harmonic signal voltages.

4-2. Explain the operation of the full-wave phase-sensitive detector of Fig. 4-16.

4-3. With the vibrator used as a modulator, what variations in output waveform are possible with direct-voltage input?

4-4. Explain how the operation of the circuit in Fig. 4-22 changes with magnitude of signal voltages.

4-5. Using Fig. 4-33, plot the output magnitude of a ring demodulator in which the voltages applied to the two inputs are equal in magnitude but differ in phase by 30°.

4-6. Using the rectifier-circuit-analysis technique, analyze the modulator circuit of Fig. 4-20, assuming finite tube impedances.

SERVO NETWORKS

5-1. Introduction. Networks are used in servomechanisms for three principal purposes: filtering signals, shifting the phase of voltages, and equalization. Filter networks are used for the attenuation of unwanted voltages. Phase-shifting networks are used for shifting the phase relationship of signals and reference voltages fed to components. Equalizing networks are used for the purpose of acting upon the actuating-signal voltage and other signals in the servomechanism to promote stability and improve servo performance by modifying the transfer function of the servomechanism. Both the theoretical and practical aspects of passive servo networks are presented in this chapter.

5-2. Review of Network Synthesis.* The design or synthesis of a servo network is based upon knowledge of the network transfer function, which is specified by a particular zero-pole configuration. It is desired to find a network with these specified characteristics. A solution may not exist; however, if it does exist, it is generally not unique. The most practical network can be chosen from a large number of equivalent possibilities.

The design procedure is generally carried out step by step, each step reducing the degree of the given transfer function. Both the network configuration and the element values are found with the procedure.

The *system function* of a network is defined as a function of the complex variable s representing the ratio of a response variable to an excitation variable. More precisely, a system function is equal to the ratio of the Laplace transform of the response, or output, variable to the Laplace transform of the driving function, or input variable. It is also the transform of the impulse response† of the network. There are two types of system functions of interest: the driving-point function and the transfer function. For a driving-point function (or, as it is often called, a two-terminal network) the input and output are measured at the same pair of terminals. Hence, any input or output impedance or admittance is a driving-point function. For a transfer function, on the other hand, the input and output are measured at two different pairs of terminals.

---

* Much of the material in Secs. 5-2 to 5-6 is taken from Ref. 38.
† See Refs. 19, 38, and 48 for further discussion.

The most general type of system function for a finite lumped-parameter network is a real rational function, which is given by a quotient of polynomials of the form

$$G(s) = \frac{N(s)}{D(s)} = \frac{a_m s^m + \cdots + a_1 s + a_0}{b_n s^n + \cdots + b_1 s + b_0} = K \frac{(s - s_1)(s - s_m)}{(s - s_1')(s - s_n')} \quad (5\text{-}1)$$

where $K = a_m/b_n$ is a constant multiplier and the a's and b's are real constants.

For absolute stability it is necessary that $D(s)$ have no zeros in the right-half plane; for limited stability, permissible in restricted instances, $D(s)$ may have first-order zeros on the imaginary axis.

5-3. Two-terminal Network Synthesis. * The design of RC driving-point functions is considered in this section. Two methods of synthesis for the driving-point functions are presented, one employing a partial-fraction and the other a continued-fraction expansion.

Foster Synthesis. The Foster form of an RC network is obtained by a partial-fraction† expansion of the impedance.

One expansion procedure for an admittance $Y(s)$ is based on a partial-fraction development of $Y(s)/s$ as follows:

$$\frac{Y(s)}{s} = \frac{k_0}{s} + \sum_{i=1}^{n} \frac{k_i}{s + s_i} \quad (5\text{-}2)$$

where all k_i's are zero or are real and positive, and all s_i's are real and positive. $Y(s)/s$ is expanded rather than $Y(s)$ so that all network elements are guaranteed positive.

As an example of such a partial-fraction expansion, consider the following admittance function:

$$Y(s) = \frac{(s + 3)(s + 9)}{(s + 6)(s + 11)} \quad (5\text{-}3)$$

To obtain an expansion with only positive coefficients, $Y(s)/s$ is expanded as follows:

$$\frac{Y(s)}{s} = \frac{(s + 3)(s + 9)}{s(s + 6)(s + 11)} = \frac{K_0}{s} + \frac{K_1}{s + 6} + \frac{K_2}{s + 11} \quad (5\text{-}4)$$

By the partial-fraction-expansion technique, the constants in Eq. (5-4) are found as follows:

---

* See Refs. 8, 21, and 49 for additional material on this topic.
† See Refs. 14 and 38 for a discussion of the partial fraction.

1. Multiply both sides of Eq. (5-4) by s, set $s = 0$, and solve for K_0:

$$\frac{s(s+3)(s+9)}{s(s+6)(s+11)} = K_0 + \frac{K_1 s}{s+6} + \frac{K_2 s}{s+11} \tag{5-5}$$

$$K_0 = \frac{(3)(9)}{(6)(11)} = \frac{9}{22}$$

2. Multiply both sides of Eq. (5-4) by $(s+6)$, set $s = -6$, and solve for K_1:

$$K_1 = \frac{(-6+3)(-6+9)}{(-6)(-6+11)} = \frac{(-3)(+3)}{(-6)(+5)} = \frac{3}{10} \tag{5-6}$$

3. Multiply both sides of Eq. (5-4) by $(s+11)$, set $s = -11$, and solve for K_2:

$$K_2 = \frac{(-11+3)(-11+9)}{(-11)(-11+6)} = \frac{(-8)(-2)}{(-11)(-5)} = \frac{16}{55} \tag{5-7}$$

In general, therefore, when the poles are first-order, the constants are found by multiplying the equation in turn by each of the poles, setting s equal to the value of the pole, and thus obtaining the value of the corresponding constant.

Finally, from Eq. (5-4) the expansion for $Y(s)$ is found by multiplying both sides of the equation by s; thus,

$$Y(s) = \frac{9}{22} + \frac{3/10 s}{s+6} + \frac{16/55 s}{s+11} \tag{5-8}$$

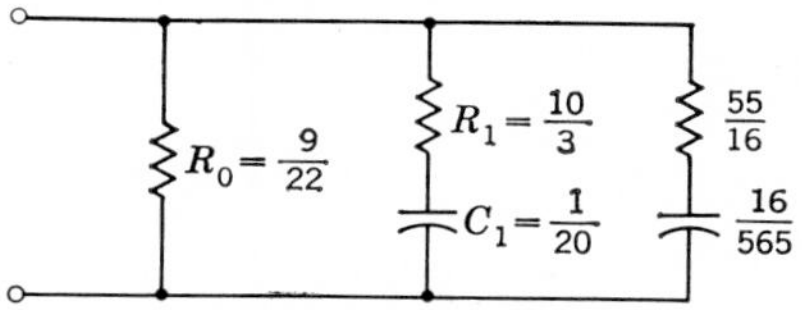

FIG. 5-1. Partial-fraction synthesis of
$$Y(s) = \frac{(s+3)(s+9)}{(s+6)(s+11)}$$

The circuit for the admittance of Eq. (5-8) is given in Fig. 5-1.

The partial-fraction expansion of an impedance $Z(s)$, which is realizable as an RC network, is expanded as follows:

$$Z(s) = k_\infty + \frac{k_0}{s} + \frac{k_1}{s+s_1} + \cdots + \frac{k_n}{s+s_n} \tag{5-9}$$

where all K_i's are zero or are real and positive quantities, and all s_i's are real and positive. As an example of such a partial-fraction expansion, consider the function given in Eq. (5-3), which, written as an impedance, is

$$Z(s) = \frac{(s+6)(s+11)}{(s+3)(s+9)} \tag{5-10}$$

The partial-fraction expansion for this impedance is

$$Z(s) = k_\infty + \frac{k_1}{s+3} + \frac{k_2}{s+9} \tag{5-11}$$

The constants, as found by the technique indicated in Eqs. (5-5) to (5-7), are as follows:

$$k_\infty = \lim_{s \to \infty} \frac{(s + 6)(s + 11)}{(s + 3)(s + 9)} = 1$$

$$k_1 = \frac{(s + 6)(s + 11)}{s + 9} \bigg|_{s = -3} = 4$$

$$k_2 = \frac{(s + 6)(s + 11)}{s + 3} \bigg|_{s = -9} = 1$$

The expansion is written as follows:

$$Z(s) = 1 + \frac{4}{s + 3} + \frac{1}{s + 9} \tag{5-12}$$

and the network is included in Fig. 5-2.

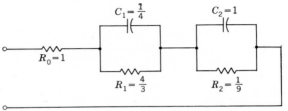

Fig. 5-2. Partial-fraction synthesis of $Z(s) = \dfrac{(s + 6)(s + 11)}{(s + 3)(s + 9)}$.

Cauer Synthesis. The continued fraction or Cauer synthesis yields a two-terminal ladder-type network. The impedance of a network can be written as a series of terms, the first of which is Z_1:

$$Z(s) = Z_1 + Z_A$$

The impedance Z_A can be written as an admittance:

$$Y_A = \frac{1}{Z_A} = Y_1 + Y_B$$

This process is continued to yield the final result:

$$Z(s) = Z_1 + \cfrac{1}{Y_1 + \cfrac{1}{Z_2 + \cfrac{1}{Y_2 + \cfrac{1}{Z_3 + \cdots}}}} \tag{5-13}$$

Any expression, for example, $Z(s) = N(s)/D(s)$, is easily written in the form of a continued fraction by a process of repeated division:

$$Z(s) = a(s) + \frac{N_1(s)}{D(s)} = a(s) + \frac{1}{D(s)/N_1(s)}$$

$$= a(s) + \cfrac{1}{b(s) + \cfrac{1}{N_1(s)/D_1(s)}} \tag{5-14}$$

Since the order of $N(s)$ and $D(s)$ does not differ by more than unity, each of the quotients $a(s)$, $b(s)$, etc., corresponds to simple two-terminal circuits. The process is carried out until a recognizable circuit is obtainable for one of the remaining fractions. The expansion may be made about infinity or zero; in each case the partial quotients all have positive coefficients. For the expansion about infinity, the polynomials are written in descending powers of s; whereas for the expansion about zero, the polynomials are written in ascending powers of s.

As an example of the continued-fraction expansion of a two-terminal admittance function, consider the function of Eq. (5-3):

$$Y(s) = \frac{(s+3)(s+9)}{(s+6)(s+11)} = \frac{s^2+12s+27}{s^2+17s+66} \tag{5-15}$$

Since $Y(s)$ has no pole at infinity, no operation is performed in the first cycle. In the second cycle, division proceeds as follows:

$$s^2+12s+27 \,\overline{)\, s^2+17s+66} \quad 1$$
$$\underline{s^2+12s+27}$$
$$5s+39 \,\overline{)\, s^2+12s+27} \quad 1/5s$$
$$\underline{s^2+\frac{39}{5}s}$$
$$\frac{21}{5}s+27 \,\overline{)\, 5s+39} \quad 25/21$$
$$\underline{5s+\frac{225}{7}}$$
$$\frac{48}{7} \,\overline{)\, \frac{21}{5}s+27} \quad 49/80s$$
$$\underline{\frac{21}{5}s}$$
$$27 \,\overline{)\, \frac{48}{7}} \quad 16/63$$

The expression is rewritten as follows:

$$Y(s) = \cfrac{1}{1 + \cfrac{1}{\frac{1}{5}s + \cfrac{1}{\frac{25}{21} + \cfrac{1}{\frac{49}{80}s + \cfrac{1}{16/63}}}}} \tag{5-16}$$

and the corresponding RC network is shown in Fig. 5-3.

The values of the components are made reasonable with an impedance-level change. To raise the impedance level by a factor α, the impedance

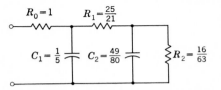

FIG. 5-3. Continued-fraction expansion of $Y(s) = \dfrac{(s+3)(s+9)}{(s+6)(s+11)}$.

of each type of element is multiplied by α. Hence, every R and L is multiplied by α, and every C is divided by α.

5-4. Elementary Lattice and Ladder Synthesis. Any realizable RC transfer function can be realized by a lattice network, which is shown in Fig. 5-4. The transfer function for this network is found for the condition of zero source and infinite load impedance. The equations about the two nodes (E_2 and E_3) with the

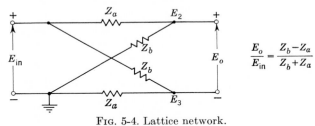

$$\frac{E_o}{E_{in}} = \frac{Z_b - Z_a}{Z_b + Z_a}$$

FIG. 5-4. Lattice network.

lower input node taken as ground are written

$$\begin{aligned}
E_2\left(\frac{1}{Z_a} + \frac{1}{Z_b}\right) &= E_{in}\frac{1}{Z_a} \\
E_3\left(\frac{1}{Z_a} + \frac{1}{Z_b}\right) &= E_{in}\frac{1}{Z_b}
\end{aligned} \tag{5-17}$$

Solution of these equations yields

$$E_o = E_2 - E_3 = \frac{E_{in}(1/Z_a - 1/Z_b)}{(1/Z_a + 1/Z_b)} = E_{in}\left(\frac{Z_b - Z_a}{Z_b + Z_a}\right) \tag{5-18}$$

The two-terminal impedance functions Z_a and Z_b are found by identifying numerator and denominator with the desired transfer function.

Either the impedance or the admittance equations can be used to determine the transfer voltage ratio. If the transfer voltage ratio, or transfer function, is written as

$$\frac{E_o}{E_{in}} = \frac{Z_{12}(s)}{Z_{11}(s)} \tag{5-19}$$

the two terminal impedances are found as follows:

$$\begin{aligned} Z_b - Z_a &= Z_{12}(s) \\ Z_b + Z_a &= Z_{11}(s) \end{aligned} \tag{5-20}$$

Adding and subtracting Eqs. (5-20) gives

$$\begin{aligned} Z_b &= \tfrac{1}{2}(Z_{11} + Z_{12}) \\ Z_a &= \tfrac{1}{2}(Z_{11} - Z_{12}) \end{aligned} \tag{5-21}$$

Each of the functions Z_a and Z_b can be divided by $Kq(s)$, where $q(s)$ is any desired polynomial in the operator s. Since a ratio of impedances is taken in Eq. (5-19), the $Kq(s)$ cancels out of the fraction. $q(s)$ is inserted to aid in realizing the two-terminal impedance functions that result. Division of Eq. (5-21) by $Kq(s)$ yields the equations

$$Z_b = \frac{1}{2}\frac{Z_{11}(s) + Z_{12}(s)}{Kq(s)} \qquad Z_a = \frac{1}{2}\frac{Z_{11}(s) - Z_{12}(s)}{Kq(s)} \tag{5-22}$$

Consider, as an example, the transfer function

$$\frac{E_o}{E_{in}} = \frac{(s + 30)^2}{(s + 50)(s + 100)} = \frac{s^2 + 60s + 900}{s^2 + 150s + 5{,}000} \tag{5-23}$$

The quantities Z_a and Z_b are found from Eq. (5-20) as follows:

$$\begin{aligned} Z_b &= \tfrac{1}{2}(s^2 + 150s + 5{,}000 + s^2 + 60s + 900) \\ Z_a &= \tfrac{1}{2}(s^2 + 150s + 5{,}000 - s^2 - 60s - 900) \end{aligned} \tag{5-24}$$

These quantities are divided by $q(s)$, which yields the following:

$$\begin{aligned} Z_a &= \frac{90s + 4{,}100}{Kq(s)} = \frac{90}{K} + \frac{4{,}100}{Ks} \\ Z_b &= \frac{2s^2 + 240s + 5{,}900}{Kq(s)} = \frac{2s}{K} + \frac{240}{K} + \frac{5{,}900}{Ks} \end{aligned} \tag{5-25}$$

In this case it is convenient to take $Kq(s) = Ks$. The two-terminal impedances Z_a and Z_b are shown in Fig. 5-5. The numerical values become reasonable in size when K is taken equal to 10^{-2}.

In general, Z_a and Z_b can be built with passive elements if the subtraction necessary in Eq. (5-22) results in all positive components. Practically, the lattice network has the disadvantage of possessing no common ground between input and output. To overcome this problem it is necessary to drive the input with a balanced signal, for example, from a transformer or difference amplifier. The load may also be driven in push-pull so that the common-ground problem can be obviated.

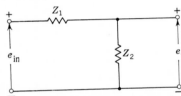

$R_a = 9,000\,\Omega \qquad C_a = 2\text{-}4\,\mu f$

$L_b = 200\,h \qquad C_b = 1.7\,\mu f$

$R_b = 24,000\,\Omega$

FIG. 5-5. Lattice elements for $\dfrac{E_o}{E_{in}} = \dfrac{(s + 30)^2}{(s + 50)(s + 100)}$.

Another difficulty with the lattice network is the number of elements necessary. For the example taken here, 10 elements are necessary to achieve the desired transfer function.

Synthesis of the necessary two-terminal impedances Z_a and Z_b is accomplished by use of any of the two-terminal synthesis procedures of Sec. 5-3.

Because of the disadvantage of an ungrounded network, considerable emphasis has been placed on three-terminal networks. One terminal is common to the input and the output and hence can be grounded. A ladder network is an example of such a grounded network. Since many synthesis procedures have been developed[*] (and are being developed), only a very simple, limited example is considered here. This limited ladder synthesis is based upon the circuit of Fig. 5-6. When this network is operated from zero or low source impedance and infinite or large load impedance, the transfer function can be written as

FIG. 5-6. Simple ladder network.

$$\frac{E_o}{E_{in}} = \frac{Z_2}{Z_1 + Z_2} = \frac{1}{1 + Z_1/Z_2} \qquad (5\text{-}26)$$

When Eq. (5-26) is rearranged and the open-circuit impedances of Eq. (5-19) utilized, the following equation results:

$$\frac{E_{in}}{E_o} - 1 = \frac{E_{12}}{E_{11}} - 1 = \frac{Z_{12} - Z_{11}}{Z_{11}} = \frac{Z_1}{Z_2} \qquad (5\text{-}27)$$

As an example of this procedure, consider the problem of finding the

[*] See Ref. 48, pp. 190–220.

equalizer that has the transfer function

$$\frac{E_o}{E_{in}} = \frac{(s + 30)^2}{(s + 50)(s + 100)}$$ (5-28)

Substituting Eq. (5-28) into Eq. (5-27) yields the ratio of Z_1/Z_2 as

$$\frac{Z_1}{Z_2} = \frac{s^2 + 150s + 5,000}{s^2 + 60s + 900} - 1 = \frac{90s + 4,100}{s^2 + 60s + 900}$$ (5-29)

To find Z_1 and Z_2, identify numerators and denominators as follows:

$$Z_1 = \frac{90s + 4,100}{Kq(s)} \qquad Z_2 = \frac{s^2 + 60s + 900}{Kq(s)}$$ (5-30)

where, as in the lattice synthesis, $q(s)$ is any desired polynomial in the operator s that is inserted to aid in realizing the two-terminal impedance functions. Since the ratio of Z_1 to Z_2 is taken, $q(s)$ cancels in the fraction. In this example take $Kq(s) = Ks$ and

$$Z_1 = \frac{90}{K} + \frac{4,100}{Ks} \qquad Z_2 = \frac{s}{K} + \frac{60}{K} + \frac{900}{Ks}$$ (5-31)

The two-terminal networks, which are easily identified by inspection, are shown in Fig. 5-7. Reasonable component sizes are obtained when K is taken equal to 10^{-2}.

$R_1 = 9,000\ \Omega$ $C_1 = 2.4\ \mu f$ $L_2 = 100\ h$ $C_2 = 11\ \mu f$

$R_2 = 6,000\ \Omega$

FIG. 5-7. Example of simple ladder synthesis.

Table 5-1 presents the circuit diagrams, the open-circuit transfer functions, and the amplitude-frequency response for several four-terminal networks with common input and output ground.

5-5. Filter Networks. Filter networks are sometimes required in servomechanisms for the attenuation of unwanted harmonic voltages that originate in the following systems: 60-cycle or 400-cycle alternators or inverters; components using magnetic materials, such as synchros and

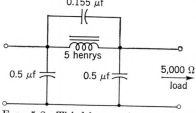

0.155 μf

5 henrys

0.5 μf 0.5 μf

5,000 Ω load

FIG. 5-8. Third-harmonic filter network.

rate generators; modulators or other circuits that are inherently nonlinear. Since the third-harmonic voltage is usually the biggest offender, a common design objective of filters is to reject completely the third harmonic and attenuate higher harmonics. Figure 5-8 shows a filter

TABLE 5-1. NETWORKS

	Network	Open-circuit transfer function	Gain curve
1	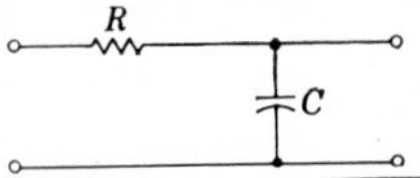	$$H = \dfrac{1}{1 + RC s}$$	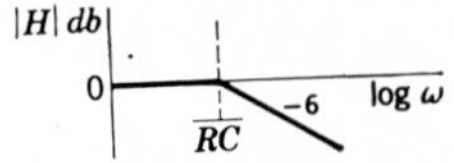
2	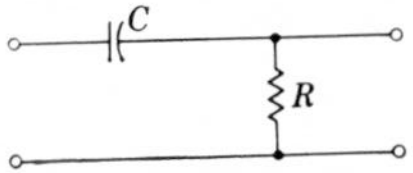	$$H = \dfrac{RC s}{1 + RC s}$$	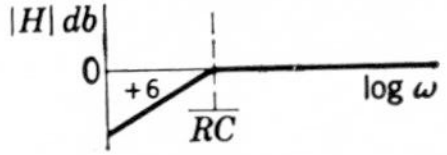
3	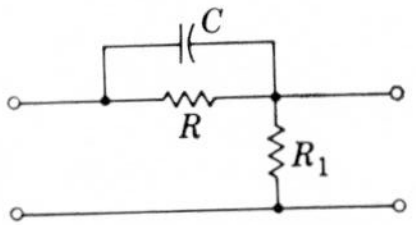	$$H = \dfrac{R_1}{R + R_1}\,\dfrac{1 + RC s}{1 + \dfrac{R_1}{R + R_1}\,RC s}$$	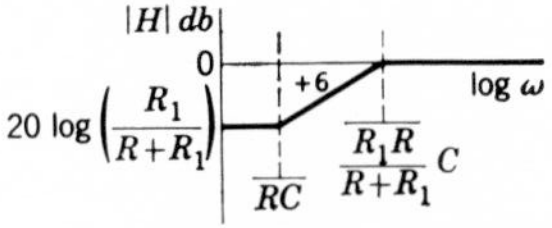
4	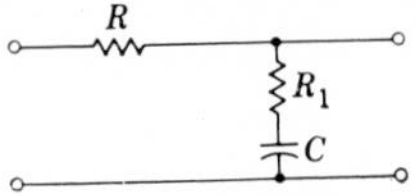	$$H = \dfrac{1 + R_1 C s}{1 + (R + R_1) C s}$$	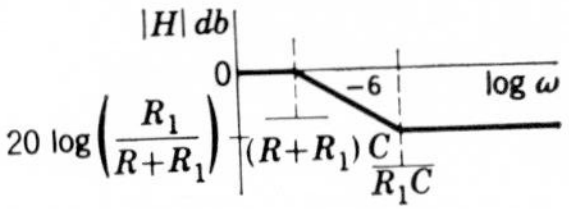
5	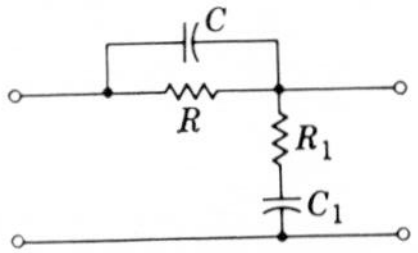	$$H = \dfrac{(1 + RC s)(1 + R_1 C_1 s)}{R R_1 C C_1 s^2 + (RC + R_1 C_1 + R C_1) s + 1}$$	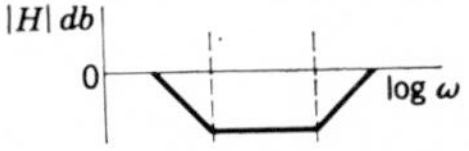
6	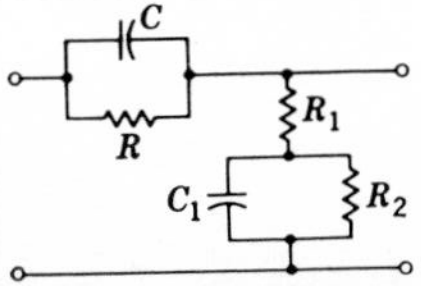	$$H = \dfrac{s^2(C_1 C R_1 R_2 R) + s(C_1 R_1 R_2 + C R_1 R + R_2 R C) + (R_1 + R_2)}{s^2(C_1 C R_1 R_2 R) + s(C_1 R_1 R_2 + C R_1 R + C R_2 R + C_1 R R_2) + (R + R_1 + R_2)}$$	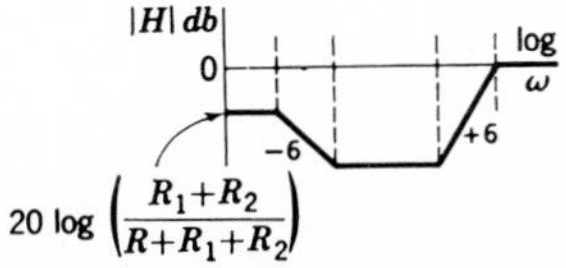

154

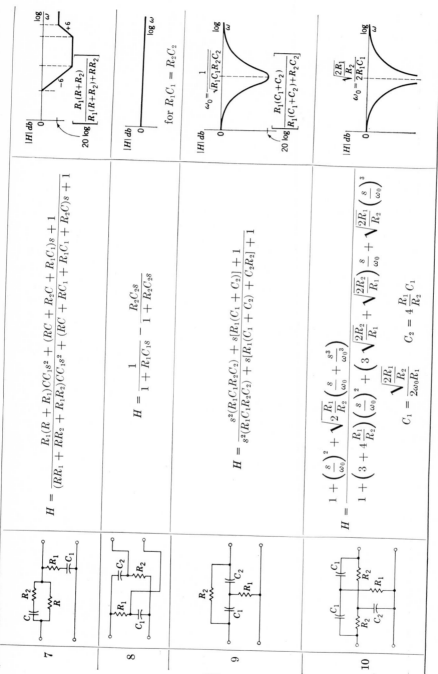

7

$$H = \frac{R_1(R + R_1)CC_1 s^2 + (RC + R_2C + R_1C_1)s + 1}{(RR_1 + RR_2 + R_1R_2)CC_1 s^2 + (RC + RC_1 + R_2C)s + 1}$$

|H| db graph, +6, −6, $20\log\left[\dfrac{R_1(R+R_2)}{R_1(R+R_2)+RR_2}\right]$, log ω

8

$$H = \frac{1}{1 + R_1C_1 s} - \frac{R_2C_2 s}{1 + R_2C_2 s}$$

|H| db graph, for $R_1C_1 = R_2C_2$, log ω

9

$$H = \frac{s^2(R_1C_1R_2C_2) + s[R_1(C_1 + C_2)] + 1}{s^2(R_1C_1R_2C_2) + s[R_1(C_1 + C_2) + C_2R_2] + 1}$$

$\omega_0 = \dfrac{1}{\sqrt{R_1C_1R_2C_2}}$, $20\log\left[\dfrac{R_1(C_1+C_2)}{R_1(C_1+C_2)+R_2C_2}\right]$

10

$$H = \frac{1 + \left(\dfrac{s}{\omega_0}\right)^2 + \sqrt{2}\sqrt{\dfrac{R_1}{R_2}}\left(\dfrac{s}{\omega_0} + \dfrac{s^3}{\omega_0^3}\right)}{1 + \left(3 + 4\dfrac{R_1}{R_2}\right)\left(\dfrac{s}{\omega_0}\right)^2 + \left(3\sqrt{\dfrac{2R_2}{R_1}} + \sqrt{\dfrac{2R_2}{R_1}}\right)\dfrac{s}{\omega_0} + \sqrt{\dfrac{2R_1}{R_2}}\left(\dfrac{s}{\omega_0}\right)^3}$$

$$C_1 = \frac{\sqrt{\dfrac{2R_1}{R_2}}}{2\omega_0 R_1} \qquad C_2 = 4\,\frac{R_1}{R_2}C_1$$

$\sqrt{\dfrac{2R_1}{R_2}}$, $\omega_0 = 2R_1C_1$

TABLE 5-1. NETWORKS (*Continued*)

	Network	Open-circuit transfer function	Gain curve
11	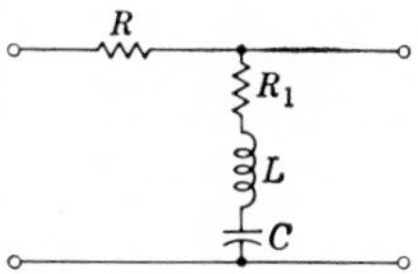	$$H = \frac{R_1 Cs + LCs^2}{(R+R_1)Cs + LCs^2 + 1}$$	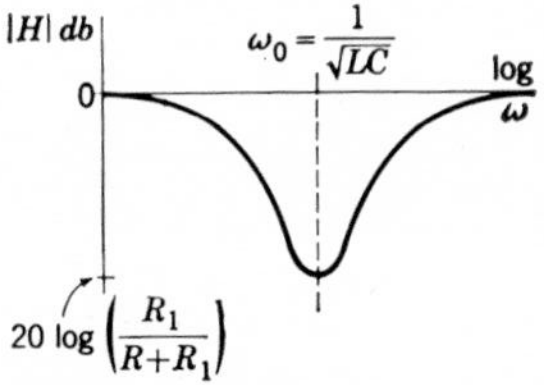
12	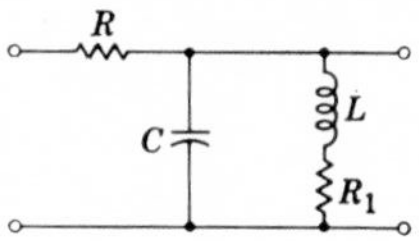	$$H = \frac{1 + \dfrac{L}{R_1}s}{\dfrac{R+R_1}{R_1} + \left(\dfrac{L}{R_1} + RC\right)s + \dfrac{L}{R_1}RCs^2}$$	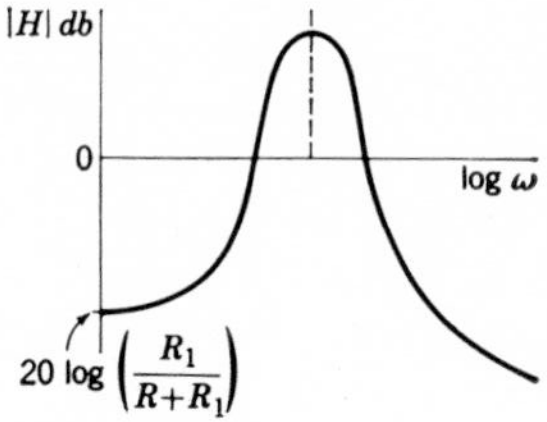
13	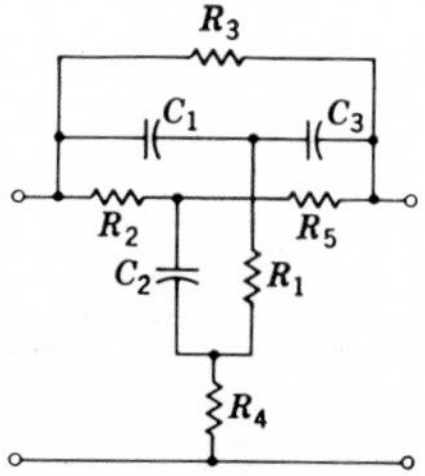	$$H = \frac{1 + (R_2C_1 s)^2}{\left[1 + R_2C_1 s\left(1+\dfrac{1}{m}+\sqrt{\dfrac{2}{m}+\dfrac{1}{m^2}}\right)\right]\left[1 + R_2C_1 s\left(1+\dfrac{1}{m}-\sqrt{\dfrac{2}{m}+\dfrac{1}{m^2}}\right)\right]}$$ $$m = 2ab \qquad C_3 = mC_1$$ $$a = \frac{R_3}{R_2} \qquad R_1 = \frac{m}{m+1}R_2$$ $$b = \frac{R_4}{R_3}$$ $$R_5 = mR_2 \qquad C_2 = \frac{m+1}{m}C_1$$	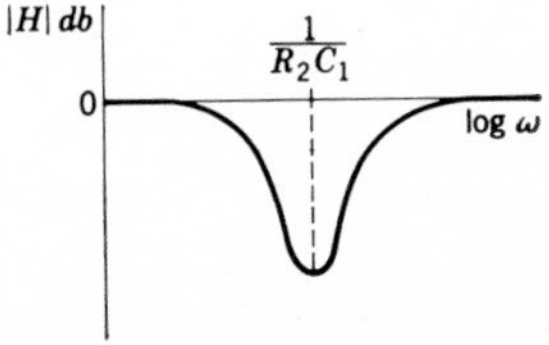

network used for this purpose, and its experimental magnitude and phase characteristics are shown in Fig. 5-9. Although the design is shown for use with 60-cycle power, a change in parameters will adapt the filter for use in 400-cycle servos. In order to minimize quadrature voltages caused by unsymmetrical characteristics of transmission about the carrier (supply) frequency, the network is fairly flat in the region of 60 cycles. While the absolute phase shift is not of very great importance in this application, it is desirable to know the phase characteristics of the filter in the region of the carrier frequency, since any shift in carrier frequency causes a phase shift in the signal being filtered. This phase shift is less than 5° for frequency changes of 10 cycles. The experimental curve is obtained with a load resistance of 5,000 ohms applied across the output terminals of Fig. 5-8.

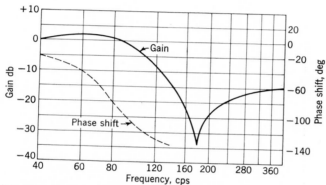

Fig. 5-9. Magnitude and phase characteristics of the network of Fig. 5-8.

Because of the size, weight, and nonlinearities of inductors, filter networks that employ only resistance and capacitive elements are often used to reject third and other harmonics. Examples of these networks are shown as Nos. 9 and 10 in Table 5-1. If these networks are used for filtering purposes, they are usually followed or preceded by a simple RC network of the type of No. 1. This network is utilized to attenuate the higher harmonics. The parallel- and bridged-T networks therefore act as more or less sharp rejection filters for the third harmonic. Higher harmonics are attenuated by the more gradual attenuation characteristics of the RC networks.

The transfer function of the parallel-T network is greatly simplified when the following conditions for symmetry are inserted:

$$R_1 = \frac{R_2}{2}$$
$$C_2 = 2C_1 \tag{5-32}$$

The transfer function is now simplified as follows:

$$H = \frac{1 + s/\omega_0 + s^2/\omega_0^2 + s^3/\omega_0^3}{1 + 5s/\omega_0 + 5s^2/\omega_0^2 + s^3/\omega_0^3} = \frac{1 + s^2/\omega_0^2}{1 + 4s/\omega_0 + s^2/\omega_0^2} \quad (5\text{-}33)$$

where $\omega_0 = 1/2R_1C_1 = 1/R_2C_1$. The design equations for the symmetrical parallel-T network are Eqs. (5-32) and the following:

$$R_2C_1 = \frac{1}{2\pi f_0} \quad (5\text{-}34)$$

Because all the design equations must be satisfied simultaneously, the parallel-T network must be carefully designed and built; and if low-tolerance network components are used, they must be measured and trimmed

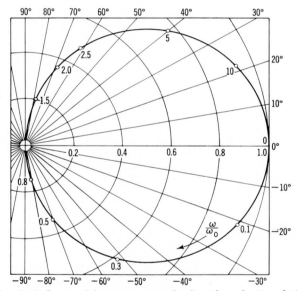

FIG. 5-10. Locus of frequency transfer function of network 10.

in order to be sure of effecting a null. The network can be nulled experimentally by varying R_1 or C_2. The limitations on the completeness of the rejection of a given frequency are pickup and the spurious resistance, inductance, and capacitance in the components.

Although the network shown has two equal capacitors and two equal resistors, this is not necessary for a null. It is more convenient in both design and assembly, however, to make these components approximately equal. The transfer locus of the network is shown in Fig. 5-10 for an infinite-load impedance on the output of the network. For frequencies lower than the nulling frequency, the network phase shift is lagging; and

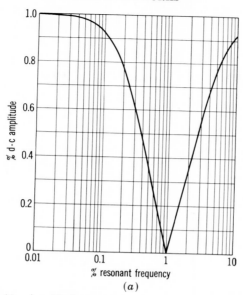

FIG. 5-11a. Amplitude response for the parallel-T network.

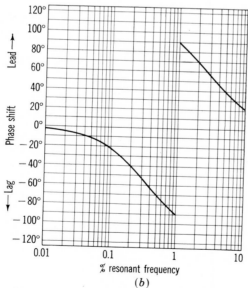

FIG. 5-11b. Phase response of the parallel-T network.

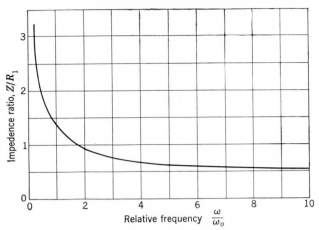

FIG. 5-12. Input impedance of parallel-T network.

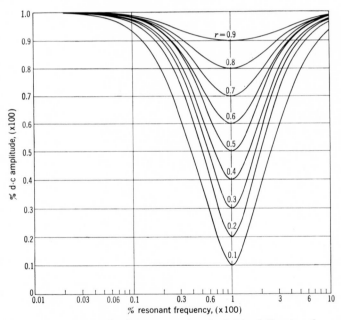

FIG. 5-13a. Amplitude response for the bridged-T network.

for higher frequencies, it is leading. Theoretically, it changes from −90 to +90° phase shift at the null, but component variations do not permit this abrupt change. As a matter of fact, some component variations can cause the transfer locus to encircle the origin—a fact that becomes significant when this network is used as a feedback network around a high-gain amplifier, because of the possibility of the amplifier being made unstable by this characteristic.

Figure 5-11 shows the variation of magnitude and phase of the symmetrical parallel-T network as a function of frequency.   If attenuation

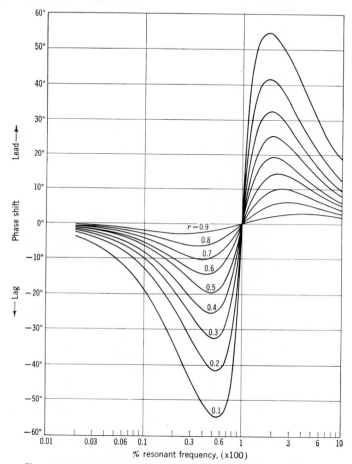

FIG. 5-13b. Phase angle response for the bridged-T network.

of higher frequencies is desired, a capacitor can be shunted across the output of the network.   The input impedance Z, again for the case of $R_2 = 2R_1$ and infinite load impedance, is given in Fig. 5-12.

The bridged-T network, No. 9, does not totally reject any frequency; although if the ratio R_2 to R_1 is made large, it can greatly attenuate voltage of a selected frequency.   The notch frequency* is given by the

* The *notch frequency* is the frequency at which the minimum amplitude occurs.

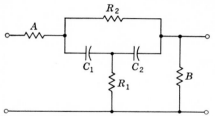

FIG. 5-14. Bridged-T network with input resistance A and output impedance B.

expression

$$\omega_0 = \frac{1}{R_1 C_1 R_2 C_2} \quad (5\text{-}35)$$

and the notch ratio γ by the equation

$$\gamma = \frac{R_1(C_1 + C_2)}{R_1(C_1 + C_2) + R_2 C_2} \quad (5\text{-}36)$$

Figure 5-13 shows the amplitude and phase response of the bridged-T network for various notch ratios.

The curves for the parallel- and bridged-T networks are based upon conditions of low (ideally zero) input and high (ideally infinite) output impedance. It is important to observe the effect on the response of the network when these conditions are not met. Consider the loaded net-

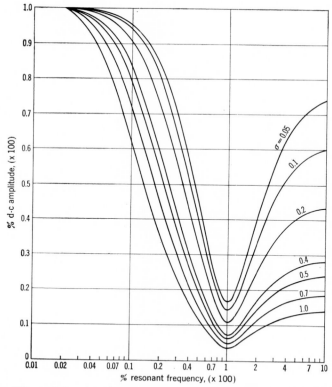

FIG. 5-15a. Effect of input resistance on amplitude response of bridged-T network. $r = 0.2$.

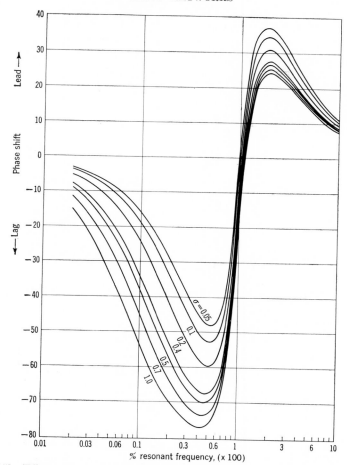

FIG. 5-15b. Effect of input resistance on phase response of bridged-T network. $r = 0.2$.

work shown in Fig. 5-14. The effects of the loading are considered separately by introduction of the following two parameters:

$$\lambda = \text{ratio of shunt output resistance to } R_2$$
$$= \frac{B}{R_2}$$
$$\sigma = \text{ratio of series input resistance to } R_2$$
$$= \frac{A}{R_2}$$

The effect on the amplitude and phase response can be seen in the curves

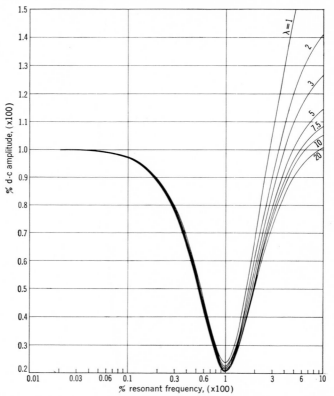

FIG. 5-16a. Effect of output resistance on amplitude response of bridged-T network. $r = 0.2$.

of Figs. 5-15 and 5-16.   The notch ratio is taken as 0.2 in both cases. It must be noted in Fig. 5-16 that the amplitude response is normalized by dividing by the d-c amplitude response.   Hence, the curves (Fig. 5-16b) showing the effect of output loading are really attenuated at zero frequency.   This fact accounts for the apparent rise in the response at higher frequencies.

With a careful selection of input and output impedance, namely,

$$A = B = R_1 = R_2 = R$$

symmetrical characteristics can again be obtained.   With equal source and load impedances a number of networks can be cascaded without the necessity of raising the impedance level of each additional network. Also, when a load is matched to its source, the insertion of this network does not disturb the match.   As an example of this loaded network,

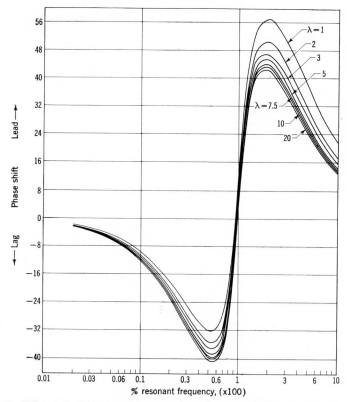

FIG. 5-16b. Effect of output resistance on phase response of bridged-T network. $r = 0.2$.

consider the capacitor-shunt bridged-T shown in Fig. 5-17. All component values are defined, along with the source impedance A and the load impedance B. The components are computed from the following equation:

$$C_1 = \frac{1}{R\omega_0}\left(\frac{1}{2r} - 1\right)^{-\frac{1}{2}}$$

$$C_2 = \frac{1}{R\omega_0}\left(\frac{1}{2r} - 1\right)^{\frac{1}{2}}$$

$$R_1 = R_2 = A = B = R \quad (5\text{-}37)$$

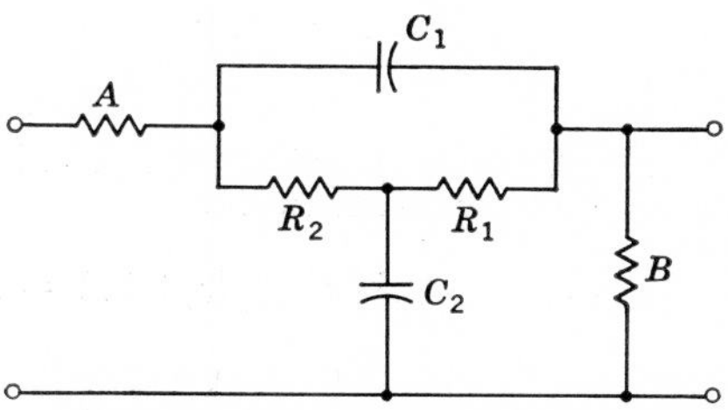

FIG. 5-17. Loaded bridged-T-network capacitor shunt.

where r is the notch ratio that has a valid range of operation between $r = 0$ and $r = \frac{1}{4}$. If necessary, the source impedance can be made equal to the load impedance by padding.

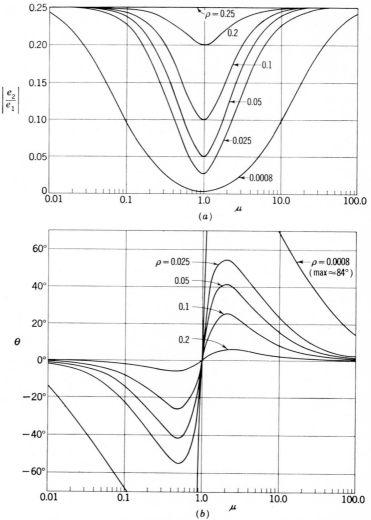

FIG. 5-18. (a) Attenuation response of loaded bridged-T network; (b) phase response of loaded bridged-T network.

As a numerical example, let $A = B = 300$ kilohms, $r = 0.25, f_0 = 26$ cps

$$\omega_0 = (6.28)(26) = 166 \text{ radians/sec}$$
$$R = A = B = R_1 = R_2 = 300 \text{ kilohms}$$
$$C_1 R \omega_0 = 1.0$$
$$C_2 R \omega_0 = 1.0$$

The attenuation and phase response for the loaded bridged-T network of Fig. 5-17 is shown in Fig. 5-18, plotted as a function of the normalized frequency $u = \omega/\omega_0$. Notice that the amplitude curves have the same symmetrical appearance and form as in the unloaded case, with two exceptions: (1) The d-c and infinite frequency gain is $\frac{1}{4}$. This means that the network acts as a four to one voltage divider at any frequency. (2) The notch width becomes excessively wide for values of $r < 0.025$.

5-6. Phase-shift Networks. Phase-shift networks are used for shifting the phase of signals or supply voltages so that the various alternating voltages in a servomechanism will have the proper phase relationship to one another. For instance, when phase-sensitive detectors are used, it may be necessary to shift the line voltage in order to supply the correct reference voltage to the detector. This is caused by the phase of the output voltage of the synchros being shifted from the line voltage by the phase shift of the synchros.

As another example of the use of phase shifters, there may be a constant phase shift between the excitation of a rate generator and its output; and it is necessary to shift the phase of the output voltage in order that the voltage can be subtracted directly from the synchro signals, since these two signals must be exactly in phase. Rather than shifting the output of the rate generators, however, networks of type 1 or 2 can be placed in series with the excitation voltage, thus shifting the phase of the excitation and interfering less with the sideband characteristics of the rate generator.

It is sometimes possible to make use of the windings of the rate generator as part of the circuit, so that the insertion of a simple capacitor in series with the rate-generator windings often can be made to achieve the proper phase shift of the voltage applied to the excitation windings.

If only single-phase power is available, it is often necessary to shift the phase of the fixed-phase excitation to a two-phase motor. This can be done by placing a capacitor in series with the constant-excitation windings; the consequences of this are discussed in Chap. 7.

Rather than shifting the phase of the constant voltage supplying a two-phase motor, the phase of the actuating-signal voltage is often shifted enough to place the control voltage at right angles to the line, thus permitting the constant-voltage windings of the two-phase motor to be excited directly from the line. Networks of type 2 in Table 5-1 are

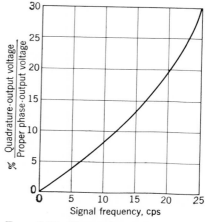

FIG. 5-19. Proportion of unwanted quadrature-voltage output for network yielding 90° phase shift of unmodulated 60-cycle carrier.

sometimes used for this purpose, since the coupling capacitors and grid resistors of the amplifier form such a network. Because this network is unsymmetrical about the carrier frequency, quadrature voltages are generated whenever the carrier is modulated. In Fig. 5-19 is shown the ratio of the magnitude of the quadrature output voltage to the magnitude of the output voltage of the proper phase as a function of signal frequency, under the assumption of equal 45° phase shifts in each of two networks. For signal frequencies of 10 cycles modulating a 60-cycle carrier, for example, the quadrature component is 8 per cent of the desired signal component.

A network that is more symmetrical about carrier frequencies is shown as No. 8 of the network table (Table 5-1). If both input and output

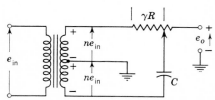

FIG. 5-20. Adjustable phase-shifting network.

must be grounded, however, a transformer is necessary. Another useful phase-shifting network is shown in Fig. 5-20. The advantage of this network is that it is adjustable and can be used to shift the phase by varying the position of the potentiometer. The transformer has a center-tapped secondary. The transfer function, for the conditions of small source and large load impedance, is

$$\frac{E_o(s)}{E_{in}(s)} = n \frac{1 - s\tau\gamma}{1 + s\tau\gamma}$$

With $s = j\omega$, the frequency transfer function becomes

$$\frac{E_o(j\omega)}{E_{in}(j\omega)} = n \frac{1 - j\omega\tau\gamma}{1 + j\omega\tau\gamma} = n < -2 \tan^{-1} \omega\tau\gamma \qquad (5\text{-}38)$$

where $\tau = RC$ and γ is the per cent rotation of the potentiometer. Since the voltages (nE_{in}) applied to this network are derived from a transformer, the transfer function of Eq. (5-38) is not applicable at zero frequency. Equation (5-38) represents a so-called "all-pass network"; i.e., as γ is varied, essentially no amplitude change results, while the phase lag is variable from 0 to $-180°$ for a fixed frequency.

It must be realized that, in the use of all networks for shifting phase of signals or supply voltages, any change in carrier frequency changes the phase shift; and if changes of carrier frequency are anticipated, this problem must be considered.

5-7. Equalizing Networks. Equalizing networks modify the character of the signal being fed into them. The equalizing network is used for stabilizing purposes and is placed in cascade with the amplifier. When the servo controlled shaft is approaching correspondence after a step-function command from rest, the network reverses the voltage applied to the servomotor before the actuating signal reaches zero, thus tending to stabilize the system by "anticipating" that correspondence is near.

Equalizing networks are of two basic types, a-c and d-c. The d-c networks operate on a direct voltage that is a measure of the servo actuating signal, and the a-c networks operate on the envelope of an alternating voltage whose magnitude is a measure of the servo actuating signal. The d-c networks are more flexible in their application, and they are capable of achieving a wider variety of effects. They require, however, that the actuating-signal voltage be demodulated if the error detector is the more common alternating-voltage type.

Two d-c equalizing networks commonly used in servomechanisms are shown as Nos. 3 and 4 in Table 5-1. The first of these is used as a lead network, the second as a lag network. Both can be used as a means of reducing the steady-state following error. The first network results in a broad-band servo, the second in a narrower-band servo. (If it is desired to minimize the servo's poor transient recovery from slewing caused by the capacitor of the lag network charging up during slewing, the magnitude of the charge can be limited by the use of a selenium-rectifier circuit.)

As an example of the use of an equalizer network, consider the passive-circuit lead network shown as No. 3 in Table 5-1. The transfer function can be written

$$H(s) = \frac{R_1}{R_1 + R} \frac{1 + RCs}{1 + \dfrac{R_1}{R_1 + R} RCs} = \frac{s + 1/\alpha\tau}{s + 1/\tau} \qquad (5\text{-}39)$$

where $\alpha = 1 + R/R_1$ and $\tau = R_1 RC/(R_1 + R)$. The network is represented on the s plane* by a pole at $s = -1/\tau$ and a zero at $s = -1/\alpha\tau$. The zero is closer to the origin than the pole and the ratio of the two distances is α. If τ is small, both the pole and the zero are remote and effectively cancel each other. As τ is made larger, the zero enters the region where the locus is affected. For very large τ, the pole also becomes significant. Consider the effect of inserting a passive-circuit lead network into a second-order system. The open-loop transfer function for the system and equalizer is

$$KGH = \underset{\text{System}}{\frac{K}{s(s + 1)}} \underset{\text{Equalizer}}{\frac{(s + 1/4\tau)}{(s + 1/\tau)}} \qquad (5\text{-}40)$$

* See the Appendix for a discussion of the root-locus method as applied to the theory of servomechanisms.

Let $K = 40$ and $\alpha = 4$. Root-locus plots are constructed for several values of τ ($=0.1$, 0.2, 0.4, 0.6, and 0.7) on Fig. 5-21a. The lead network produces a different effect, depending upon the value of τ. From Fig. 5-21a the damping ratio ζ and the frequency of oscillation ω_n are obtained and are shown plotted on Fig. 5-21b as a function of τ. For fixed K and α, the optimum value of τ is approximately 0.1 sec.

Network 5 is a combination of the two networks and can be used when it is necessary, for example, to extend the corner frequency of a servomotor and still have the high gain at low frequency necessary for a

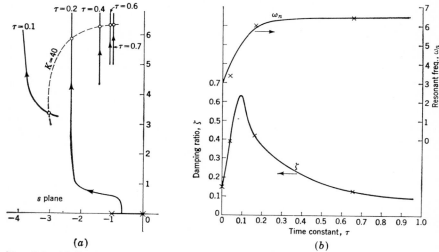

$$(a) \hspace{7cm} (b)$$

FIG. 5-21.(a) Root-locus diagrams for the system transfer function:

$$G(s) = \frac{40}{s(s + 1)} \frac{s + \frac{1}{4}\tau}{s + 1/\tau}$$

(b) variation of ζ and ω_n as τ is varied for the system of Eq. (5-40).

small velocity following error. There is, however, a rigid relationship between the corner frequencies of the network, which restricts its flexibility. Networks 6 and 7 accomplish the same result as network 5 but do not have this difficulty. To achieve the same results, networks 3 and 4 are sometimes used in cascade, although more components are required and the impedance-loading problem is more difficult. The denominators of the transfer functions of networks 5, 6, and 7 and the numerators of 6 and 7 can each be factored into two overdamped factors, thus locating two corner frequencies.

If only a lead network is desired, the circuit of Fig. 5-22 can be used to encompass the entire process of demodulation, equalization, and modulation all in a single stage of amplification. The tube is biased so that it rectifies, and the cathode capacitor-resistor combination is of such a time constant that the amplifier is degenerate only to low signal frequencies. The amplifier acts, therefore, like a lead network since it has low gain at low signal frequencies and high gain at high signal frequencies. Experimental data on the amplifier are shown in Fig. 5-23.

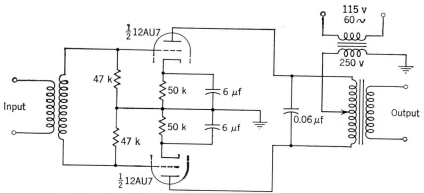

FIG. 5-22. Demodulation-equalization-modulation network.

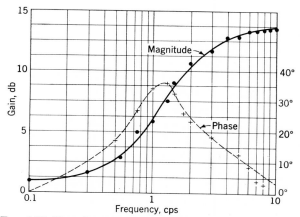

FIG. 5-23. Experimental results of the circuit of Fig. 5-22.

One difficulty in the use of any lead networks in equalization at signal frequencies is that low frequencies are attenuated more than high frequencies. If there is any ripple in the signal from the phase-sensitive detector, it may have to be filtered in order to prevent the amplifier from saturating or the motor from overheating owing to these noise voltages.

Equalization at carrier frequency can be accomplished by network 9, 11, 12, or 13. Network 9 (the bridged-T), network 11 (the resonant-damper), and network 13 (the bridged-parallel-T) when used for equalization all have frequency characteristics that produce a notch (i.e., a V shape in the db-magnitude vs. log-frequency plot) at the carrier frequency. They introduce a phase lead to the envelope representing the actuating signal. Of course, the network does not actually operate on the envelope of the actuating-signal voltage. Each of the sideband frequencies undergoes independent magnitude and phase changes, and the output is the sum of the two signals, each of which has been so modified. In introducing a simple, sinusoidally modulated carrier to the network, the network may be thought of as modifying the voltage components that make up the input envelope; and the combination of the modified components produces an output envelope that is different in magnitude and phase from the input envelope. (See the Appendix for a more complete treatment).

If a network of type 11 is used, the LC circuit is made resonant at the carrier frequency; hence it is extremely susceptible to any supply-frequency fields that may exist. It is necessary, therefore, to shield this network carefully and ground the shields in order to reduce pickup.

The use of any of the a-c lead networks attenuates carrier frequency and sideband frequencies close to the carrier and transmits other frequencies with less attenuation. Since many noise signals are harmonics of the carrier frequency, such as harmonic voltages from the synchro or any rate generator that may be in the circuit, these networks attenuate the signal frequencies more than the harmonic voltages, often by a factor of 10 or more. It is therefore almost always necessary to use a filter in conjunction with the networks to attenuate the harmonics. The design of such a filter network requires the producing of a narrow-band filter to attenuate harmonics and undesirable noise frequencies while keeping the bandwidth wide enough so that the desirable equalization effect of the network is not nullified.

Network 12 can be used for equalization at carrier frequency when a high gain at low signal frequencies is desired. This network produces a peak at the carrier frequency, hence increases the servo stiffness (i.e., its control torque sensitivity per unit of error), and reduces the velocity following error. Its unstabilizing effect, however, is similar to that of network 4 used in equalization at signal frequencies.

As with all networks designed to equalize a servo at carrier frequencies, there is the problem of lack of symmetry about the carrier frequency. The effect on servomechanism performance of any quadrature component generated by lack of symmetry depends on servo design. Some servo components, such as phase-sensitive detectors, are relatively insensitive to quadrature voltages; although if equalization is taking place at carrier frequency, it is unlikely that an a-c equalizing network will be followed by a phase-sensitive detector. Two-phase motors are somewhat affected by the quadrature component generated in unsymmetrical networks, but this component can easily be 10 per cent of the desired signals without any noticeable deterioration of the performance.

Although a-c equalizing networks are designed to be as symmetrical as possible about the carrier frequency, their severest limitation is that the supply frequency may change, thus causing them to be highly unsymmetrical about the new supply frequency. The deterioration of performance depends upon the narrowness of the notch, which is a function of the corner frequencies of the network. It creates enough of a problem, however, to render a 60-cycle servomechanism designed to be critically damped by the use of an a-c equalizing network highly oscillatory by power-supply frequency variations on the order of 10 per cent. While a-c equalizing networks introduce fewer complications into the servo-amplifier, the presence of this severe limitation may render them useless.

5-8. Practical Considerations in the Design of Servo Networks. Although commercially available networks, especially filter types, can be found, it is often necessary to fabricate the servo network along with the other components, such as gear trains and amplifiers. For this reason, care must be exercised in the design and fabrication of networks for servo applications. The following practical points, which affect the performance of the network, should be considered: (1) the effect of input and output impedance, (2) the effect of component tolerances, (3) the effect of encapsulating the network, and (4) the effect of temperature on the transfer function.

The effects of input and output impedance are considered in Sec. 5-5 for the bridged-T network. Many networks can be designed to operate with a finite-load impedance. Quite often, however, the network produces the desired transfer function only when operating from low (ideally zero) source impedance and high (ideally infinite) load impedances. Frequently a 10:1 ratio of impedances is satisfactory to yield the desired transfer function. That is, the source impedance should be $\frac{1}{10}$ the magnitude of the network input impedance at the frequencies of operation. The load impedance should be 10 times the magnitude of the network output impedance at the operating frequencies. When an impedance ratio of less than 10:1 is not possible, the frequency response is usually altered unless the lower impedance ratio is provided in the design.

An example of a synthesis procedure that provides for an output load impedance is the loaded ladder network. The constant-resistance ladder network is derived from the circuit shown in Fig. 5-24. The transfer function for this network is written as follows:

$$\frac{E_o}{E_{in}} = \frac{R_o Z_2}{R_o Z_1 + R_o Z_2 + Z_1 Z_2} = \frac{Z_2/R_o}{Z_1/R_o + Z_2/R_o + Z_1 Z_2/R_o^2} \quad (5\text{-}41)$$

and the input impedance is given by

$$Z_{in} = \frac{Z_1 R_o + Z_2 R_o + Z_1 Z_2}{R_o + Z_2} = \left(\frac{\dfrac{Z_1}{R_o} + \dfrac{Z_2}{R_o} + \dfrac{Z_1 Z_2}{R_o^2}}{1 + \dfrac{Z_2}{R_o}} \right) R_o \quad (5\text{-}42)$$

When the input impedance is equal to the load impedance, i.e., $Z_{in} = R_o$, Eq. (5-42) is equaled to R_o with the result:

$$\frac{Z_1}{R_o} + \frac{Z_2}{R_o} + \frac{Z_1 Z_2}{R_o R_o} = 1 + \frac{Z_2}{R_o} \quad (5\text{-}43)$$

Substituting from Eq. (5-43) into Eq. (5-41) gives the following design expression:

$$\frac{E_o}{E_{in}} = \frac{Z_2/R_o}{1 + Z_2/R_o} \quad \text{or} \quad \frac{Z_2}{R_o} = \frac{1}{E_{in}/E_o - 1} \quad (5\text{-}44)$$

Similarly, the design equation for Z_1, as written from Eq. (5-43), is

$$\frac{Z_1}{R_o} = \frac{1}{1 + Z_2/R_o} = 1 - \frac{E_o}{E_{in}} \quad (5\text{-}45)$$

Application of Eqs. (5-44) and (5-45) for the constant-resistance ladder is similar to that for the simple ladder network as discussed in Sec. 5-5.

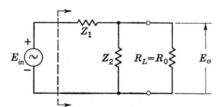

Fig. 5-24. Loaded ladder network.

Because of the variation of component values owing to production tolerances a network may not produce the desired transfer function. When servo networks are built in production quantities, the variation in transfer function may be substantial. The problem can be solved by tightening up on the component tolerances. This approach, however, usually results in an expensive product. It is usually more desirable to build the network with ± 5 per cent tolerance components and to calibrate the response by varying one component. Usually phase-shift and equalizer networks are less critical than filter networks. For this reason it is often possible to fabricate the entire network from relatively standard components (± 2 to ± 5 per cent). Filter networks, which are frequently more critical, are brought into tolerance by variation of one component in the network. For example, the parallel-T network (No. 10 in Table 5-1) is easily nulled by variation of either R_1 or C_2. A resistance decade can be inserted into the network and varied until the null occurs at the correct frequency. The correct value is read from the decade box.

To increase reliability, servo networks are often totally encapsulated with a plastic material. This technique prevents damage to the network under such conditions as vibration, shock, or humidity. Similar benefit is obtained by mounting the network components on a terminal board and dipping the assembly into an epoxy resin.* Care must be exercised in the encapsulating of certain components, especially inductors and capacitors. In certain cases the encapsulation procedure causes these components to shift in value owing to one of several causes: (1) increased stress due to changes in dimension of the plastic material, (2) changes in air gap in the inductors, and (3) change in dielectric constant for capacitors.

The major effect of temperature on servo networks is in the variation of the inductive elements. For small inductances, powdered-iron-alloy cores (for example, Molybdenum Permalloy Powder Cores) show small variation with temperature. For stabilized cores the inductance variation is less than ± 0.1 per cent over a temperature range of 30 to 130°F. Ordinary magnetic steels show much greater variation. Since the permeability and hence the inductance of magnetic components vary with temperature, it is often desirable to design resistance-capacitance networks.

When an RC network is designed to operate over a wide temperature range, the resistance-temperature characteristics must be considered. For example, a ½ watt carbon resistor can vary ± 3 per cent in resistance over a temperature range of -15 to $+105$°C. Up to $+65$°C the resistance variation is much less (approximately 1 per cent). The resistance variations are usually not important for phase-shifting and equalizer networks. If the resistance variation in RC filter networks is unacceptable, a thermistor† may be used in series or parallel with the resistor. A *thermistor* is a nonlinear resistance with a negative temperature coefficient. The thermistor compensates for the positive temperature coefficient of the resistor, and the combination can be designed to exhibit relatively little resistance variation with temperature.

PROBLEMS

5-1. Explain the purposes of each of the three types of network used in servomechanisms.

* This is one type of plastic that is frequently employed for this purpose.
† See Chap. 6 for the application of thermistors in transistor-amplifier design.

5-2. Determine four different networks for the following RC admittance:

$$Y = \frac{(s+1)(s+3)}{(s+2)(s+5)}$$

Each expansion is to possess only positive coefficients.

5-3. Find lattice networks for the following transfer voltage ratios:

(a) $\dfrac{s^2}{(s+6)(s+50)}$

(b) $\dfrac{s(s+1)}{(s^2+s+10)}$

(c) $\dfrac{s^2+9}{(s+12)(s+20)}$

(d) $\dfrac{s^2+s+10}{(s+10)^2}$

5-4. Design a resistance shunt and a capacitor-shunt bridged-T network with a resonant frequency of 400 cps, a notch depth of 0.2, and a d-c impedance level of 50 kilohms.

5-5. Derive the equation for the phase shifter of Fig. 5-20 and show how this network is useful for a-c servo systems.

5-6. Derive the transfer functions shown in the network tables (Table 5-1).

5-7. For the network of type 11, substitute the following component values: $L = 10$ henrys, $C = 0.0158$ μf, $R = 5,400$ ohms, $R_1 = 600$ ohms. What is the equation for the output voltage of this network if the carrier frequency is 400 cycles and the signal frequency is a 5 cycle/sec sinusoidal voltage?

5-8. Compare the advantages and disadvantages of equalization at carrier frequency as opposed to equalization at signal frequency.

CHAPTER 6

SERVOAMPLIFIERS

6-1. Description of Servoamplifiers. In this chapter those character-istics and design features of many types of amplifiers which are peculiar to servomechanisms are discussed. Since the subject of amplifier design is well-covered in numerous texts,* only the salient features of servo-amplifier design are summarized. Vacuum-tube, transistor, thyratron magnetic, and rotating motor-generator amplifiers are discussed in this chapter.

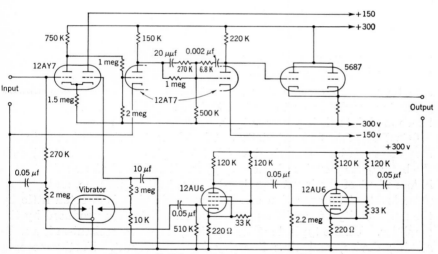

Fig. 6-1. Self-balancing d-c servoamplifier.

A typical a-c servoamplifier is shown in Fig. 1-2; a d-c amplifier used in servomechanisms is shown in Fig. 6-1. Although both a-c and d-c amplifiers are used in servomechanisms, the a-c amplifiers are by far more common because of the problems associated with d-c amplification. These problems include drift, which is the low-frequency variation of the output voltage with no change of input, and the necessity of providing

* See Refs. 8, 31, and 43 for a further discussion of both transistor- and vacuum-tube-amplifier design.

special bias voltages in cascaded stages.   Drift in d-c amplifiers can be caused by changes in power-supply voltage or the variation of component values, which in turn are often due to temperature and aging effects. Despite the advantages of simplicity and flexibility of utilizing d-c equalizing networks, d-c amplifiers are generally avoided because of the necessity of keeping the amplifier free from drift during long periods of time.   This latter advantage can be obtained by means of demodulation and modulation as shown in Fig. 5-22, thus not requiring any d-c amplification.   Another type of d-c amplifier uses a chopper to modulate the input voltage and a chopper to rectify the output.   Such an amplifier is actually an a-c amplifier, however, even though its input and output are both d-c.

Both a-c and d-c amplifiers are used as the entire voltage- and power-amplifying source of signal voltages for instrument servomechanisms. Typical output stages of servoamplifiers for smaller instrument servomechanisms employ 6AQ5's, 12AU7's and 6L6's.   When it is desired to obtain more power from the amplifier and to permit a higher output voltage, such transmitting tubes as the 807's or 6146's can be used. Since more powerful transmitting tubes require larger plate voltages, which are often dangerous and clumsy, an auxiliary amplifying means is often used.   In these cases, electronic amplifiers are used as preamplifiers to drive both electric- and hydraulic-power amplifiers.   They can also be used to drive either magnetic amplifiers or rotating motor-generator amplifiers or to control the valves of hydraulic systems and hence modulate their power output.

6-2. Desirable Characteristics.   The characteristics desirable in a-c amplifiers can be summarized as (1) flat amplitude response (gain) over the band of frequencies of interest, (2) small and fixed phase shift that is independent of the input signal, (3) low output impedance, and (4) low noise level.   The operation of the servomechanism is affected little by the nonlinearity of amplifiers and waveform distortion produced by the amplifier.   Unlike typical audioamplifiers, the servomechanism is a null-seeking device, and thus linearity is unimportant.   Furthermore, a servomotor or other power-amplifying device that might be fed from the servoamplifier can withstand an immensely higher level of distortion than can the human ear.   To obtain the maximum power in a given space and at a minimum cost, the tubes are usually driven far beyond the limit of distortionless output.

So that unfavorable dynamics are not introduced, the amplifier gain should be constant with frequency to a point well beyond the frequency range of the servomechanism.   The term "amplifier" in this section implies the pure amplification means exclusive of any equalizing networks that might be inserted for improvement of the dynamic characteristics of the servomechanism. For d-c amplifiers, this requirement means that the amplifier should be flat for several octaves beyond the highest servo-actuating-signal frequency.

The a-c servoamplifier must be flat over a band of frequencies. This band extends from the carrier frequency minus the highest modulation frequency the servo will transmit to the carrier frequency plus the highest servo modulation frequency. For example, if the carrier frequency of the servomechanism is 60 cps and the highest signal frequency is 20 cps, the servoamplifier should be flat from less than 40 to over 80 cps. An amplifier that is not flat over this range can produce one of two deleterious effects. This unsymmetrical transmission about the carrier frequency can introduce unwanted time lags into the servo loop, or it can introduce distortion into the signal by the generation of quadrature components. Suitable design of the coupling and bypass networks is the usual solution to this problem since it ordinarily resolves itself into improvement of low-frequency response. Because of the need for improved low-frequency response and other desirable characteristics gained from the use of feedback, cathode bypass capacitors are not ordinarily used in servoamplifiers. If any filters are used for the suppression of undesired harmonics, they must also be flat over the range of sideband frequencies of interest.

Another desirable characteristic of an a-c servoamplifier is that there be no change in phase shift with the level of the input signal. Servo components operate more effectively on signals of the proper phase. In saturating, some amplifiers change the phase of the carrier and cause the servomotor or power-amplifying device to deliver less output than if the phase shift did not occur.

The output impedance of servoamplifiers is made as low as possible to improve the dynamic performance of the device it feeds. Often it is not economically feasible to reduce it to as low a value as desired from the dynamic-performance standpoint. A typical value of amplifier output impedance is on the order of 800 ohms resistance. In the case of instrument servomechanisms, low output impedance in the amplifier is desirable because of the effect of this impedance on the performance of the servomotor and because of the increased gain and performance obtained from a low output impedance when other power amplifiers are driven. When a servomotor is driven by the amplifier, the impedance of the motor changes with the speed and applied voltage, so that it is impossible to match the amplifier to the motor. For a given output impedance of the amplifier, this represents the condition of maximum power transfer to the servomotor.

6-3. Amplifier Feedback. Voltage feedback is often used in servoamplifiers for reducing output impedance, distortion, and internally generated noise. It is also used to introduce favorable dynamics into the servo loop.

For an amplifier of forward-loop gain KG and with negative voltage feedback H, the internally generated noise, distortion, and output impedance are reduced by the factor $1/(1 + GH)$. Since the feedback amplifier gain is reduced by $1/(1 + GH)$, a preamplifier with low distortion and noise may be added ahead of the feedback amplifier to compensate for loss in gain. One type of feedback used in the output stages of amplifiers for reducing the distortion and lowering the output impedance is shown in Fig. 6-2. Normally the output transformer feeds back 10 per cent of the output voltage to the cathodes of the power tubes. The resulting 10 per cent change of amplifier gain is scarcely noticed in servo performance, but the use of this circuit in typical amplifiers reduces the

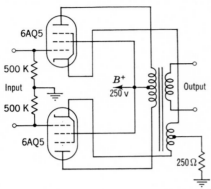

FIG. 6-2. Amplifier output stage using feedback.

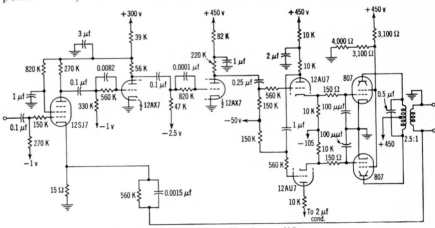

FIG. 6-3. Servo feedback amplifier.

impedance from 800 to the order of 400 ohms. Experiments on actual circuits should be conducted, however, to determine whether the improved circuit performance is outweighed by the following disadvantages: (1) need for a more complicated transformer and (2) reduction of amplifier gain.

Feedback can also be used for the improvement of over-all stability of

the amplifier, i.e., to reduce the effect of tube aging and power-supply variations on the gain of the amplifier. A circuit using feedback for this purpose is shown in Fig. 6-3.

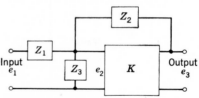

Feedback is employed in electronic amplifiers to achieve equalization. Although feedback can be used in both d-c and a-c amplifiers, the dynamic effect is more easily accomplished with d-c amplifiers. A

FIG. 6-4. Use of feedback to achieve favorable dynamics with a d-c amplifier.

schematic diagram from which equations can be derived is given in Fig. 6-4. Assume that Z_1, Z_2, and Z_3 are impedances and that K is the gain of a high-gain amplifier. From Fig. 6-4,

$$\frac{e_1 - e_2}{Z_1} + \frac{e_3 - e_2}{Z_2} = \frac{e_2}{Z_3} \qquad (6\text{-}1)$$

and
$$e_3 = Ke_2 \qquad (6\text{-}2)$$

From these equations, e_2 can be eliminated by letting $K \to \infty$:

$$\frac{e_3}{e_1} = -\frac{Z_2}{Z_1} \qquad (6\text{-}3)$$

If Z_2 is a capacitor and Z_1 a resistor, the transfer function of the feedback amplifier is

$$\frac{E_3}{E_1} = -\frac{1}{RCs} \qquad (6\text{-}4)$$

which is an integrator. If Z_1 is a capacitor and Z_2 a resistor, a differentiator results. Similarly, combinations of these effects can be obtained. (The benefits of these effects are discussed in the Appendix.)

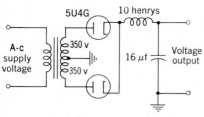

FIG. 6-5. Power supply.

6-4. Power Supplies for Servoamplifiers.

A typical power supply for servoamplifiers is a full-wave rectifier and filter such as shown in Fig. 6-5. In some applications it is desirable to use selenium rectifiers instead of vacuum-tube rectifiers. Because of their relatively low inverse voltage rating and their critical-temperature requirement, selenium rectifiers are somewhat limited. Both germanium and silicon rectifiers are finding wider use in power supplies. Germanium diodes also suffer from temperature. Silicon rectifiers are less temperature sensitive and have a higher inverse voltage rating than either germanium or selenium. Fig. 6-6

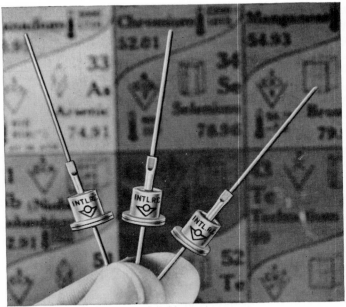

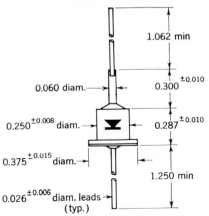

0.060 diam.

1.062 min

0.300 ±0.010

0.250 ±0.008 diam.

0.287 ±0.010

0.375 ±0.015 diam.

1.250 min

0.026 ±0.006 diam. leads (typ.)

FIG. 6-6. Photograph and dimensional diagram for silicon diodes. (*International Rectifier Corp., El Segundo, Calif.*)

shows a photograph and a dimensional diagram for a fused-junction silicon diode. These units are capable of carrying 750 ma without a heat sink and can operate with low leakage and optimum reliability over a temperature range of −65 to +165°C. Units of this type provide the answer to many power-supply problems.

When a number of amplifiers are to be supplied, a motor-generator set is sometimes used. To reduce ripple and power-supply impedance, the early stages of servoamplifiers are often supplied from a regulated section of the main power supply.

Special care must be exercised when several servoamplifiers are fed from the same power supply, especially if the power-supply impedance is high. One of two effects may be observed. The first is cross-talk effect; i.e., the transient operation of one of the servomechanisms causes the other servomechanisms to move. The problem typically results from the application of a common power supply to operate both train and elevation servos for a fire-control system. The other effect which may exist is that all the servomechanisms which are connected to a common power supply may oscillate at a low frequency, since they are all coupled into a large multiple-loop system. Both problems can be eliminated by adequate decoupling and reduction of power-supply impedance, at least for the first stages of the amplifiers.

In many applications it is necessary to provide a regulated voltage from the power supply. The zener voltage effect can be used with considerable success for this purpose. The silicon zener diode is especially useful in applications where it is important to maintain a constant voltage level under conditions of high temperature, severe shock, and vibration. In view of the many advantages they offer over their counterpart, the glow-discharge gas tube, silicon zener diodes find widespread use as regulator or reference elements in the design of new equipment. Their ability to regulate over a wide current area and the present availability of types in a voltage range from three to several hundred volts readily qualify them for servomechanism use.

Silicon diodes, which are shown in Fig. 6-7, are characterized by a high ratio of reverse to forward resistance. The reverse current of a silicon diode remains small until the reverse voltage reaches a nondestructive breakdown point known as the *zener voltage*. In this region the current increases very rapidly, while the voltage drop across the diode remains almost constant. The breakdown voltage at which this phenomenon occurs is controlled to a great degree during manufacture. From Fig. 6-8 it can be seen that over a wide range of current, a substantially constant voltage drop exists. The slope of the curve

$$\frac{\Delta e}{\Delta i}$$

illustrates the regulation ability of the diode and may be expressed as a resistance. It is equivalent to a fraction of an ohm for low-voltage zener diodes and up to several hundred ohms for higher-voltage types.

The zener breakdown is similar to the ionization that occurs in the more familiar glow-discharge gas tubes; a cumulative action takes place as a result of the current carriers being given sufficient energy to release

Fig. 6-7. Zener-diode types.   (*International Rectifier Corp., El Segundo, Calif.*)

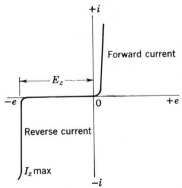

Fig. 6-8. Typical voltage drop and reverse resistance.

additional current carriers, thus making possible a high reverse current flow. Beyond breakdown, the characteristics of the silicon diode most resemble the sustaining characteristics of the gas regulator tube and may be considered to be the semiconductor equivalent. The effect can be used in exactly the same manner to provide a constant voltage output.

The zener diode, however, possesses certain advantages over the gas tube:

1. Zener diodes are available with any required voltage in the range from 3 to

1,000 volts; gas tubes are limited to specific values between 60 and 150 volts.

2. No special provision need be made to ensure a minimum starting potential, since this and the working potential are virtually the same in a zener diode.

3. Encapsulated zener diodes exhibit negligible photoelectric effects.

4. Zener diodes may be shunted by large values of capacitance without danger of oscillation.

5. Zero-temperature coefficients may be obtained.

6. Zener diodes are of more rugged construction and can withstand very high operating temperatures, shock, and vibration.

7. Zener diodes are smaller in size and weight.

Figure 6-9 shows a typical use of the zener diode in regulating the output of a d-c power supply. Depending upon the load requirements, the diode shunt regulator draws variable current through the resistor R.

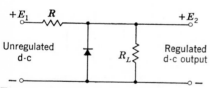

FIG. 6-9. Zener diode in reference circuit.

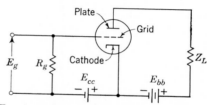

FIG. 6-10. Schematic diagram for a triode amplifier.

As the load decreases or increases, the zener shunt element draws more or less current. The net result is a practically constant output voltage across R_L. The maximum current that can flow through the diode is limited by the heat generated at the junction. Thus the use of a zener diode as a voltage regulator is limited only by its rated current-handling capabilities.

6-5. Design Considerations for Vacuum-tube Amplifiers. Complete volumes are written on the subject of electronic amplifiers. The basic points of linear analysis are considered in this section. The reader may consult Refs. 2, 31, and 43 for additional material.

Design Parameters. The approach to the analysis and design of vacuum-tube circuits is based upon the equivalent circuit. Figure 6-10 shows a schematic diagram for one stage of a triode amplifier. The analysis of this circuit is accomplished with conventional circuit analysis by finding an equivalent circuit for the vacuum tube. The performance of a vacuum-tube triode is obtained from a plot of the static plate characteristics, which are shown in Fig. 6-11 for the medium $-\mu$ twin triode 12AU7. These curves are a plot of plate current i_b vs. plate

voltage e_b for various values of grid voltage e_c.   The curves intersect
the horizontal axis at points that are called *cutoff points*.

The effect of the grid in controlling the plate current is clearly demonstrated by the curves of Fig. 6-11, and the specific operating points indicated by the letters a, b, and c.   Suppose the tube is operating at point
a (i.e., $E_c = -8$ volts, i_b at 10 ma, and e_b at 265 volts).   When the grid
voltage is changed to -6 volts with the plate voltage held fixed, the plate
current changes to 16 ma (point c).   To return the plate current to its
original value of 10 ma requires a 45-volt change in plate voltage (point b).
Hence a 2-volt change in grid voltage causes the same change in plate
current as a 45-volt change in plate voltage.   In this region of operation,
the grid is 22.5 times more effective in controlling the tube than the

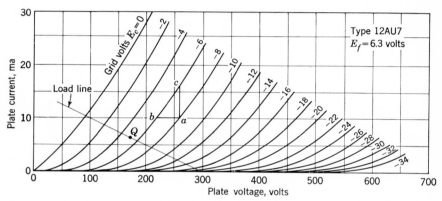

FIG. 6-11. Average plate characteristics for the 12AU7 twin triode.   (*Radio Corp. of
America, Harrison, N.J.*)

plate.   The amplification factor μ is defined as this ratio, or stated
mathematically,

$$\mu = \frac{\Delta e_b}{\Delta i_b}\bigg|_{e_c = \text{const}} \tag{6-5}$$

For the 12AU7 of Fig. 6-11, $\mu = {}^{45}\!/_2 = 22.5$.   Hence for characteristics
that can be approximated by parallel straight lines, the amplification
factor μ is constant.

The internal resistance of the vacuum tube is also an important design
quantity.   This internal resistance is defined by r_p and is termed the
plate resistance.   The plate resistance is defined mathematically by the
equation

$$r_p = \frac{\Delta e_b}{\Delta i_b}\bigg|_{e_c = \text{const}} \tag{6-6}$$

which is the average slope of the $e_p - i_p$ curve.   Reference to the small

triangle on the plate characteristics of Fig. 6-11 yields the plate resistance.
Along the line $e_c = -6$.

$$r_p = \frac{265 \text{ volts} - 220 \text{ volts}}{16.5 \text{ ma} - 10 \text{ ma}} = \frac{45}{6.5} \times 10^3 = 7,000 \text{ ohms}$$

These two parameters are sufficient to describe the behavior of a vacuum
tube for linear analysis. A third parameter, which is related to the
previous two, is useful for describing a vacuum tube in terms of the

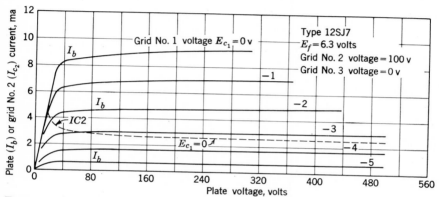

FIG. 6-12. Average plate characteristics for the 12SJ7 sharp-cutoff pentode. (*Radio Corp. of America, Harrison, N.J.*)

current equivalent circuit. This is called the *mutual conductance* g_m and
is defined as

$$g_m = \frac{\Delta i_b}{\Delta e_c}\bigg|_{e_b = \text{const}} \tag{6-7}$$

This ratio is computed from Fig. 6-11 along the vertical line $a - c$ as
follows:

$$g_m = \frac{(16.5 - 10)(10^{-3})}{(-6) - (-8)} = 3.25 \times 10^{-3}$$
$$= 3,250 \text{ micromhos}$$

Comparison of the defining equations for the three parameters yields the
expression

$$\mu = g_m r_p \tag{6-8}$$

For the example of the 12AU7, $\mu = (3,250 \times 10^{-6})(7,000) = 22.5$.
Plate characteristics and these tube parameters are given by the manufacturer for each of the tube types.

The average plate characteristics for a 12SJ7 pentode are shown in
Fig. 6-12. These characteristics are significantly different from the

triode curves. The computation of the parameters is the same as for the triode. The average parameters for the 12SJ7 are approximately $\mu = 1,500$, $r_p = 1$ megohm, and $g_m = 1,600$.

Equivalent Circuit for a Vacuum Tube. The performance of a vacuum tube can be approximated by an equivalent circuit. For assumed linear plate characteristics, the equivalent circuit provides a method of linear analysis. The form of this equivalent circuit can be reasoned from a knowledge of the tube parameters μ and r_p. The voltage E_g on the grid circuit of Fig. 6-10 is amplified into the plate circuit μE_g. The plate resistance represents the internal impedance of the tube. The equivalent circuit, which is shown in Fig. 6-13, is applicable for alternating (a-c) quantities only. The unidirectional voltage E_{bb}, which is the B+ voltage, and E_{cc}, which is the bias voltage, are omitted from the circuit. The superimposed direct currents are found from the original diagram, Fig. 6-10.

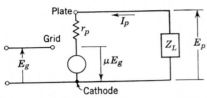

FIG. 6-13. Equivalent circuit for vacuum tube.

In application, the equivalent circuit replaces the actual circuit at the points marked plate, cathode, and grid. The equivalent circuit of Fig. 6-13 provides no path for grid current, hence the grid must be kept negative with respect to the cathode. The gain E_p/E_g for this circuit is found by means of standard methods of circuit analysis. For example, the current is

$$I_p = \frac{\mu E_g}{r_p + Z_L} \qquad (6\text{-}9)$$

The output voltage E_p is

$$E_p = -I_p Z_L = \frac{-\mu E_g Z_L}{r_p + Z_L} \qquad (6\text{-}10)$$

and the voltage amplification is

$$K = K \underline{/\theta} = \frac{E_p}{E_g} = \frac{-\mu Z_L}{r_p + Z_L} \qquad (6\text{-}11)$$

When the load is a pure resistor, the voltage gain is a real negative number,

$$K = -\frac{\mu R_L}{r_p + R_L} \qquad (6\text{-}12)$$

For typical values $\mu = 22.5$, $r_p = 7K$, and $R_L = 10K$, the gain is -13.5.

Another example is the equation for the cathode follower, which is shown both in schematic-diagram form (Fig. 6-14a) and in equivalent-circuit form (Fig. 6-14b). This circuit utilizes negative feedback for the purpose of obtaining a high input and low output impedance. The plate-current equation is

$$(R_L + r_p)I_p = \mu E_g \tag{6-13}$$

where $E_g = E_{in} - I_pR_L$. This expression is substituted into Eq. (6-13):

$$(R_L + r_p)I_p = \mu E_{in} - \mu I_pR_L$$

which is rewritten

$$[R_L(1 + \mu) + r_p]I_p = \mu E_{in} \tag{6-14}$$

The output voltage is

$$E_o = +I_pR_L = \left[\frac{\mu R_L}{R_L(1 + \mu) + r_p}\right]E_{in} \tag{6-15}$$

The gain of the stage is

$$K = \frac{E_o}{E_{in}} = \left[\frac{\mu R_L}{R_L(1 + \mu) + r_p}\right] \tag{6-16}$$

Quiescent Values. The equivalent circuit for a vacuum tube describes the performance of the tube when it is operating in an assumed linear

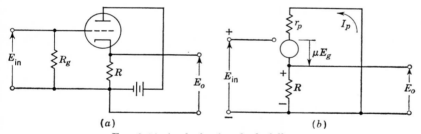

Fig. 6-14. Analysis of cathode follower.

fashion. Before the tube will operate, it must be supplied with certain constant-grid bias and supply voltages and loaded with an appropriate load resistance. The setting of these fixed values is important to the proper operation of the tube. Quiescent conditions exist when the signal voltage applied to the grid is zero. Under these conditions, the input terminals are effectively shorted and the bias voltage E_{cc} appears on grid. The grid resistor shown in Figs. 6-10 and 6-14 provides a conductive path between grid and cathode. Since the grid draws no current, the resistor has no effect on the circuit. If the source has a sufficiently low output impedance (0.1 to 1 megohm), it is not necessary to add this resistor. If a conductive path is not provided, however, the grid becomes charged electrostatically and the tube becomes blocked; i.e., the plate current drops to zero.

The operating conditions of a vacuum tube are plotted on the plate characteristics by means of a "load line." The equation for the load line is found from the vacuum-tube circuit diagram

$$e_b = E_{bb} - R_L i_b \tag{6-17}$$

where e_b = plate voltage (total alternating and direct current)
E_{bb} = supply voltage
R_L = load resistance
i_b = plate current (total alternating and direct current)

This straight line is easily drawn by finding the intersection with the i_b and e_b axes. The intersection with the e_b axis is found by setting i_b equal to zero with the result

$$e_b = E_{bb} \tag{6-18}$$

The intersection with the i_b axis is found by letting $e_b = 0$ with the result

$$i_b = \frac{E_{bb}}{R_L} \tag{6-19}$$

A load line for the 12AU7 is shown in the plate characteristics of Fig. 6-11 for $E_{bb} = 300$ volts and $R_L = 20$ kilohms. The intersections are $e_b = 300$ volts and $i_b = {}^{300}\!/_{20}$ kilohms = 15 ma. With the grid bias selected at approximately -5 volts, the grid can swing through ± 2 volts about -5, and the plate can swing almost ± 60 volts about 175. The quiescent point Q is shown in Fig. 6-11. As the grid voltage changes, the point moves along the load line in accordance with the applied signal. The plate current and plate voltage both follow the grid variation. For a sinusoidal grid-voltage variation, the waveforms will have the shape shown in Fig. 6-15. As the grid swings positive, the plate current is in phase while the plate voltage is 180° out of phase with the grid voltage. The waveforms of both plate current

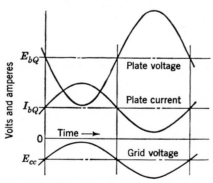

FIG. 6-15. Waveforms of plate voltage and current with a sinusoidal grid voltage.

and plate voltage will be sinusoids provided that in the operating region the $e_b - i_b$ curves are parallel straight lines separated by equal distances.

In choosing the operating point it is desirable to make use of the most linear portion of the plate characteristics. In this way the least distortion in output waveform results. The grid voltage is chosen so that the signal does not drive the grid into cutoff during the negative swing nor cause the grid to draw current during the positive swing. In either case the waveform of the output becomes distorted. For best results, even the curved portion of the $e_b - i_b$ curves should be avoided.

6-6. A Typical Vacuum-tube Circuit and Its Operation. A typical vacuum-tube servoamplifier is shown in Fig. 6-3. This amplifier utilizes three stages of voltage amplification comprising an input preamplifier (12SJ7 pentode) and two additional stages of voltage amplification (two halves of a 12AX7 dual triode). The output from the second half of the 12AX7 drives a pair of cathode followers (two halves of a 12AU7 dual triode). These tubes are utilized to provide a push-pull* signal for the final power amplifier (two 807's). Notice that the signal from the plate of the upper half of the 12AU7 is fed to the grid of the lower half of the 12AU7. Hence the voltages across the cathode resistors are of equal magnitude but 180° out of phase. This is the form of balanced signal required to drive the power tubes. The output-power tubes (two 807's) drive the load through an output transformer. This amplifier is capable of delivering 30 watts of power into the servomotor. Voltage from the secondary of the output transformer is fed back to the cathode of the first tube. An equalizer network (0.0015-μf capacitor in parallel with a 560-kilohm resistor) is utilized to stabilize the loop. Other parallel RC circuits, which appear at both grids of the 12AX7, are used to prevent the amplifier from oscillating.

The large capacitors (1, 2, and 3 μf) that are connected from the supply-voltages lead to ground are used to "decouple" the stages. These RC networks reduce the variations which exist in other stages and which may be fed through the common power supply. This amplifier is known as an *RC coupled amplifier* because each stage is coupled to the following and preceding stage with an RC net-work of the form shown in Fig. 6-16. It is important that the cutoff frequency ($\omega_{\text{cutoff}} = 1/RC$) of this RC network be chosen so that it does not attenuate any signal frequencies. Because of the use of RC coupling

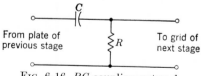

FIG. 6-16. *RC* coupling network.

networks and a transformer output, this amplifier is not suited to operate with direct current or low frequencies.

Since many servomechanisms employ suppressed-carrier modulation, it is only necessary to amplify signals that lie in a passband about 60 or 400 cps. In the design of a-c servos, the signal to noise ratio is considerably improved by using tuned amplifiers. The design is based upon the concept of eliminating from the response characteristics of the system

* This is a signal which varies about ground potential which is in the center rather than at either end. See Ref. 43, p. 178.

all frequencies except in the relatively narrow region about the carrier frequency. Careful design of the tuned circuit is necessary since sharp tuning adds phase lag to the signal. Parallel-tuned LC circuits, as shown in Fig. 6-17a, can be inserted in the forward path of the servo to produce a narrow-band system. Tuned transformer coupling, as shown in Fig. 6-17b, produces essentially the same results as Fig. 6-17a, since both methods are inserted in the forward loop of the amplifier.

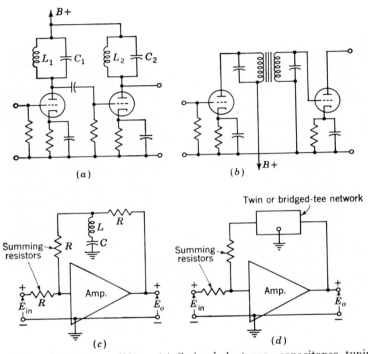

FIG. 6-17. Tuned servoamplifier. (a) Series inductance—capacitance tuning; (b) transformer capacitance tuning; (c) LC feedback tuning; (d) twin-T feedback tuning.

An alternate method of tuning the amplifier is shown in Fig. 6-17c. A series LC coil is used in the feedback path of the amplifier. The transfer function of the amplifier with a network $H(p)$ in the feedback is

$$\frac{E_o}{E_{in}} = \frac{A}{1 + AH} \approx \frac{1}{H} \tag{6-20}$$

for large values of gain A. The gain of the closed-loop amplifier is large only when H is small. In particular, at a frequency where $H = 0$, the over-all gain is A. Outside of this frequency band the gain drops off.

One of the difficulties with these networks is the temperature sensitivity of iron core inductors. As the temperature varies, the magnetizing impedance varies and the gain of the stage may vary by a factor of 2. To avoid such problems with iron core inductors, RC networks, such as twin- and bridged-T networks, are used (Fig. 6-17d). Figures 5-11 and 5-13 show the amplitude and phase response for a twin-T and a bridged-T

FIG. 6-18. Internal construction of vacuum-tube servoamplifier. (*Servomechanisms, Inc., Hawthorne, Calif.*)

network. The networks are driven from a low-source impedance and into a large-load impedance.

Figure 6-18 shows the internal construction of a commercially available vacuum-tube amplifier, the SA112H. This amplifier is a miniaturized, hermetically sealed, fluid-filled, plug-in electronic amplifier designed to control a 400-cycle two-phase servomotor requiring 3 watts electrical-control input (Kollsman 1623B, Kearfott RB106, or equivalent motors). This amplifier is intended primarily for use in analog-computer servo loops. The plug-in feature incorporated in the design facilitates the application of the amplifier to any control-system equipment requiring this function and reduces the maintenance problem by permitting simple and quick replacement of the complete amplifier. The amplifier is designed to operate over a temperature range of −65 to +175°F.

The amplifier comprises four stages of voltage amplification, a phase-inverter stage and an output-power stage that is transformer-coupled to the servomotor. The input impedance to the amplifier is greater than 1 megohm. Input connections are provided for two separate simultaneous signals. Each connects to the grid of the first tube through a 1-megohm resistor. The ground return for the input is supplied externally. Input to the second amplifier stage for such applications as tachometer feedback is made through another pin. The amplifier gain is graphically shown in Fig. 6-19. With an input signal of 0.01 volt a-c rms at 400 cps, the voltage gain is 2,250 ± 15 per cent. The amplifier

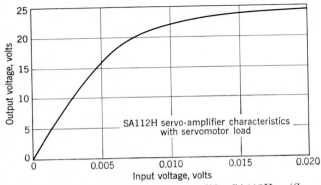

FIG. 6-19. Gain characteristics of vacuum-tube amplifier SA112H. (*Servomechanisms, Inc., Hawthorne, Calif.*)

saturates at approximately 0.01 volt. Since the amplifier provides 90 ± 5° lagging phase shift at the carrier frequency of 380 to 420 cps, little additional phase shift is required to drive the two-phase motor. Damping is provided by tachometer feedback into the second stage of the amplifier. When used with a Kearfott RB106 or equivalent, the output of the amplifier is 26 volts. For power-factor correction, a tuning capacitor is provided as an integral part of the amplifier. The unit weighs approximately 1½ lb and has the physical dimensions shown in Fig. 6-20.

A typical instrument type servo application of the SA112H servo-amplifier is indicated in Fig. 6-21, which shows the essential components of the servo loop, and Fig. 6-22 indicates the step-function response of this system. Since this is only one typical application, systems having different loop gain and different frictional and inertia loads will exhibit divergent characteristics.

6-7. Noise, Linearity, and Distortion in Vacuum-tube Amplifiers.

Because the voltage gain of servoamplifiers is often over 100,000, the noise level of the amplifier must be low. Considered here is such noise, or spurious voltage, as originates not in synchros or other devices outside the amplifier but in the amplifier itself. This consists of hum, pickup, ripple, and thermal noises generated in the amplifier.

Hum can be caused by the alternating voltage applied to the filament windings of the tubes, particularly in the first stage. Tubes should be

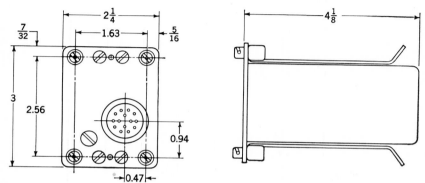

FIG. 6-20. Physical specification for the SA112H servoamplifier. (*Servomechanisms, Inc., Hawthorne, Calif.*)

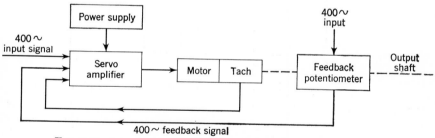

FIG. 6-21. A typical application for the SA112H servoamplifier.

selected with care since some are more susceptible to hum than others. A microphonic tube must not be used in this first stage if the amplifier is subject to any type of mechanical vibration. Ripple voltage is generated by the power supply, and adequate filtering can prevent this. Pickup usually originates from lead wires that are too long or is the result of circuits operating at high-impedance levels. This problem can normally be eliminated or greatly reduced by reasonable care in wiring, proper location of the components, and adequate shielding.

Thermal noise is caused by the thermal agitation of the molecules that make up the resistors and other components. Another component of noise is generated in vacuum tubes as a result of the shot effect of electrons in transit from cathode to plate. Pentode tubes are more susceptible than triodes because of the additional grid structure. This noise is also a function of tube g_m and, in general, becomes smaller for larger values of g_m. The use of double-speed synchro systems minimizes these problems because of the reduction in amplifier gain permitted with the same loop gain of the servomechanism.

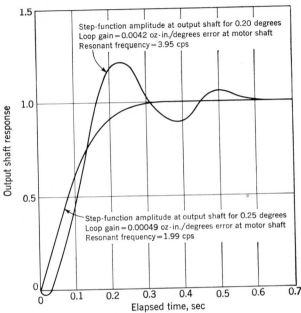

Step-function amplitude at output shaft for 0.20 degrees
Loop gain = 0.0042 oz-in./degrees error at motor shaft
Resonant frequency = 3.95 cps

Step-function amplitude at output shaft for 0.25 degrees
Loop gain = 0.00049 oz-in./degrees error at motor shaft
Resonant frequency = 1.99 cps

Output shaft response

Elapsed time, sec

Fig. 6-22. Step-function response for system of Fig. 6-21.

Use of a tuned amplifier, which produces a narrower passband, eliminates most of the noise since the amplifier does not respond to signals outside of the narrow passband.

The linearity of a servoamplifier is not of great interest. It is not necessary that double the input voltage result in exactly double the output voltage. Since the servomechanism operates to reduce the input voltage to zero, any nonlinearity introduced is merely a secondary effect. All servoamplifiers saturate with increase in input voltage, usually at the grids of the output stage. When a certain output voltage is reached, increase in input voltage effects only a deterioration of output waveform, and no increase in maximum voltage occurs. (As a matter of fact, an actual decrease may result.) This means that, for large servo errors, as in slewing from a large distance away from null, the output voltage of the amplifier becomes constant.

The fact that the amplifier saturates may also introduce a problem when there are large residual voltages, as from synchros or a rate generator. When these signals are large enough to saturate the amplifier, the addition of true signal voltages does not result in as much gain for the signals as if the residual voltages were absent. Servomotors and the servomechanisms in which they are used are usually capable of withstanding high levels of residual voltages. Often harmonic and quadrature noise can be as much as one-third of the full output of the amplifier without introducing serious problems. If residual voltages are a problem, they should be attenuated by filtering or other means.

If the amplifier is used in an instrument servo, it is generally designed to saturate on the maximum, or rated, voltage of the servomotor; a typical value is on the order of 110 volts. For an amplifier with a gain of 100,000, an input signal on the order of 1 mv will saturate the amplifier.

Even though voltages above saturation voltage result in poor output waveform, the motor-output torque does not normally reduce appreciably, since distortion of waveform is not of major importance in servoamplifiers. It is often the practical consideration of motor heating, rather than performance, that requires a reduction in distortion. A common and simple way to do this is by placing a capacitor across the primary of the output transformer. This often achieves the additional purpose of eliminating spurious oscillations in the amplifier. The value should be chosen, however, so that the bandpass of the amplifier is not reduced to so narrow a value as to introduce the equivalent of a time lag in the amplifier.

6-8. Design Considerations for Transistor Amplifiers. Recently many fine texts have been written on the theory and application of transistors. Only an outline of the aspects of transistor-circuit design that are applicable to servomechanisms is presented here. The reader is directed to Refs. 14, 28, 33, and 44 for detailed information on transistor-circuit design.

Design Parameters. One of the essential differences between transistor and vacuum-tube circuits lies in the impedances. For circuits that draw no grid current, the vacuum tube does not load the source. In other words, the output circuit is isolated from the input circuit. The impedances of a transistor circuit are such that the input and output circuits are conductively coupled and circuit isolation does not exist. The schematic diagram for a junction-transistor amplifier (only junction transistors, as contrasted to point-contact transistors, are considered here) is shown in Fig. 6-23. Comparison with Fig. 6-10 indicates the following similarities:

Transistor	Vacuum-tube triode
Base terminal	Grid terminal
Emitter terminal	Cathode terminal
Collector terminal	Plate terminal

Two types of transistor exist: the n-p-n type, in which the emitter is biased negative and the collector is biased positive with respect to the base, and the p-n-p, in which the biasing is the reverse of the n-p-n. The circuit of Fig. 6-23 shows the bias polarities for a p-n-p junction

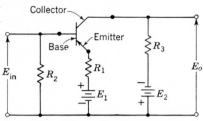

transistor. The type of transistor, either n-p-n or p-n-p, is indicated schematically by the direction of the small arrow on the emitter connection. When the arrow points toward the base, as it does in Fig. 6-23, the transistor is of the p-n-p variety. An n-p-n transistor is represented by a similar symbol but with the arrow pointing away from the base. The p-n-p and n-p-n

Fig. 6-23. Schematic diagram of one transistor-amplifier stage; p-n-p transistor is used.

transistors are complements of one another. Frequently a circuit designed for use with an n-p-n transistor can be used with a p-n-p unit if the polarities of all bias voltages are reversed.

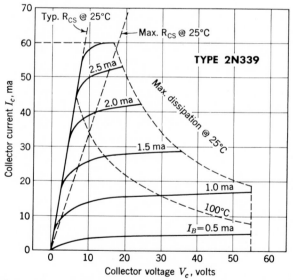

Fig. 6-24. Typical collector characteristics for type 2N339 transistor. (*Texas Instruments, Inc., Dallas.*)

The starting point for an analysis of transistor circuits is the performance characteristics of the transistor. Figure 6-24 presents typical collector characteristics for the type 2N339 n-p-n grown-junction silicon transistor. The curves are a plot of collector current vs. collector-to-base voltage with base current as a parameter. The 2N339, 2N340, 2N341, 2N342, and 2N343 transistors have similar characteristics except for the current amplification and breakdown voltages. Each unit is heat-cycled from −65 to +175°C for 10 cycles and then humidity-cycled at temperature from −65 to +75°C in air at 95 per cent relative humidity. The hermetic seal is tested by subjecting immersed units to hydraulic pressure. A rigorous tumbling test subjects each unit to a number of random mechanical shocks to ensure maximum mechanical reliability. Each unit is thoroughly tested to determine the electrical-design characteristics.

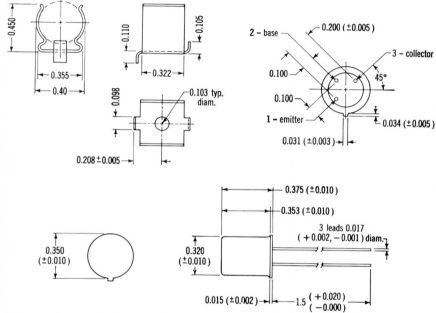

Fig. 6-25. Dimensional outline for 2N339 silicon transistor. (*Texas Instruments, Inc., Dallas.*)

Production samples are life-tested periodically to determine the effects of storage and dissipation and ensure maximum attainable reliability.

The transistor that is shown in Fig. 6-25 has a welded case with glass-to-metal hermetic seal between case and leads. The approximate weight is 1.2 g. Case and leads are tinplated, and the case is black-enameled. A noninsulated mounting clip (also shown in Fig. 6-25) is provided with each transistor. It is suitable for applications where thermal dissipation to a heat sink is desired. The emitter is in electrical contact with the case. Maximum ratings and typical characteristics are included in Table 6-1.

The collector characteristics for the 2N339 indicate another major

TABLE 6-1*

Parameter	2N339 Min	2N339 Max	2N340 Min	2N340 Max	2N341 Min	2N341 Max	2N342 Min	2N342 Max	2N343 Min	2N343 Max	Unit
Collector breakdown voltage	55		85		125		60		60		volts
Collector cutoff current		1		1		1		1		1	μa
at 150°		250		250		250		250		250	μa
Input impedance		30		30		30		30		30	ohms
Output admittance		2		2		2		2		2	micromhos
Feedback-voltage ratio		300		300		300		300		300	$\times 10^{-6}$
Current-transfer ratio	0.9	0.989	0.9	0.989	0.9	0.989	0.9	0.97	0.966	0.989	
Saturation resistance		300		350		400		350		350	ohms
Power gain	30		30		30		30		30		db

* Texas Instruments, Inc., Dallas.

difference between the transistor and the vacuum tube: the transistor is a current amplifier rather than a voltage amplifier. The parameter on this curve is base current. The maximum current amplification is obtained with a low-input impedance and a large-output impedance. Since this is the form of the impedances in a transistor, it is useful to consider a transistor as a current amplifier.

Four quantities are required to define the operation of a transistor. These quantities can be written in several forms. The most common set of parameters, which are termed T *parameters*, are the following:

1. r_b = base resistance and is defined

$$r_b = \frac{\Delta V_e}{\Delta I_c}\bigg|_{I_e = \text{const}} \tag{6-21}$$

where V_e is the emitter voltage, I_c is the collector current, and I_e is the emitter current. Values for r_b, which is the forward resistance of the emitter-base diode, lie in the range 200 to 800 ohms.

2. r_c = collector resistance and is defined

$$r_c \cong \frac{\Delta V_c}{\Delta I_c}\bigg|_{I_c = \text{const}} \tag{6-22}$$

where V_c is the collector voltage and r_c is the back resistance of the collector-base diode and ranges in value between 0.1 and 1 megohm.

3. r_e = the emitter resistance and is defined

$$r_b + r_e = \frac{\Delta V_e}{\Delta I_e}\bigg|_{I_c = \text{const}} \tag{6-23}$$

where r_e is the forward resistance of the emitter-base diode and lies in the range of 10 to 30 ohms.

4. α = current-amplification factor and is defined

$$\alpha = \frac{\Delta I_c}{\Delta I_e}\bigg|_{V_c = \text{const}} \tag{6-24}$$

The current amplification lies in the range of 0.9 to 1.0 and is essentially independent of the operating point. These quantities are given in the manufacturer's literature or can be derived from the static characteristics for the transistor.

Another set of parameters, which are called the *hybrid parameters*, is often more useful in transistor representation. These parameters, which are also applicable only for small-signal performance, are defined from the following equations:

$$\begin{aligned} v_1 &= h_{11}i_1 + h_{12}v_2 \\ i_2 &= h_{21}i_1 + h_{22}v_2 \end{aligned} \tag{6-25}$$

The currents and voltages are defined by the grounded-base circuit of Fig. 6-26. These parameters can be found from the following expressions:

$$h_{11} = \frac{v_1}{i_1}\bigg|_{v_2=0} \qquad (6\text{-}26)$$

which is the input impedance with the output terminals short-circuited, and

$$h_{21} = \frac{i_2}{i_1}\bigg|_{v_2=0} \qquad (6\text{-}27)$$

which is the current gain with the output terminals shorted. Both

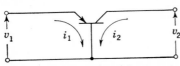

FIG. 6-26. Definition of currents and voltages for hybrid parameters; *p-n-p* transistor is shown.

of these are found by setting $v_2 = 0$, which can be accomplished by shorting the output terminals to a-c signals. This can be accomplished with a large capacitor. The remaining hybrid parameters are found by setting $i_1 = 0$, which can be accomplished by placing a large inductance in series with the emitter lead. They are defined by the expression

$$h_{12} = \frac{v_1}{v_2}\bigg|_{i_1=0} \qquad (6\text{-}28)$$

which is the reverse voltage gain under open-circuit conditions, and

$$h_{22} = \frac{i_2}{v_2}\bigg|_{i_1=0} \qquad (6\text{-}29)$$

which is the output admittance with the input circuit open.

Numerical values for the hybrid parameters are summarized in Table 6-2 for the type 952 (Texas Instruments, Inc.). The *n-p-n* grown-junction silicon transistor is especially designed for use in audio or servo-amplifier stages requiring medium power output. Silicon transistors can be operated at ambient temperatures up to 150°C. Each unit is thoroughly temperature-cycled. This process consists of four temperature-shock cycles from −55 to +150°C and four cycles at 95 per cent relative humidity from −55°C to +75°C. In addition, the hermetic seal is checked by vacuum testing. Every unit is tested for design characteristics and undergoes a tumble test to check for mechanical reliability. A typical set of common-base characteristics is included in Fig. 6-27.

The equivalent T parameters provide a more convenient way to describe circuit performance than the hybrid parameters. Unfortunately they cannot be measured directly and can only be arrived at indirectly.

TABLE 6-2*

Symbol	Parameter	Minimum	Design	Maximum	Unit
I_{CO}	Collector cutoff current			6	μa
R_{CS}	Collector saturation resistance			350	ohms
VV_{BE}	Bias voltage			1	volts
h_{11}	Input impedance		12	30	ohms
h_{22}	Output admittance		1	2	micromhos
h_{12}	Feedback-voltage ratio		60	300	$\times 10^{-6}$
h_{21}	Current-transfer ratio	-0.9	-0.94	-1	
PG_e	Power gain	30			db

* Texas Instruments, Inc., Dallas.

The most common method of obtaining the T parameter is to develop a set of expressions that give T parameters in terms of h parameters. The h parameters are usually provided by the manufacturer in their printed literature. The conversion from one set of parameters to the other is

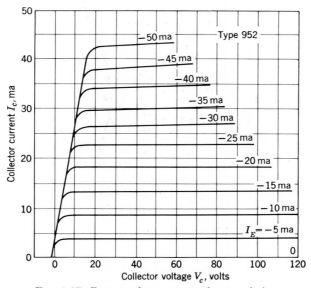

FIG. 6-27. Common-base output characteristics.

achieved by comparing the following equations, which define the T parameters:

$$v_1 = i_1(r_e + r_b) + i_2 r_b$$
$$v_2 = i_1(r_b + r_m) + i_2(r_b + r_c) \tag{6-30}$$

with the defining equations for the h parameters [Eqs. (6-25)]. The

h-parameter equations are repeated:

$$v_1 = i_1 h_{11} + v_2 h_{12}$$
$$i_2 = i_1 h_{21} + v_2 h_{22} \tag{6-31}$$

The origin of Eqs. (6-30) becomes more apparent from a consideration of the equivalent circuit for a common-base connection for a transistor. The same conditions are imposed on both sets of equations. When $v_2 = 0$, the hybrid equations yield

$$\frac{v_1}{i_1} = h_{11}$$
$$\frac{i_2}{i_1} = h_{21} \tag{6-32}$$

and the T equations yield

$$\frac{v_1}{i_1} = r_e + \frac{r_b(r_c - r_m)}{r_b + r_c}$$
$$\frac{i_2}{i_1} = - \frac{r_b + r_m}{r_b + r_c} \tag{6-33}$$

Solution of these equations yields

$$h_{11} = r_e + \frac{r_b(r_c - r_m)}{r_b + r_c} \tag{6-34}$$

$$h_{21} = - \frac{r_b + r_m}{r_b + r_c} \tag{6-35}$$

With $i_1 = 0$, the hybrid equations yield

$$\frac{i_2}{v_2} = h_{22} \quad \text{and} \quad \frac{v_1}{v_2} = h_{12} \tag{6-36}$$

and the T equations yield

$$\frac{i_2}{v_2} = \frac{1}{r_b + r_c} \quad \text{and} \quad \frac{v_1}{v_2} = \frac{r_b}{r_b + r_c} \tag{6-37}$$

Solution of these equations yields the following:

$$h_{22} = \frac{1}{r_b + r_c} \tag{6-38}$$

$$h_{12} = \frac{-r_b}{r_b + r_c} \tag{6-39}$$

With suitable algebra, the reverse set of equations is found:

$$r_e = h_{11} + \frac{h_{12}}{h_{22}} (1 + h_{21})$$

$$r_b = -\frac{h_{12}}{h_{22}}$$

$$r_c = \frac{1 + h_{12}}{h_{22}}$$ (6-40)

$$r_m = \frac{1}{h_{22}} (h_{12} - h_{21})$$

A common approximation made in a-c transistor analysis should be pointed out. As a practical matter, h_{12} is on the order of 1×10^{-4} and h_{21} is nearly one; consequently,

$$r_c \cong \frac{1}{h_{22}}$$

and

$$r_m = \frac{-h_{21}}{h_{22}} \cong -h_{21}r_c \cong -r_c$$

(6-41)

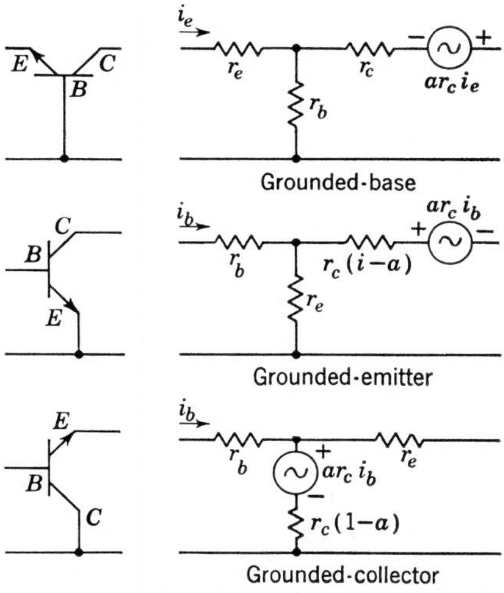

Transistor Equivalent Circuit. The common equivalent circuits for the three possible connections of a transistor are shown in Fig. 6-28. The T parameters are utilized in these circuits, but with the aid of Eqs. (6-40) the conversion to h parameters is relatively simple. Other texts (see Ref. 28) show all

FIG. 6-28. Transistor equivalent circuits; *n-p-n* transistor is shown.

equivalent circuits. The three connections in the figure bear the following similarities to vacuum-tube circuits:

Grounded grid	Grounded base
Grounded cathode	Grounded emitter
Grounded plate	Grounded collector

These circuits are for a-c quantities only. The quiescent operating voltages are not included in these circuits. Each of the connections presents unique characteristics. These are summarized as follows:

Grounded base	No phase reversal, less than unity current amplification, low input impedance, high output impedance
Grounded emitter	Phase reversal, large current amplification, low input impedance
Grounded collector	No phase reversal, high input impedance

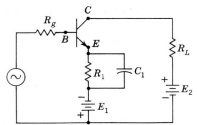

Fig. 6-29. Single-stage transistor amplifier.

The various quantities of interest are found from application of Kirchhoff's laws to the equivalent circuit. For example, suppose it is necessary to find the voltage gain for the grounded-emitter amplifier shown in Fig. 6-29. The resistor R_1 is often used to provide some degree of stability against temperature variation. It is shunted with a capacitor. The equivalent circuit for this amplifier is shown in Fig. 6-30. The quantities of interest are found with the aid of Kirchhoff's laws as follows:

$$e_g = i_b(R_g + r_b + r_e) + i_2 r_e$$
$$r_c i_b = i_b r_e + i_2[r_e + r_c(1 - \alpha) + R_L] \tag{6-42}$$

The output voltage is $e_o = -i_2 R_L$. Solution for i_2 from Eqs. (6-42) yields, after some algebra,

$$\frac{e_o}{e_g} = \frac{R_L(r_e - \alpha r_c)}{(r_b + R_g)[r_e + r_c(1 - \alpha) + R_L] + r_e(r_c + R_L)} \tag{6-43}$$

Because of the magnitudes of the various terms, i.e., R_L and $R_g \gg r_e + r_b$, $R_g \ll r_c$, and $R_L \ll r_c (1 - \alpha)$, the following approximation is obtained from Eq. (6-43):

$$\frac{e_o}{e_g} = \frac{-\alpha R_L}{R_g(1 - \alpha) + r_e} \tag{6-44}$$

For typical values $\alpha = 0.96$, $R_L = 40$ kilohms, $R_g = 800$ ohms, and $r_e = 25$ ohms, the voltage gain is -670. The student is directed to the

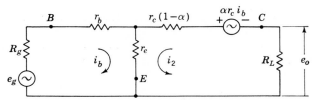

Fig. 6-30. Equivalent circuit for single-stage transistor amplifier.

fine Refs. 14, 28, and 44 for equations for input and output impedance and current, voltage, and power gain. These quantities can be derived from the equivalent circuit.

Quiescent Values. As with vacuum tubes, transistors must be biased with direct voltages so that they will operate along the linear portion of their characteristics. Because of the variation of transistor parameters with temperature, the operating point may require stabilization. This technique, which is not usually required for vacuum tubes, is discussed in the next section.

The common-emitter output characteristic shown for the Texas Instruments Type 903 transistor in Fig. 6-31 is used to demonstrate the method of establishing the operating point. For a class A linear amplifier the operating point is set so that the magnitude of the input signal does not drive the collector current (or voltage) into saturation or cutoff. The operating point for the class A operation of the common-emitter connection of the Type 903 transistor is shown in Fig. 6-31. This point is established by setting the load resistor R_L and the supply voltage V_{bb}.

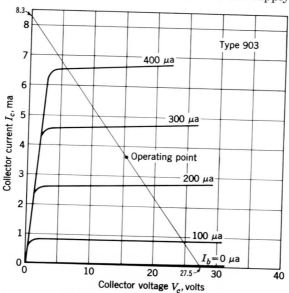

Fig. 6-31. Common-emitter output characteristics for Type 903 junction transistor. (*Texas Instruments, Inc., Dallas.*)

The intersection of the load line with the horizontal axis is the supply voltage; in this case, $V_{bb} = 27.5$. R_L is computed from the slope of the load line by

$$R_L = \frac{V_{bb}}{I_{cbb}} \tag{6-45}$$

For the example of Fig. 6-31, the load resistor is

$$R_L = \frac{27.5}{8.3 \times 10^{-3}} = 3.2 \text{ kilohms} \tag{6-46}$$

The quiescent point (zero-input-signal point) on the load line is determined by the value of the bias current that flows through the base of the transistor.   For this example, a bias current of 250 μa is chosen.   A base-current signal variation of ±150 μa should provide a linear output.   This base-current bias is positive for the *n-p-n* transistor and can be provided by a separate battery supply as indicated in Fig. 6-29.   More frequently it is obtained from the collector supply voltage in the manner shown in

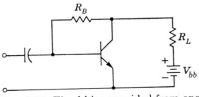

Fig. 6-32.   The value of the bias resistor R_B is obtained from the approximate expression

$$R_B = \frac{V_{bb}}{I_{bc}} - R_L \qquad (6\text{-}47)$$

where V_{bb} is the collector supply voltage and I_{bc} is the desired base-current bias.   It is assumed that the

FIG. 6-32. Fixed bias provided from one source.

voltage between the base and collector during operating conditions is small with respect to the supply voltage and is hence neglected.   For the transistor of Fig. 6-31, the bias resistor is

$$R_B = \frac{27.5}{250 \times 10^{-6}} - 3.2 \text{ kilohms} = 0.11 \text{ megohm}$$

6-9. A Typical Transistor Circuit and Its Operation.   Figure 6-33 shows a photograph of a transistor resolver amplifier that features small

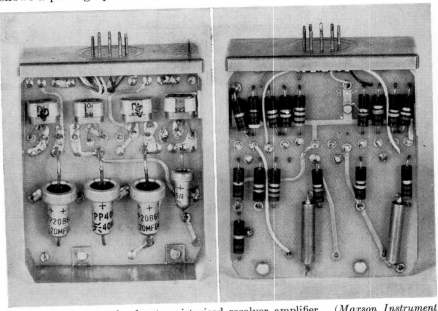

FIG. 6-33. Photograph of a transistorized resolver amplifier.   (*Maxson Instrument Corp., Long Island City, N.Y.*)

size, light weight, dependable long life, and extreme accuracy. Etched wiring and silicon transistors and diodes are utilized to allow operation under maximum temperature conditions.

Smaller than a package of cigarettes, these 400-cps a-c amplifiers have withstood the most rigorous life and environmental tests with no failures and no appreciable change in characteristics—even after a full year (over 8,000 hours) of continuous operation at elevated temperatures.

Typical of the performance characteristics for this amplifier are:

Output voltage (rms)	8 (into 3,500 ohms)
Nominal open-loop gain	2,000
Nominal input impedance	1.5 megohms
Max phase shift	1
Accuracy	$\pm 0.1\%$
Feedback	2,000–1, typical
Input-power requirements	+45 volts at 7.3 ma
	− 20 volts at 0.3 ma
Weight	1.1 oz

The schematic diagram for a transistorized servoamplifier is shown in Fig. 6-34. This amplifier utilizes three 905 transistors in three essentially identical voltage amplifiers. The output from this amplifier is phase-inverted with a transformer that drives a pair of 2N497's in push-pull as power transistors. The output from the power transistors drives the motor load directly with no output transformer required. Feedback voltage from the collectors of the output transistors is subtracted from the input signal. Three matched summing resistors are provided to add three signals at the input.

Base-current bias is supplied the first three transistors with 200 kilohms (or 240 kilohms) resistors from collector to base. This transistor amplifier is capable of driving a size 11 or size 15 servomotor (3 watts) directly from the collectors of the output transistors. With all components encapsulated, the amplifier is capable of delivering this power under severe temperature (−55 to 110°C), vibration, and life. The operating specifications for this amplifier can be summarized as follows:

Output power	3 watts
Gain stability	$\pm 20\%$ from −55 to 110°C
Gain	50–5,000, adjustable by varying the external feedback resistor
Input impedance	80 kilohms with minimum gain
Max output voltage	70 volts rms with 1,400 ohms center-tapped load
Max input voltage	22 volts rms

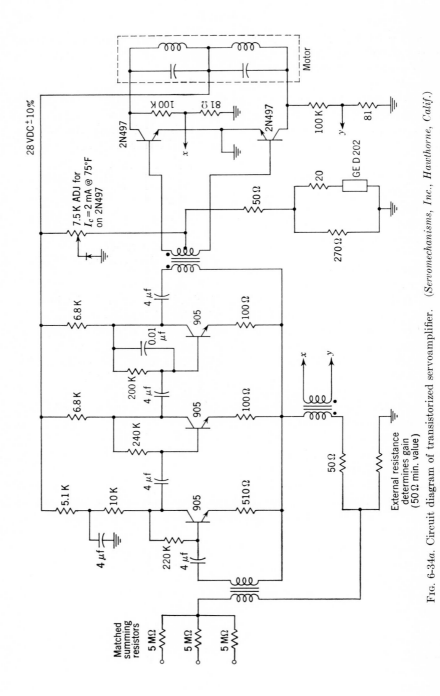

Fig. 6-34a. Circuit diagram of transistorized servoamplifier. (Servomechanisms, Inc., Hawthorne, Calif.)

210

The "sandwich" form of packaging for a transistor amplifier is shown in Fig. 6-34b. This unit encloses two silicon transistor amplifiers in a single package. The entire unit is covered with a protective metal enclosure, and the amplifier is then encapsulated. Notice how various elements are mounted between the center and outer circuit boards. The power transistors are mounted rigidly to the base for the purpose of obtaining a good heat sink for the dissipation of power in the transistors. Tests on this amplifier indicate a linearity that is shown in Fig. 6-35a. The effect on input impedance of gain change and the variation of gain vs. feedback resistance is shown in Fig. 6-35b.

FIG. 6-34b. Photograph of servoamplifier. (*Servomechanisms, Inc., Hawthorne, Calif.*)

6-10. Noise, Linearity, and Temperature Stability in Transistor Amplifiers. Although the theory of noise in transistor circuits is not so well developed as that for vacuum tubes, experimental work has produced some results. Point-contact-type transistors are, generally, more noisy than the junction type. For lower-frequency applications (audio and servoamplifiers) the junction transistor is less noisy than the vacuum tube. This performance makes the transistor ideally suited for low-level input and preamplifier stages of audio and servoamplifiers.

Noise is generated at both the emitter-base junction and the collector-base junction and within the semiconductor material. For the low frequencies utilized in transistor servoamplifiers the noise power per cycle of bandwidth is approximately an inverse function of frequency. Other noise that is generated within the transistor amplifier is due to spurious voltages from the power supply. Because of the lack of a filament in a transistor, the unit does not suffer from hum as does the vacuum tube. Pickup, which is caused by long lead wires and high-impedance circuits, is substantially reduced because the size of the transistor lends itself to small and neat packaging and because the impedance levels are frequently lower in transistor circuits. Since these noise voltages become more serious as the amplifier gain is increased, it is frequently an advantage to use a double-speed synchro system, which permits the use of a much lower gain.

As in the case of vacuum-tube amplifiers, the effect of linearity on transistor amplifiers is of less importance than are other spurious effects. Since the servoamplifier operates about a null voltage, little deterioration in performance results if the amplifier does not produce double the output voltage for double the input voltage.

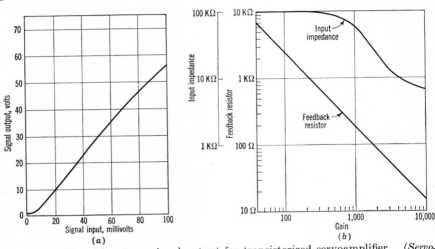

FIG. 6-35a. Signal input vs. signal output for transistorized servoamplifier. (*Servomechanisms, Inc., Hawthorne, Calif.*)

FIG. 6-35b. Input impedance and feedback resistor vs. gain. (*Servomechanisms, Inc., Hawthorne, Calif.*)

One of the most significant effects that require careful attention in transistor-amplifier design and use is temperature. The temperature problem is far more difficult with transistor amplifiers than it is with vacuum-tube amplifiers. The germanium transistor can operate only over a very narrow band of temperature. At the higher temperatures the transistor behaves like a resistor in that the conductivity depends upon the material rather than upon the impurities that are used to control its conductivity at lower temperatures. The allowable junction temperatures are approximately 80°C for germanium and 150°C for silicon. Although the silicon transistor is capable of withstanding a wider range of temperatures, the parameters often vary by as much as a factor of 2. This effect is shown in Fig. 6-36 for the Type 903 grown-junction transistor.

Use of feedback around the transistor amplifier can result in a reduction of the effects of variation of many of the parameters. The most significant problem that is caused by temperature is the shift of the bias points. Bias stabilization must be provided to accommodate the temperature variations and also variation from transistor to transistor. The load line, shown in Fig. 6-31, is applied to the V_c vs. I_c curves for constant base current. Both a-c and d-c load lines can be drawn on these characteristics, which are for the grounded-emitter connection. The d-c load line is shown in this diagram. In practice it is not advisable to operate the transistor in this fashion because of the wide variation of the characteristics with a change in α. The current gain of the grounded-emitter transistor is approximately equal to $\alpha/(1 - \alpha)$, which is called β.

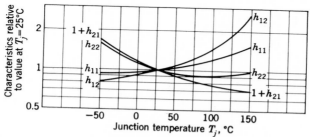

Fig. 6-36. Common-base characteristics vs. junction temperature for Type 903 transistor. (*Texas Instruments, Inc., Dallas.*)

For $\alpha = 0.95$, the current gain for the common-emitter connection is $\beta_1 = 0.95/(1 - 0.95) = 19$. With $\alpha = 0.99$, the current gain is

$$\beta_2 = \frac{0.99}{1 - 0.99} = 99$$

Hence a 4 per cent change in α causes almost a 500 per cent change in β and the V_c-I_c characteristics. Because of this variation, constant base-current biasing affords very poor stability.

The current gain for the common base connection is approximately α. Hence a 4 per cent change in α causes only a 4 per cent change in current gain. The V_c-I_c curves for constant emitter current, which are included in Fig. 6-37, then remain considerably more fixed for variations in α. Thus for bias stability, the transistor must be operated in the grounded-base configuration for direct current. For a-c quantities the transistor can be operated in the grounded-emitter configuration. Use of the characteristics of Fig. 6-37 is quite similar to that discussed in connection with the constant base-current characteristics of Fig. 6-31. These characteristics are even easier to use because the curves are essentially parallel and equidistant—straight lines that are separated by a distance $\Delta I_c = \alpha \, \Delta I_e$.

As an example of simultaneous operation of a transistor in the grounded-base configuration for direct current and in the grounded-emitter configuration for alternating current, consider the circuit of Fig. 6-38, which can be redrawn as it appears to a-c and d-c quantities, as shown in Fig. 6-39. For a-c quantities, the capacitor C_e effectively

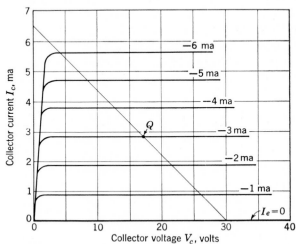

FIG. 6-37. Common-base output characteristics for Type 903 transistor. (*Texas Instruments, Inc., Dallas.*)

short-circuits R_e, and the transistor is operating in the grounded-emitter configuration. With a low internal-impedance power supply, the bias resistor R_1 is in parallel with R_2. For bias purposes, the equivalent circuit for d-c quantities has the configuration as shown in Fig. 6-39b when the parallel combination of R_1 and R_2 is small. The load line is drawn on the common-base output characteristics of Fig. 6-37 for the following values:

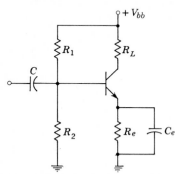

FIG. 6-38. Grounded emitter for a-c and grounded base for d-c quantities.

$$V_{bb} = 30.0 \text{ volts}$$

$$R_L = \frac{V_{bb}}{I_{cbb}} = \frac{30.0 \text{ volts}}{6.5 \text{ ma}} = 4.6 \text{ kilohms}$$

The operating point is chosen at -3.0 ma, which is set by choosing values of V_e and R_e. Although the designer has some degree of latitude in his choice of these quantities, it is usually good practice to choose R_e in the range of 2 to 5 kilohms so that I_e is maintained constant. In this case, R_e

is taken to be 4 kilohms and $V_e = $ (4 kilohms)(3 ma) $= 12$ volts. In the circuit of Fig. 6-38 the bias is obtained from the same supply that furnishes collector voltage through the bleeder resistors R_1 and R_2. The choice of these values is based upon the gain requirements of the a-c equivalent circuit (Fig. 6-39a) and the above-determined bias conditions. Since it is not possible to cover the topic adequately in this text, the reader is directed to several excellent references.*

6-11. The Theory of Thyratron Control. Transistor and vacuum-tube amplifiers are used for power applications where the output power is on the order of 25 watts or less. Grid-controlled thyratrons can be used for applications requiring powers up to 10 hp.

Thyratrons consist of an envelope containing an inert gas, a heated cathode, an anode, and a control grid located between the cathode and the anode. An additional grid, called a shield grid, is sometimes used to

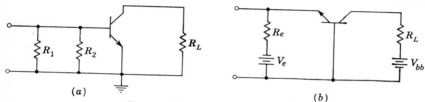

(a)

(b)

Fig. 6-39a. A-c equivalent circuit.
Fig. 6-39b. D-c equivalent circuit.

reduce the control-grid current and to effect more flexibility in control-circuit design. Commercial tubes are available that can reliably control loads from a few milliamperes to several amperes.

When the anode of a thyratron is made positive with respect to the cathode, electrons flow from the emissive cathode to the anode. Thus, the gas is ionized and the ions neutralize the space charge, thereby reducing the internal tube drop to a low level. The current flow in the tube is therefore determined almost entirely by the external load resistance and the supply voltage. The grid voltage operates to permit or to prevent the flow of current, but once the flow has started, it has no further effect. The grid loses control once conduction has started because a sheath of ions forms on the grid structure and varying the grid potential only serves to make the sheath thinner or thicker. Since the tube can never conduct when the anode is negative with respect to the cathode, the tube can be extinguished only by lowering the plate voltage.

The *critical grid voltage* is defined as the voltage between the grid and cathode that will just prevent the tube from conducting when the anode is positive. This critical grid voltage is a function of anode voltage. A typical graph given in the manufacturer's data sheet is illustrated in

* See, for example, Ref. 49, Secs. 8-12 to 8-44.

Fig. 6-40. It is seen that for each anode voltage there is a range of critical grid voltages. For high anode voltages, in this instance above 1,100 volts, the grid no longer has control, and the tube conducts for any negative grid voltage. For low anode voltages, the grid must be made positive, and control is uncertain.

Since the control characteristic is not sharply defined and the grid can be used only to start conduction, the circuits used for thyratrons are much different from those used in ordinary vacuum-tube amplifiers. In servos it is common to use alternating voltage as a supply to thyratrons to solve the problem of extinction, and it is therefore of interest to see how

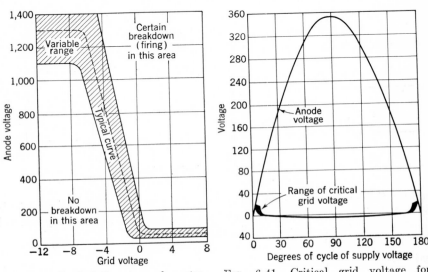

FIG. 6-40. Typical thyratron character-istics.

FIG. 6-41. Critical grid voltage for sinusoidal anode voltage.

the grid range of critical grid voltage appears for sinusoidal anode volt-age. This is shown in Fig. 6-41. Any grid voltage above the critical value causes the tube to conduct. Voltages below the critical value prevent conduction. Voltages in the critical range cause some tubes to conduct but not others. There exists uncertainty even with the same tube at different times. Again, when the anode voltage is low, as at the beginning and end of the cycle, the range of critical voltage is quite large.

In the application of thyratrons to any servo circuit, there are two principal ratings that must be observed. These are the current rating and the inverse peak voltage rating. The current rating is usually the greatest continuous current that a tube can pass without danger of over-heating and reducing of life. It is possible, however, for instantaneous currents to be as much as 100 times the average rating if they are carried for only a short period of time. Peak recurring currents of 10 times the average rating can be safely carried.

The *peak inverse voltage* is the maximum instantaneous negative voltage that can safely be applied to the anode. If this voltage is exceeded, a tube may arc back and conduct in the reverse direction, thus suffering serious damage. There is also a limit to the peak positive voltage that can be applied to the anode without loss of control, as is shown in Fig. 6-40. No damage will result to the tube, but it is undesirable to lose control of it at any time.

Other ratings that must be observed are the maximum negative grid voltage and maximum grid current. If these ratings are not observed, tube life can be seriously shortened. Long life is attained by applying proper filament voltage and taking care to heat the cathode to operating temperatures before applying anode voltage.

Although the use of thyratron control does not materially alter motor dynamic characteristics, servomotors, when used with thyratron control, must have a low armature inductance. This is necessary to minimize the inductive voltage transient developed across the load as the tube stops firing. This negative voltage appears at the cathode of the opposite tube, thus reducing the d-c bias and causing the tube to fire incorrectly.

Another serious problem is that of circuit noise. Any pulse or harmonic voltage that might cause a tube to fire at an incorrect time reduces the net output power and may produce pulsations of motor torque and even cause jitter in the control shaft of the servomechanism. Precautions must be taken to reduce noise caused by stray pickup and to avoid circuit arrangements that might permit coupling between tubes. Where high-frequency anode supplies are used, deionization time is a limiting factor, but this is no problem in the low frequencies (such as 60 and 400 cycles) normally used in servomechanism. The critical grid voltage, however, is somewhat affected by the frequency of the supply. A further difficulty in the use of thyratrons is that the on-off character of their operation may affect the waveform of the supply voltage and ruin it for application to other circuits using the same supply and may even cause radiation of electromagnetic waves.

6-12. Control of Thyratrons. In servomechanisms, it is desirable to control the output current continuously from zero to maximum value. The magnitude of grid voltage that must be applied in order for plate current to flow for a particular waveform of the plate voltage can be determined from a knowledge of the critical grid voltage for each value of plate voltage.

When a thyratron anode is energized from an a-c line, there are two methods used for controlling the amount of power delivered. Both rely on varying the interval of conduction period as a function of the control signal. This interval can be controlled by varying the magnitude of the grid voltage or the phase of the grid voltage with respect to the anode voltage. The magnitude method uses a variable-magnitude a-c signal and permits control from one-half the maximum output to full-output current. The grid waveform can be continuous (d-c), a pure sine wave, or a peaked voltage. The fact that control is not usually obtained over the entire cycle, however, makes this means less satisfactory than that of phase control.

There are a number of phase-shift methods and combinations of phase-shift and magnitude methods that can be used to obtain smooth control

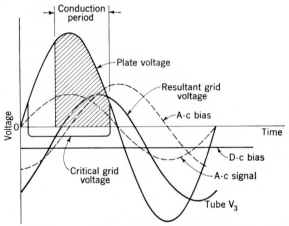

FIG. 6-42. Voltage relationship for phase control of thyratrons.

over the entire range. Typically, a combination of alternating and direct current is used. It is desired to intercept the critical-voltage curve at any chosen point in the anode voltage cycle in order to cause current to flow over any desired portion of the cycle and hence to be able to control the current flow from zero to a maximum. If a small fixed magnitude of alternating voltage that lags the anode voltage by 90° is added to a variable- and reversible-polarity direct voltage proportional to the actuating signal, the conduction period can be varied as desired. The point at which an alternating grid voltage exceeds the critical grid voltage can also be varied by means of the addition of an alternating voltage proportional to the actuating signal to various a-c and d-c biases, so arranged that the net grid voltage varies over the full-conduction half cycle of the thyratron. Figure 6-42 shows the voltage relationships for this latter method.

D-c motors are more commonly used with thyratron servomechanisms than a-c motors. A typical control circuit is shown in Fig. 6-43, in which control of the torque of the motor is obtained by controlling the point (during the half cycle in which the plate is positive) when the grid voltage is more positive than its critical value. If the average current of each tube is equal during the time interval on one cycle, the motor does not produce torque. If, however, the upper tube carries more current by having its critical grid voltage exceeded for a larger proportion of the positive half cycle than the lower tube, the motor rotates in one direction. The motor is reversed when the critical voltage of the lower tube is exceeded for a larger proportion of the positive half cycle than the upper tube. The motor does

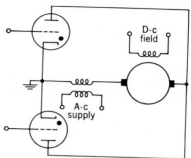

FIG. 6-43. Thyratron motor control.

not respond to each cycle of current but rather to the average excess of current in one of the two directions. Because of the form factor of current in the half-wave circuit, the heating value of this current is greater than the torque-producing value.

6-13. A Typical Thyratron Control System and Its Operation. A servomechanism using the amplified actuating-signal voltage to control the thyratrons is shown in Fig. 6-44, along with the block diagram of the system. The block diagram is drawn with emphasis on the principle of operation, hence the position of the block marked "synchros" and the use of the reference-input and controlled-shaft signals with no concern given to the command and the primary-feedback signals. These would be necessary only if a study of the operation of the synchros and their errors were of interest in this analysis.

The servo response is damped by a-c rate-generator feedback, which is subtracted from the actuating-signal voltage. The resulting signal is amplified by vacuum tubes. The controlling grid voltage is the sum of an alternating-voltage bias of constant magnitude, a constant direct-voltage bias, and an amplified signal voltage.

When the servo is at rest with zero actuating signal and the bias voltages are properly adjusted, the thyratrons fire with equal currents for a portion of the cycle, and the motor receives no net torque. Under these conditions, the thyratron voltages are shown in Fig. 6-45. The plate voltage is shaded to indicate the portion of the cycle in which the plate current is flowing. If the plate circuit were of pure resistance, this shaded portion would be proportional to the current flow at every instant. The tube drop is approximately 10 volts, and the critical grid voltage is assumed to be zero.

When the actuating-signal voltage is something other than zero, however, the addition of the a-c signal voltage to the bias voltages causes the resultant grid voltage to intercept the critical grid voltage at two different portions of the cycle for the two different tubes. This effect is shown in Fig. 6-46 (see also Fig. 6-42). The plate current is therefore increased in one tube and decreased in the other.

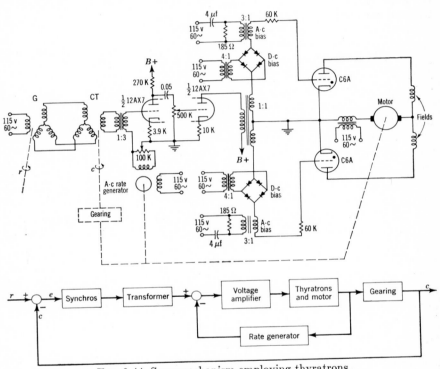

Fig. 6-44. Servomechanism employing thyratrons.

Another servo that employs thyratron control is illustrated in Fig. 6-47. A fact of economic importance is that the only transformer of any size required for the thyratron is the filament transformer; the signal and bias transformers are quite small. The servomechanism is stabilized by means of a d-c equalizing network, appearing between the two choppers, and a feedback voltage, appearing across the resistor R_5. This feedback voltage is proportional to the motor armature current and is filtered by an RC network, and the d-c value is blocked by a capacitor. The a-c component is fed back to the second synchronous chopper, where it is converted to a 60-cycle square wave and is of such polarity as to subtract from the actuating-signal voltage. This voltage is similar to that which might be obtained from a rate generator since it is roughly proportional to the armature current, which is proportional to the motor speed.

In this design, armature control of the motor is used, rather than field control as in the former example. A special problem is introduced by this method of control, however. Assume that the actuating signal is of such a direction that V_1 is the conducting tube. The voltage across V_2 is equal to the voltage drop across V_1. At the end of the current conduction through V_1, however, the voltage appearing across V_2 is the line

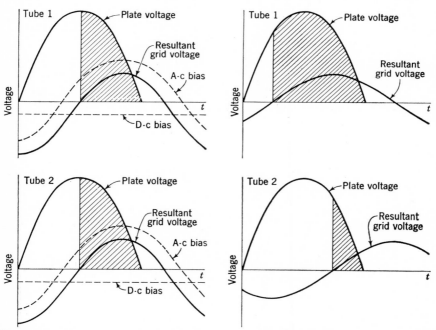

FIG. 6-45. Thyratron voltages for zero control signal.

FIG. 6-46. Thyratron voltages for typical control signal.

voltage, plus the back emf of the armature. Therefore, when the motor is rotating, the anode voltage in the off tube is positive for more than 180°. The method of grid control chosen must be such as to avoid misfiring of the off thyratron.

Figure 6-48 shows the waveform appearing at various points across the circuit for a constant actuating signal. At the output of the control transformer, the voltage is a sine wave (part a). At the output of the first chopper, the voltage is a full-wave rectified signal (part b). After filtering and equalization, the input to the second chopper is roughly a d-c signal. The output of the second chopper is a 60-cycle square wave (part c), and part d shows the voltage appearing at the grids of the

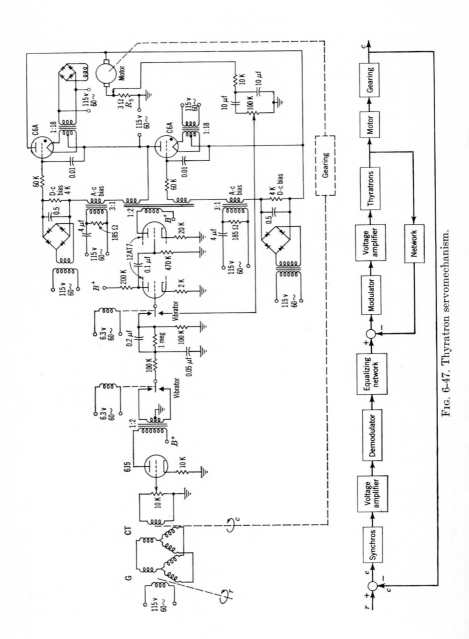

FIG. 6-47. Thyratron servomechanism.

thyratron. The drop across R_5 is the armature current of the motor and is a portion of a sine wave (part e). Under maximum-error conditions, and hence saturation, the armature current is a half-wave rectified direct current.

A-c servomotors can also be controlled by the use of thyratrons, and a typical circuit is shown in Fig. 6-49. If the tubes V_1 and V_2 are conducting, the voltage is applied to phase 1 of the two-phase motor, and a voltage at right angles is applied to phase 2 through the capacitor. The

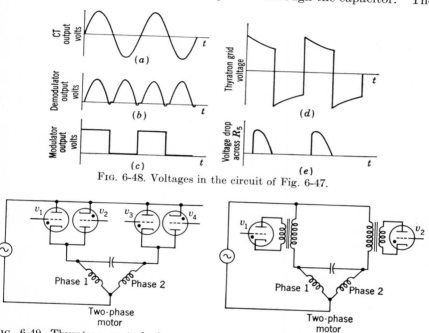

Fig. 6-48. Voltages in the circuit of Fig. 6-47.

Fig. 6-49. Thyratron control of an a-c motor.

Fig. 6-50. Thyratron control of an a-c motor.

magnitude of the torque applied by the motor is a function of the amount of current flowing through the tubes, which can be varied by the grid control as before. To reverse the direction of the motor, the tubes V_3 and V_4 are made to fire. In this case, line voltage is then applied to phase 2, and a voltage at approximately right angles to line voltage is applied to phase 1. The motor therefore reverses. It is significant that in this circuit a constant voltage is not applied to one phase of the two-phase motor, and therefore no appreciable heating occurs during zero actuating-signal conditions.

A variation of this circuit is shown in Fig. 6-50. Whereas the circuit of Fig. 6-49 is a full-wave circuit, Fig. 6-50 is a half-wave circuit. It can, however, be made full-wave by merely placing two more thyratrons back to back with the original two in the manner shown in Fig. 6-49. In this circuit, the primary of a step-up transformer is connected in series with the load and the thyratron connected directly across the secondary. During the portion of the cycle in which V_1 is made to conduct, the alternating voltage across the primary is very small. Since V_2 is not conducting, the impedance of the primary of its transformer is very large and therefore very nearly full line voltage is applied to phase 1 of the motor and across the capacitor to phase 2. The motor is reversed by making V_2 conducting and V_1 nonconducting. Again the proportion of control torque applied in the servo is dependent upon the proportion of the cycle during which conduction takes place. This circuit is similar to that of a magnetic-amplifier circuit.

6-14. Advantages and Disadvantages of Magnetic Amplifiers. A magnetic amplifier is a device used for controlling the flow of power to a

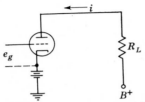

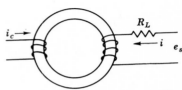

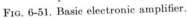

FIG. 6-51. Basic electronic amplifier.

FIG. 6-52. Basic magnetic amplifier.

load by means of saturation of a magnetic core. In the simplest sense, its operation can be thought of as analogous to that of the electronic amplifier shown in Fig. 6-51. For a certain grid potential e_g, the current i is determined by the B+ voltage, the load resistance R_L, and the plate resistance presented by the vacuum tube. The resistance of the vacuum tube can be changed by varying e_g. Small changes of e_g result in a considerable change in the resistance of the tube and hence cause a considerable change in the current i, resulting in a large change of voltage drop across R_L. The electronic amplifier, therefore, uses the principle that a small voltage change e_g changes the resistance of a vacuum tube, and hence the current that can flow through the load R_L, when a supply voltage B+ is applied to the entire circuit.

The analogous magnetic circuit is shown in Fig. 6-52. Here the alternating-voltage power supply e_s is applied to the load resistance R_L and a coil of wire wrapped around magnetic material, which presents an inductive impedance. When the control current i_c is zero, the magnetic material, the frequency of the power source, and the coil winding are such that a large impedance is presented to the load circuit, and therefore the current i is small. As the control current i_c is increased, the inductance of the core is made smaller and hence the load current increases. The number of turns can be so chosen that a small control current i_c results in a large change in voltage across the load R_L. The simplest magnetic amplifier, therefore, involves the change in load-circuit impedance by shifting the d-c level in the control circuit and is referred to as a saturable reactor. Although magnetic amplifiers are used for other purposes, the discussion in this text will be confined to the application to servomechanisms.

The advantages of magnetic amplifiers as compared with vacuum tubes are numerous. The principal one is their long life; like transformers, they can operate for years with no maintenance. Furthermore, they can be hermetically sealed, with only the terminals exposed to the elements. Since no filament supply is necessary, they are ready for immediate operation without warmup. Low heat dissipation and low temperature rise are in part results of the fact that no filament supply is necessary. No high-voltage d-c supply is required. These factors often result in a smaller total amount of equipment. The circuits are quite simple, and the impedances can be made so that no output transformer is necessary to match the amplifier with the servomotor. They are highly resistant to shock and vibration. The input circuits can be completely isolated from the output circuits. They are capable of a very high gain per stage and can control large output powers.

The disadvantages of magnetic amplifiers are principally the time lags associated with inductive circuits, often necessitating higher-frequency supplies, such as 400 cycles rather than 60 cycles. In addition, the size of 60-cycle units may be prohibitive for the application. There is a certain lack of flexibility of the circuits, in part caused by the input-impedance limitations of the coils of wire. The fact that the waveforms of the currents are not pure sinusoids also prevents certain types of application such as unity-gain a-c amplifiers. Furthermore, the non-sinusoidal waveforms can cause radio interference in airborne and ship-borne applications. In addition, they are normally confined to a temperature range of -55 to $+100°C$ because of the change of core properties and the change of metallic-rectifier properties outside this range. Also the gain that is available without excessive drift is limited.

Some of the disadvantages can be minimized by the use of combinations of vacuum-tube or transistor and magnetic amplifiers. Such a combination, in which an electronic amplifier is used for the early stages and a magnetic amplifier is used for the output stage, often provides the gain, speed of response, and input-impedance advantages of an electronic amplifier without the disadvantages of a magnetic amplifier.

6-15. Theory of Magnetic Amplifiers. The theory of magnetic amplifiers is demonstrated with an elementary circuit that has a refinement over the simplest magnetic-amplifier circuit of Fig. 6-52. In Fig. 6-52 the load current that flows during one half cycle is in such a direction as to nullify partially the effect of the control current and hence tends to desaturate the core. In practice, this results in a relatively large input power to the magnetic amplifier and a reduction in its gain. The simplest half-wave self-saturating magnetic amplifier, which is shown in Fig. 6-53, produces a load current that contributes a d-c component to the control ampere turns.

It is instructive to examine the operation of this circuit during steady-state conditions. To do so requires consideration of Fig. 6-54, which is a plot of the flux for this particular size of core vs. the magnetic intensity H, which is proportional to ampere turns surrounding the core. For simplicity, hysteresis effects are eliminated in Fig. 6-54. When the voltage of the supply e_s is negative and opposes the direction of the rectifier, the entire voltage drop appears across the rectifier. Assuming zero rectifier leakage, no current flows opposite to

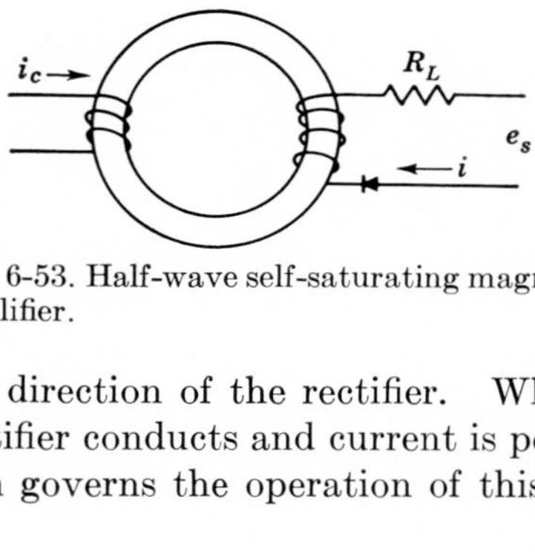

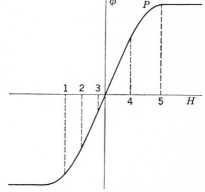

FIG. 6-53. Half-wave self-saturating magnetic amplifier.

FIG. 6-54. Magnetic saturation curve.

the direction of the rectifier. When the supply voltage is positive, the rectifier conducts and current is permitted to flow. The following equation governs the operation of this current:

$$e_s = Ri + N \frac{d\phi}{dt} \tag{6-48}$$

The voltage appears either as an iR drop in the load circuit or as an induced voltage $e = N \, d\phi/dt$ across the reactor.

For the first example assume that the control current i_c is of such a negative value that the initial coercive force H is as shown at point 1 in Fig. 6-54. As the current starts to flow through the rectifier, the coil, and the load resistance, the magnetic flux changes to some point P on the saturation curve. This is accomplished with small load current or with a small change in H. The inductance of the coil is large, and most of the voltage drop appears across the coil. Assume that the supply

voltage reverses polarity.   The load current ceases, and the core flux
returns to its original value under point 1 in Fig. 6-54, in accordance with
the following equation:

$$\phi = \frac{1}{N} \int_o^t e\, dt \tag{6-49}$$

Figure 6-55 shows an oscillogram of the supply voltage, the resulting
load current, and the core flux for this condition.

Assume for the second example that the control current i_c is such as to
bias the core to point 2 of Fig. 6-54 and the magnitude of the supply

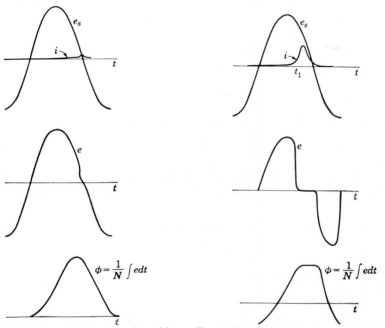

FIG. 6-55. One cycle of operation (bias
point 1).

FIG. 6-56. One cycle of operation (bias
point 2).

voltage e_s is the same as in the previous example.   To understand the
operation of the circuit requires consideration of Eq. (6-49).   Before
time t_1 on the oscillogram of Fig. 6-56, the current and hence the iR drop
have been small, and most of the supply voltage has been absorbed across
the coil.   Consequently, the coil voltage is nearly equal to the supply
voltage e_s.   At t_1, the time integral of e/N results in a flux sufficient to
bring the operation to point P on the saturation curve of Fig. 6-54.   At
this point, saturation is reached, and the current suddenly jumps.   A
small change in ϕ requires a large change in H (or ampere turns, hence

load amperes) since the curve of Fig. 6-54 governs the operation of the magnetic circuit. The current is limited almost entirely by the load resistance. Because the slope of the flux curve is almost zero, the second term $N \, d\phi/dt$ of Eq. (6-48) is approximately zero, and therefore the load resistance absorbs practically the entire supply voltage.

As the supply voltage e_s decreases, the current also decreases, since the current is virtually proportional to the supply voltage as long as the load resistance offers practically the only impedance in the circuit. When the current reduces to the value it had at time t_1, the status of the core is as given by the point P in Fig. 6-54. Thereafter, the current decreases slowly as the flux decreases in accordance with Eq. (6-49). The oscillograms of Fig. 6-52 illustrate the steady-state relation of load current and supply voltage for various other bias values of current (and hence magnetizing force H) as given in Fig. 6-54.

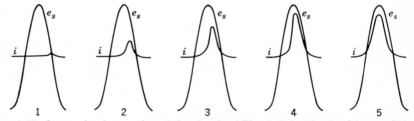

FIG. 6-57. One cycle of operation of the circuit of Fig. 6-53 for the five bias conditions of Fig. 6-54.

Notice that the operation of the simple type of magnetic amplifier is much like that of a thyratron. Once the thyratron grid voltage exceeds the critical value that ionizes the gas, load current surges through the tube and is limited only by the magnitude of the supply voltage and the load resistor. The resulting waveform of the current is similar to that of Fig. 6-57.

The purpose of the rectifier of Fig. 6-53 is to prevent reverse load current from affecting the initial operating point as established by the value of control current. The control current is thus permitted to "set" the operating point of the core on the nonconducting half cycle without this operating point being affected by the load current. The current through the output winding of the reactor contributes to the saturation of the core as in any reactor or transformer, so that the load current tends to increase the saturation rather than decrease it.

6-16. Operation of a Typical Full-wave Circuit. Most magnetic-amplifier circuits employ pairs of simpler circuits to obtain full-wave performance. A typical circuit using d-c control but producing alternating current through the load is shown in Fig. 6-58. This circuit illustrates a self-saturating full-wave magnetic amplifier using two reactors. The load circuit contains series rectifiers to keep the load current in each reactor from reversing. No induced voltage of fundamental frequency appears across the winding terminals of the control circuit, although even harmonic voltages do appear. These undesirable voltages may feed back to the control voltage.

To explain the operation of this and subsequent circuits, the following convention is adopted for a-c portions of the circuit: Voltage polarities and direction of current flow are indicated by unencircled plus and minus signs and unencircled arrows during the first half cycle. During the second half cycle, they are indicated by signs and arrows enclosed by circles. Net control currents are indicated in boldface.

The supply voltage and frequency, the number of load-winding turns, the area of the core, and the maximum possible flux density of the

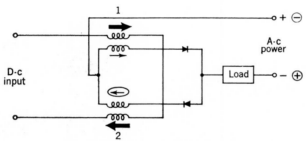

FIG. 6-58. Full-wave self-saturating circuit.

magnetic material are so chosen that the flux varies between that of point 1 and point P (Fig. 6-54) of each core, when the control current biases the core to point 1.

The operation of the circuit of Fig. 6-58 is explained as follows: Assume first that the control current is negative and of such a value as to place the initial operating point at 1 of Fig. 6-54. Neither core fires for either polarity of supply voltage. Suppose now that the current is changed to a value of zero at the start of the first cycle. During the first half cycle, only a small magnetizing current flows in the load circuit of reactor 1, and because of the polarization of the rectifier, no load current flows in rectifier 2. During this half cycle, core 2 is being set by the control current (in this case, by its zero value). During the second half cycle, in which polarities and direction marks are enclosed in circles, core 2 fires halfway through the cycle, while core 1 is being set by the control current. During the third half cycle, core 1 fires halfway through the cycle.

Increasing the control current in the positive direction (i.e., the direction shown by the boldface arrows of Fig. 6-58) causes the firing

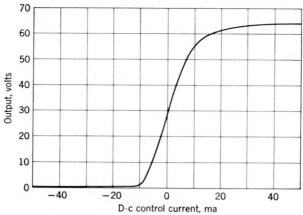

FIG. 6-59. Measured characteristic of the circuit of Fig. 6-58.

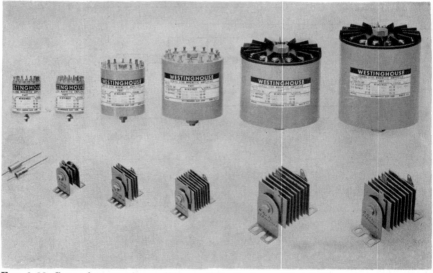

FIG. 6-60. Several magnetic amplifiers.   (*Westinghouse Electric Corp., East Pittsburgh, Pa.*)

point to be advanced farther in each half cycle.   Thus, in this full-wave circuit the load is energized during both halves of the cycle of the a-c power source and is always in phase with the source.   Figure 6-59 illustrates the measured characteristic (output volts vs. control current) of a full-wave magnetic amplifier of the type shown in Fig. 6-58.   It shows an output of 28 volts to the load with zero control current, the output cut off for − 10 ma control current, and the output saturated for +12 ma control-current input.

Figure 6-60 shows a variety of magnetic amplifiers and Fig. 6-61 shows an open construction form of a completely assembled magnetic amplifier.

6-17. A Complete Amplifier. Considered now is a complete magnetic amplifier, which includes a phase-sensitive detector, a voltage-amplifier stage, and a power amplifier. To use the circuit of Fig. 6-58 with synchros in servomechanisms, it is necessary to have a phase-sensitive rectifier to convert the alternating actuating-signal voltage to a d-c

Fig. 6-61. Open-construction magnetic amplifier. (*Westinghouse Electric Corp., East Pittsburgh, Pa.*)

control signal. A circuit that accomplishes this is shown in Fig. 6-62, and its performance is shown in Fig. 6-63.

Each of the two d-c signals of the circuit of Fig. 6-62 becomes the input to one side of the push-pull magnetic amplifier shown in Fig. 6-64. This stage consists of four reactors with two control windings on each magnetic core. One set of the control windings is connected in series to one of the d-c input signals; the other set is connected in series to the other d-c input signal. The a-c power source is a secondary winding of a transformer, and the reactor output windings are connected in parallel to this source through appropriate rectifier units.

Because of the operation of the phase-sensitive rectifier, the input polarity does not change with the actuating signal. For zero actuating signal the net control ampere turns in each of the cores is zero. The net control ampere turns, for a given polarity of actuating signal, increases in one direction in one core and increases in the other direction in the other core. Reversal of polarity of the actuating signal reverses the polarity of the net ampere turns in each core. Because of the rectifiers in the output windings, the polarities of the output terminals 5 and 6 and

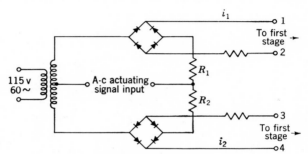

FIG. 6-62. Phase-sensitive rectifier.

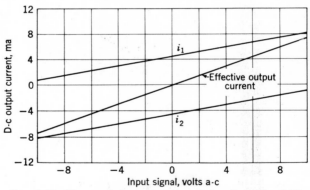

FIG. 6-63. Measured characteristics of circuit of Fig. 6-62.

7 and 8 are also determined and cannot be changed. Thus, for either cycle of the a-c source, terminal 5 is always positive and terminal 6 always negative.

Assume net ampere control turns in the direction of the boldface arrows. During the first half cycle, cores 1 and 4 fire, and cores 2 and 3 are being set. During the first half cycle, core 1 fires early in the cycle (since the control-current flux is in the direction of the load-current flux), and core 4 fires late. During this same half cycle, core 2 is being set to fire early, and core 3 is being set to fire late (since its control flux is opposite to the direction in which the load-current flux will be in the next half cycle). During the second half cycle, core 2 fires early and core 3 late. Thus, a greater current flows from terminal 5 through its load (the power stage) and back through 6 than flows out of 8. For a reversal of polarity of control ampere turns, more current flows from

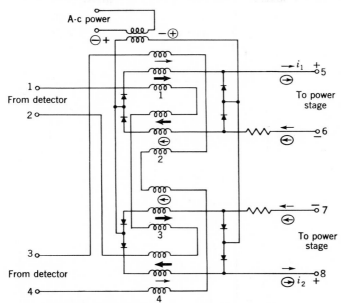

FIG. 6-64. Push-pull magnetic amplifier, first stage.

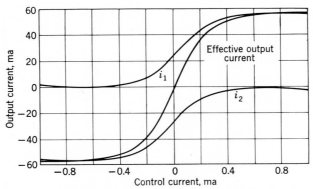

FIG. 6-65. Measured performance of the circuit of Fig. 6-64.

terminal 8 than from 5. Figure 6-65 shows the measured performance of this circuit.

The push-pull power amplifier of Fig. 6-64 is used to feed the power stage shown in Fig. 6-66. The load of this amplifier is a servomotor

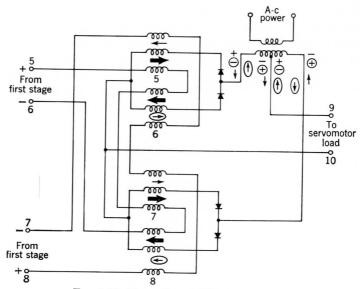

FIG. 6-66. Magnetic-amplifier power stage.

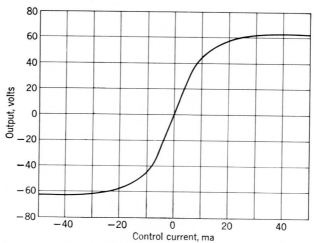

FIG. 6-67. Measured performance of the circuit of Fig. 6-66.

rated at 115 volts, 400 cycles, 9 watts. The amplifier of Fig. 6-66 contains four reactors with a pair of control windings on each and connected in two groups as in the previous stage. The output windings are connected in parallel to the center tap of the transformer secondary and to the load.

Assume that more control current is flowing through terminals 5 and 6 than 7 and 8. The net control ampere turns is in the direction of the boldface arrows. During the first half cycle, cores 5 and 7 are firing, and cores 6 and 8 are being set. Core 7 fires sooner; so, by tracing the currents resulting from each half of the excitation voltage, it is seen that a net current flows toward terminal 9. On the second half cycle, core 8 fires sooner, and current flows from terminal 9. Thus an alternating

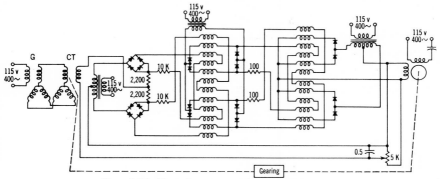

FIG. 6-68. Complete magnetic-amplifier servo.

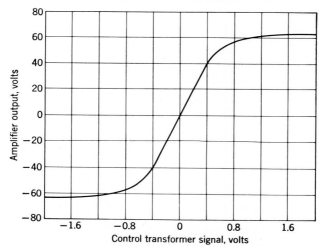

FIG. 6-69. Static measurement of the circuit of Fig. 6-68.

current flows through the servomotor load. Zero load current flows for balanced input and the load current reverses polarity when more current flows through 7 and 8 than 5 and 6. Figure 6-67 shows the steady-state operating characteristics of this stage.

The complete magnetic amplifier is shown in Fig. 6-68. The stages are the same as those described in the previous pages except for the addition of balance and load resistors and an over-all feedback. The steady-state characteristics of the magnetic amplifier are shown in Fig. 6-69 for no feedback, and the complete design data are shown in Table 6-3. The use of feedback reduces the static gain by a factor of about 6 but improves the dynamic performance from a measured corner frequency of 2.4 to 3.4 cycles. The motor has a corner frequency of 4 cycles, the gear ratio is 250, and the measured open-loop characteristics of the amplifier, motor, and gear train are shown in Fig. 6-70. The measured velocity-error constant of about $\frac{1}{20}$ is consistent with the frequency response data. The controlled-shaft torque sensitivity is 45 oz-in./deg.

TABLE 6-3. DESIGN DATA OF MAGNETIC AMPLIFIER

Detector rectifiers	Bridge circuit: 4 series $\frac{1}{2}$-in. plates per arm, Radio Receptor Co. 16Y1 (2 each)
First-stage power rectifiers	Doubler circuit: 1 series 1-in.^{2} plate per arm, Radio Receptor Co. MIDIE (3G (4 each)
Output-stage power rectifiers	Doubler circuit: 6 series $1\frac{3}{16}$-in.^{2} plates per arm, Radio Receptor Co. P6DIE3G (2 each)
Input-stage reactors	Core: ID 0.75 in., OD 0.94 in.
	Hymu 80: 0.001-in. tape, 0.25 in. wide, dry-hydrogen-annealed
	Case: ID 0.68 in., OD 0.01 in., height 0.33 in.
	Control windings: 750 turns each, No. 34 HF
	Power winding: 700 turns, No. 34 HF
Output-stage reactors	Core: ID 1.00 in., OD 1.25 in.
	Orthonol: 0.002-in. tape, 0.25 in. wide, dry-hydrogen-annealed
	Case: ID 0.93 in. OD 1.32 in., height 0.33 in.
	Control windings: 50 turns each, No. 32 HF
	Power winding: 3,300 turns, No. 32 HF
Power and reference transformer	Core: ID 1.25 in., OD 1.88 in.
	Orthonol: 0.002-in. tape, 0.5 in. wide
	Case: ID 1.18 in., OD 1.95 in., height 0.61 in.
	Primary: 690 turns, tapped at 360, No. 25 HF
	Section 1: 1,100 turns, CT, and tapped 90 turns each side of center, No. 28 HF
	Section 2: 60 turns, no. 28 HF

6-18. BH Curves and Bias Windings. The shape of the BH curve of the magnetic material is most important in the operating characteristics of the magnetic amplifier. In the initial study of the theory of magnetic amplifiers the flux vs. magnetizing-force curve, or BH curve, is considered as a single-valued function. The effects of hysteresis loops on the theory of operation of magnetic amplifiers are considered. The effect of other factors influenced by the shape of the BH curves is also discussed.

Figure 6-71 shows a typical rectangular-loop BH curve of a magnetic material. Also drawn are some minor loops that show the relationship of flux and magnetizing force for various initial magnetizing forces. In explaining the effect of hysteresis on the operation of magnetic amplifiers, use is made of the circuit of Fig. 6-53. If the control current is zero, the state of the core material is initially at point 1 in Fig. 6-71, assuming no past history of the core. During the positive half cycle of the voltage, the flux and current build up along the dotted line and, assuming the

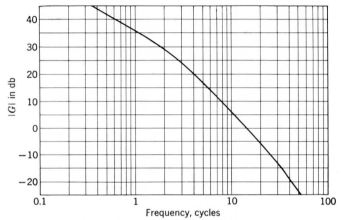

FIG. 6-70. Frequency response of the servo of Fig. 6-68.

coil goes to saturation, reach a maximum value. The core fires, and the current is again limited only by the resistance in the circuit. As the voltage reduces, the current also reduces. When the current is zero the magnetizing force is also zero, but the flux is not zero because of the retentivity of the core.

The state of the core material is now at point 2. Subsequent positive half cycles of supply voltage cause the core to fire almost immediately after starting the half cycle. Thus, full current, limited only by the resistance of the circuit, flows during the entire positive half cycle, and control is effectively lost. In using core material with a rectangular-shaped BH curve, there-fore, a bias current is necessary to bias the

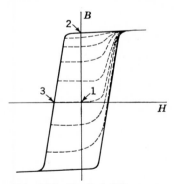

FIG. 6-71. Typical BH curve.

magnetizing force in a negative direction so that the initial operating point is on the left-hand curve of Fig. 6-71, and possibly at point 3. This bias current can flow in a separate winding.

For a second illustration, assume an initial control current and a bias-current combination that will magnetize the core initially to point 3.

Now the explanation of circuit operation is the same as that given with Fig. 6-54 during the positive half cycle of supply voltage. As the supply voltage becomes negative, the net ampere turns in the core decreases to

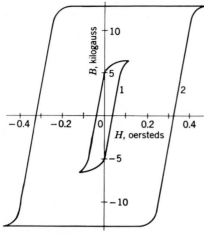

the initial value and the core again assumes the state of point 3. The finite hysteresis loop has not affected the amplifier materially except that a greater magnetizing current is necessary to change the flux from its initial value to its maximum value.

Figure 6-72 shows a comparison of hysteresis loops, for a frequency of 60 cycles, of two magnetic materials commonly used in magnetic amplifiers. Loop 1 is for a high-nickel alloy of about 75 to 80 per cent Ni. Loop 2 is for a nickel-tin alloy of about 50 per cent Ni. The high-nickel alloy is obtainable under several names, such as Mumetal, Hymu 80, Supermalloy, and 1040 alloy.

FIG. 6-72. Hysteresis loops of two mag-netic materials.

The material of loop 2 is known variously as Deltamax, Orthonik, Orthonol, and Hypernik V.   Both materials are dry-hydrogen-annealed.

The method of annealing has an important effect on the shape of these loops. For example, Orthonik can be annealed in a slightly different way to have rounded corners and to resemble more the shape of the Mumetal *BH* curves with a change of scale.   Ordinary silicon iron, even of the best grade, is not normally used in lower-power magnetic amplifiers because of the large magnetizing currents necessary to achieve maximum flux density.

Mumetal is normally used for the first stage of the magnetic amplifier because of the smaller magnetizing current necessary.   If the magnetic amplifier draws a large magnetizing current, the signal source will normally supply this magnetizing current and therefore be required to supply appreciable power to the servoamplifier.   This problem is avoided when Mumetal is used.   Mumetal has the added advantage that the *BH* curve is not so rectangular as the Deltamax loop, and hence no bias winding is necessary.   Mumetal is also better for the first stage since the loop is not so rectangular and two cores exhibit less difference in magnetic properties.   The problem of output noise voltage, which is controlled in the input stage, is reduced.

For the second stage, the magnetizing current is less important, since it comes from a previous stage rather than from the signal source.   The amount of power output that the second stage (if it is the output stage) is capable of producing is important. Mumetal has a maximum flux density on the order of 4 to 5 kilogauss, whereas Deltamax has maximum flux density of about 15 kilogauss. Hence, it can handle three to four times the power for the same sized core, and for a given number of turns a much higher output voltage can be obtained. Some of the points discussed are summarized as follows:

1. The width of the hysteresis loop should be narrow to minimize the magnetizing current.

2. In order to minimize the amplifier-unbalance noise, the first stage should be of material with a less rectangular hysteresis loop; i.e., it should have a low retentivity.

3. For high gain, the sides of the hysteresis loop should be as vertical and as close together as possible.

4. For a high output power, the saturation flux density should be as high as possible to minimize the size of core and the number of load turns required.

Oddly distorted *BH* curves are usually the result of nonuniformity of the core and are caused by variations in thickness of the material, in properties across the width of the strip of magnetic material, and in grain size. Distorted curves can also be caused by stresses or by turns of a strip that are electrically short-circuited. The deleterious effect of stresses caused by bending, punching, shearing, and other mechanical processes is normally relieved by heat treatment of the core. Since any of these distorted shapes can result in poorer operation of the amplifier, stresses, such as those induced by clamping or potting, should be kept to an absolute minimum.

It is often necessary to bias the core in order to retain control over the portion of the cycle in which firing will take place. The purpose of the bias winding is to establish, in the absence of control current, the flux necessary to bring the core to the desired initial operating point during the flux-setting half cycle. Superposed upon this flux is that established by the control windings. Although cores can be biased at other values, normally the core is biased so that the cores fire midway in the cycle for zero control current. For biasing purposes, the quiescent current from the previous stage or from the phase-sensitive rectifier can be used, and the bias current flows in the control winding. It is often necessary or desirable, however, to put an additional bias winding in each core to keep the core biased to the value desired.

The bias winding can be excited by either direct or alternating current. Figure 6-73 shows the addition of a bias winding to the elementary self-saturating circuit. If a d-c bias is used, the direction of current flow is usually chosen to be opposite that of the load current. Its magnitude would be such as to bring the flux to point 3 of Fig. 6-71, in the absence of all other currents.

When a-c bias is used, Fig. 6-71 can also be used to illustrate the proper design proportions of the windings. For ease of explanation, assume that the bias and load windings have an equal number of turns. Consider first that only the bias winding is connected to a power source whose magnitude for the normal biasing arrangement is half that which the core is capable of supporting in the steady state without firing. That is, the voltage is one-half that which in the steady state would cause the core to alternate between values of negative and positive flux just short of saturation. The state of the core during the first (positive) half cycle proceeds from point 1 to a flux value just under saturation to a point close to point 3 and back to a point close to 1, so that the core never fires with just the bias winding connected.

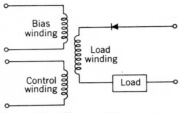

FIG. 6-73. The addition of bias winding to an elementary circuit.

Assume now that the full supply voltage, double that applied to the bias winding, is applied to the rectifier, load winding, and load in series. Assume also that the control current is zero. During the first half cycle, after starting at point 1, the core fires about halfway through the cycle. Before firing, the load-winding voltage induces in the bias winding a voltage twice that applied by its power source and in the opposite direction. Currents circulate through the source in the direction reverse to that when the load winding is not supplied with power. During the flux-setting half cycle, however, the bias voltage produces a time integral such as to reset the flux to position 3 and thence to position 1 again, its initial value. The bias winding must be connected in the direction to cause current to flow in the direction opposite to that in which the load current will flow in the half cycle. The purpose of the control current is to add to or subtract from the bias ampere turns to effect firing earlier or later than the mid-point of the positive half cycle.

It is customary to put fewer turns on the bias winding than are on the control winding; for example, the ratio 10:1 in turns might be employed. This turns ratio is chosen so that there will be smaller induced voltages from the load winding to the bias winding during the portion of the half cycle in which voltage appears across the load winding. Therefore, if the full voltage across the load windings is 100 volts, that applied to the bias winding would be 5 volts, which is half the reflected voltage through the turns ratio. While the induced voltage from the load winding bucks the supply voltage to the bias winding, the important action of the bias winding occurs during the flux setting of the half cycle in which it is not opposed by any induced voltage caused by the load winding on the core. On the negative half cycle, the voltage induced by the bias winding into the load winding tends to reduce the voltage appearing across the rectifier.

6-19. Various Magnetic-amplifier Circuits. There are a number of variations of the basic circuit that is shown in Fig. 6-58. These can be designed to have d-c output and a-c input rather than a-c output and d-c input as is the case with Fig. 6-58. The purpose of this section is to consider the operation of circuits having different operating principles and hence different features.

The first of these circuits is shown in Fig. 6-74 and is an output stage. The circuit as shown employs d-c control, although if one of the d-c control windings is reversed as shown within the dotted lines, the circuit can be used with a-c control instead. This circuit has several features not found in the circuit of Fig. 6-58. Although it utilizes the self-saturation principle, i.e., the load currents do not reset the cores, it does so in a somewhat different manner. Also, a direct current is caused to flow through the load under conditions of zero input signal. This direct current provides servomotor viscous damping that can be made to decrease with the magnitude of the control signal so that, when there is a large error in the servo and the control signal is large, there is less damping and the motor can slew rapidly to the new position. When the actuating signal approaches zero, however, the direct current in the motor, and consequently the viscous drag in the motor, increases to provide stability.

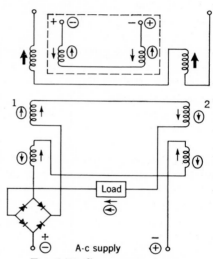

FIG. 6-74. Geyger output stage.

Consider the operation of the circuit assuming zero d-c control current. For the first half cycle the polarities are shown unencircled, and for the second half cycle, the polarities are shown encircled. The two windings on core 1 are producing flux in the same direction, whereas in core 2 they are in opposing directions. If the turns are accurately matched, the windings on core 1 have a finite impedance, whereas those on core 2 have no inductive impedance. Current flows through the load in the direction of the arrow.

On the other half cycle, core 1 has opposing fluxes and consequently zero impedance, whereas core 2 has finite impedance.   A full-wave pulsating direct current still flows in the same direction through the load.

In the presence of control current in the direction shown, increased current flows through the coils on core 1 during the first half cycle, and the coils on core 2 are so connected that zero impedance appears across them. A larger current therefore flows through the load to the left than during the zero control-current condition.   On the same half cycle, the control current is setting the flux in core 2 in such a direction that during the second half cycle there is a reduction in load-current flow.   During the second half cycle, the coils on core 1 are opposing and present zero impedance.   The coils on core 2, having been set to produce less current per cycle, do produce current over a smaller portion of that cycle.   The total effect of the two half cycles is some direct current and a net alternating current.

If the control current is assumed in the opposite direction, the greatest current flows during the second half cycle and flows in the same direction as before.   The first half cycle has less current flow, and therefore the polarity of the fundamental component of the resulting wave is in the opposite direction.

This circuit, which is shown in Fig. 6-74, can also be used with a-c control by the control winding that is enclosed with the dotted lines. During the first half cycle, load current is flowing in core 1 and core 2 is being set in a direction to reduce the current flow during the next half cycle.   During the second half cycle, the current is reduced in core 2, whereas core 1 is being reset in the direction to increase load current. In order to put the initial operating point of the cores where desired, either d-c or a-c bias windings can be added to this circuit, as to all the output stages.

Variation in the damping can be obtained by means of these bias windings.   If the cores are biased so that they fire at a point halfway through the cycle, there is no net change in direct current with magnitude of control signal or hence of the output voltage.   If, however, the cores are biased for firing earlier in the cycle, the load current flows over more than half of each of the half cycles and the direct current decreases with magnitude of control signal.   This, however, requires a greater flow of current under quiescent conditions.

It is often desirable to improve the time-lag characteristics of the magnetic amplifier by the use of feedback circuits.   These feedback circuits can be fed to the control windings of the first or second stage, or they can be fed to separate and distinct feedback windings that are wound on the same cores but are isolated (except through coupling) from the other windings.   Figure 6-75 shows the addition of some resistors to the circuit of Fig. 6-66 that permit a full-wave direct voltage to be fed back. This voltage is of zero magnitude for zero input signal and has a magnitude dependent upon the magnitude of the input signal (and hence the load voltage) and a polarity dependent upon the direction of the input signal. Arrows are placed on this circuit for each of the half cycles involved. Those of the first half cycle are not enclosed in circles, and the polarity and directions in the second half cycle are enclosed in circles. Analysis of a complete cycle of operation for each of the various conditions of control current, i.e., zero control current and control current in each direction, indicates that the output across the feedback resistors is of the type necessary for use with d-c equalizing networks.

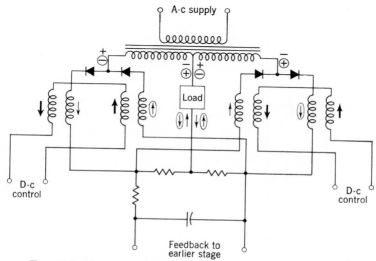

Fig. 6-75. The addition of feedback to the circuit of Fig. 6-66.

An equalizing lag network that consists of a resistor and capacitor is shown in the feedback path. This lag network produces a lead in the over-all feedback amplifier. The voltage appearing across the capacitor can be fed back into the feedback windings of the first stage. The difficulty with magnetic-amplifier feedback circuits, not present to a large degree in transistors or electronic-tube feedback circuits, is that the input impedance of the windings to which signals are fed back is rather small. Consequently, the capacitor is shunted by a rather low impedance circuit. Some beneficial effect can be obtained from this feedback without the RC network, however, since the inductance of the feedback circuit together with its resistors causes a time lag that, when in the feedback circuit, appears as a time lead in the over-all amplifier.

One of the basic difficulties of magnetic amplifiers is the time lag associated with the control. This is caused by the L/R—the inductance over the resistance—ratio of the control winding. Figure 6-76 shows a circuit that attempts to reduce the inductance of the control circuit and hence increase the speed of response of the amplifier. It does this by causing all the cores (in this case, two) that are in the control circuit to be fully saturated during a portion of the cycle. During the portion in which the cores are fully saturated, the inductance of the circuit is small and consequently does not contribute to the time lag of establishing the current in the control circuit. It is a half-wave circuit; i.e., load current flows only during one half cycle. This load current has as its fundamental the frequency of the supply and consequently drives the servomotor in the proper direction depending upon the polarity of the input signal.

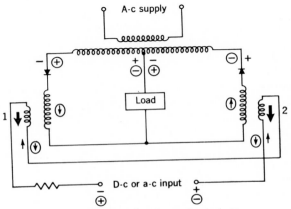

Fig. 6-76. Low-time-lag output stage.

The polarity of the two half cycles of operation is marked. Either alternating or direct current can be used in the control circuit without modification of the diagram, but for simplicity it is assumed that d-c control is used and that this control current is in the direction shown by the arrows. During the first half cycle no load current flows, since it is in opposition to the rectifier in both cores. During the second half cycle, both cores fire at an instant of time depending upon the initial flux value to which they have been set during the previous half cycle. For the direction of control currents shown, core 1 fires first during the cycle, and hence the direction of load current is as given. At the latter part of the cycle, core 2 also fires, producing a load current flowing in the opposite direction. From this portion of the cycle when both cores are firing, the inductance in the control circuit is small. Consequently, if the control voltage is changing, the current has no difficulty in quickly coming to a new value without appreciable inductive lag. Both core 1 and core 2 are set to initial values determined by the magnitude of the control current. With the cores unsaturated the inductance in the control circuit increases to its full value, and the control current is consequently diminished by this increase in circuit impedance. It decreases with time as a function of the inductance and resistance of the circuit. For a given control voltage, however, the same current is available at the beginning of each flux-setting half cycle. For different control voltages, the current available at the beginning of each flux-setting half cycle is different, although it will diminish because of the change of inductance in the circuit. In this case, the inductance does not limit the establishment of the flux-setting current since it can change over a given cycle almost instantaneously.

Because of the collapsing of the fields within the cores, no transient in the control circuits is permitted to last longer than the period of time between the times when the cores are collapsed. Therefore the response of the system to a given control signal cannot exceed one cycle. Variations of this circuit include elimination of the center-tapped transformer by use of bridge circuits and use of a-c control rather than d-c control.

6-20. Practical Design Considerations and Amplifier Construction. After the desired circuit has been chosen, it is necessary to set forth certain design information on the amplifier so that it can be constructed. For each of the various stages, it is necessary to know each core size, the wire size, and the rectifier size and to have the following information: (1) the number of control-current turns, (2) the number of load turns, (3) the number of bias-winding turns, and (4) the number of feedback-winding turns. Some amplifiers employ only control and load turns, so that the last two items can be ignored. Figure 6-77 presents a few of the numerous core shapes that are available for magnetic amplifiers. Each half of the C- and E-type cores (two half cores are cut from the square-0-shaped cores) are banded together to keep the air gap to a minimum. These types can accommodate a prewound coil. A special toroidal winding machine is required to wind the toroidal cores. All of these cores are made from magnetic material (Deltamax, Supermalloy, Mo Permalloy, etc.) that is in the form of 1- to 4-mils-thick tape. This tape is covered with an insulating material and is wound in the desired shape. The C- and E-type cores are separated with a precision cut and, after the windings are placed on the core, are held together with a metal band.

The number of control turns on the input core is determined by a knowledge of the range of voltage available from the signal source from zero signal to full-saturation signal. There is often a large resistance placed in series with the control winding in order to increase the input impedance of the amplifier, so that the input voltage and this resistance largely determine the current. Although this resistor reduces the gain, it also increases the speed of response because the L/R ratio is made smaller. To keep the inductance small, the actual number of turns used is the smallest that can be employed for the range of currents necessary.

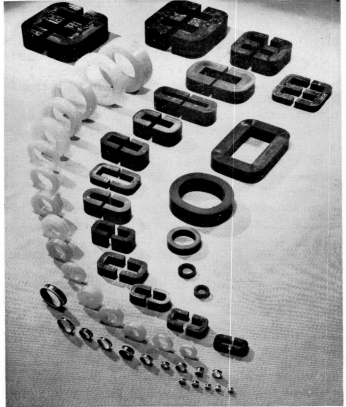

FIG. 6-77. Tape-wound cores for magnetic amplifiers.   (*The Arnold Engineering Co., Marengo, Ill.*)

The control winding of the second and subsequent stages is chosen to saturate for full output current of the preceding stage.

The number of load turns is largely determined by the line voltage used.   For a full-wave circuit, the line voltage must be about 150 per cent of the desired load voltage to allow for voltage drop in the amplifier circuits.   The following standard transformer equation is used to calculate the number of turns:

$$E = 2.87 \times 10^{-3} KNBAf \qquad (6\text{-}50)$$

where E = voltage absorbed by reactor, volts
  B = maximum flux density, kilogauss
  N = number of turns on power winding
  A = core cross-sectional area, in.^{2}
  f = power frequency, cycles

and the magnetizing force H in oersteds is given by the equation

$$H = 0.496 \frac{NI}{l} \tag{6-51}$$

where l = length of core, in.

I = winding current, amp

In this case, the wire size is as large as practical in order that the drop across the reactor during saturation will be as low as possible. The core size, which is also determined by this equation, is an empirical determination because the number of turns of wire, the core window area, and the length of the magnetic path are all interdependent. It is normally necessary to make a few calculations before arriving at the right combination of dimensions. The procedure generally followed is to choose the power-winding wire size that will carry the required load current and to select a core size of minimum window area that will permit the number of turns of wire to be wound in the area. Table 6-4, which presents the dimensional characteristics of heavy formvar wire, and Table 6-5, which gives the dimensional characteristics of toroidal cores, are of considerable value to the engineer in choosing the core and wire size.

If it is necessary to use bias windings, the number of ampere turns is chosen to achieve the proper bias for the zero-input-signal operating point on the BH curve of the amplifier. A small number of turns is normally selected to keep the inductance and induced voltage of this winding low; it might amount to about one-tenth the number of load-winding turns. All this bias power is supplied by the line, so that there is no serious power-loss problem. If feedback turns are necessary, sufficient window area must be provided and the number of turns for proper operation of these circuits must be chosen from a knowledge of the operating conditions of the amplifier.

The rectifier size is chosen to carry the amount of current necessary for the circuit in which the rectifier is placed. This current determines the size of the plates, and the number of plates is determined by the back emf, which should be on the order of 8 volts per plate.

A perfect rectifier has zero resistance in one direction and infinite resistance in the reverse direction. Actual rectifiers do not achieve this perfection. Normally, selenium rectifiers are used for magnetic amplifiers. They have a low reverse leakage current capable of handling large currents and reliable, long life.

The reason leakage current is so important can be seen from Fig. 6-53. During the negative half cycle, it is desirable that the entire supply voltage be across the rectifier. If there is any leakage current, there results a net reverse-current flow, which helps to set the core, and the point of firing in the positive half cycle therefore is controlled not entirely by the

TABLE 6-4. HEAVY FORMVAR DATA

Size, Awg	Turns, in.^{2}	Resistance, ohms/1,000 ft	Diameter, in.	Area, c.m.*
8	57	0.63	0.1324	16,510
9	72	0.79	0.1182	13,090
10	90	1.0	0.1056	10,380
11	113	1.26	0.0943	8,234
12	141	1.58	0.0842	6,530
13	176	2.0	0.0853	5,178
14	220	2.52	0.0673	4,107
15	273	3.18	0.0602	3,257
16	350	4.016	0.0539	2,583
17	432	5.064	0.0482	2,048
18	540	6.38	0.0432	1,624
19	668	8.05	0.0387	1,288
20	850	10.15	0.0346	1,022
21	1,045	12.9	0.0310	810.1
22	1,300	16.14	0.0278	642.4
23	1,650	20.36	0.0249	509.5
24	2,030	25.67	0.0224	404.0
25	2,500	32.37	0.0201	320.4
26	3,160	40.81	0.0180	254.1
27	3,880	51.47	0.0161	201.5
28	4,770	64.9	0.0145	159.8
29	5,920	81.83	0.0130	126.7
30	7,300	103.2	0.0116	100.5
31	9,260	130.1	0.0105	79.70
32	11,100	164.1	0.0095	63.21
33	13,900	206.9	0.0085	50.13
34	16,900	260.9	0.0075	39.75
35	22,300	329.0	0.0067	31.52
36	26,900	414.8	0.0060	25.00
37	33,100	523.1	0.0055	19.83
38	40,000	659.6	0.0049	15.72
39	51,800	831.8	0.0043	12.47
40	66,200	1,049	0.0038	9.888
41		1,323	0.0034	7.845
42		1,670	0.0030	6.250
43		2,104	0.0027	4.928
44		2,654	0.0025	3.915

* c.m. is the abbreviation for circular mils.

control current but rather by the combination of the control current and the leakage current that flows during the negative half cycle. The capacitance of rectifiers also causes some flow of leakage current. It is possible to shunt the rectifier with a resistor, however, to use the reverse-load-current flow to provide bias without the necessity of additional windings.

The current and reverse-voltage characteristics required of the rectifier can be obtained by a study of the circuit. It is necessary to compute the inverse-voltage rating, not only for the possible supply voltage but also for load voltage that may add to the reverse voltage during a portion of the cycle. Conservative practice dictates that about 8 volts per plate should be the maximum used. For example, if the peak reverse voltage across a rectifier is on the order of 40 volts, a five-plate rectifier should be used. The area of the plate is determined by the current requirements.

A typical selenium-rectifier curve is shown in Fig. 6-78. For small voltages, selenium cells do not act as rectifiers but merely present a high impedance to the current. It is only after the application of about 0.5 volt for a 1-in.^{2} plate that the forward resistance drops off. Difference in the forward resistance is not important, since the forward resistance of rectifiers is usually a small part of the total circuit impedance, except in interstage connections of some circuits. Differences in the back resistance are very important, since the back current flows in the flux-setting half cycle, and reverse currents can easily differ by a factor of 2, thereby causing unbalance in the output. The use of 8 to 10 volts per plate results in keeping this difference of current small. Variation in temperature, which causes variation in

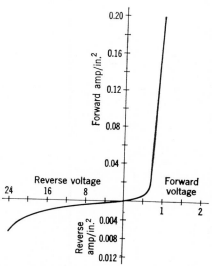

Fig. 6-78. Typical selenium-rectifier characteristics.

the leakage- or reverse-current flow, results in differences in the two halves of the push-pull amplifiers and therefore causes the amplifier to have a high noise output, with attendant drift and unbalance.

In the manufacture of magnetic amplifiers, it is necessary that certain precautions be taken in order to obtain the full advantage of the magnetic materials used. Since stresses cause peculiarities in the shape of the BH curve that may result in impairment of the operation of the amplifier, it is normal to suspend the magnetic material in a silicone grease in a plastic box so that the turns are not wound directly on the magnetic material and hence do not induce stresses in the core.

Since air gaps in the magnetic path may require extremely large magnetizing currents and thus reduce the gain of the magnetic amplifier,

TABLE 6-5. DIMENSIONAL CHARACTERISTICS OF TOROIDAL CORES*

Nominal core dimensions							Nom. core vol.	Cross core area, A_c†		Cased core window area, A_w			Mean core length		Wire-wound core dimensions‡								Core size
ID		OD		Ht.											Maximum OD		Maximum ht.		Mean winding length				
In.	Cm	In.	Cm	In.	Cm		In.³	In.²	Cm²	In.²	Cm²	Circular mils × 10⁶	In.	Cm	In.	Cm	In.	Cm	Ft	In.	Cm		
0.500	1.270	0.625	1.588	0.125	0.318		0.0138	0.0078	0.0504	0.136	0.877	0.173	1.77	4.49	0.822	2.09	0.461	1.17	0.098	1.18	3.00		T8043
0.500	1.270	0.750	1.905	0.125	0.318		0.0307	0.0156	0.101	0.123	0.794	0.157	1.96	4.99	0.941	2.39	0.451	1.15	0.111	1.33	3.37		T5340
0.500	1.270	0.750	1.905	0.250	0.635		0.0613	0.0313	0.202	0.123	0.794	0.157	1.96	4.99	0.941	2.39	0.576	1.46	0.131	1.58	4.00		T6592
0.625	1.588	1.000	2.540	0.188	0.478		0.0900	0.0353	0.227	0.213	1.38	0.271	2.55	6.48	1.22	3.10	0.577	1.47	0.141	1.69	4.30		T5958
0.625	1.588	1.000	2.540	0.250	0.635		0.120	0.0469	0.302	0.213	1.38	0.271	2.55	6.48	1.22	3.10	0.639	1.62	0.151	1.82	4.61		T5651
0.650	1.651	0.900	2.286	0.125	0.318		0.038	0.0156	0.101	0.234	1.51	0.298	2.44	6.19	1.14	2.90	0.526	1.34	0.122	1.46	3.72		T5515
0.650	1.651	1.150	2.921	0.375	0.953		0.265	0.0938	0.605	0.234	1.51	0.298	2.83	7.18	1.37	3.47	0.776	1.97	0.184	2.21	5.62		T6180
0.750	1.905	1.000	2.540	0.250	0.635		0.0859	0.0313	0.202	0.328	2.11	0.417	2.75	6.98	1.28	3.25	0.701	1.78	0.150	1.81	4.58		T5502
0.750	1.905	1.125	2.858	0.188	0.478		0.104	0.0353	0.227	0.328	2.11	0.417	2.95	7.48	1.39	3.53	0.639	1.62	0.151	1.81	4.59		T5504
0.750	1.905	1.250	3.175	1.000	2.540		0.786	0.250	1.01	0.328	2.11	0.417	3.14	7.98	1.50	3.81	1.45	3.69	0.296	3.56	9.03		T5762
1.000	2.540	1.250	3.175	0.125	0.318		0.0552	0.0156	0.101	0.631	4.07	0.803	3.53	8.98	1.62	4.13	0.701	1.78	0.149	1.78	4.53		T4168
1.000	2.540	1.250	3.175	0.250	0.635		0.110	0.0313	0.202	0.631	4.07	0.803	3.53	8.98	1.62	4.13	0.826	2.10	0.169	2.03	5.17		T7699
1.000	2.540	1.375	3.493	0.250	0.635		0.175	0.0469	0.302	0.645	4.16	0.821	3.73	9.48	1.73	4.38	0.836	2.12	0.180	2.16	5.48		T4635
1.000	2.540	1.500	3.810	0.250	0.635		0.245	0.0625	0.403	0.631	4.07	0.803	3.93	9.98	1.84	4.67	0.831	2.11	0.191	2.29	5.83		T5800
1.000	2.540	1.500	3.810	0.375	0.953		0.368	0.0938	0.605	0.631	4.07	0.803	3.93	9.98	1.84	4.67	0.956	2.43	0.212	2.54	6.46		T5233
1.000	2.540	1.500	3.810	0.500	1.270		0.491	0.125	0.806	0.631	4.07	0.803	3.93	9.98	1.84	4.67	1.08	2.75	0.233	2.79	7.10		T6847
1.125	2.858	1.625	4.128	0.500	1.270		0.540	0.125	0.806	0.819	5.28	1.04	4.32	11.0	2.01	5.10	1.14	2.91	0.242	2.91	7.39		T5778
1.250	3.175	1.750	4.445	0.250	0.635		0.295	0.0625	0.403	1.03	6.65	1.31	4.71	12.0	2.18	5.54	0.956	2.43	0.210	2.52	6.41		T5387
1.250	3.175	1.750	4.445	0.500	1.270		0.589	0.125	0.806	1.03	6.65	1.31	4.71	12.0	2.18	5.54	1.21	3.06	0.252	3.02	7.68		T7441
1.250	3.175	1.750	4.445	1.000	2.540		1.18	0.250	1.61	1.03	6.65	1.31	4.71	12.0	2.18	5.54	1.71	4.33	0.335	4.02	10.2		T4189

1.250	3.175	2.000	5.080	0.375	0.953	0.718	0.141	0.907	1.03	6.65	1.31	5.11	13.0	2.40	6.09	1.08	2.75	0.252	3.02	7.68	T5772
1.500	3.810	2.500	6.350	0.500	1.270	1.57	0.250	1.61	1.47	9.45	1.87	6.28	16.0	2.97	7.54	1.34	3.41	0.320	3.84	9.75	T5320
1.625	4.128	2.000	5.080	0.250	0.635	0.267	0.0469	0.302	1.59	10.2	2.02	5.69	14.5	2.54	6.45	1.09	2.78	0.229	2.75	6.98	T4179
1.625	4.128	2.000	5.080	0.500	1.270	0.534	0.0938	0.605	1.82	11.7	2.31	5.69	14.5	2.59	6.58	1.39	3.54	0.269	3.23	8.21	T6114
2.000	5.080	2.500	6.350	0.500	1.270	0.884	0.125	0.806	2.73	17.6	3.48	7.07	18.0	3.23	8.20	1.59	4.05	0.316	3.80	9.65	T4178
2.000	5.080	3.000	7.620	0.500	1.270	0.196	0.250	1.61	2.73	17.6	3.48	7.85	19.9	3.65	9.26	1.59	4.05	0.358	4.30	10.9	T6110
2.000	5.080	3.000	7.620	1.000	2.540	3.93	0.500	3.23	2.73	17.6	3.48	7.85	19.9	3.65	9.26	2.09	5.32	0.441	5.30	13.5	T8027
2.250	5.715	4.250	10.795	1.125	2.858	11.5	1.13	7.26	3.52	22.7	4.48	10.2	25.9	4.87	12.4	2.34	5.95	0.565	6.78	17.2	T6464
2.500	6.350	3.000	7.620	0.500	1.270	1.08	0.125	0.806	4.40	28.4	5.60	8.64	21.9	3.93	9.97	1.84	4.68	0.355	4.25	10.8	T4180
2.500	6.350	3.500	8.890	0.500	1.270	2.36	0.250	1.61	4.40	28.4	5.60	9.43	23.9	4.34	11.0	1.84	4.68	0.396	4.75	12.1	T6100
2.500	6.350	3.500	8.890	1.000	2.540	4.71	0.500	3.23	4.40	28.4	5.60	9.43	23.9	4.34	11.0	2.34	5.95	0.480	5.75	14.6	T5468
2.500	6.350	3.750	9.525	1.250	3.175	7.67	0.781	5.04	4.40	28.4	5.60	9.82	24.9	4.55	11.5	2.59	6.59	0.542	6.50	16.5	T5479
2.500	6.350	3.750	9.525	1.500	3.810	9.20	0.938	6.05	4.40	28.4	5.60	9.82	24.9	4.55	11.5	2.84	7.22	0.584	7.00	17.8	T5690
3.000	7.620	4.500	11.430	1.500	3.810	13.3	1.13	7.26	6.14	39.6	7.82	11.8	29.9	5.47	13.9	3.06	7.77	0.649	7.79	19.8	T5581
3.000	7.620	5.000	12.700	1.000	2.540	12.6	1.00	6.45	6.14	39.6	7.82	12.6	31.9	5.91	15.0	2.56	6.50	0.607	7.29	18.5	T6379
3.100	7.874	5.850	14.859	1.375	3.493	26.6	1.89	12.2	6.45	41.6	8.21	14.1	35.7	6.75	17.2	2.97	7.54	0.745	8.94	22.7	T5582
3.250	8.255	4.500	11.430	1.500	3.810	11.4	0.938	6.05	7.63	49.2	9.71	12.2	30.9	5.58	14.2	3.22	8.18	0.641	7.69	19.5	T5737
3.250	8.255	5.000	12.700	1.500	3.810	17.0	1.31	8.47	7.63	49.2	9.71	13.0	32.9	6.01	15.3	3.22	8.18	0.683	8.19	20.8	T9259
4.000	10.160	5.250	13.335	2.000	5.080	18.2	1.25	8.06	11.7	75.7	14.9	14.5	36.9	6.63	16.8	4.09	10.4	0.781	9.38	23.8	T5611
4.000	10.160	6.000	15.240	2.000	5.080	31.4	2.00	12.9	6.91	44.6	8.80	15.7	39.9	6.81	17.3	3.64	9.26	0.850	10.2	25.9	T9260

* The Arnold Engineering Co., Marengo, Ill.

† For calculating net core area, multiply by the following stacking factors:
    For 0.0005-in. strip, multiply by 0.50
    For 0.001-in. strip, multiply by 0.75
    For 0.002-in. strip, multiply by 0.85
    For 0.004-in. strip, multiply by 0.90
    For 0.006-in. strip, multiply by 0.90

‡ Based on the assumption of a zero residual hole and negligible bowing of the coil away from the core case.

"gapless" construction is generally used. This can be accomplished by two different methods, one by use of a stack of washer-shaped disks of magnetic material, the other by use of a tape core wound like a roll of electrical tape. In each method the insulating material is normally magnesium oxide. During annealing, it serves to keep the metal from fusing together and at all times causes the adjacent pieces of material to be insulated from one another. The washer-shaped disks, while they completely eliminate the air gap, cannot result in so sharp a rectangular loop as with the other type because of the grain orientation of the material caused by the rolling process. Since with the tape cores the flux is always traveling in the direction of the rolling, they are therefore preferred. Various sizes of tape-wound cores are shown in Fig. 6-77. There is, however, a small air gap, but the area of the adjacent magnetic surfaces across which the flux flows is so large that this effect is almost negligible.

Normally a thickness of six-thousandths is used for 60-cycle amplifiers and two-thousandths for 400-cycle magnetic amplifiers. Because of this gapless construction, the winding process is somewhat more difficult than for normal E cores used in transformers. Each turn of wire must be threaded through the center of the core, the circular window, and it is somewhat more difficult to make the turns completely uniform because of the larger circumference of the outside of the core compared with that of the window.

A number of these cores, constituting a complete amplifier, can be stacked lightly on top of one another. The entire amplifier, together with its rectifiers, can be potted with Acme Star Compound, made by the Acme Wire Company. In order to eliminate some of the inner-winding capacitances, the coils should first be dipped in wax. To avoid some of the problems of low-temperature operation, the rectifiers themselves should be completely coated with silicone grease. It is not necessary, however, to pot the amplifier if it can be supported in the can in such a way as to prevent shock and vibration stresses being imparted to the core. The entire amplifier can be hermetically sealed, leaving the only access to the amplifier through terminals. Figure 6-79 shows the cores and internal construction of a commercially available 400-cycle magnetic amplifier, together with the complete potted unit. Figure 6-61 shows the construction of an open-type magnetic amplifier.

6-21. Transistor Magnetic Amplifiers. Each type of amplifier possesses certain advantages and disadvantages. In many cases the transistor amplifier is superior to the magnetic amplifier (magamp). In other cases, the reverse is true. For this reason an amplifier which is comprised of the two types may provide performance which exceeds that of either type separately. Commonly, transistors and magamps are combined into a single amplifier. Since it is impossible to cover all the numerous circuits* that are possible, only two types are considered in this book: (1) magnetic preamplifier and transistor power amplifier and (2) transistor preamplifier and magnetic power amplifier.

The transistor amplifier is a better a-c amplifier than the magamp. When d-c response is required, the magamp is more suitable. In terms

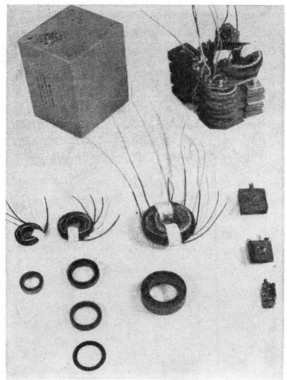

FIG. 6-79. Magnetic amplifier and its construction. (*The Ahrendt Instrument Co., College Park, Md.*)

of power source the transistor amplifier requires a d-c supply whereas the magamp is more conveniently operated from an a-c supply. This is not a severe limitation for lower power applications, since both a-c and d-c power are usually available. For larger sizes (500 watts or greater) a d-c supply can become a serious problem. Although the field of power transistors is developing rapidly, a magamp can be designed to handle more power than a transistor amplifier.

* See Ref. 27 for other transistor-magamp circuits.

D-C to A-C Amplifier. When a unidirectional signal is to be amplified with an a-c output, the first type of amplifier may be used. With a magnetic preamplifier and a transistor power amplifier, the over-all amplifier will possess a high gain with a relatively small time constant.

Since the magamp acts only as a direct-voltage amplifier, it can be of small size. A self-saturating single-ended magamp of the type shown in Fig. 6-58 can be used as the first stage. This drives a class B push-pull transistor output stage. Such an amplifier is shown in Fig. 6-80a driving a servomotor load. The power supply for the magamp operates at rated frequency. In this circuit, greater linearity is achieved if the power source approaches a square wave in shape and if the magamp is biased for a 90° firing angle. The motor is tuned for unity power factor at stall. A maximum of power is delivered to the motor when the output of the magamp is sufficient to drive the transistors into saturation.

A-C to D-C Amplifier. Since the time constant of a magamp increases with gain, for even fairly large output power, the transistor power amplifier may be superior. The transistor is a superior a-c amplifier; however, a magamp may be more attractive for various reasons, including (1) capability of supplying large-power-output requirements, (2) high-temperature operation, and (3) limited d-c power source. To reduce the time constant without sacrificing gain, the combination amplifier comprising a transistor preamplifier and a magnetic power amplifier may prove most suitable. One such combination amplifier is shown in Fig. 6-80b.

This amplifier is capable of supplying a low-voltage size-18 a-c servomotor. The amplifier operates at 115 volts ± 10 per cent, 400 cps ± 5 per cent. The input impedance is greater than 10,000 ohms. For regions about the null, the gain of the complete amplifier is approximately 2,500. With larger signal inputs, for example 25 to 30 mv, the gain drops to about one-half the null gain or 1,300. Because the amplifier is used about the null, this amount of saturation usually does not degrade performance. Use of 905 silicone transistors and IN336 silicone rectifiers permits the operation of this amplifier over a temperature range of -40 to $+175°$F.

Most of the component values of the amplifier are specified on the drawing. Precise values of some components are set when the amplifier is tied into the servomotor. For example, R_{13} is used to adjust the amplifier gain. Its nominal value is 200,000 ohms. As R_{13} is reduced, the gain of the magnetic amplifier is reduced. R_{12} and R_{14}, nominal values 10,000, are adjusted so that the amplifier output can be balanced.

When this amplifier is properly encapsulated, it is capable of operation under severe vibration (± 15 g at frequencies of 50 to 100 cps) and high shock loads (30 g along any axis).

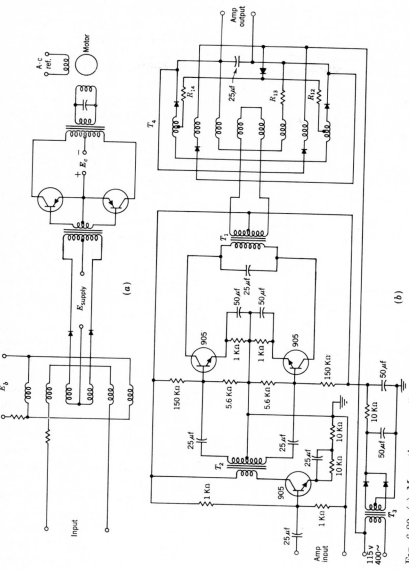

FIG. 6-80. (a) Magnetic preamplifier and transistor power amplifier. (b) Transistor preamplifier and magnetic power amplifier.

255

6-22. Controlled Rectifier. * This semiconductor device shows promise of replacing many magamp and thyratron applications. The unit consists of two *p-n* junctions and one *n-p* junction as shown in Fig. 6-81*a*. The schematic for the controlled rectifier is similar to that for a diode except for the addition of the gate lead. The unit is analogous in operation to the thyratron except that the controlled rectifier operates at high voltages and with smaller switching times. Figure 6-81*b* shows the voltage-current characteristic that displays the switchlike action of the controlled rectifier.

The operation of the controlled rectifier may best be understood by comparing it to the operation of a gas thyratron, a rectifying device in which the conduction cycle is controlled by power applied to a third

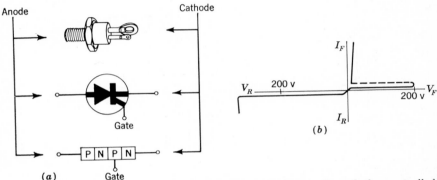

Fig. 6-81. (*a*) Sketch of schematic, and internal construction of the controlled rectifier. (*General Electric Co., Syracuse, N.Y.*) (*b*) Controlled rectifier-voltage current characteristics.

electrode (the thyratron grid). In the controlled rectifier this third electrode is called the *gate*. As is the case with a thyratron, conduction can be achieved either by exceeding some critical anode to cathode voltage or by applying a signal to the grid or gate.

Consider a controlled rectifier with no applied gate signal and a forward breakover voltage of 200 volts. Assume the reverse breakdown to be at a substantially higher voltage. The voltage-current characteristic appears in Fig. 6-81, and the voltage relationships of a device in an a-c circuit are shown in Fig. 6-82*a*. In this figure, losses due to forward voltage drop during conduction and forward and reverse leakage during blocking have been exaggerated for clarity. It can be seen that the controlled rectifier blocks current flow in each direction until the forward breakover voltage is exceeded, at which time the device "fires" and

* The controlled rectifier is the trade name of this device, which was introduced by General Electric Co. early in 1958.

continues to conduct until the forward voltage is removed. (Actually there is a small forward holding current required to maintain forward conduction.)

Now consider the same device with a signal applied to the gate. This signal is generally applied from a high impedance source of the order of several volts. The source may be a-c or d-c; however, for firing control, the gate voltage should be positive with respect to the cathode. The gate input impedance ranges from 10 to 100 ohms at the firing point. (See diagram of Fig. 6-82b.) As the gate current is increased, a critical point is reached at which the device breaks down at any positive anode to cathode voltage greater than a few volts. After breakdown, the impedance of the device is low and the current is essentially limited only

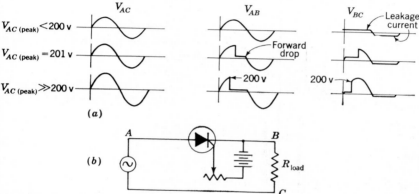

Fig. 6-82. (a) Voltage relationships in an a-c circuit. (b) Circuit used to generate waveforms of (a).

by the load. The gate loses control after breakdown, and the device can be cut off only by reducing the anode voltage to zero. This, of course, is identical to the loss of grid control in a thyratron. Firing of the controlled rectifier may be accomplished in as many ways as have been devised for firing thyratrons.

Lower temperatures require higher gate currents to fire. Thus the gate circuit should be designed to provide a firing current and voltage greater than the maximum required to fire and less than the maximum allowable gate current of 300 ma and maximum allowable gate voltage of 5 volts. Reverse gate current (out of the gate terminal) should be limited by a diode in series with the gate lead if reverse voltages appear in the gate circuit.

Peak voltages of up to 400 volts are presently available with higher-voltage models under development. Many of the thyratron circuits of Secs. 6-12 and 6-13 are directly applicable to use with controlled rectifiers.

Units can be connected in series, parallel, or multiphase for the purpose of meeting a wide variety of control applications. The unit operates at power gains of greater than 150,000 and is capable of switching at 1 μsec. Because of its low internal resistance (approximately 0.2 ohm), the unit operates at high efficiency. The voltage drop is on the order of 1 volt.

6-23. Rotating Amplifiers: Ward Leonard Control. When servomechanisms are required to control large power loads, the choice generally resolves itself into one between hydraulic systems or electrical systems involving d-c motors. If it is desirable to keep the system all electrical and a d-c motor is chosen, about the only choice of power amplifier to excite the d-c motor is a rotating amplifier. Such amplifiers are of three basically similar types—the Ward Leonard system, the Regulex or Rototrol generator, and the Amplidyne generator. Each consists essentially of a generator driven by an induction motor at a relatively constant speed (about 3,600 rpm, except in the very large sizes, where the speed is usually 1,800 rpm). Operation is based upon the principle that a small change in field current can produce a large change in armature current.

The Ward Leonard system employs a simple motor-generator set. The servoamplifier excites the fields of the generator, which is generally of the split type, fed from a push-pull d-c amplifier. The field is split in order to allow the net field flux to be reversed easily. When the currents in the two halves are equal, the flux is zero and the output voltage is almost zero. An increase in current in either one of the two sides of the split field causes an output voltage that is proportional to the field excitation (but at a much higher level) to appear across the brushes of the armature. The polarity of the voltage is dependent upon which of the two fields has the greater current.

A servomechanism employing the Ward Leonard system is shown in Fig. 6-83. In this circuit, the synchro actuating-signal voltage is rectified and amplified by means of triodes that are excited with supply frequency. The rectified signal is filtered and applied to a push-pull d-c power amplifier, whose load is the differentially wound field coils of the power generator. Actuating-signal voltages cause unbalance of the currents in these tubes, which are initially balanced to have equal field strength for zero actuating signal. As is the case in all circuits employing the Ward Leonard system, the generator field coils of the circuit of Fig. 6-83 load the electronic amplifier, so that their characteristics cannot be considered separately.

The voltage from the power generator is applied to the armature of the d-c motor, whose field is excited with a constant direct current. The servomotor also loads the power generator, and their combined characteristics must be considered. As a stabilizing means, the armature voltage is fed back to the input of the amplifier. It passes first through an

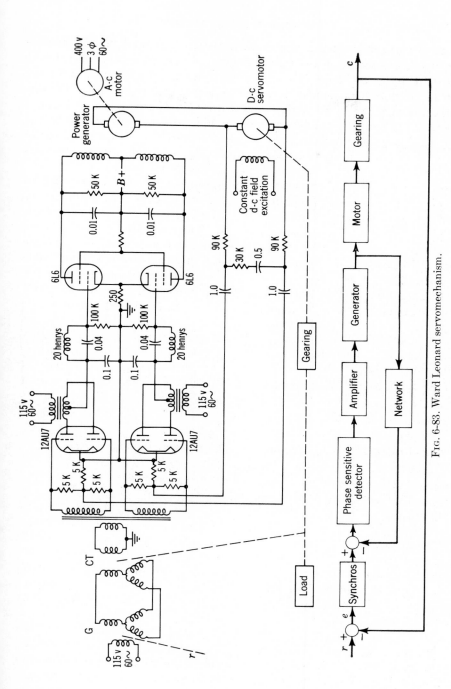

FIG. 6-83. Ward Leonard servomechanism.

259

equalizing network, which blocks the feedback signal when it is unvarying but passes it when the armature voltage is changing. The polarity of the voltage fed back to the input of the amplifier is of such a direction as to produce degeneration. Since no degeneration occurs when the armature voltage is unvarying, the static gain of the amplifier is high, thus causing a high torque sensitivity for the servomechanism. Reduction of the gain of the amplifier under dynamic conditions permits the servomechanism to be stable.

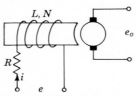

FIG. 6-84. Generator circuit.

One of the problems of rotating amplifiers, and in fact of all electrical power amplifiers of large power output, is the presence of unfavorable dynamics. There are a number of time lags in the Ward Leonard system—one in the generator field and the principal one in the armature circuit. The system transfer function can be derived in the following manner.

Figure 6-84 shows a simple generator for which K = generated volts per field ampere turn ($K = e_o/Ni$). If R is the total field resistance,

$$e = Ri + L \frac{di}{dt} \qquad (6\text{-}52)$$

Transforming and defining $A = KN/R$ volts/volt and $\tau = L/R$,

$$\frac{E_o}{E} = \frac{A}{1 + \tau s} \qquad (6\text{-}53)$$

This is the transfer function of the open-circuited rotor. If the generator feeds the armature of a motor and the sum of the resistances of the generator and motor armatures is R_a and the sum of the inductances is L_a, the following additional equation governing the motor current i_a is obtained:

$$R_a i_a + L_a \frac{di_a}{dt} = e_o \qquad (6\text{-}54)$$

On the assumption of no armature reaction the transfer function from generator field voltage to motor current is

$$\frac{I_a}{E} = \frac{A}{1 + \tau s} \frac{1/R_a}{1 + \tau_a s} \qquad (6\text{-}55)$$

where $\tau_a = L_a/R_a$.

To keep the resistance of the field circuit high and thus reduce the time lag, the power amplifiers generally employ pentodes. If the power amplification is to be kept high, however, the resistance of the armature circuit must be made fairly low, and as a result, its time constant is appreciable. A more quantitative discussion of time constants is presented in the later sections since many of the design factors and dynamic properties of the various systems are similar.

The brush drop in both the generator and the motor can be kept small enough to be no problem, but hysteresis is a difficulty in these systems that is not common to electronic power amplifiers. Even though the field currents are balanced, the output of the power generator may be some finite voltage because of hysteresis in the iron. The use of a higher-quality iron in these Ward Leonard systems reduces the hysteresis.

For the control of large-power d-c motors, the Ward Leonard system does not make as economical use of materials as do the other rotating amplifiers. The Ward Leonard system has a large physical size for the same voltage gain. Furthermore, the other rotating amplifiers can be driven directly from vacuum tubes, which is possible only in the smaller-size Ward Leonard system. Power on the order of 100 watts or less is more economically controlled with the Ward Leonard system, but in larger powers up to 40 kilowatts the Regulex, Rototrol, or Amplidyne generator is used, often in combination with the Ward Leonard system.

6-24. Regulex and Rototrol Generators. The Regulex generator (Allis-Chalmers) and the Rototrol generator (Westinghouse) are both basically d-c generators that use self-excitation as a means of increasing amplification. The Rototrol generator in most applications uses a series field for self-excitation; the Regulex generator more often uses a shunt field. It is somewhat easier to explain the fundamentals in terms of the latter. Since the characteristics of the two machines are basically similar, reference is made only to the Regulex generator after the initial theory is explained.

Figure 6-85 presents the excitation curve of an ordinary d-c generator, showing the relationship of output voltage e_o to ampere turns Ni_f flowing through the field windings. If the generator is externally excited as in the Ward Leonard system, the curve shows the ampere turns that must be supplied by the control source to maintain any given output

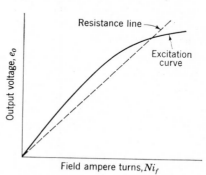

FIG. 6-85. Generator characteristics.

voltage. With a voltage applied across the field winding, including any external resistance, the straight line shows the field current that flows. If the generator is self-excited, the output voltage is the intersection of the two curves, since any smaller output voltage on the excitation curve

causes a larger field current.   This in turn causes a larger output voltage
until the point of intersection is reached.

Suppose that the resistance of the self-excited field is increased until it
has the slope shown in Fig. 6-86 and

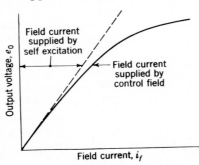

the ampere turns necessary to maintain any given voltage are supplied
by an auxiliary control field.   Up to
saturation of the iron, the output
voltage is proportional to the applied
control current, which is a small percentage of the total field ampere turns
required.   As a consequence, a voltage gain much higher than that of the
Ward Leonard system is obtained in

Fig. 6-86. Regulex-generator characteristics.

the same-sized machine.   Dynamically, the Regulex generator has a

smaller time lag than a Ward Leonard system having the same voltage
gain.

The Regulex generator is made with a number of field windings for
various purposes—up to eight separate windings can be put on a single
machine.   Isolation of the several control signals is then possible.   For
a given power output, this added flexibility increases the size somewhat
over a conventional d-c generator.   Two of the windings may be used
for push-pull control in place of a single split winding.   Another winding
may be used to compensate for voltage drop caused by load current;
however, the compensating field is normally excited by the drop of a
resistor in the armature circuit.   Rather than waste power in a resistor
that serves no useful purpose, the voltage drop across the interpole windings may be used for this compensation.   The other fields are used for
auxiliary control purposes, bias signals, and antihunt circuits.   Typical
field-winding data are shown in Table 6-6.

It is instructive to develop the equations that show the effect of mutual

TABLE 6-6. TYPICAL REGULEX-GENERATOR DATA
(3 kw, 250 volts, 1,750 rpm; $K = 0.75$ volt per field amp-turn)

Field winding	Turns	Resistance, at 25°C	Inductance, henrys	Max current, amp
Shunt	650	90.5	9.34	
Reference	1,200	215	31.8	0.65
Control	400	12.1	3.53	0.54
Auxiliary	300	42.2	1.99	1.75
Damping	52	0.083	0.015	0.35

coupling among the various field windings, since similar relationships exist for all the rotating amplifiers when more than one field is involved. First the transfer function of the two-field separately excited generator is derived to compare it with the derivation already given for the single-field generator. The results are extended to a multiple-field generator, and the transfer function of the Regulex generator is derived.

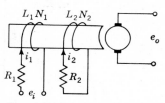

Figure 6-87 is a diagram of the two-field generator, and to determine the transfer function of the generator from e_1 to e_o, the second field is assumed short-circuited through the total resistance of that circuit, including its excitation. The source of any

Fig. 6-87. Two-field generator circuit.

field circuit may contain complex impedances, which are treated in the same way as resistance by using operational impedance (Ls and $1/Cs$). Any shunt impedances are reduced to the equivalent series impedance with the aid of Thevenin's theorem. The equations governing this circuit are

$$e_1 - R_1 i_1 - L_1 \frac{di_1}{dt} - M_{12} \frac{di_2}{dt} = 0 \qquad (6\text{-}56)$$

$$-M_{21} \frac{di_1}{dt} - R_1 i_2 - L_2 \frac{di_2}{dt} = 0 \qquad (6\text{-}57)$$

$$i_1 K N_1 + i_2 K N_2 = e_o \qquad (6\text{-}58)$$

where the K's are defined as before and the M's are the mutual inductances. When perfect coupling is assumed,

$$M_{12} = \sqrt{L_1 L_2} = L_1 \frac{N_2}{N_1} \qquad (6\text{-}59)$$

The above equations are Laplace-transformed:

$$\frac{E_o}{E_1} = \frac{A_1}{1 + (\tau_1 + \tau_2)s} \qquad (6\text{-}60)$$

where $A_1 = KN_1/R_1$, $\tau_1 = L_1/R_1$, and $\tau_2 = L_2/R_2$. This derivation can be extended, as before, to include the cascaded lag of the armature circuit.

Equation (6-60) reveals that the effect of the additional field winding is to add to the time lag of the field circuit. This takes into account the full mutual effect of the two fields. By superposition, the effect on e_o of an additional signal in the second field winding is found by using an expression corresponding to Eq. (6-60), which relates e_o to e_2.

This analysis, again assuming perfect coupling so that

$$M_{km} = \sqrt{L_k L_m} = \frac{L_k N_m}{N_k}$$

can be extended to the N field generator, with the result that

$$\frac{E_o}{E_1} = \frac{A_1}{1 + (\tau_1 + \tau_2 + \cdots \tau_n)s} \qquad (6\text{-}61)$$

The effect of eddy currents can be treated as an additional short-circuited field if the time constant is known. The sum of the inherent-field time constants, neglecting external resistance, is a function only of the volume of the copper and iron used and is independent of the number of turns, the size of the wire, or any other considerations.

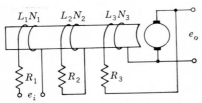

FIG. 6-88. Regulex generator.

A third field can be added to the two-field generator of Fig. 6-84. If this field is excited from the armature of the generator itself, the circuit diagram of the Regulex generator with two control fields is as shown in Fig. 6-88. The equations describing the circuit are written and yield the following for the open-circuit output of the Regulex generator:

$$\frac{E_o}{E_1} = \frac{A_1/(1 - A_3)}{1 + (\tau_1 + \tau_2 + \tau_3)s/(1 - A_3)} \qquad (6\text{-}62)$$

where $A_1 = KN_1/R_1$ and $A_3 = KN_3/R_3$, the fraction of self-excitation. The Regulex generator still has a single time constant, but it increases linearly with gain. A_3 can be made as close to unity as desired by decreasing the field resistance R_3, as shown in Fig. 6-86. When $A_3 > 1$, the system is unstable. It is often adjusted to unity, however, despite the fact that it may shift to a value greater than 1, since it is the stability of the over-all system that is of primary importance, and the over-all system can be stable with one of the loops unstable (see the Appendix). In the limiting case of $A_3 = 1$, Eq. (6-62) reduces to a simple integration.

Equation (6-62) can be extended to include the inductance and resistance of the armature circuit when the output of the Regulex generator is feeding the rotor of a d-c motor or the field of another generator.

The transfer function, from voltage input e_1 to armature current i_a, is

$$\frac{I_a}{E_1} = \frac{\dfrac{1}{R_a} \dfrac{A_1}{(1 - A_3)}}{(1 + \tau_a s)\left(1 + \dfrac{\tau_1 + \tau_2 + \tau_3}{1 - A_3} s\right)} \qquad (6\text{-}63)$$

where $\tau_a = L_a/R_a$, the ratio of total resistance to total inductance in the armature circuit.

Figure 6-89 is an example of a typical electronic circuit that feeds the Regulex-generator fields and shows the stabilization means commonly employed. The 6L6's control the Regulex-generator fields, which have a resistance of about 1,000 ohms. The Regulex generator feeds a large power generator, which supplies power to the motor. The rate generator provides damping for the system. The other feedback voltage is proportional to the rate of change of the applied motor voltage. It is degenerative to high frequencies and hence reduces the gain at high frequencies but has no feedback of direct current and hence leaves the gain high for

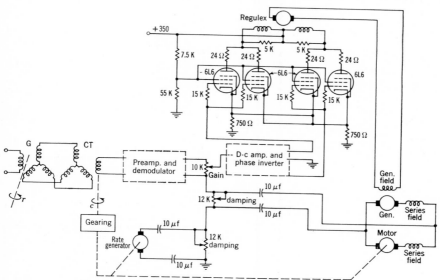

FIG. 6-89. Regulex-generator follow-up control system.

low frequencies. To increase the power gain for supplying large motors, two Regulex generators powered mechanically by the same drive motor can be used in series.

To lower residual voltages and hysteresis, the Regulex generator is constructed with a laminated field structure, usually employing 14-mil punchings of a good grade of transformer iron. It can be seen from a study of Fig. 6-86 that hysteresis lowers the voltage gain of the system. The field structure is operated at a low level of saturation to improve linearity. Interpoles are used to improve commutation. The various windings and performance characteristics are normally designed specifically for the application.

6-25. Theory and Practice of the Amplidyne Generator. The Amplidyne generator incorporates two generator stages in one frame. For a given weight and space, the Amplidyne generator has a higher voltage gain than the Regulex generator. As with all rotating amplifiers, the power gain for good designs is more a function of the amount of copper and iron in the unit than of the operating principle of the device. There tend to be more problems in commutation and brush-position adjustment in the Amplidyne generator than in the others.

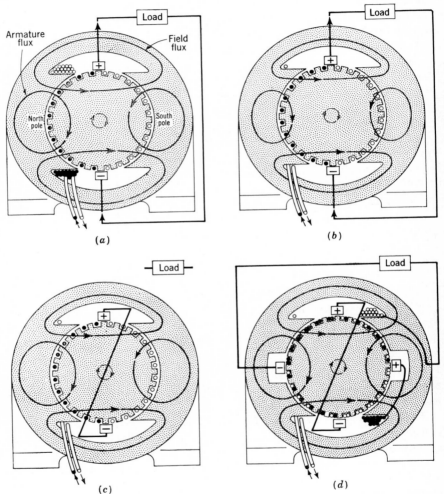

Fig. 6-90. Schematic diagrams of the Amplidyne generator.

The basic principle of the Amplidyne generator is generally explained by using the diagram shown in Fig. 6-90. A conventional d-c generator (10 kw) driven at constant speed is shown schematically in Fig. 6-90a. For the sake of simplicity, the armature also serves as the commutator.

About 100 watts of excitation power supplied to the field coil creates the excitation flux. This flux produces a full-load voltage of 100 volts, which circulates 100 amp (full-load current) through a 1-ohm resistance load. However, the load current, in flowing through the armature conductors, creates an armature flux. This flux is of about the same magnitude as the excitation flux but is not doing any useful work. (Note: The small circles show conductors carrying current toward the reader. The small shaded circles show conductors carrying current away from the reader.)

With a smaller field coil and with excitation power reduced from 100 to 1 watt, the same conventional d-c generator appears as shown in Fig. 6-90b. The new reduced excitation power, and the fact that the number of field turns has been reduced to $\frac{1}{100}$ of the former value, creates only 1 per cent of the original excitation flux. Voltage at the brushes is reduced from 100 to 1 volt. The current load, reduced from 100 to 1 amp, produces only 1 per cent of the former armature flux. The excitation power thus has been reduced to a value where it can readily be supplied and handled by precise control devices.

A short circuit (see Fig. 6-90c) across the brushes restores the armature current and, consequently, the armature flux to their full original values. This occurs because the internal resistance of the armature winding is assumed to be $\frac{1}{100}$ of the load circuit resistance. The load has been disconnected. The excitation and the flux continue to be extremely small, but they now control the full-size armature flux.

To put the short circuit to work, two new brushes are added (shown in Fig. 6-90d), one in the center of each armature-flux loop, just as the conventional brushes are located in the center of the excitation flux. The armature flux is full-sized and so produces 100 volts (full voltage) between the new brushes. The new brushes are then connected to the load—one directly and the other through a compensating field, as shown. Full current, 100 amp, now circulates through the load. In the same armature conductors the new load current adds to and subtracts from the short-circuit current.

The function of the compensating winding is to neutralize any tendency of the load current to set up its own armature flux in opposition to the control flux.

Assume that excitation current is suddenly doubled (an increase in excitation power from 1 to 4 watts). This instantly doubles the short-circuit current, producing double voltage (200 volts) and double load current (200 amp). Thus, by raising control input by 3 watts, output is raised from 10 to 40 kw.

To obtain comparable amplification by conventional means, two generators would be required—one excited by the control signal, the second excited by the output of the first. This would result in a cumulative delay in the response.   The Amplidyne generator combines these two generators into one.   By means of armature excitation, it utilizes the same structure twice.   Response is practically instantaneous.

A photograph of a 1.5-kw Amplidyne generator having a 250-volt 6-amp output is shown in Fig. 6-91, complete with its electronic preamplifier.

The power gain obtainable from such an Amplidyne generator varies from about 700 to 100,000, with the larger gains obtainable most efficiently from the larger generators.   For example, typical gains are 5,000 for a 375-watt unit and 20,000 for an 8-kw unit.   Figure 6-92 shows a servomechanism employing an Amplidyne generator to supply power to

Fig. 6-91. Amplidyne generator and electronic amplifier. (*General Electric Co., Erie, Pa.*)

the servomotor.   The rectifier and power amplifier are much the same as those used in a Ward Leonard system, and the split field is again used in the Amplidyne generator.   This system, however, uses a somewhat more complicated feedback scheme than is used in the Ward Leonard system shown.   The feedback damping signal consists of the sum of voltages from a rate generator (which is, of course, a very small unit compared with the servomotor or the Amplidyne generator), the motor series field, and a special quadrature-axis winding on the Amplidyne generator.   All of these are added together and fed through a network to be subtracted from the actuating signal.

One example of the use of the Amplidyne generator is shown in the photograph of Fig. 6-93.   This planar-type horizontal boring mill is equipped with Amplidyne-generator feed drives and three-dimensional

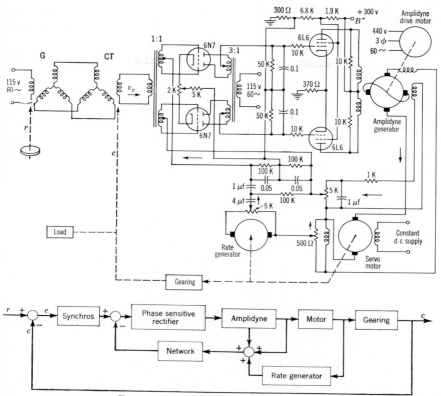

FIG. 6-92. Amplidyne servomechanism.

FIG. 6-93. Horizontal boring mill controlled with Amplidyne generator. (*General Electric Co., Erie, Pa.*)

tracer control. Machining of irregular shapes requires the accurate and rapid positioning of a tracing-head stylus so that it can automatically follow the shape of a template or model. This must be done with accuracy and at a constant rate of speed. It will be noted that the tracing head is mounted on the same machine member as the cutting tool, and therefore as the stylus follows the model, the tool duplicates its shape in the work. Electric signals from the tracing head, which indicate the angle and amount of stylus deflection, are modified by the electronic control to provide two d-c output voltages. These voltages indicate by their polarity and magnitude, respectively, the direction and speed at which two Amplidyne-generator feed drives must run to cause the tracing-head stylus to follow the contour of the model.

The Amplidyne generator has two principal sources of time lag—one caused by the control-field inductance and the other caused by the quadrature-circuit inductance. As in the case of the Ward Leonard system and the Regulex generator, the control field loads the electronic power amplifier and its effect must be considered in determining the control-field lag. Again, this lag is kept small by the use of pentodes in the electronic power amplifier.

The quadrature time lag is the largest time lag in the generator and the most difficult to reduce. The magnitude of desired output voltage determines the number of turns in the quadrature-circuit windings, and the use of added resistance in the quadrature circuit, while it reduces the time lag in the quadrature circuit, also reduces the quadrature current and consequently the output of the generator. Reduction of the quadrature time lag to about equal the control-circuit time lag is usually the best that can be obtained. The control-field time lag is a few tenths of a second, and the quadrature time lag ranges from about 0.025 to 0.20 sec. A third time lag in the direct axis is about 0.002 sec, unless it is feeding a Ward Leonard system. In this case the time lag of the generator field can add as much as a second or two.

For a given machine and driving speed there is a definite time-lag-gain relationship. Increasing the gain causes an increase in time lag. Decreasing the time lag, through the use of field resistance, decreases the gain in proportion. Decreasing the air gap increases the gain but also increases the time lag. An increase in the driving speed, and thus the gain, results in no increase in time lag. This is generally done in aircraft installations through the use of higher motor speeds. Increasing the number of poles also increases the gain with a somewhat smaller increase in time lag, thus improving the performance. The result of any coupling between the quadrature axis and direct axis produces degenerate feedback, which again reduces the gain and quadrature-axis time delay.

When the complete Amplidyne generator is connected to the servo circuit, its transfer function from control-field-voltage input to servo-motor-current output is

$$\frac{I}{E} = \frac{K}{(1 + \tau_c s)(1 + \tau_q s)(1 + \tau_d s)}$$ (6-64)

where $\tau_c = L_c/R_c$ = control-field time constant
L_c = control-field inductance
$\tau_q = L_q/R_q$ = quadrature-circuit time constant
L_q = total inductance of quadrature circuit
$\tau_d = L_a/R_a$ = armature-circuit time constant
L_a and R_a = total inductance and resistance of Amplidyne-generator armature and servomotor armature circuit
K = armature-circuit sensitivity in open-circuit volts per control-field volt. This is equal to $K_1 K_2/R_a$, where $K_1 = K_c/R_c$, $K_2 = K_q/R_q$, K_c is the quadrature-circuit sensitivity in volts per control-field ampere, and K_q is the output sensitivity in volts per quadrature-circuit ampere.

L_c and R_c include the complete control-field current, which comprises the output impedance of the preamplifier added to the Amplidyne-circuit control fields. Table 6-7 presents values of the constants for various size Amplidyne generators. (τ_d is omitted, since it is dependent upon the total armature-circuit constants.)

TABLE 6-7. AMPLIDYNE-GENERATOR CONSTANTS

Power, kw	GE type	$K_1 K_2$	τ_c control field, sec	τ_q quadrature axis, sec
0.5	AM-73	6.46	0.046	0.06
3	AM-610	9.6	0.11	0.17
10	AM-622	5.4	0.15	0.19
25	AM-654	5.19	0.288	0.081
50	AM-658	3.6	0.434	0.13

The transfer function of Eq. (6-64) is based on the following assumptions, which are valid for a well-designed generator and the use of which causes only second-order errors:

1. No coupling exists between the quadrature-axis and direct-axis flux.
2. The output circuit is perfectly compensated so that the output current has no effect on the control flux.
3. Brush-resistance drop is a linear relation.
4. Hysteresis and eddy-current losses are negligible.

The Amplidyne generator can be designed and built to meet a given transfer function within practical tolerances. Extreme changes in temperature, however, may change the transfer-function coefficients by 10 to 20 per cent. Any increase in time lag from this source, however, is accompanied by a decrease in gain, so that the stability of the over-all servomechanism is generally not substantially changed.

The transfer function of the output of the Amplidyne generator can be measured in any one of several ways. One method consists in applying a step-function signal to each of the various stages and measuring the output vs. time. When plotted on semilogarithmic paper, the slope of the output vs. time curve yields the time lag for that stage.

The time lag of the control field can be determined by applying a step-function voltage to the control field with the quadrature circuit open and measuring the output voltage of the quadrature circuit vs. time. The quadrature-circuit time lag can be measured by placing a small resistance in the quadrature circuit and measuring the current of the quadrature circuit for a step-function current applied to the control field. The same result can be obtained by measuring the output voltage of the Amplidyne generator under no-load conditions, since under open-circuit conditions no dynamics are contributed by the output field. The direct-axis time lag is itself usually not of great interest, since the over-all time lag of the direct-axis circuit and the servomotor armature is of primary consequence. The portion contributed by the Amplidyne-generator direct axis can be determined by putting a resistive load on the output and measuring the rise of output current upon the application of a step-function current applied to the quadrature axis. Probably the best method of measuring the over-all transfer function of an Amplidyne generator and motor is to apply sinusoidal signals, plot amplitude and phase shift, and thus determine the corner frequencies and time constants.

The position of the brushes in the Amplidyne generator is quite critical and difficult to set. On generators of less than 1,500 watts, the four brushes are usually on the same holder and fixed with respect to each other. It is necessary to adjust carefully their position relative to that of the field. The quadrature-axis brushes are generally made of a high-resistance material to reduce the residual output voltage. The brushes of the quadrature axis do not wear so well as the others because of the poor commutation in the quadrature axis and the larger ampere-hour load. This can easily be seen from the following example: When the servomotor is running at full speed and the load current is small, the direct-axis brushes are required to carry only this small current. The Amplidyne-generator output, however, is full-voltage, and the quadrature-axis brushes must therefore carry the maximum current to generate this full voltage.

To obtain good regulation, it is necessary for the direct axis to be well commutated. The direct-axis windings used are either concentrated or distributed windings. Good commutation of the quadrature axis is obtained by the large air gap adjacent to the coils under commutation, since only the larger machines have interpoles and quadrature-axis commutation windings. This small segment-to-segment induced voltage resulting from a large number of coils per slot and high brush resistance in the quadrature circuit usually makes further compensation unnecessary.

Both wave and lap windings are used in the armature. The induced voltage per coil and the voltage between commutator segments are kept low by the use of only three coils per slot. The generator is operated at low saturation and good iron is used, thus keeping nonlinearities and hysteresis in the output negligible. The residual output for most machines is on the order of 5 per cent, which can be canceled by the use of a killer, or "dither," winding, if necessary. In some machines this consists of a field winding or a few turns connected to a 60-cycle a-c supply. It is also possible to connect permanent magnets to the armature and produce the same effect, although usually this small residual output does not create enough problems to warrant its elimination. Bar and slot ripple exists on the order of 1 to 10 per cent in the output of the Amplidyne generator. Eddy currents, which cause additional time lags, are reduced by laminating the entire field structure.

There are a number of equalizing circuits used in conjunction with Amplidyne generators. Many of them are not peculiar to the Amplidyne generator and are not discussed here. One common type of equalization, however, consists in feeding back the voltage drop across the

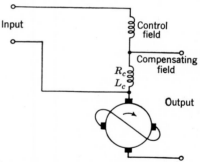

FIG. 6-94. Amplidyne feedback circuit.

direct-axis compensating field to the input of the Amplidyne, as shown in Fig. 6-94. Since the voltage fed back is proportional to the output current of the Amplidyne generator and since the motor drive acceleration is proportional to this current, acceleration damping is produced.

In terms of the resistance R_c and the inductance L_c of the compensating field, the transform relating the Amplidyne-generator armature current and the voltage fed back from the compensating field is

$$\frac{E}{I} = R_c + L_c s \qquad (6\text{-}65)$$

The resistance term provides damping proportional to motor acceleration, whereas the inductance term provides damping proportional to rate of change of motor acceleration. The time constant L_c/R_c of this circuit may be about $\frac{1}{60}$ sec for typical applications. Eddy current, however, produces an additional time lag, thus reducing the over-all transfer function to

$$\frac{E}{I} = \frac{R_c(1 + L_c/R_c s)}{1 + \tau s} \tag{6-66}$$

Ripple voltage in the output must be filtered. Frequencies desired in the feedback circuit, however, are usually high enough so that the ripple frequencies do not affect the dynamic characteristics of the system.

The voltage induced in the quadrature-axis field is another method used in conjunction with the Amplidyne generator. A feedback voltage that is proportional to the rate of change of motor acceleration is provided by the schematic diagram of Fig. 6-95. The diagram can be explained as follows: For a given instantaneous load impedance, the change in quadrature-axis flux results in a change of the output current. Since the motor acceleration is proportional to the output current, any changes in output current result in a change of motor acceleration. Since a voltage is induced in the quadrature-axis winding only when there is a change in quadrature-axis flux, this induced voltage is proportional to changes in acceleration. If it is desired to reduce the time lag of the system at the expense of gain, the output voltage of the Amplidyne generator can be fed back degeneratively to a point in the preamplifier. Consideration of the block diagram and the equations involved shows the conventional manner of reducing this time lag. The feedback can also be made degenerative only at high frequencies and zero at zero frequency.

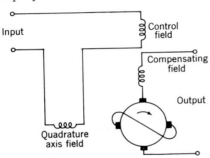

Fig. 6-95. Amplidyne feedback circuit.

PROBLEMS

6-1. Sketch a single-stage d-c amplifier using a chopper to modulate input voltage and a chopper to rectify the output.

6-2. Name properties important to servoamplifiers and properties important to audioamplifiers but unimportant to servoamplifiers.

6-3. Name three beneficial effects from the use of feedback in servoamplifiers.

6-4. Explain how a common power supply could cause cross talk in two servomechanisms.

6-5. Discuss the vacuum-tube performance that depends upon equivalent-circuit analysis and that which depends upon load-line analysis.

6-6. Make a comparative analysis of the use of transistors and vacuum tubes in servomechanism amplifiers.

6-7. Why are four parameters required to define the performance of a transistor amplifier when only three are required for a vacuum tube?

6-8. Explain the advantages and disadvantages of thyratron amplifiers as against vacuum-tube and transistor amplifiers for the power stage of a servoamplifier.

6-9. Discuss advantages and disadvantages of controlled diodes as compared to thyratron amplifiers.

6-10. Cite applications of servomechanisms that would make the advantages of magnetic amplifiers more important than the disadvantages.

6-11. Cite applications of servomechanisms that would make the disadvantages of magnetic amplifiers more important than the advantages.

6-12. A servomechanism uses a magnetic amplifier, but there is in the amplifier a time lag that for the purpose of this problem can be considered of the form $1/(1 + \tau s)$. The time constant is proportional to the gain of the amplifier. It is proposed that it be reduced by means of feeding back a portion of the output signal of the amplifier to its input. Assuming that the servo has a given gain requirement, discuss the merit of this proposal.

6-13. Sketch ϕ and e for each of the oscillograms given in Fig. 6-57.

6-14. Explain how hysteresis reduces the gain of a magnetic amplifier.

6-15. What are the disadvantages of using ordinary transformer iron in magnetic amplifiers?

6-16. Show how bias windings can improve the performance of magnetic amplifiers.

6-17. Explain the operation of the feedback circuit of Fig. 6-75 by going through a complete cycle of operation for each of the various conditions of control current.

6-18. Explain why the shape of the BH curve of the magnetic material influences the necessity of bias windings.

6-19. For a tape-wound core, derive an equation yielding the equivalent air gap.

6-20. Explain how ambient-temperature variations can cause drift in magnetic amplifiers. Which of the circuits would be most susceptible?

6-21. Compare the advantages and disadvantages of the Ward Leonard system, the Regulex generator, and the Amplidyne generator.

6-22. Derive Eq. (6-61).

6-23. Show that the sum of the inherent-field constants of a rotating amplifier, neglecting external resistance, is a function only of the volume of copper and iron used and is independent of the number of turns, the size of wire, or any other consideration.

6-24. Derive Eq. (6-63).

6-25. Explain how hysteresis lowers the voltage gain of the Regulex generator.

6-26. Give a circuit diagram that would show the use of regenerative feedback to increase the gain of the Amplidyne generator.

CHAPTER 7

SERVOMOTORS

7-1. Applications of Servomotors. Most of the smaller motors used in servomechanisms are a-c and are of the two-phase induction-motor type. Their mechanical output power varies from about $\frac{1}{2}$ to 100 watts. A-c motors in sizes larger than this are too inefficient and, if constructed with the desirable torque-speed curves for servo use, are difficult to cool. D-c servomotors vary in size from about $\frac{5}{100}$ to many horsepower

Fig. 7-1. Shaded-pole reversible motor. (*Barber Coleman Co., Rockford, Ill.*)

and are more generally used in larger power servomechanisms. Although universal a-c or d-c motors are sometimes employed in instrument servomechanisms, the most common a-c motor used is one with two-phase excitation, for which approximately half the power is supplied by the line and the other half by the servoamplifier. The voltages applied to the two windings are at right angles to one another, and normally one winding is excited with a fixed voltage. The other winding is excited by the control voltage, which is the output of the servoamplifier.

The output torque of the motor is roughly proportional to the applied control voltage, and the direction of the torque is determined by the polarity of the control voltage. Whenever the "error" of a simple proportional servo reverses its direction, the actuating signal reverses its polarity and the motor therefore reverses its direction of application of torque. The fixed-voltage winding is usually excited from the supply source, which is shifted in phase until it is 90° from the variable control voltage. The phase of the fixed voltage can be shifted by means of a capacitor, and the variable phase of the motor is fed from the output of the servoamplifier, generally through an output transformer. Some servomotors are designed, however, so that they have a high-impedance center-tap winding and may be fed directly from push-pull tubes with somewhat higher dielectric stress to ground. The other winding may or may not be of different impedance.

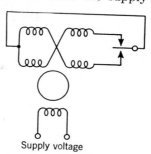

Supply voltage

Fig. 7-2. Control circuit for shaded-pole motor.

Fig. 7-3. Cutaway view of a precision servomotor. (*G-M Laboratories, Chicago, Ill.*)

Applications for motors are so numerous that it would be difficult to list them all. Small motors are used for vending machines, appliances, clocks, office machines, industrial and projection equipment, fans, displays, toys, etc. A motor of this type is shown in Fig. 7-1. Shaded-pole reversible motors of this type are controlled by shorting one pair of shorting coils with a double-throw switch (see Fig. 7-2).

Precision servomotors of the type shown in Fig. 7-3 find application in accurate control systems. Motors of this type are used in instrument servos, computers, inertial-guidance systems, and numerous applications where precision angular motion is required. Because of the large slip frequency and hence the large eddy-current losses in a-c servomotors, these units are utilized primarily in small power applications. The two-phase servomotor is most desirable for instrument servomechanism use.

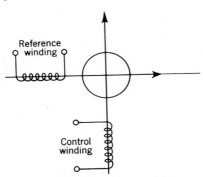

FIG. 7-4. Schematic diagram of a two-phase servomotor.

This motor provides a stall torque that is proportional to the control-field voltage, and the torque-speed characteristics are linear. This type of motor is emphasized in this chapter.

7-2. Theory of A-C Servomotors.

A two-phase servomotor operates as an induction motor. The motor comprises a stator winding, which is a group of coils fitted into the laminated-iron stator structure, and a rotor, which may take one of several forms: (1) squirrel-cage, (2) drag cup, or (3) solid iron. The theory of operation of each type of rotor is similar. The two stator coils are 90 electrical degrees apart in space, as indicated in the schematic of Fig. 7-4. In actual practice, the windings are distributed about the stator. The effect, however, is as shown in the schematic. The windings are excited with alternating voltages that are separated 90° in time phase. The vector diagram of Fig. 7-5 indicates the resultant of the two time-varying vectors that are 90° apart in space. These two component vectors combine to produce a resultant V_{tot} of constant magnitude that rotates at synchronous speed:

$$N_s = \frac{120f}{p} \qquad (7\text{-}1)$$

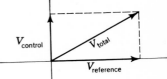

FIG. 7-5. Vector diagram showing operation of induction motor.

where N_s is the synchronous speed in rpm, f is the frequency in cps, and p is the number of poles. For example, in an eight-pole 400-cps motor the resultant field rotates at $(120)(400)/8 = 6,000$ rpm.

The components in the vector diagram of Fig. 7-5 can be combined analytically. The reference voltage is

$$V_{ref} = V \sin \omega t \qquad (7\text{-}2)$$

and the control voltage is written

$$V_{con} = jV \cos \omega t \qquad (7\text{-}3)$$

For balanced operation, which is analyzed here, the magnitudes of each of these vectors are made equal. The two vectors are separated 90° in time phase, as indicated by the use of sin ωt for the reference sinusoid and cos ωt for the control voltage. The operator j indicates 90° space difference between the two vectors. Addition of these vectors yields

$$V_{tot} = V(\sin \omega t + j \cos \omega t) = Ve^{j\omega t} \qquad (7\text{-}4)$$

This is the equation for a vector of constant magnitude that is rotating at $N_s = 120f/p$.

The rotating flux vector intersects the conductors in the rotor and induces voltage which in turn produces currents which flow in these conductors. These currents are determined by the magnitude of the voltage and the motor impedance. With the rotor stationary, the rotor currents are of the same frequency ω as the stator frequency. Because the rotor currents are induced by the rotating field, these currents produce a rotor field with the same number of poles as the stator. The rotor and stator fields do not move with respect to each other. Thus, the two magnetic-field vectors, which rotate together at synchronous speed, produce a starting torque. This torque begins to accelerate the rotor until it reaches its operating speed, which is determined by the windage, friction, and load torques. The rotor, however, can never reach synchronous speed because at this speed the rotor conductors are stationary with respect to the rotating-field vector and no voltage would be induced in them.

When the rotor is turning at N_a rpm (actual speed), the rotating-stator flux vector is turning at N_s (synchronous speed). The slip of the rotor is $N_s - N_a$ and the per cent slip is

$$S = \frac{N_s - N_a}{N_s} \qquad (7\text{-}5)$$

For example, if $N_s = 6{,}000$ rpm, and the no-load speed is $N_a = 5{,}000$ rpm, the per cent slip is

$$S = \frac{6{,}000 - 5{,}000}{6{,}000} = \frac{1}{6} = 1.67 = 16.7\%$$

Since the relative velocities of the rotating-stator field and the rotor differ by $N_s - N_a$, the frequency of the voltages induced in the rotor is $S\omega$. The magnitude of the currents again depends upon the induced voltage and the rotor impedance evaluated at the slip frequency. The rotor field produced by these currents rotates at SN_s, the per unit slip multiplied by the synchronous speed. Since the rotor is mechanically turning at $(1 - S)N_s$, the space angular velocity of the field vector is $SN_s + (1 - S)N_s$ or N_s. Hence the rotor and stator fields remain stationary with respect to each other and torque is produced.

In servo applications, the reference winding is excited continuously, but the control winding is supplied from the output of the error detector and hence is variable. In this manner the torque output is varied by varying this voltage. With fixed reference and control voltages the torque characteristics of an induction motor vary widely with rotor resistance. The torque is proportional to the product of the stator- and rotor-field strengths multiplied by the size of the angle between these *flux vectors*. As the control winding voltage is reduced in magnitude, the stator flux and hence the rotor flux is reduced, which results in a reduction of torque output. The optimum angle between the flux vectors is 90°. It is usually less than this and depends largely upon the impedance of the rotor.

The speed-torque characteristics of a servomotor are most important to its performance. The shape of this characteristic depends largely on the value of rotor resistance. The curves of Fig. 7-6 show typical speed-torque characteristics for several values of rotor resistance. The rotor resistance is usually controlled by increasing the resistance of the conducting material used in the rotor. Induction motors used for delivering power are designed with a minimum of rotor resistance so that maximum torque occurs for small values of slip. Increasing the rotor resistance linearizes the speed-torque characteristic. With a large resistance R_4, the maximum torque is less but the curve is more linear. The variation of starting torque with rotor resistance is obtained from the curves of Fig. 7-6 by observing the intersection of the curves with the zero-speed ordinate. The optimum starting torque is obtained when the value of rotor resistances is R_3. For both large and smaller values the starting torque is less. The maximum product of torque and speed occurs at about half speed with a servomotor and close to synchronous speed with a power motor.

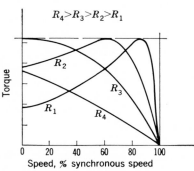

Fig. 7-6. Variation of torque-speed characteristics with rotor resistance.

7-3. Dynamic and Static Characteristics of Servomotors. The speed-torque curves for a typical servomotor are shown in Fig. 7-7. These are important curves that are required to determine servomotor performance. They are typical of servomotor characteristics. The torque is large at zero speed to aid in servo static sensitivity, to give internal damping to the servomechanism, and to prevent single phasing* of the servomotor.

* *Single phasing* means that the motor runs with only one winding excited.

Servo stability cannot depend totally on this internal damping without investigation of the damping at various constant velocities and near zero speed. Since this damping decreases with increasing speed, the stability margin may also decrease in following a moving command. The curves are plotted with rated voltage (115 volts) on the fixed phase and with various values of control voltage. For purposes of analysis, these curves are usually linearized.

The input impedance of a servomotor also shifts with operating conditions. The impedance is largely reactive, and a plot of input impedance for a typical servomotor is shown in Fig. 7-8. The variation of impedance shown on the graph indicates how impossible is the task of choosing a

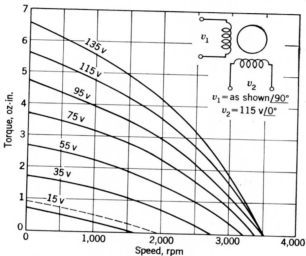

FIG. 7-7. Typical torque-speed performance of a servomotor.

transformer to match the tube impedance with the motor impedance. The back emf developed with rotation is responsible for the major portion of this impedance change.

The back emf developed can be advantageously used. Since its magnitude varies with shaft speed, circuits can be devised that produce output voltages simulating a rate-generator output. Figure 7-9 shows one such circuit in which the bridge circuit on the output of the amplifier is balanced to have zero output voltage when the motor is stalled. The voltage that develops is then proportional to motor velocity and, after harmonic filtering, is fed back to the input of the amplifier.

The speed-torque curves can be obtained experimentally with the aid of a dynamometer. One such unit is discussed in Sec. 14-6. Figure 7-10 shows another method of plotting the speed-torque curves. The test motor is geared to a d-c tachometer and is loaded with a large inertia disk. The angular velocity, which is converted to a voltage with the tachometer, is applied to the horizontal axis of the oscilloscope. The velocity is also passed through a passive circuit that approximately differentiates the velocity. The output is the acceleration that is proportional to the motor torque. The acceleration is applied to the vertical

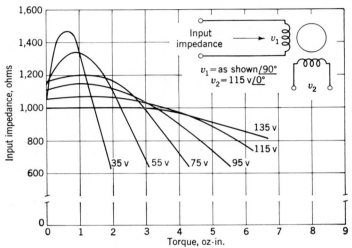

FIG. 7-8. Impedance characteristics of a typical servomotor.

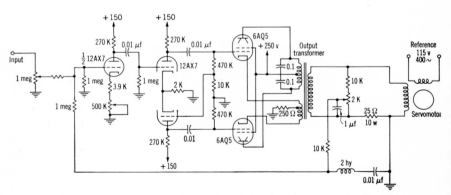

FIG. 7-9. Simulated rate-generator feedback using motor back emf.

plates of the oscilloscope. The speed-torque curve is plotted on the face of the oscilloscope.

The stalled torque of the servomotor is proportional to the voltage applied to the control phase, and since the output torque decreases approximately linearly with speed, it can be considered as producing its stalled torque diminished by the torque absorbed in internal damping. The *viscous-damping coefficient* is proportional to the slope of the speed-torque curve and for a given control voltage is proportional to the stalled torque divided by the no-load speed. Figure 7-11 shows the speed-torque curve and other data for the Mk 8 motor, and Fig. 7-12 gives its physical dimensions. Both figures are based on manufacturer's (Kearfott) catalogue data. The power-in and the power-factor curves in each phase are measured with the voltages held constant at rated value, and the load is varied from zero to stall. The speed-torque curve, the power output,

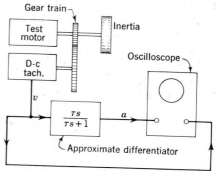

FIG. 7-10. Speed-torque plotter.

and the efficiency are plotted with constant rated-voltage input per phase and with varying load. The no-load speed and stall-torque curves are plotted with fixed-phase voltage constant and with the control-

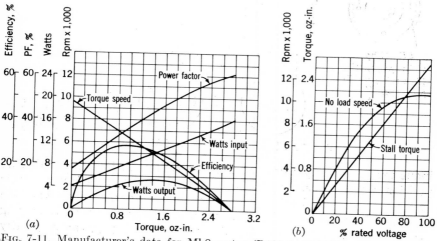

(a)

(b)

FIG. 7-11. Manufacturer's data for Mk8 motor (R160-2, R160-3). (*Kearfott Company, Inc., Little Falls, N.J.*)

phase voltage varied from zero to rated value. Notice the linearity of the speed-torque curve in Fig. 7-11a and the linearity of the stall-torque vs. control-voltage curve of Fig. 7-11b. These are the most important curves for the servo engineer. The power curves are of importance in determining whether a particular motor is of sufficient size to handle the load.

A characteristic in addition to bearing friction that affects the smoothness of operation of a servomotor is the magnetic effect of slot lock, or cogging; this is present to an appreciable degree only in squirrel-cage rotors.   The effect is caused by variation of motor torque with position of the motor shaft.   Although all well-designed servomotors have skewed (i.e., the rotor bars are not parallel to the motor shaft but are skewed as shown in the cutaway view of Fig. 7-3) rotor bars or armature slots to reduce the slot-lock or cogging effect, it is present to some extent in all two-phase squirrel-cage motors.   In some applications, and particularly in use with integrating circuits, a servomechanism having a two-phase

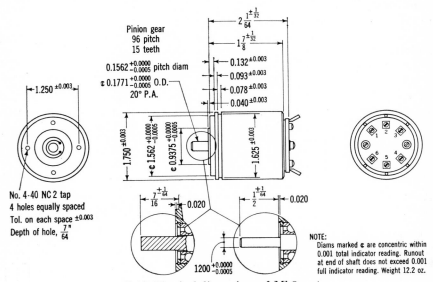

Fig. 7-12. Physical dimensions of Mk8 motor.

induction motor may have an appreciable jitter in its controlled-shaft position when the command is rotating at constant velocity.   It is even possible for cogging to introduce instability into the system when the command is stationary.   Particularly when integrating-type equalizing networks are used, any problem of slot lock, or cogging, can be greatly minimized by the employment of a drag-cup construction or a solid-core rotor.

Although in preliminary calculations it is assumed that the servomotor is linear, there are many nonlinear factors that make it difficult to describe its properties for use in servo design.   For example, the output torque varies with temperature, the torque sensitivity varies with voltage, and the internal damping and input impedance are affected by speed and voltage.

The fact that motors are nonlinear is further demonstrated by measuring the effectiveness of methods of achieving the 90° phase shift between the control-voltage and the fixed-voltage windings. There are two ways of accomplishing this 90° phase shift. Either the phase of the control voltage can be shifted in the amplifier, which is discussed in the chapters on networks and amplifiers, or the phase of the reference voltage can be shifted. If a three-phase supply voltage is available, the necessary two-phase power can be obtained from a pair of the supply lines or by the use of Scott-T connected transformers as is shown in Fig. 7-13. The three-phase voltage is applied to the primary and a two-phase voltage appears at the secondary. Such methods yield a low impedance source for the fixed-voltage winding. Typically, however, the 90° phase shift is obtained by placing a capacitor in series with the constant-excitation winding. The capacitance value is normally chosen by stalling the motor

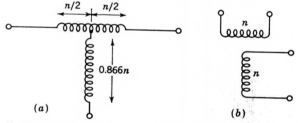

FIG 7-13. Scott-connected transformer. (a) Three-phase primary. (b) Two-phase secondary.

and adjusting its value until the fixed voltage is 90° from the control voltage. Nonlinearities in the operation of the motor, however, affect both the phase shift and the applied voltage.

If this normal procedure is followed with the 5-watt Diehl motor, shown in Fig. 7-14, the value of the capacitance is found to be 1.7 μf, and 115 volts is obtained at the motor winding with the application of 177 volts to the input of the capacitor and motor combination. When the shaft of the motor is released and allowed to run free, the phase of the motor voltage shifts 15° and the voltage on the windings increases to 185 volts. By measuring the phase of the input signal to the amplifier (for example, the synchro-control-transformer output), the motor capacitor is adjusted to result in a motor voltage at right angles to this phase when the signal is made zero and the motor is neither rotating nor stalled but only has its fixed phase excited. A different value of capacitance is obtained from that previously found, even if the phase shift in the amplifier is zero.

For the 400-cycle Mk 8 motor shown in Fig. 7-12, a capacitance of 0.52 μf and a potential of 59 volts applied to the capacitor and fixed-voltage winding in series will produce 115 volts at 90° to the line across the winding when the motor is stalled. When the shaft is allowed to run free, the winding potential becomes 133 volts and the phase shifts an additional 18°.

One measure of the dynamic properties of a servomotor is given by two commonly cited figures of merit: the torque-to-inertia ratio and the torque-squared-to-inertia ratio. In a typical design problem, the engineer has a choice of the gear ratio between motor and load. A gear ratio can be chosen so that the inertia of the load reflected to the motor

FIG. 7-14. Five-watt Diehl servomotor. (*Diehl Manufacturing Company, Somerville, N.J.*)

shaft is equal to the motor inertia. For a matched gear ratio, the maximum acceleration of the load is produced by a motor with the largest torque-squared-to-inertia ratio. This can be seen from the analysis in which the following nomenclature is used:

$$J_m = \text{motor inertia}$$
$$J_L = \text{load inertia (fixed)}$$
$$N = \text{gear ratio} = \text{motor speed/load speed}$$
$$T_s = \text{stall torque of motor}$$
$$\alpha = \text{angular acceleration}$$

The angular acceleration of the motor is the torque divided by the inertia of the motor plus the reflected inertia of the load, which is written

$$\alpha_m = \frac{T_s}{J_m + J_L/N^2} \tag{7-6}$$

But the acceleration of the load α_L is related to α_m by the gear ratio

$$\alpha_L = \frac{1}{N}\,\alpha_m = \frac{T_s}{NJ_m + J_L/N} \tag{7-7}$$

To determine the value of N that will cause the maximum α_L, Eq. (7-7) is maximized. The maximum is found by determining the minimum of the denominator as follows:

$$\frac{d}{dN}\left(NJ_m + \frac{J_L}{N}\right) = 0 = J_m - \frac{J_L}{N^2} \tag{7-8}$$

which reduces to

$$N_p{}^2 = \frac{J_L}{J_m} \tag{7-9}$$

The maximum angular acceleration of the output is found by substituting Eq. (7-9) into Eq. (7-7) with the result that

$$\alpha_{L,\max} = \frac{T_s}{\sqrt{\dfrac{J_L}{J_m}}\,J_m + \sqrt{\dfrac{J_m}{J_L}}\,J_L} = \frac{T_s}{2\sqrt{J_L J_m}} = \frac{1}{2\sqrt{J_L}}\frac{T_s}{\sqrt{J_m}} \tag{7-10}$$

Hence the motor with the greatest $T_s{}^2/J_m$ produces the greatest angular acceleration of the load.

This figure of merit takes into account the speed of the motor. If a 2:1 gear ratio is placed on a motor to produce a lower speed but higher torque output, the torque-squared-to-inertia ratio either at the motor shaft or at the geared-down shaft is the same, but the torque-to-inertia ratio is lower at the geared-down shaft.

If, however, the gear ratio is fixed and is large enough so that the factor determining the acceleration of the load is the same as the acceleration of the motor, the motor with the largest torque-to-inertia ratio will accelerate the load the most. In each case, the torque chosen is the stalled torque at rated voltage (which also varies with winding temperature; for example, as the winding temperature of the 5-watt Diehl motor increases 60°F, the torque drops 15 per cent).

In order to keep the speed within reason, 400-cycle motors must be designed with more poles than 60-cycle motors. For example, the synchronous speed of a two-pole 400-cycle motor is 24,000 rpm, which presents severe bearing problems as well as the requirement of considerable gearing to reduce the speed and increase the torque to useful values. Within a given frame size, which theoretically sets a limit on the power rating of the motor, the designer must obtain a number of poles. Theoretically, doubling the number of poles halves the speed and doubles the torque. In practice, the speed is halved, but the torque is not quite doubled. Thus, the power output of the motor diminishes with reduced speed. The torque-squared-to-inertia figure is improved, however, which results in a higher-performance motor. Most 400-cycle servomotors have four, six, or eight poles.

7-4. Servomotor Transfer Function. Before the transfer function is determined, the performance of the motor is considered from a physical point of view. The two phases of an a-c motor are the excitation, or fixed, phase and the control, or variable, phase. If the fixed field is excited and the control field is shorted, the output torque is zero. If, while in this state, the shaft is turned with the fingers, a distinct tendency to drag is felt. This is "internal" electrical damping. The motor shaft acts as if the rotor had been dipped into molasses. As the shaft is turned, currents are induced in the rotor. The magnitude of these currents is proportional to the velocity in the same manner as in the a-c rate generator, which is discussed in Chap 8. The internal damping is reduced, however, unless the control winding is driven from a low impedance source.

Suppose full reference voltage is applied to the fixed phase while a variable voltage is applied to the control phase. As the control voltage is increased, the torque increases uniformly. Hence the motor produces a damping torque proportional to velocity and a torque proportional to the control voltage. This physical reasoning is borne out by the following analysis, which is based on the speed-torque curves of Fig. 7-15. These curves, together with a knowledge of load conditions and motor inertia, are sufficient for determining the motor transfer function. A simple inertia load J is assumed, and a transfer function is found from these linearized speed-torque curves, from which is written the expression

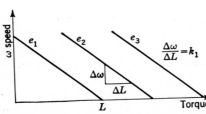

FIG. 7-15. Linearized speed-torque curve for servomotor.

$$\omega = k_1 L + k_2 e \qquad (7\text{-}11)$$

where k_1 is the slope of the speed-torque curve and k_2 is found from the intersection of the speed-torque curves with the $L = 0$ axis. Equation (7-11) is easily rewritten in the form

$$L + m\omega = k e_{in} \qquad (7\text{-}12)$$

where m is the slope $= -1/k_1 = -\Delta L/\Delta\omega$ and k is the ratio k_2/k_1.

Suppose the motor drives an inertia load $\bar{L} = Js^2\Theta$, where Θ is the angle of the motor shaft. The shaft velocity $\bar{\omega}$ is

$$\bar{\omega} = s\Theta$$

The equation is obtained by combination with the above expression:

$$Js^2\Theta = k\bar{e}_{in} - ms\Theta \qquad (7\text{-}13)$$

and is rearranged as follows:

$$\Theta = \frac{k\bar{e}_{in}}{s(Js + m)} \qquad (7\text{-}14)$$

Figure 7-16 shows the block diagram of a motor. In this figure, $K_m = k/m$ and $\tau = J/m$. It must be emphasized that the block diagram of Fig. 7-16 and the transfer function of Eq. (7-14) are applicable only for a motor driving an inertia load.

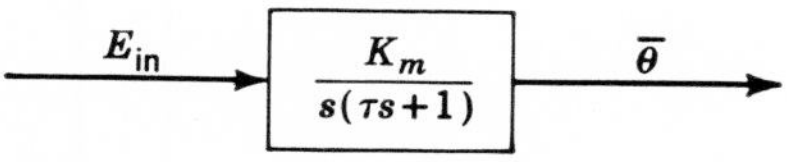

FIG. 7-16. Block diagram of servomotor.

In the actual design of a servo system it is necessary to obtain numerical values for the transfer function of Eq. (7-14) from the manufacturer's literature. A speed-torque curve similar to Fig. 7-11 is usually supplied by the manufacturer. Since the speed-torque curve is given only for full-rated applied voltage, approximations must be made to obtain the transfer function. Since a position servo generally operates about a null, i.e., for values of control voltage near zero, the slope of the zero-voltage speed-torque curve is more accurate than the slope of the rated-voltage curve. This slope is approximately one-half the slope of the full-rated-voltage curve. Hence as a first approximation

$$m = \frac{1}{2}\frac{\text{stall torque (rated voltage)}}{\text{no-load speed (rated voltage)}} \qquad (7\text{-}15)$$

where the $\frac{1}{2}$ accounts for the difference in slope between the zero-voltage and rated-voltage speed-torque curve. The other constant is

$$k = \frac{\text{stall torque}}{\text{rated control voltage}} \qquad (7\text{-}16)$$

The stall torque is read from the speed-torque curve at the point where the speed is zero, and the no-load speed is read at the point where the torque is zero. For the motor of Fig. 7-11,

Stall torque = L_0 = 2.75 oz-in.

No-load speed = ω_0 = 9,800 rpm = $\dfrac{(9,800)(2\pi)}{60}$

= 1,030 radians/sec

Rated control voltage = 115 volts

The constants are:

$$k = \frac{2.75}{115} = 2.39 \times 10^{-2} \text{ oz-in./volt}$$

$$m = \frac{1}{2}\frac{2.75}{1,030} = 0.269 \times 10^{-2} \text{ oz-in.-sec}$$

For an inertia load that is equal to the inertia of the motor:

$$J = (2)(4.0) = 8.0 \text{ gm-cm}^2$$
$$= \frac{8.0}{980} \text{ gm-cm-sec}^2 = \frac{8.0}{980}(0.0137) \text{ oz-in.-sec}^2$$
$$= 11.2 \times 10^{-5} \text{ oz-in.-sec}^2$$

The transfer-function quantities are

$$\text{Time constant} = \tau = \frac{J}{M} = \frac{11.2 \times 10^{-5} \text{ oz-in.-sec}^2}{0.258 \times 10^{-2} \text{ oz-in.-sec}}$$

$$\text{Motor constant} = K_m = \frac{k}{m} = \frac{2.39 \times 10^{-2} \text{ oz-in./volt}}{0.268 \times 10^{-2} \text{ oz-in.-sec}}$$

$$= 8.93 \frac{\text{radians/sec}}{\text{volt}}$$

The approximate transfer function is

$$\frac{\Theta}{e} = \frac{8.93}{s(0.0418s + 1)} \tag{7-17}$$

If a family of speed-torque curves is available or can be run, a more accurate transfer function can be obtained. The servomotor shown in Fig. 7-14 was run on a dynamometer.* Speed-torque curves for various control voltages are plotted in Fig. 7-17a. The intersections with the $\omega = 0$ axis of the various curves are taken from Fig. 7-17a and plotted on Fig. 7-17b. The slope of the speed-torque curve for zero control voltage is used for m since the servo operates near the null (zero control volts):

$$m = \frac{(+1.5) - (1.5)}{(2\pi/60)(-1,700 - 2,350)} = -\frac{3}{(4,050)(6.28/60)}$$
$$= 7.09 \times 10^{-3} \text{ oz-in.-sec}$$

The slope of the linear portion of Fig. 7-17b is used to determine the second constant:

$$k = \frac{3.9 - 0.2}{0.5 \times 115} = 64 \times 10^{-3} \text{ oz-in./volt}$$

The transfer-function quantities and the motor inertia

$$J_m = 0.14 \text{ oz-in.}^{-2}$$

* The dynamometer is discussed in Sec. 14-6.

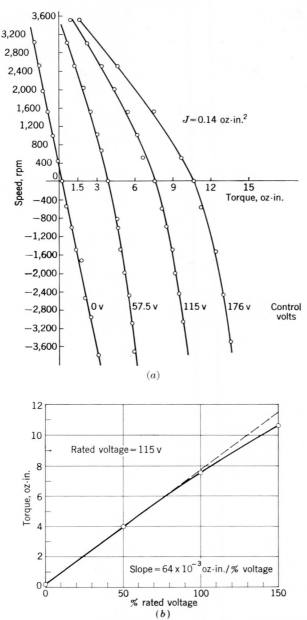

FIG. 7-17. (a) Experimental speed-torque curves for 5-watt Diehl servomotor shown in Fig 7-14. (b) Torque-voltage curve taken from Fig. 7-17a.

are found from these values. For an inertia load that is equal to the motor inertia:

$$J = \frac{2(0.14)}{32 \times 12} \frac{\text{oz-in.}^2}{\text{in./sec}^2} = 0.73 \times 10^{-3} \text{ oz-in.-sec}^2$$

The time constant and motor constant are:

$$\tau = \frac{J}{m} = \frac{0.73 \times 10^{-3}}{7.09 \times 10^{-3}} = 0.103 \text{ sec}$$

$$K_m = \frac{k}{m} = \frac{64 \times 10^{-3}}{7.09 \times 10^{-3}} = 9.04 \frac{\text{radians/sec}}{\text{volt}}$$

It is interesting to compare the values of k and m found accurately with those found approximately. The approximate values are found from the manufacturer's literature:

$$k = \frac{7.5}{115} = 65.2 \times 10^{-3} \text{ oz-in./volt}$$

$$m = \frac{1}{2} \frac{7.5}{(3,600)(2\pi/60)} = 9.95 \times 10^{-3} \text{ oz-in.-sec}$$

Notice that although the torque-voltage constant k compares closely, the slope of the speed-torque curve m shows some error.

Use of the ½ factor is justified on the basis of the shape of the speed-torque curves of Fig. 7-17a. The nonlinear shape of the speed-torque curves and the change of slope with voltage preclude a high degree of accuracy.

The corner frequency of the 5-watt Diehl motor is greater than 3 cycles when fed from a zero-source-impedance control amplifier. When the amplifier impedance is raised to 400 ohms, the corner frequency drops about a half, or to 1½ cycles. If the amplifier is designed to match motor impedance and hence has an output impedance of about 800 ohms, the corner frequency is further reduced to about 1 cycle. These values do not change appreciably whether the 90° phase shift of the fixed windings is obtained from the low impedance source or from a phase-shifting capacitor.

Figure 7-18 shows an experimentally obtained frequency response from the 5-watt Diehl motor, as obtained from an essentially zero impedance source, with a constant 115-volt line applied to the fixed-voltage winding and various control voltages (each at 90° to the line) applied to the control winding. Although balanced sideband suppressed carrier signals were used in obtaining these data, further experimentation reveals that the response data are little affected by the use of unbalanced sidebands. For example, in a particular experiment in which the control voltage had a magnitude of 10 volts, the addition of a quadrature suppressed carrier voltage of a magnitude of 5 volts had no appreciable effect on motor performance despite the greatly unbalanced sidebands resulting.

7-5. Construction of A-C Servomotors. Figure 7-14 is a photograph of a two-phase 5-watt servomotor, the characteristics of which are

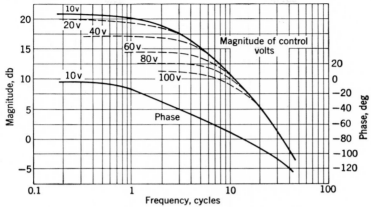

FIG. 7-18. Experimental transfer locus of 5-watt Diehl motor (Fig. 7-14).

described in the previous section. It has a no-load speed close to 3,600 rpm and is constructed for 115-volt 60-cycle operation.

The construction of two-phase servomotor rotors can be either squirrel-cage, solid, or drag-cup. All of these types have distributed windings in the stator.

Squirrel Cage. The most common of these is shown in Fig. 7-3 and is the squirrel cage. It has the same appearance as the rotor of any squirrel-cage induction motor except that its diameter is made very small to reduce inertia and thus improve its acceleration characteristics. Although reducing the rotor diameter also reduces the torque output, the inertia is reduced by the square of the diameter, whereas the torque is reduced only by the first power of the diameter. Practical considerations limit the extent to which this fact can be advantageously applied. A

FIG. 7-19. Squirrel-cage servomotor. (*Boston Div., Minneapolis-Honeywell, Boston.*)

typical high-performance squirrel-cage servomotor is shown in the photograph of Fig. 7-19, and an assembly drawing of another squirrel-cage servomotor is shown in Fig. 7-20.

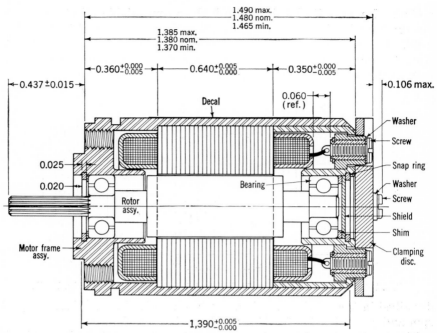

FIG. 7-20. Assembly drawing of squirrel-cage servomotor. (*American Electronics, Inc., Los Angeles.*)

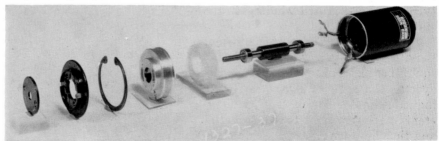

FIG. 7-21. Servomotor using solid rotor. (*Ford Instrument Company, Long Island City, N.Y.*)

Solid Iron Rotor. A solid rotor is normally made of such magnetic material as Swedish iron and is used to carry both the flux and the induced rotor currents. The net result is that the motor acts as if bars were present to carry current, although the torque per watt input is about 20 per cent less. Figure 7-21 illustrates a commercial motor that uses this type of rotor construction. This motor is designed to operate directly from the plates of the output tubes of an electronic amplifier. Use of a high-voltage motor eliminates the need for an output transformer and, hence, results in a saving in amplifier space and weight.

Drag Cup.   The drag-cup motor is much like the drag-cup generator, and its cup is constructed of copper, aluminum, or an alloy.   A photograph of several of these units is shown in Fig. 7-22.   A sketch of this type of motor is shown in Fig. 7-23.   For the same size and weight as the squirrel-cage construction, it generally has lower torque.   Since all the

Fig. 7-22. Several drag-cup servomotors.   (*Arma Corporation, Hempstead, N.Y.*)

heavy iron laminations are stationary and only a light cup is rotating, the inertia is quite small.   In order to further reduce the inertia of servo gear trains, some motors have pinions cut integral with the shaft, thus making the inertia of the first pinion of the train extremely small.

Servomotors often utilize flange mountings for ease in construction of servo gear trains, and their shaft is held fairly concentric to the flange-mounting surface.   The tolerance can be somewhat relaxed over that used in synchros, since the motor operates at a much higher speed in the gear train and a given angle of backlash has much less effect on the stability and accuracy of the system. Bearing friction is generally kept to

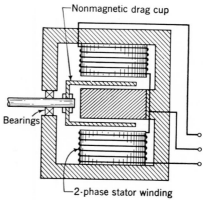

Fig. 7-23. Sketch of a drag-cup servomotor.

a minimum by the use of ball bearings.   The bearing friction of a 5-watt servomotor is about $\frac{1}{100}$ oz-in.   This friction requires a control voltage of 1 volt on the control winding to be overcome, assuming that the other winding is excited with 115 volts at 90° phase angle.

Because servomotors are often required to stand still for long periods of time with full excitation on the fixed-voltage winding, cooling is often a severe problem.   It is common to design servomotors above 10 watts output with a blower attached to the frame.   This blower is powered by a separate constant-speed motor and permits the over-all dimensions of the motor to be reduced considerably.   Such a construction is shown in the drawing of Fig. 7-24.   The use of the auxiliary blower permits a 25-watt-output motor in the same frame size as a 10-watt motor that does not have a blower.   For the larger power, higher-current windings are used, and although the frame size is the same, the blower occupies an additional volume about the same size as the motor itself.

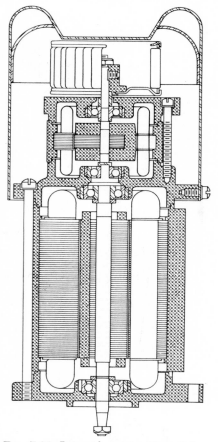

FIG. 7-24. Internal construction of fan-cooled motor.

Frequently it is possible to stabilize a feedback system by adding viscous damping to the motor shaft. Motors are available that have adjustable eddy-current dampers. Units of this type usually are built for small-size motors since a large waste of power would occur in larger (20 watt and greater) applications.   Damping is accomplished by the relative motion between a low-inertia drag cup connected to the rotor and a fixed magnetic field. As the cup cuts lines of flux set up by the magnetic field, eddy currents are induced in the cup.   These currents create a drag or damping effect proportional to the speed of the rotor.   The degree of damping is varied by adjusting the strength of the fixed magnetic field.   This is accomplished by a screwdriver adjustment on the back cap of the motor.   This type of damping, which is included in the motor of Fig. 7-25, is simpler and more rugged than other conventional methods.   In contrast with network damping, this viscous-drag damping is insensitive to line-frequency changes.   It is cheaper and more compact than tachometer-generator feedback but not always equivalent.

Frequently viscous damping is used in small servomotors. A small paddle wheel is affixed to the shaft and caused to move through grease or heavy oil.

An integral motor and a-c tachometer provide a power source with an output-velocity voltage available to be fed back for damping in large power systems. Since these units utilize one housing and one shaft, a saving in size and cost results. The resulting servo possesses a greater adjustability of damping. A typical combination unit is shown in Fig. 7-26. The drawing of Fig. 7-27 shows the internal construction of a servomotor-tachometer assembly.

FIG. 7-25. Damped control motor utilizing an adjustable eddy-current disk. (*Servomechanisms, Inc., Hawthorne, Calif.*)

Notice the drag-cup rotor used on the tachometer section. D-c motors and tachometers on one shaft are also available for use in d-c systems.

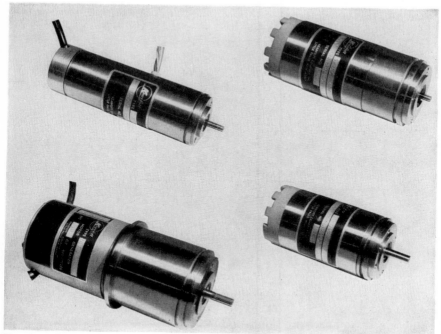

FIG. 7-26. Servomotor and tachometer combined on one shaft. (*Kearfott Company, Inc., Clifton, N.J.*)

For very low power instrument applications, a drag-cup servo-motor, not designed for excitation directly from the vacuum-tube amplifier, can be used without an output transformer, as shown in the circuit of Fig. 7-28. In this instance, the constant direct current from the B+ supply, which is the quiescent current of the output tube, also

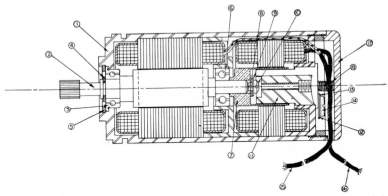

FIG. 7-27. Assembly drawing of a servomotor tachometer within an integral frame. (1) Motor-frame assembly, 1; (2) rotor assembly, 1; (3) flanged bearing, 1; (4) C ring, 1; (5) snap ring, 1; (6) bearing, 1; (7) drag cut, 1; (8) flat washer, 1; (9) lock washer, 1; (10) screw, 1; (11) slug, 1; (12) flat washer, 2; (13) lock washer, 2; (14) screw, 2; (15) black sleeving, 1; (16) red sleeving, 1; (17) end cap, 1; (18) screw, 2; (19) decal, 1. (*American Electronics, Inc., Los Angeles.*)

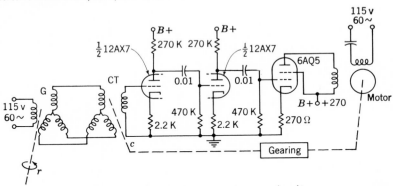

FIG. 7-28. Simple instrument-servo circuit.

produces a viscous drag on the motor and thus helps to stabilize the servomechanism. The entire amplifier can thus be made quite compact even in this vacuum-tube version.

The characteristics of various a-c servomotors are given in Table 7-1, as obtained from information supplied by the manufacturers.

7-6. D-C Servomotors. Among the various d-c servomotors are the series motor, the shunt (armature- or field-controlled) motor, and the per-

TABLE 7-1. A-C SERVOMOTORS

Manufacturer	Type	Frequency	Weight, lb	Power output, watts	J, oz-in.^{2}	Stall torque, oz-in.	No-load speed, rpm	Voltage		Impedance at stall, ohms		Stall power factor	Remarks
								Main	Control	Main	Control		
Kollsman	951-0160	60	0.50	0.50	0.057	0.55	3,450	115	115	2900	2000	0.88	Induction type
Kollsman	999-0462	400	0.38	1.6	0.057	0.45	10,950	110	110	1200	1200	0.70	Induction type
Kollsman	890-0120600	60	2.6	4.0	0.096	4.6	3,400	32	32	43.5	43.5	0.83	Induction generator built-in
Kollsman	1204-01611	60	0.475	0.24	0.0222	0.41	3,030	115	115	1700	1700	0.83	Drag-cup type
Kollsman	863-04640	400	1.1	4.0	0.0183	0.65	19,500	120	120	740	740	0.80	Drag-cup type
Arma	1A60	60	0.80	1.5	0.03	1.9	3,250	40	40	137	137	0.66	Solid rotor
Arma	1A400	400	0.8	1.5	0.030	0.80	9,800	115	115	700	700	0.38	Solid rotor
Kearfott	R110-2	400	0.46	1.7	0.018	1.45	5,000	115	115/57.5	1030	4500/1125	0.49	Induction type
Kearfott	R111-2	400	0.77	2.6	0.022	2.25	5,000	115	115/57.5	640	3400/850	0.43	Induction type
Kearfott	R119-2A	400	0.281	1.0	0.0058	0.63	6,200	115	115/57.5	2175	6600/1650	0.575	Induction type
Ford	629842	60	1.7	5	0.056	7.0	3,400	115	115	640	640	0.65	Solid rotor
Ford	840079	400	1.7	7.0	0.050	3.6	7,800	115	115	295	295	0.324	Solid rotor
Ford	839866	60	7.1	37	3.31	26	3,500	115	115	156	156	0.95	Solid rotor
American Electronics	172	400	0.9	6.0	0.018	2.7	9,000	115	115/57.5	495	495/121	0.60	Induction type
Diehl	SM-15	400	0.45	1.8	0.016	1.5	4,800	115	115/57.5	1030	1030/257	0.49	Induction type
Diehl	SSFPE 25-32-1	60	1.5	2	0.077	4.5	1,750	115	115	500	500	0.6	Induction type
Diehl	SSFPE 49-7	60	2.9	10	0.66	12.0	3,300	115	115	440	440	0.87	Induction type
Diehl	SSFPF 49-9	60	4	25	0.66	20.0	3,500	115	115	240	240	0.90	Blower cooling
Diehl	SSFPF 66-11-1	60	10	50	1.10	55.0	3,600	115	115	82	82	0.93	Blower cooling
Diehl	SSFPF 85-18-1	60	11.2	100	2.0	95.0	3,500	115	115	70	70	0.95	Blower cooling
Minneapolis-Honeywell	SM-080	400	0.76	2.5	0.022	2.35	4,800	115	115/57.5	640	640/160	0.43	Induction type

299

manent-magnet fixed-excitation shunt motor. These units develop high output power in a given size and, in the case of the field-controlled shunt motor, require little control power. Radio-interference generation, brush wear, and d-c amplifier drift are problems. Isolation and matching of d-c circuits are difficult as compared with a-c circuits.

The series motor has high starting torque and current with poor speed regulation. Reversibility is obtained with a switching system that reverses the field terminals or with a split-series winding, one winding for each direction of rotation. The latter reduces motor efficiency. A typical speed-torque curve shows a high stall torque and rapid reduction of torque with increasing speed. This results in good damping but gives a large velocity error.

The shunt motor has good speed regulation and starting torque. Reversibility may be obtained with an armature or field-polarity-reversal switching system or by using a split-shunt winding, one winding for each direction of rotation. The latter reduces motor efficiency. Armature control or field control is available with a shunt motor.

The permanent-magnet motor is a fixed-excitation shunt motor where the field is actually supplied by a permanent magnet. Performance is similar to the shunt motor with armature control and fixed field.

D-c motors can be controlled by using either the current of the field winding or the armature current. The control of field current is less common, since it is undesirable to supply the large fixed armature current necessary for large d-c servomotors. There are also dynamic advantages in armature control. This arises from the fact that the transfer function from armature voltage v_a to motor shaft angle θ is idealized to the following expression:

$$\frac{\theta}{V_a} = \frac{1}{K_a s(1 + \tau_m s)} \qquad (7\text{-}18)$$

where K_a is the torque of the motor per ampere of armature current and is dependent upon its instantaneous speed and voltage. If armature resistance loss is neglected, the d-c motors have the same value of K_a for a given speed and voltage. It can be calculated from the following expression:

$$K_a = K_v(550/746) \qquad (7\text{-}19)$$

where K_v is the back emf developed by the armature per radian per second of rotation. A typical figure for a 110-volt, 1,500-rpm d-c servomotor is $K_a = 1.4$ lb-ft/amp.

The value of τ_m in Eq. (7-18) can be calculated from the expression

$$\tau_m = \frac{RJ}{K_a K_v} \qquad (7\text{-}20)$$

where R is the armature resistance and J is its inertia.

The transfer function for the d-c servomotor [Eq. (7-18)] can be derived from the speed-torque curve as shown in Sec. 7-4 for a-c servomotors. Two characteristic curves are shown in Fig. 7-29. The speed-torque curve is quite similar to that for the a-c servomotor. A more accurate but more complicated transfer function includes the effects of such things

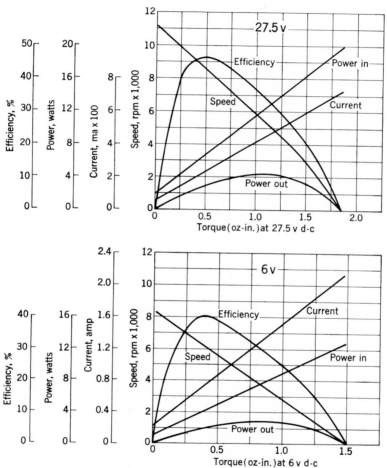

FIG. 7-29. Characteristic curves for d-c servomotor.

as winding time lags and armature inductance. The speed-torque characteristics are greatly affected by the type of excitation, i.e., series, shunt, or fixed. D-c machines develop large power output in a small size. Extreme environmental conditions can be withstood by sealing the units. The major application of d-c motors in aircraft control systems is in power actuators where weight and space limitations demand a unit with a large power per volume ratio.

For the field control of d-c motors, the idealized transfer function from field voltage to motor shaft angle is

$$\frac{\theta}{V_f} = \frac{K_f}{R_f J} \frac{1}{s^2(1 + \tau_f s)} \tag{7-21}$$

where K_f = torque developed per ampere of field current
R_f = field resistance
J = armature inertia
$\tau_f = L_f/R_f$ = field time constant

The presence of the s^2 term in Eq. (7-21) compared with the s term of Eq. (7-18) indicates that field control introduces a greater stability problem.

Because windings are necessary in the armature of a d-c motor, the inertia of d-c motors tends to be larger than that of squirrel-cage a-c motors. The added friction drag of the brushes is another factor to discourage their use in instrument servomechanisms. Slot lock is important as in the case of a-c motors, and the armature slots are normally skewed to avoid this effect at slow speeds.

Commutation is also a problem, and interpoles are sometimes used in the larger d-c servomotors to improve this. The problem is accentuated at high altitudes, and units have been hermetically sealed to avoid the difficulty. Sometimes the worst commutator problems arise from the fact that the motors operate at stalled condition most of the time, and large currents must flow from the brush to the slowly moving commutator bars. The brushes also require maintenance attention, and arcing can cause radio interference. Commutating windings are generally used in order to keep the torque vs. armature-current curve linear beyond the rated torque. Their use reduces armature inductance by about one-third, thus yielding a lower armature-circuit time constant.

The field of d-c servomotors of all sizes is normally operated well beyond the knee of the saturation curve to keep the torque less sensitive to changes in field voltage and to increase the torque sensitivity of the motor. If the motor is used in an instrument servomechanism and has a permanent-magnet field, good compensation is necessary to avoid demagnetization of the field magnets upon sudden reversal of signal. A typical permanent-magnet-field d-c servomotor is shown in Fig. 7-30. The characteristic curves for this machine are shown in Fig. 7-29 for two values of voltage. The field structure for this machine consists of Alnico VI cast in the form of a circular ring that completely surrounds the armature. This unique construction provides a strong magnetic flux, concentrated in a motor that measures slightly over 1 in. in diameter. A flat wafer-type commutator is used to reduce over-all length. This design allows the brushes to be inserted through the rear of the motor. This motor is manufactured with a rotatable brush holder that is adjustable for best commutation and power output. The armatures are wound with heavy Formvar wire over Mylar insulation. After winding, the armatures are ground, impregnated, baked, and sprayed with corrosion-inhibiting material.

The effect of hysteresis and eddy currents is generally negligible. The pole pieces are of laminated construction to reduce arcing of the brushes in their rapid rates of signal change. Further improvement is sometimes obtained with a completely laminated flux path. Circuits to control d-c servomotors for thyratron and rotating-amplifier control are given in Chap. 6.

7-7. Motor Dampers. A servomechanism can be stabilized in any number of ways. Perhaps the first that comes to mind is load stabilization. One method of accomplishing this is to add viscous damping to the motor shaft or to the controlled shaft. While this method is effective, it has a number of disadvantages. If a viscous fluid is used to achieve this damping, provision must be made for a housing to contain the fluid and for some means of maintaining its characteristics constant with variations in temperature. Another objection to the use of ordinary viscous damping is its inflexibility. While networks can be varied to achieve a number of

FIG. 7-30. Permanent-magnet-field d-c servomotor. (*Servo-Tek Products Co., Hawthorne, N.J.*)

dynamic effects, viscous damping can achieve the variations of but one parameter. This is often insufficient to change the loop transfer function to have the proper characteristics.

One of the principal disadvantages of the application of viscous damping is the power consumption involved. The use of this method of providing damping dissipates considerable power in dragging the motor shaft through the viscous medium. Consequently viscous damping, and in some cases an approximation of viscous damping through the utilization of dry friction, is used only with servomechanisms of the smallest power. A device that does have considerable application, however, is the friction damper, sometimes called the Lancaster damper. It applies damping to the motor shaft during transients and while the motor is accelerating rapidly, but it absorbs no power during steady-state velocity commands.

A cutaway view of the Lancaster damper is shown in Fig. 7-31.   It consists essentially of a disk and bushing, which can be clamped to the motor shaft; a flywheel, which is free to rotate with respect to the pressure disk which is attached to the motor shaft; a felt washer, which is soaked in oil and which restrains the relative motion between the flywheel and the pressure disk; and a spring, which adjusts the restraining force.

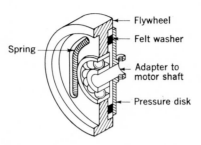

FIG. 7-31. Construction of friction damper.

If this device is clamped on the motor shaft and the flywheel held fixed, a viscous drag acts on the motor shaft because of the viscous drag of the pressure disk on the felt washer.   The motor shaft is damped with a simple viscous drag.   When in actual use, however, the flywheel is free to rotate, so that during rapid changing motions of the motor shaft, the flywheel inertia causes it to stand relatively still and a viscous drag is exerted on the motor shaft.   When the servomechanism is tracking a constant-velocity command and the motor shaft is rotating at relatively constant angular velocity, the drag of the felt washer on the flywheel causes it to rotate at motor speed and hence no drag is exerted on the motor shaft.   The velocity following error is reduced, and no power is required to rotate the friction damper.

The viscous-damping characteristic of the friction damper can be varied by changing the spring pressure with which the felt presses against the inertia disk.   The inertia can be changed by a relatively simple redesign of the friction damper.   There are many types of friction damper other than the one shown, one of which actually uses a reservoir of oil and paddle wheels to couple the inertia viscously to the motor shaft.

It is easily seen that friction dampers are restricted to use with small motors, generally on the order of 10 watts or less.   This, in turn, restricts their application to instrument servomechanisms or small motors.   One of the principal difficulties with these devices is the variation in viscosity of the fluid with operating temperature.   Silicone fluids, however, have been developed that have a very small change of viscosity with temperature.   The ranges of temperature encountered in military applications often cause the performance obtained from an ordinary friction damper to be insufficiently consistent.   Therefore, in some of these applications the temperature of the fluid or the case is thermostatically controlled.

Another design of friction damper devised to minimize the effect of temperature variation adds a spring between the inertia and motor shaft on an ordinary friction damper.   The addition of such a spring permits the use of the friction damper despite changes in operating temperatures up to 150°F.   Other schemes have been used for reducing temperature effects, such as the elimination of the use of fluid entirely.   Powders, such as graphite and other lubricating materials, are sometimes used. Even dry friction has been used as a means of coupling the inertia to the motor shaft.   To give some element of proportionality to the "viscous" damping, the more complicated of these employ several sets of friction disks with various spring pressures.   The varying accelerations of the motor produce varying amounts of friction applied to the shaft, thus approximating to some extent the linear characteristics of viscous friction.

One of the more successful methods of eliminating the temperature effect utilizes the principles of magnetic coupling and is illustrated in Fig. 7-32.   This damper consists of permanent magnets and an inner rotor, which is free to turn; a thin copper shell, which is coupled rigidly to the servomotor shaft; and an outer keeper of soft magnetic iron, which

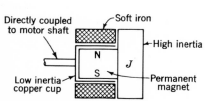

FIG. 7-32. Magnetic-coupled damper.

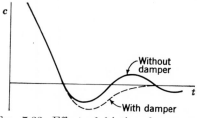

FIG. 7-33. Effect of friction damper on servo transient response.

completes the magnetic circuit and is fixed to the frame of the servomotor.   Additional inertia is coupled to the permanent magnet.   The use of such a device reduces the change in damping constant over extreme changes of temperature to about 2:1.   Any residual temperature effect is almost solely due to changes in the conductivity of the copper cup.

The dynamic effect of the use of friction dampers can be seen by a study of Fig. 7-33, which shows the transient recovery of a servomechanism without and with the use of a friction damper in recovering from the same transient.   The solid line shows the transient response of the servo controlled shaft without the use of the friction damper, and the dotted curve shows the transient when the friction damper has been added.   At the peak of the overshoot, the additional inertia of the friction damper causes the motor to rotate in the same direction for a longer period of time, thus causing a larger overshoot.   The inertia on the inertia damper continues to rotate in this direction, however, as the motor shaft reverses its direction, and causes a strong damping force to be applied to the motor.   Under ideal conditions the inertia disk stops rotation at the same time as the motor shaft ceases to rotate.

This transient response hints at a difficulty encountered with friction dampers, i.e., poor transient recovery from slewing. If the servomechanism has been slewing at a constant velocity for any length of time, a large amount of energy is stored in the inertia of the damper. It may take considerable time to absorb the energy in the damper when recovering from this slewing condition. This difficulty cannot be minimized by the reduction of inertia of the damper, since this is one of the dynamic-design characteristics of the damper. With some additional mechanical complexity, however, it is possible to disengage the damper during slewing. A device to accomplish this can take the form of a slip clutch that disengages the damper when the servomotor is slewed for any length of time. This feature prevents large overshoots and does not affect the dynamic performance of the servo under normal operation.

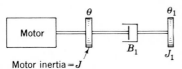

Motor inertia = J

Fig. 7-34. Schematic of Lancaster damper.

The dynamic effect of the use of the friction damper for load stabilization can be investigated with the following notation:

J = moment of inertia of servomotor
B = viscous-damping coefficient of servomotor
J_1 = moment of inertia of friction damper
B_1 = viscous-damping coefficient of friction damper

These quantities are shown in the schematic diagram of Fig. 7-34. The over-all transfer function is obtained by writing two equations, one each about θ and θ_1.

$$kE_{in} - Bs\theta = Js^2\theta + B_1s(\theta - \theta_1) \qquad (7\text{-}22)$$
$$0 = J_1s^2\theta_1 + B_1s(\theta_1 - \theta) \qquad (7\text{-}23)$$

where $kE_{in} - Bs\theta$ represents the equation for the motor torque. Solution of these equations yields the transfer function from servomotor torque input to position of the motor-shaft output:

$$G = \frac{(1/J)(s + B_1/J_1)}{s\left(s^2 + \dfrac{J_1B + JB_1 + J_1B_1}{JJ_1}s + \dfrac{B_1B}{JJ_1}\right)} \qquad (7\text{-}24)$$

The transfer function without the damper is found by setting $B_1 = 0$ in Eq. (7-24) with the result that

$$G = \frac{1/J}{s(s + B/J)} \qquad (7\text{-}25)$$

If the quadratic factor in the denominator of Eq. (7-24) is assumed to be overdamped, this equation can be written

$$G = \frac{(1/J)(s + B_1/J_1)}{s(s + \omega_1)(s + \omega_2)} \qquad (7\text{-}26)$$

By a proper choice of damping characteristics, ω_1 can be made as small as desired. The maximum value of ω_2 is as follows:

$$\omega_2 = \frac{B}{J} + \frac{B_1}{J_1} + \frac{B_1}{J} \qquad (7\text{-}27)$$

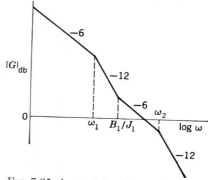

The amplitude response and the various corner frequencies are shown in the diagram of Fig. 7-35. When the servo performance with and without the damper is compared it can be seen that low-frequency servo gain can be increased. The veloc-ity following error is reduced, servo

FIG. 7-35. Asymptote plot of Eq. (7-24).

resistance to external torque loads is increased, and the corner frequency is extended from B/J to $(B/J + B_1/J_1 + B_1/J)$. Sufficient flexibility of design is desirable to allow adjustment of the parameters of the damp-ers so that the various corner frequencies can be properly selected for any given application.

It sometimes helps, in thinking roughly about this device, to consider the motor and damper combination at low- and high-oscillation fre-quencies. At low frequencies, the inertia disk keeps in step with the motor shaft; therefore the first corner frequency is the motor damping B divided by the total inertia $J + J_1$. At high frequencies, the inertia disk practically stands still; so the high corner frequency is the total damping $B + B_1$ divided by the motor inertia J. It is recognized, by comparison with the actual equations, that this method yields only approximate results, but it is a method of obtaining a physical picture of what happens in the frequency domain, even as Fig. 7-33 helps give a picture of what happens in the time domain.

In the event that the servomotor has negligible viscous-damping effect from internal eddy-current characteristics (in other words, if the motor has a flat torque-speed curve), the transfer function of the servo-motor is a straight line having a slope of -12 db/octave. If such a motor were used with a proportional amplifier, instability would be the inevitable result. The addition of a friction damper, however, causes the motor-damper characteristics to be as follows:

$$G = \frac{(1/J)(s + B_1/J_1)}{s^2 \left(s + \dfrac{J + J_1}{J J_1} B_1\right)} \qquad (7\text{-}28)$$

The servo can now be stabilized because the slope can be made to be −6 db/octave at gain crossover (see the Appendix). Theoretically, the velocity following error of such a servo is zero.

Friction dampers can be used to contribute to the favorable dynamics of a servomechanism. A simple a-c amplifier can be used in conjunction with a servomotor without the necessity of a rate generator or electrical-network equalization. The use of a friction damper also permits more gear-train backlash than is possible with cascaded equalizing networks. Friction dampers are, however, an additional piece of mechanical equipment that can become disadjusted.

As an example of the type of performance that can be expected from an instrument servomechanism using only a friction damper as a means of stabilization, a servomechanism was constructed utilizing the 5-watt Diehl servomotor with the spring-coupled friction damper and a 100:1 gear ratio. The torque sensitivity of the servo was 0.2 oz-in./deg at the motor shaft, and the natural frequency of the servomechanism was about 15 cps. The servomechanism was tested, among other things, with a constant-velocity command of 60°/sec. The maximum error of the servomechanism under these conditions was 1½°, and the transient completely decayed in about ³⁄₁₀ sec.

7-8. Clutches. Many types of clutches are used to couple two shafts. The amount of coupling can be varied in a continuous (proportional-coupling) manner or in a steplike (on-off) fashion. To be satisfactory for servomechanism application a clutch must exhibit certain characteristics. The control of the coupling must be accomplished with relatively low-power signals, and the coupling must be capable of fast response. The clutch must exhibit a minimum of hysteresis and should transmit zero torque when the control signal is zero. For the continuous type of units the torque transmitted should be linear with respect to the control signal.

Clutches find less application in instrument servomechanisms. They are utilized to a larger extent in larger power (¹⁄₁₀ to 3 hp) applications. In this application, clutches act as a prime mover that consists of a constantly rotating shaft driven by a motor. The power drive of the servomechanism is coupled by a clutch to this rotating shaft. Clutches offer a response that is quite different from other forms of actuators. Very high accelerations can be obtained by suddenly coupling a stationary load into a large inertia wheel that is rotating at high velocity. A large source of torque can be controlled with a relatively low source of power, and a single drive can be clutched to several output shafts. The following four types are considered: (1) magnetically actuated friction disk, (2) hysteresis, (3) eddy current, and (4) magnetic particles (fluid or power).

Magnetically Actuated Friction Disk. This type of clutch is most widely used in servo systems. Fast response time (5 msec) and long life are achieved by careful selection of the friction-surface material. Figure 7-36 shows the principle of operation of a single-end magnetic clutch. This magnetic clutch is designed with single-end concentric input and output shafts (shaft through shaft) located at the mounting end of the unit. This type of design permits the engineer to mount the clutch in a manner similar to a standard servomotor or synchro, for example. This results in a single-line gear train and convenient assembly and servicing. Input and output shafts are coupled when the coil is energized. Couplings are designed with flat faces to minimize angular-displacement error upon engagement. The operation of this clutch is similar to a solenoid. As current is passed through the magnetic coil a field is

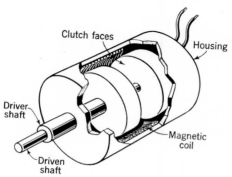

Fig. 7-36. Single-end magnetic clutch. (*Sterling Precision Corp., Flushing, N.Y.*)

established. The two plates are attracted and the clutch is thus engaged. This operation is not continuous but is of the on-off type.

Figure 7-37 shows a cutaway view of a magnetic clutch which utilizes crown-tooth couplings which provide nonslip contact between the input and output shafts. The driving surfaces of a friction coupling are flat rather than having teeth. A flat-type clutch cannot clutch so large a torque. It is ideal for use with potentiometers or other units that have built-in stops. The unit shown in the sketch of Fig. 7-37 has a 1.750-in. diameter with a body length of 2.062 in. The engage time is less than 10 msec, and the following typical specifications are achieved:

Rated load:

Crown-tooth coupling	80 oz-in.
Friction coupling	16 oz-in.
Output-end inertia	0.042 oz-in.^{2}
Input-end inertia	0.030 oz-in.^{2}
Coil voltage	24 or 110
Weight	12 oz

Numerous variations in clutching and braking can be provided. For example, it may be desired to brake the output shaft when the clutch is not energized. This is made possible by spring loading the movable member so that when the coil is not energized the moving member is held with either a crown-tooth or friction brake.

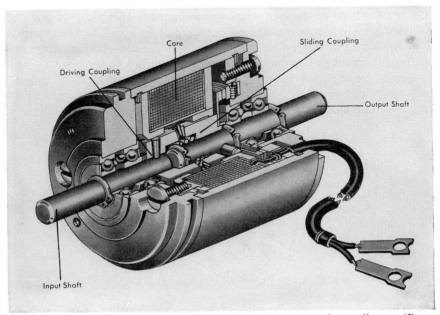

Fig. 7-37. Cutaway view of a magnetic clutch with crown-tooth couplings. (*Reeves Instrument Corp., New York.*)

Hysteresis Clutch. The schematic diagram of Fig. 7-38 shows the principle of operation of this type of clutch. The d-c control signal generates a magnetic field that magnetizes the permanent-magnet ring. Flux poles are generated within the ring, but because of the motor load torque these poles are at an angle to the axis of the applied field. The entire assembly shown on the schematic rotates. The d-c control excitation is brought into the moving coil by means of slip rings.

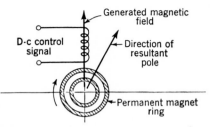

Fig. 7-38. Schematic diagram of a hysteresis clutch.

With no d-c excitation the input shaft, which carries the coil and pole structure, rotates independent of the output shaft. As the d-c signal is applied, the permanent-magnet material becomes polarized and is caused to rotate. The transmitted torque depends upon the d-c control current in a manner similar to the torque vs. control characteristic shown in Fig. 7-39. This curve is nonlinear and varies depending upon the amount of slip. If the torque demanded from the clutch is greater than can be sustained by the applied d-c signal, the clutch will slip. At any one torque and d-c signal setting, the rotor output shaft lags behind the coil or input shaft in a manner similar to a synchronous motor.

Eddy-current Clutch. The hysteresis clutch operates in a manner similar to a synchronous motor. The operation of the eddy-current clutch is based upon the same principles as an induction motor. A d-c field

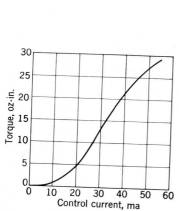

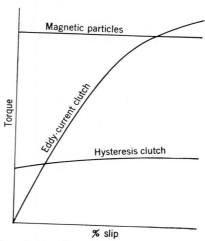

FIG. 7-39. Torque vs. control current for a typical hysteresis clutch.

FIG. 7-40. Comparison of torque-slip curves for three types of clutch.

is rotated by the input shaft. This field generates voltages and hence currents in a conducting disk that is attached to the output shaft. The field produced by these induced (eddy) currents interacts with the d-c rotating field and produces a torque. (The theory of induction motors upon which this is based is presented in Sec. 7-2).

Although small slip results in a higher-efficiency unit, large-slip clutches are frequently utilized to obtain high starting torques. Unlike the hysteresis clutch the eddy-current clutch depends upon the slip for its operation. No torque is developed without a difference in speed between the input and output shafts. The torque-slip curve for the eddy-current clutch is compared with the torque-slip curves for the other two types in Fig. 7-40.

The characteristic torque vs. control current for an eddy-current clutch is not linear. Since both the d-c flux and the induced eddy currents depend upon the control current, the torque varies as the square of the control current.

Magnetic Particles. Magnetic particles, either fluid or powder, are packed between a pair of plates. One each of these plates is connected to the input and output shafts respectively. When a magnetic field is applied, the particles become a rigid mass and torque is transmitted through the magnetic particles from input to output shaft.

Although the fluid operates more smoothly than the powder, leakage of the fluid through the shaft seals frequently requires the use of powder. Dry lubricants comprised of molybdenum or graphite aid in the performance of the powder unit.

The torque-excitation characteristic curve for a magnetic-particle clutch deviates from linearity at the low signal levels. Torques in magnitude of 8 lb-in. can be transmitted when control currents of 6 to 8 ma

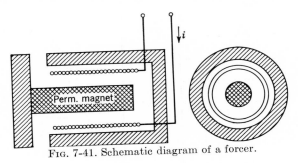

Fig. 7-41. Schematic diagram of a forcer.

are applied. The zero-excitation drag torque, which is caused by residual magnetism and viscous coupling, is approximately ¼ per cent.

7-9. Torquers and Forcers. In many applications, such as the force-balance accelerometer (Secs. 9-6 and 9-7) and the precision gyroscope (Chap. 10), a force (or a torque) is required with no appreciable motion. The term "forcer" or "torquer" is applied to such a unit. Figure 7-41 shows a simplified diagram of a forcer. A permanent magnet is free to move a small distance through the field coil. A direct current through the field coil produces a flux that interacts with the fixed flux of the permanent magnet and hence develops a force whose sign depends upon the polarity of the magnet and direction of current through the field winding.

Careful stabilization of the magnet and compensation of the magnetic path for temperature changes can result in a precision unit whose equation can be written:

$$F = K_s i \qquad (7\text{-}29)$$

where K_s is the sensitivity in force units per ampere. The unit resembles the d-c rate pickoff, which is described in Sec. 8-7. The methods of stabilization are similar.

7-10. Actuators. For applications where very large forces are required to be moved through small distances, a linear or rotary actuator can be

Fig. 7-42. Linear-motion actuator.   (*Airborne Accessories Corp., Hillside, N.J.*)

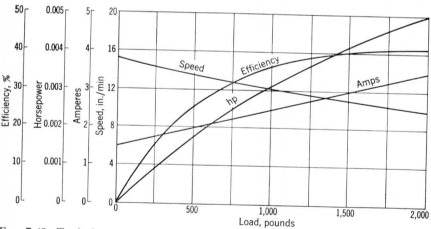

Fig. 7-43. Typical actuator characteristics.   (*Airborne Accessories Corp., Hillside, N.J.*)

utilized. A typical unit is shown in Fig. 7-42. The unit comprises a d-c or a-c motor that drives a screw-jack assembly. Operating loads up to 12,000 lb can be controlled at speeds up to 0.2 in./sec. Actuators are available with load-limiting protection, intermediate-position switches, and thermal-overload protection. Typical performance characteristics of a 1,000-lb, 26-volt d-c actuator are shown in Fig. 7-43.

PROBLEMS

7-1. What are the advantages and disadvantages of squirrel-cage, solid-rotor, and drag-cup-type motors?

7-2. Two two-phase induction motors, one with a high-resistance rotor and the other with a low-resistance rotor, are rotating at full speed in one direction. Reverse voltage is applied to one phase of each of the motors. Which of the two has the higher decelerating torque?

7-3. Show that the viscous-damping coefficient of a motor together with its voltage-torque sensitivity can be obtained from the speed-torque curve of the motor, assuming linearity.

7-4. With a motor whose fixed-voltage winding is excited through a capacitor, what is the effect of phase shifts in the fixed-voltage winding caused by changes of operating speeds?

7-5. Compare the advantages and disadvantages of a-c and d-c servomotors.

7-6. Prove that the back emf of a d-c shunt motor gives rise to an apparent damping.

7-7. Name the factors and characteristics that should be considered in selecting a servomotor. Discuss each and how it affects servo operation.

7-8. Obtain the transfer function for the motor speed–torque curve which is shown in Fig. 7-7. Rated voltage is 115 volts and the total motor inertia is 2.4×10^{-2} oz-in.-sec^2.

CHAPTER 8

RATE-MEASURING INSTRUMENTS

8-1. Theory of Rate Generators. A rate generator (or tachometer) is an electromechanical component which resembles a small motor and which develops an output voltage proportional to its shaft speed. The direction of the shaft is indicated by the polarity of the output voltage. Units are available for use with both ac and dc systems. The d-c units generally have a permanent-magnet-field excitation. The a-c units are excited by the alternating-voltage supply and produce an output voltage of supply frequency whose phase is dependent upon the direction of shaft rotation and whose amplitude is proportional to the magnitude of the shaft velocity. It is also possible to excite an a-c unit with direct current to obtain a d-c output proportional to the angular acceleration of its shaft. An ideal rate-measuring instrument should possess the following characteristics:

1. The output voltage is linear with respect to shaft speed.

2. The magnitude of the output voltage is the same for either direction of rotation.

3. The output is relatively free from undesirable voltages such as noise, harmonic, and quadrature.

4. At any one speed the output voltage is proportional to input voltage.

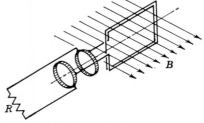

Fig. 8-1. Schematic of a-c rate-measuring instrument.

5. High sensitivity is available, i.e., appreciable output voltage with small shaft speed.

The theory underlying the performance of rate-measuring instruments is based upon Faraday's law of induction. This law states that when the magnetic flux through a closed conducting circuit changes, a current is generated in the circuit. The method used to change the flux is unimportant. The source of the flux can be changed, the circuit can be moved, or the shape of the circuit can be varied.

The induced emf in each turn of wire in the coil shown in Fig. 8-1 is

$$v = -\frac{d\phi}{dt}$$

where ϕ is the flux through the coil.   For this figure, the flux is given by the expression

$$\phi = AB \cos \alpha \qquad (8\text{-}1)$$

where A = area enclosed by the coil
$\quad\quad B$ = flux density (assumed constant through the coil)
$\quad\quad \alpha$ = angle between the plane of the coil and the vertical
The voltage induced in a coil with N turns is given by

$$v = -N \frac{d\phi}{dt} = NAB \, \omega \sin \alpha \qquad (8\text{-}2)$$

where ω is the angular velocity of the coil.   With constant flux density B and with constant angular velocity ω the output voltage is easily written

$$v = K\omega \sin \omega t \qquad (8\text{-}3)$$

With A and N constant the voltage gradient K is constant, and $\alpha = \omega t$. Hence the coil of wire rotating in a constant magnetic field develops a sinusoidal alternating voltage.   The amplitude of this voltage is proportional to the angular velocity.   A unidirectional voltage is obtained by connecting the coil to a commutator, as shown in Fig. 8-2.   At the instant when the current in the coil reverses, the connections to the external circuit are interchanged and the current through the external resistor, although pulsating, is always in the same direction.   In practice, more coils and more segments on the commutator are utilized.   The output voltage is unidirectional, with a small ripple.   The amplitude of this voltage is proportional to the angular velocity—which is one of the desired characteristics of the d-c tachometer.

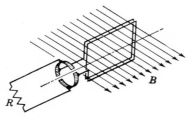

Fig. 8-2. Schematic of d-c rate-measuring instrument.

The theory underlying the operation of the a-c rate generator is also based on the laws of electromagnetic induction.   The application, however, is unique to a particular type of a-c signal.   The a-c rate generator must produce a sinusoidal signal of *constant frequency* whose amplitude is proportional to the angular velocity.   The sign of the velocity (either clockwise or counterclockwise) depends upon the phase (either in phase or 180° out of phase) of the constant-frequency reference.

The a-c generator shown in Fig. 8-1 does not meet this requirement. As can be seen from Eq. (8-3), the amplitude of the voltage from this type of rate generator is proportional to angular velocity ω, but the frequency of the a-c signal varies with angular velocity.

The a-c rate generator used for servo applications is shown in the schematic of Fig. 8-3. The unit has two stator windings, i.e., an excitation and an output winding. No electrical connections are made to the rotor of an induction motor.

The excitation winding and the output winding are placed in the stator so that they are geometrically at right angles, and one of the windings is excited by an alternating supply voltage. Because of the geometry of the coils, no output voltage is induced whenever the rotor is stationary. When the rotor is stationary, eddy currents are induced in the rotor by the reference frequency. The combined flux of the reference winding and these eddy currents produces no component of flux that can generate a voltage in the output winding. With the rotor stationary, then, the rate generator behaves like a transformer whose windings are oriented at right angles to each other. The combined alternating flux is in such a direction that it does not generate a voltage in the output winding.

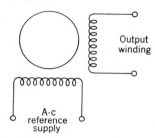

FIG. 8-3. Schematic of an a-c rate generator.

As the rotor is caused to rotate, the flux produced by the eddy currents changes direction and produces a component of flux in the direction of the output winding. Hence, a voltage of reference frequency is developed across the terminals of the output winding. The amplitude of this voltage is proportional to the shaft angular velocity.

The direction of the shaft velocity is indicated by the phase of the output voltage. If the output is in phase with the reference voltage, the velocity direction is defined as positive. If the output is 180° out of phase with the reference voltage, the velocity direction is negative.

8-2. Applications of Rate Generators. Rate generators have extensive applications, such as computing instruments, damping devices, and components of velocity servomechanisms. Applications in computers include both differentiators and integrators. If it is necessary to obtain the rate of change of a signal that is in the form of a shaft position or can be converted to a shaft position, then a rate generator coupled to the shaft generates a voltage proportional to the first derivative of the shaft position.

The feedback circuit of Fig. 8-4 can be used to generate the integral of a quantity. The function of which the integral is desired must be in the form of the envelope of an alternating voltage (suppressed carrier modulation) and can be fed directly into the terminals marked ab. If, however, the function of which the integral is desired is in the form of a shaft position, the shaft must be coupled to a potentiometer arm and thus converted into a voltage.

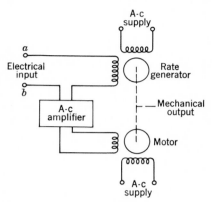

FIG. 8-4. Integrator using a rate generator.

The rate generator is excited from the same a-c source as the potentiometer or other origin of the reference voltage across ab. The high-gain amplifier driving the motor, which in turn is geared to the rate generator, tends to reduce the amplifier input voltage to zero. At all times the rate-generator voltage matches the voltage across the terminals ab, and its shaft must therefore rotate with a speed instantaneously proportional to the input voltage. If the unit is ideal, the position of the rate-generator shaft is proportional to the integral of the voltage appearing across ab (or the shaft position of the potentiometer) since its rate of change is at all times proportional to the voltage across ab.

This operation is analyzed by referring to the idealized block diagram of Fig. 8-5. The closed-loop transfer function is

$$\frac{C}{R} = \frac{G}{1 + GH} = \frac{\dfrac{K_1 K_2}{Js^2 + Bs}}{1 + \dfrac{K_1 K_2 K_3 s}{Js^2 + Bs}} \tag{8-4}$$

$$= \frac{K_1 K_2}{Js^2 + (K_1 K_2 K_3 + B)s} \tag{8-5}$$

where G is the transfer function of the forward path and H is the transfer function of the feedback path. The use of a high-gain amplifier reduces Eq. (8-5) to the following:

$$C = \frac{1}{K_3 s} \tag{8-6}$$

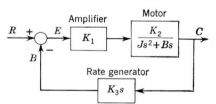

FIG. 8-5. Block diagram of the integrator.

This same equation can be found from a more general property of feedback systems. That is, a high forward gain results in the reciprocation of the feedback transfer function. This can be seen from an examination of the closed-loop transfer function

$$\frac{C}{R} = \frac{G}{1 + GH} = \frac{1}{H}\frac{GH}{1 + GH} \tag{8-7}$$

where G is the forward-loop transfer function and H is the feedback transfer function. For a high-gain system, Eq. (8-7) simplifies to

$$\frac{C}{R} \approx \frac{1}{H} \tag{8-8}$$

For the example of Fig. 8-5, with a high-gain amplifier K, the system equation is written from Eq. (8-8) as follows:

$$C = \frac{1}{K_3 s} R \tag{8-9}$$

which verifies Eq. (8-6). In the time domain the output of the system of Fig. 8-5 is

$$c = \frac{1}{K_3} \int_0^t r \, dt \tag{8-10}$$

Although both a-c and d-c rate generators are utilized for computing applications, the a-c unit finds wider application because of its freedom from threshold (due to lack of brushes) and better linearity.

Such conditions as linearity, threshold, and sensitivity independent of direction of rotation are less important in the use of rate generators for damping in servomechanisms, which represents the other major use of rate generators. A typical servo application of a rate generator, utilized in an instrument servomechanism, is shown in the circuit diagram of Fig. 8-6. The actuating-signal voltage is obtained from a pair of synchros and is fed to the input of the conventional audioamplifier, the output of which feeds one phase of a two-phase motor. Subtracted from the synchro signal is a voltage from the a-c rate generator, whose phase is adjusted to be exactly the same as that of the synchro output. The synchros, the rate generator, and the servomotor must all be excited from the same a-c reference voltage.

A physical explanation of how the rate generator contributes to the stability of the system should aid comprehension. Assume first that the voltage applied to the control winding of the motor produces a torque approximately proportional to that voltage. If the rate-generator signal is disconnected, the actuating-signal voltage from the synchros produces a torque proportional to the control voltage. Suppose that the synchro output voltage is short-circuited and that the motor shaft is rotated externally. Rotation of this shaft causes a voltage proportional to the speed of rotation to be developed at the output terminals of the rate generator and hence applied to the input terminals of the amplifier. Since the motor produces a torque proportional to the input voltage of the amplifier, a torque exists on the motor proportional to the speed of rotation of the generator shaft. As the shaft speed is increased, the torque output of the motor is increased but in a direction that opposes the rotation of the motor. When the motor shaft is rotated by hand, a viscous-drag effect is experienced. As a matter of fact, the effect actually produced is dynamically equivalent to a viscous drag; i.e., the retarding torque is proportional to the speed of the motor shaft. Therefore, use of the rate generator produces a viscous damping that tends to stabilize the system.

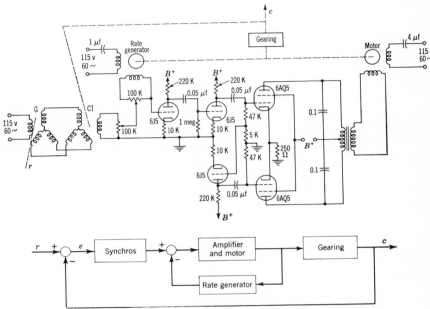

FIG. 8-6. Typical servomechanism employing a rate generator.

From the idealized block diagram of Fig. 8-7, the following equation can be written:

$$\frac{E}{R} = \frac{1}{1 + G} = \frac{1}{1 + K_1 K_4 \dfrac{\dfrac{K_2 K_3 s}{J s^2 + B s}}{\dfrac{K_2 K_3 K_5 s}{J s^2 + B s}}} \tag{8-11}$$

$$\frac{E}{R} = \frac{J s^2 + (B + K_2 K_3 K_5)s}{J s^2 + (B + K_2 K_3 K_5)s + K_1 K_2 K_3 K_4} \tag{8-12}$$

This equation indicates that the rate-generator constant multiplied by the amplifier gain adds directly to the viscous-damping coefficient of the motor. Thus, when the rate generator is added to the system, the servo behaves dynamically as if the damping B of the motor were increased to a value $B + K_2K_3K_5$. The damping of the servo is easily adjustable by varying K_5 (usually accomplished with a potentiometer).

In this application the rate generator also tends to linearize the servomechanism. It is normal to expect wide variation in motor damping as the operating conditions of motor voltage and speed change. However, if the viscous damping that is produced by the rate generator is large compared with the internal damping of the motor, variations in motor damping can take place without materially affecting the total damping in the system.

Because of the additional damping provided by the rate generator, the amplifier gain can be considerably increased for the same degree of stability of the servomechanism. Thus, if the motor corner frequency is too low, which results in a servo that is too sluggish to follow a rapidly

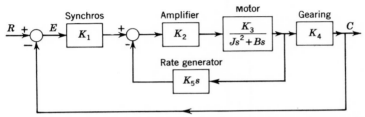

Fig. 8-7. Block diagram of a simple idealized servo using a rate generator.

changing command, the use of a rate-generator feedback can extend this value an octave or more. The corner frequency ω_1 of the servo of Eq. (8-12) is extended from

$$\omega_1 = \frac{B}{J} \tag{8-13}$$

its value before the addition of the rate generator, to

$$\omega_1 = \frac{B + K_2K_3K_5}{J} \tag{8-14}$$

Thus, the bandwidth of the servo, and therefore its ability to follow higher-frequency signals, is increased. The desirability of extending the corner frequency by this amount depends on the noise content of the command and the time lags in this system.

Increased amplifier gain, which is permitted by the addition of rate feedback, produces a servo that has a lower velocity error and an increased torque sensitivity at the controlled shaft. Increased torque sensitivity reduces the effect of torque disturbances on the controlled shaft and reduces the sensitivity of the servo to friction, which tends to produce a static error.

In addition to the dynamic advantages of using rate generators in servomechanisms, a further advantage is obtained because the system is less susceptible to instability caused by backlash of the gearing. This results from the fact that the motor and the generator are usually coupled directly. Backlash that may exist in the larger loop causes less trouble when a rate generator is utilized.

If a modulator is used to convert the direct-voltage signal to an alternating voltage, a d-c rate generator can be substituted for the a-c rate generator in Fig. 8-6. One advantage of the use of d-c rate generators

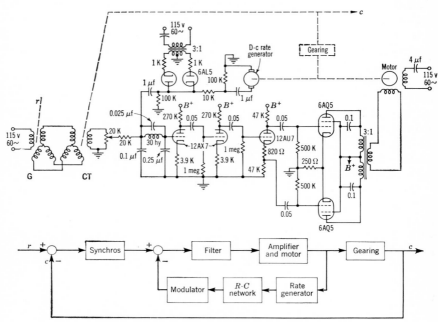

Fig. 8-8. Servo employing a d-c rate generator.

is that the rate-generator signal developed when the servo is rotating at a constant velocity can be blocked by means of a high-pass network. This reduces even further the velocity error and reduces the bandwidth of the servo for a given static torque sensitivity of velocity-error constant. A typical circuit, which has wide application, is shown in Fig. 8-8. The d-c rate generator is followed by a blocking capacitor and a modulator that converts the rate-generator signal to an alternating voltage. This signal is altered, and the filter is placed in the main amplifier channel to obtain some beneficial filtering effects for the synchros as well. If the time constant of the RC network at the output of the rate generator is made fairly long, the capacitor has little effect during the normal transient operation of the servomechanism. When, however, the servo is tracking a constant-velocity command, the constant voltage from the rate generator is blocked. It therefore does not subtract from the actuating-signal voltage and thus makes no contribution to the velocity following error. In effect, viscous damping is eliminated under those conditions.

8-3. Construction of A-C Rate Generators. The a-c rate generator resembles a two-phase a-c motor. An a-c reference voltage is applied to one phase of the tachometer generator, and a voltage of reference frequency and amplitude proportional to shaft speed is generated on the other phase. Two typical types of a-c rate generator exist: the induction generator, using a squirrel-cage rotor, and the drag-cup generator, using a light conducting cup as rotor. Since the rate generator is often coupled directly to the servomotor shaft and adds directly to that inertia, the rate-generator inertia is kept small. For this reason the drag-cup unit finds widest application.

The construction of the induction rate generator is similar to that of two-phase servomotor.* Except for the size (less power is transmitted through the tachometer), the squirrel-cage induction rate generator is quite similar.

The drag-cup generator consists of the same type of stator as the two-phase induction generator. Its rotor, however, consists of a thin aluminum or copper cup, and the rotor flux is carried by a stationary magnetic core within the cup. A sketch of the drag-cup tachometer is shown in Fig. 8-9. Although this construction necessitates two air gaps, the inertia of the cup can be made very small and can thus improve the acceleration characteristics.

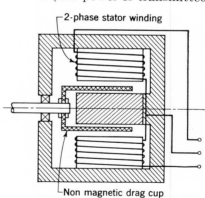

FIG. 8-9. Sketch of a drag-cup a-c tachometer.

A photograph of a drag-cup rate generator is shown in Fig. 8-10.

Other types of rate generator have solid rotors consisting of magnetic material. The solid iron rotor carries both the flux and the induced currents that serve to generate voltage in the output winding. These units are a compromise between the other two types in that they have only one air gap but usually have more inertia than the drag-cup types.

In order to minimize the backlash between servomotors and rate generators, these units are sometimes constructed on the same shaft and

* See Chap. 7 for a discussion of servomotors.

Fig. 8-10. Exploded view of a drag-cup rate generator.

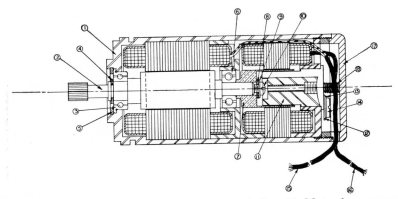

Fig. 8-11. Servomotor and tachometer on common shaft. (1) Motor-frame assembly, 1; (2) rotor assembly, 1; (3) flanged bearing, 1; (4) C ring, 1; (5) snap ring, 1; (6) bearing, 1; (7) drag cup, 1; (8) flat washer, 1; (9) lock washer, 1; (10) screw, 1; (11) slug, 1; (12) flat washer, 2; (13) lock washer, 2; (14) screw, 2; (15) black sleeving, 1; (16) red sleeving, 1; (17) end cap, 1; (18) screw, 2. (*American Electronics, Inc., Los Angeles.*)

frequently built with a common outer housing. An assembly drawing of such a unit is shown in Fig. 8-11.

As with any electromechanical unit used in servomechanisms, the rate generators must have accurate and concentric shaft and mounting surfaces. Rate generators are often flange-mounted to prevent mechanical strains from affecting the path of magnetic flux.

8-4. Characteristics of A-C Rate Generators. A-c rate generators have a sensitivity ranging from about $\frac{1}{10}$ to 1 volt/100 rpm, with an output impedance on the order of 3,000 ohms. The phase angle of the output voltage can vary from 0 to 90°, depending upon the construction and design of the unit. If the phase angle of the output of the rate generator is constant under all operating speeds, the phase of the excitation of the rate generator can be appropriately shifted by a series capacitor, as shown in Fig. 8-6. The output voltage is thus brought in phase with that of the output voltage of the synchros. If the phase is not adjusted, the difference in phase causes a quadrature voltage, which tends to saturate the amplifier and heat the motor.

Because of the change of leakage resistance and reactance, the output phase angle is not always constant with speed. Figure 8-12 shows an experimental plot of the phase angle of the output voltage of a rate generator as a function of speed. This unit has a sensitivity

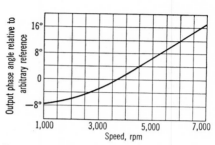

FIG. 8-12. Phase angle vs. speed of an a-c rate generator.

of $\frac{9}{10}$ volt/1,000 rpm. The amount of phase shift obtained varies widely for units from different manufacturers and even between units of the same design and manufacture. It is possible, however, to obtain units whose phase shift is less than ±5 minutes for all operating speeds.

Nonsinusoidal output voltage is another difficulty with a-c rate generators. The presence of third and fifth harmonic voltages in the output is caused by the nonlinearity of the iron in the magnetic circuit. As in the case of synchros, these harmonics can saturate the servoamplifier without producing useful results.

Of more concern is the fact that the output voltage is not zero when the speed of the rate-generator shaft is zero. As with synchros, these voltages are at both fundamental and harmonic frequencies. If the residual voltages are large enough, they can saturate the amplifier. The magnitude of harmonic voltages at zero shaft speed is different for each unit. For the rate generator used in the experiment of Fig. 8-12, the null voltage is on the order of 8 to 50 mv. Units with the same sensitivity are available, however, whose harmonic voltages are on the order of 5 to 7 mv. The harmonic voltages can be filtered if necessary.

The other component of the residual voltage cannot be filtered since it is of fundamental frequency. If it is in phase quadrature with the proper output voltage, it can saturate the amplifier and heat the motor with no useful effect. If it is in phase with the desired signal, it can cause an error in the servomechanism since the synchro must be offset by the amount necessary to null the total input voltage to the amplifier. Thus fundamental residual voltage varies in both magnitude and phase. For the generator described in Fig. 8-12, the diagram of Fig. 8-13 shows the experimentally obtained, fundamental component of null-voltage output as a function of rotor position.

Any constant component of voltage can be subtracted to reduce the over-all magnitude by placing a voltage in series with the output of the rate generator. The portion that varies with shaft angle cannot be diminished by this means. Units are available that, for the same sensitivity, have about one-tenth of the fundamental residual voltage as shown in Fig. 8-13.

Residual voltages are caused by magnetic circuit dissymmetries, which can be the result of nonuniformity of the magnetic material and the conducting material and irregular machining of the air-gap surfaces. Just as in the case of the synchros, careful machining reduces the residual

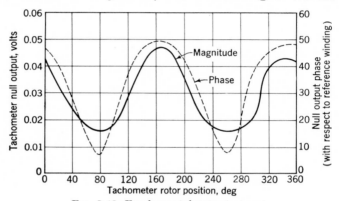

FIG. 8-13. Fundamental output at rest.

voltages, and both good design and workmanship improve the linearity, phase-shift, and the residual-voltage characteristics.

In normal mathematical calculations it is generally assumed that the rate-generator transfer function from shaft-position input to voltage output is given by

$$e_0 = K\omega \tag{8-15}$$

where K is the voltage gradient in volts/(radians/sec) and ω is the shaft speed. An ideal instrument should have a constant K invariant with shaft speed ω, voltage level, and carrier frequency and a constant phase shift of the output voltage with respect to the reference voltage.

The voltage gradient K is found from the manufacturer's literature. Often the manufacturer gives the K information as follows: Output volts at 1,000 rpm = 3 volts with rated reference voltage applied. With data in this form the gradient is assumed linear and K is computed as follows:

$$K = \frac{3}{(1,000)(2\pi/60)} = 2.87 \times 10^{-12} \text{ volts/(radians/sec)} \tag{8-16}$$

An experimental determination of the transfer function of the rate generator whose characteristics are plotted in Figs. 8-12 and 8-13 is given in Fig. 8-14. This curve is close to 6 db/octave and rises to 23 cycles. At frequencies of this magnitude, there is degradation of the waveform caused by the inequality of the size of the upper and lower sideband voltages.

Equation 8-15 is written in operational form as follows:

$$\frac{E_o}{\theta} = Ks \qquad (8\text{-}17)$$

where s is the Laplace-transform operator. A summary of characteristics of commercially available a-c rate generators is given in Table 8-1.

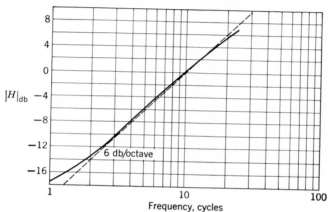

FIG. 8-14. Frequency response of rate generator.

8-5. Construction of D-C Rate Generators.

Although a-c rate generators are more common, d-c generators are often required for d-c servo applications such as d-c servo damping and d-c velocity servo comparison. Because of the necessity for brushes and commutation in d-c machines, d-c rate generators are less accurate, produce both electrical and radio noise, are subject to drift, and quite often operate with a different gradient in one direction from the other.

The d-c generator is similar in appearance and operation to the d-c motor. A fixed field is established with a direct current through a field coil or with a permanent magnet. As the rotor windings cut the constant magnetic field, a voltage that is proportional to velocity is generated in the rotor windings. The transfer function can be written

$$\frac{E_o}{\theta} = Ks \qquad (8\text{-}18)$$

where K is the d-c generator gradient in volts/(radians/sec).

TABLE 8-1. A-C RATE-GENERATOR CHARACTERISTICS

Manufacturer	Type	Frequency	Weight, lb	Sensitivity, volts/100 rpm	Phase shift, deg	Voltage (zero speed) In phase, mv	Voltage (zero speed) Quadrature, mv	Voltage (zero speed) Harmonic, mv	Input, volts	Rotor inertia, oz-in.^{2}
Arma	1A60	60	1.5	0.33 ± 5%	0 ± 1.5	10	10	10	24	0.22
Arma	5E	60	6.3	1.0 ± 1%	0 ± 0.5	5	5	15	90	0.75
Kearfott	R807	400		0.04	±10	0.005			26	0.0048
Kearfott	R800	400		0.32	5 ± 1	1	8	5	115	0.0288
						Total				
Kearfott	320650	400		0.275	0 ± 1	15			52	0.0205
Kollsman	863-01621	60	1.07	1 ± 1%	0	20		18	115	0.0465
Kollsman	863-04302	400	1.07	0.42 ± 10%	34	37		20	115	0.0465
Kollsman	945B-01600	60	0.97	0.45 ± 10%	14	28		72	115	0.0164
Kollsman	XA1994E	400	1.06	0.03	0 ± 1	1		0.5	26	0.009
Ford Instrument	951196	400	1.0	0.46 ± 0.04%	90	30			115	0.075
American Electronics	MT12	400	0.49	0.05 ± 7%	±10	19			115	0.0072
American Electronics	SMT155E	400		0.22	0 ± 0.5	12			115	0.0275

A typical d-c rate generator is shown in Fig. 8-15, and a cutaway of a similar unit is given in Fig. 8-16. As in the case of a-c tachometers, the d-c units must be carefully constructed so that the high precision required for servo operation can be achieved. Symmetry of the magnetic material is essential for bidirectional operation. The unit shown in the photograph of Fig. 8-17 and in the outline drawing of Fig. 8-18 features relatively small size, high linearity, low torque, and high-speed operation. These generators are built in machined aluminum housings that are protected with an anodized finish. Both flange-type and servo-type mountings are available.

FIG. 8-15. D-c rate generator. (*Electric Indicator Company, Inc., Springdale, Conn.*)

8-6. Characteristics of D-C Rate Generators. A d-c rate generator usually obtains its magnetic field by means of a permanent magnet and

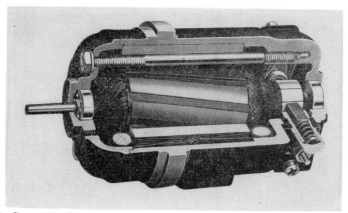

FIG. 8-16. Cutaway view of a d-c rate generator. (*Electric Indicator Company, Inc., Springdale, Conn.*)

therefore requires no excitation voltage. Because its output is direct voltage, however, it does require brushes operating on a commutator. The appreciable friction load from these brushes is a disadvantage to its application. This friction is on the order of 1 oz-in., and if the motor is coupled directly to the rate generator, it can be an appreciable percentage of the total output torque of the motor.

A d-c rate generator usually has a somewhat higher voltage sensitivity

Fig. 8-17. D-c rate generator. (*Servo-Tek Products Co., Hawthorne, N.J.*)

than an a-c generator, on the order of ½ volt/100 rpm. Voltage-rpm curves for the unit shown in Fig. 8-18 are included in Fig. 8-19. Its output resistance is about 300 ohms, but this is not usually a significant advantage over a-c rate generators, since no power is taken from the signal output and it is normally fed into high-impedance circuits.

Unlike the a-c rate generator, there is no residual voltage on its output terminals when the shaft is stationary. When the shaft is rotating, however, there is ripple voltage caused by rectification of the voltage generated in the rotor by means of commutator bars and brushes. Typical rate generators use either 9 or 18 bars; the smaller the rotor diameter, the fewer the number, although to reduce the ripple voltage a large number is desirable. When the direct-voltage output of a typical unit is 20 volts, the ripple may be ½ volt rms a-c. In

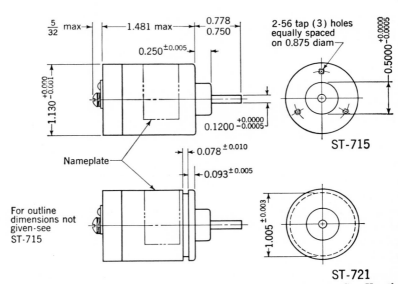

Fig. 8-18. Outline drawing of d-c rate generator. (*Servo-Tek Products Co., Hawthorne, N.J.*)

many servo applications, this characteristic of d-c rate generators is not a serious disadvantage, although it is a disadvantage if the servo or integrator is required to rotate at a very low velocity. Brush jump at high velocities also causes additional spurious voltages.

Dynamically, the transfer function of the rate generator is like that of the a-c rate generator and is very close to 6 db/octave. There is no problem of unequal sideband transmission at the higher oscillating frequencies.

The permanent magnets are stabilized against demagnetizing effects such as mechanical shock and short circuits. This is accomplished by applying an alternating field, of particular magnitude, to the magnetic circuit after the initial charging of the magnet. The instrument is made

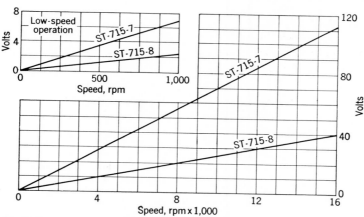

FIG. 8-19. Voltage-rpm curves for d-c tachometer. (*Servo-Tek Products Co., Hawthorne, N.J.*)

insensitive to temperature changes by using a "carpenter-metal" shunt in the magnetic path. This shunt has a permeability that changes with temperature in a sense opposite to the permeability changes of Alnico. This technique maintains an essentially uniform flux in the magnetic core. Adjustable magnetic cores (or slugs) permit an adjustment of the sensitivity K.

8-7. Linear-motion D-C Rate Generators. Permanent magnets are often used for measuring linear-motion velocities. This type of pickoff consists of a coil mounted on the fixed member and a magnet mounted on the movable member. A sketch of a linear motion, d-c rate pickoff is shown in Fig. 8-20. As the magnet moves in and out of the coil, a unidirectional voltage is generated at the output terminals of the coil, which voltage is proportional to the linear velocity. The proportionality constant K_2 is the voltage gradient in volts/(in./sec). If the magnet is stabilized against demagnetization and compensated for temperature changes, a precise transducer is obtained.

This transducer is often fabricated as an integral part of another assembly. Frequently the rate generator is simply an additional winding on the forcer, which is described in Sec. 7-9. Since the d-c forcer con-

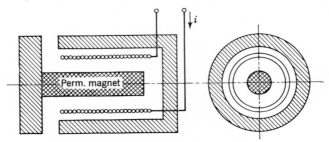

Fig. 8-20. Simplified diagram of a rate generator.

figuration is similar, the same permanent magnet can be utilized to generate this rate signal.

PROBLEMS

8-1. What properties of a rate generator are important when it is used as part of an integrator circuit, as opposed to its use in a servomechanism as a stabilizing means? What properties are important for both applications?

8-2. Based on the theory of rate generators, is it possible to obtain a rate voltage by changing the reluctance in a magnetic circuit?

8-3. Design an electromechanical integrator utilizing an a-c rate generator with a sensitivity equal to 2.87×10^{-12} volts/(radians/sec). Lay out the system block diagram so that an output rate of 0.1 radian/sec results when a step of 1.0 radian is applied to the input.

8-4. A simple idealized servomechanism has its corner frequency at 1 cycle and a phase margin of 45°. It is desired to modify this servomechanism, keeping it a 6–12 servomechanism with a 45° phase margin but with a corner frequency of 5 cycles. This can be done either by the use of a network or by the use of rate-generator feedback. Compare the torque sensitivities of the servos resulting from each of the two methods.

8-5. Derive an idealized loop transfer function for the diagram of Fig. 8-8.

8-6. List the characteristics of a rate generator, such as quadrature voltage and linearity, and determine which, if any, can be reduced by appropriate compensation. Discuss the compensation.

8-7. Compare the advantages and disadvantages of a-c rate generators with d-c rate generators.

CHAPTER 9

ACCELERATION-MEASURING INSTRUMENTS*

9-1. Introduction. Since force is proportional to linear acceleration ($F = ma$) and torque is proportional to angular acceleration ($L = I\alpha$), the measurement of acceleration is essential for a wide range of applications. For example, an accelerometer can be used to measure the thrust of a rocket engine, the torque on the wings during pull-out from a dive, the vibrational forces on a shake table, and the force effects of an earthquake. These and many other forces and torques are measured with linear and angular accelerometers.

Although many types of acceleration transducers are manufactured, most of these instruments are based upon a common principle of operation: the measurement of the motion of a restrained mass when it is subjected to acceleration. Variations as to linear or angular accelerations, fluid or solid mass, fluid or pneumatic damping, a-c or d-c pickoff, do not change the fundamental theory underlying the operation of the accelerometer. Two types of accelerometer are considered: one is basically a mechanical unit in which the acceleration measurement depends upon the mechanical system; the other is a force-balance unit in which a servo corrects some of the inaccuracies in the basic mechanical system. Both types produce an output voltage that is proportional to the acceleration along or about a certain axis.

Many of the measuring instruments in general use, such as electric meters, galvanometers, pressure gauges, and vibration pickups, have characteristics in common that place them in a single group for the purpose of response analysis. Each of these instruments may be represented as a mass suspended on a spring member and damped by viscous fluids or electric currents. Since a large percentage of these measuring instruments can be treated as a simple single-mass and single-spring system, a detailed analysis of the linear accelerometer provides the basis for the understanding of the operation of other measuring instruments.

9-2. Seismic Accelerometers: Theory of Operation. Consider as a representative example the *seismic* or mechanical accelerometer that is

* The authors are indebted to Statham Laboratories for the use of their Instrument Notes in the preparation of this chapter.

333

represented by the schematic of Fig. 9-1. The instrument may be used to measure acceleration, velocity, or displacement, depending upon the portion of its frequency range that is utilized. This instrument consists of a mass suspended from the frame by a spring. Damping is provided

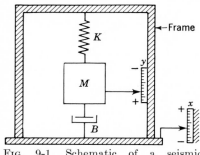

either mechanically or electrically, and an electrical pickoff measures the position of the mass with respect to the frame. The variable x is the displacement of the frame that is fastened to the body whose acceleration is to be measured. The variable y is the displacement with respect to the frame of the suspended mass M. The position pickoff measures

FIG. 9-1. Schematic of a seismic accelerometer.

the variable y. K is the spring constant of the suspension, and B is the viscous damping constant. The equation relating the recorded variable y to the forcing variable x is desired. The constants of the system may be measured in any consistent set of units. For example, if cgs units are used, then x and y are in centimeters; K is the force in dynes required to deflect the mass 1 cm; B is the viscous drag in dynes when the mass has a velocity of 1 cm/sec; and M is in grams.

Since y is measured with respect to the frame, the force on the mass due to the spring is $-Ky$ and that due to the damper is $-B(dy/dt)$. The motion of the mass in space is $(y - x)$. The Laplace-transformed equation for the sum of the forces on the mass is

$$Ms^2(Y - X) + BsY + KY = 0 \qquad (9\text{-}1)$$

where zero initial conditions are assumed. Eq. (9-1) can be rearranged as

$$(Ms^2 + Bs + K)Y = MA(s) \qquad (9\text{-}2)$$

where $s^2X(s) = A(s)$ is the transform of the acceleration to be measured and is a function. The same analysis is applicable to other instruments. For a velocity pickoff, $s^2X(s)$ is replaced by $sV(s)$ where $V(s)$ is the transform of the velocity to be measured.

The transfer function of the accelerometer between acceleration input $A(s)$ and the response $Y(s)$ is

$$\frac{Y(s)}{A(s)} = \frac{M}{Ms^2 + Bs + K} = \frac{1}{s^2 + B/Ms + K/M} \qquad (9\text{-}3)$$

This equation can be recast in standard form

$$\frac{Y}{A} = \frac{1}{s^2 + 2\zeta\omega_n s + \omega_n{}^2} \qquad (9\text{-}4)$$

where the natural frequency is $\omega_n{}^2 = K/M$ and the damping ratio is

$$\zeta = \frac{B}{2\sqrt{KM}} \tag{9-5}$$

The natural frequency and the damping ratio are two of the three parameters that suffice to specify the response of the accelerometer, as well as many other similar instruments. The third factor is the sensitivity (i.e., defined as the volts per g output from the accelerometer), which is related to the output position instrument. Almost any of the position instruments discussed in Chap. 3 can be used to measure the accelerometer output. Commonly, either a linear motion potentiometer or an E pickoff is used to measure $y(t)$. If the transfer function of the position instrument is K_s, the over-all accelerometer transfer function

$$\frac{Y}{A} = \frac{K_s}{s^2 + 2\zeta\omega_n s + \omega_n{}^2} \tag{9-6}$$

corresponds to the block diagram shown in Fig. 9-2. $K_s/\omega_n{}^2$ is the sensitivity of the accelerometer in volts per g. The three factors of damping ratio, natural frequency, and sensitivity are simple figures of merit for comparison of instruments. In a system containing a

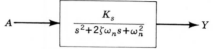

FIG. 9-2. Block diagram of a mechanical accelerometer.

mass and a spring restraint, the natural frequency is given by

$$\omega_n = 2\pi f_n = \sqrt{K/M} \tag{9-7}$$

Viscous damping in the system has no effect on the undamped natural frequency f_n; accordingly, the damping can be varied at will without alternating f_n.

The frequency-response characteristics of the mechanical acceleration are found from the equation

$$\frac{Y}{AK_s/\omega_n{}^2} = \frac{1}{(1 - \mu^2) + 2j\zeta\mu} \tag{9-8}$$

where ζ is the damping ratio and μ is the frequency ratio ω/ω_n. The amplitude and phase response of the mechanical accelerometer are shown in Figs. 9-3 and 9-4 for various values of damping ratio.

In order for an accelerometer to have the widest possible frequency range over which its measurements will be without waveform change, its response should not only have a flat amplitude curve but its phase-shift curve should be linear with frequency. A linear phase-shift curve corresponds to a time delay of the recorded signals but causes no distortion

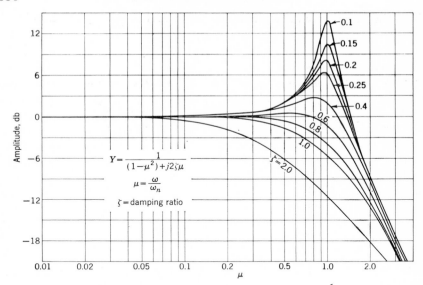

FIG. 9-3. Amplitude of transfer function. $Y = \dfrac{1}{(1 - \mu^2) + j2\zeta\mu}$.

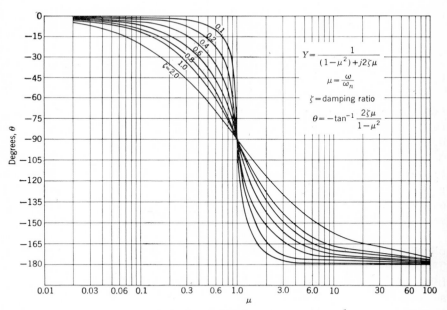

FIG. 9-4. Phase shift for transfer function. $Y = \dfrac{1}{(1 - \mu^2) + j2\zeta\mu}$.

by unequal relative shifts of different frequency components. Notice that a $\zeta = 0.707$ results in a flat amplitude curve, within close limits, out to 0.9 of the natural frequency; and further, the phase-shift curve is more nearly linear than is any on either side of it. For these reasons, accelerometers and many other instruments are commonly designed to operate with a 0.7 critical damping. As is expected, increased damping decreases the magnitude of the response peak in the neighborhood of the natural frequency and thus minimizes transient oscillations due to high-frequency excitation. However, the most important reason for damping is that of increasing the frequency range in order to reproduce transient waveforms faithfully. In many cases, the design of instruments to have a high natural frequency is a technical problem of considerable difficulty. Hence, the damping is usually adjusted to provide as wide a frequency range as is possible.

There are special cases in which 0.7 critical damping does not lead to the best response characteristics. If the natural frequency of the measuring instrument is several times higher than the highest frequency to be measured, a smaller damping coefficient is desirable. From Fig. 9-3 it can be seen that, within close limits, the response is flat below $0.2\omega_n$ for any reasonable value of ζ. From the phase-shift curve, it can be seen that a low value of ζ in this range results in low phase shift and hence in low signal delay. Further, the peak response is outside the range of frequencies being measured; hence it is not likely to lead to large excitations. Consequently, a ζ of 0.3 or even lower is often used in instruments with a relatively high natural frequency.

It is important to clarify several frequencies that occur in the frequency response of Fig. 9-3. The frequency at which the maximum of the amplitude response occurs is not the natural frequency. Only if the damping is zero does the maximum response occur at the natural frequency. As the damping is increased, the frequency at which peak response occurs is lowered; and at a damping ratio of $1/\sqrt{2}$ the peak response is at zero frequency. For greater damping, no real maximum exists at all. The frequency at which maximum response occurs is shown in Fig. 9.5.

If the instrument is displaced and then allowed to execute a typical damped transient, it may be found that the transient decay is oscillatory. The frequency that can be assigned to this oscillation is not the natural frequency. Only at zero damping is the frequency of the oscillatory transient the same as the natural frequency. As the damping is increased, the frequency of oscillation decreases; and at a damping ratio of unity (by definition) the oscillatory nature of the transient entirely disappears. The frequency of transient oscillation is plotted in Fig. 9-6.

In plotting Figs. 9-5 and 9-6, it is assumed that the damping can be varied without affecting either the spring constant or the suspended mass of the instrument. Although such is the case with magnetic damping, where a magnetic field can be varied without altering the suspended mass, such is not the case with fluid damping. If the fluid is removed from a fluid-damped instrument, it is an elementary procedure to determine the frequency of free oscillation of the system, and the natural frequency of the instrument without fluid is thus determined. When

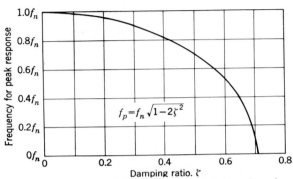

$$f_p = f_n \sqrt{1 - 2\zeta^2}$$

FIG. 9-5. Frequency for peak sinusoidal response vs. damping ratio.

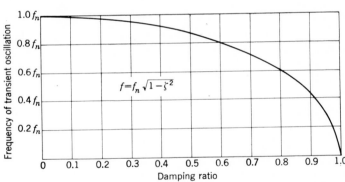

$$f = f_n \sqrt{1 - \zeta^2}$$

FIG. 9-6. Frequency of transient oscillation vs. damping ratio.

the fluid is replaced, a different system exists since the mass is changed. Since a damping fluid has mass and must be moved by the suspended mass in order to damp, it consequently has kinetic energy; hence it has a reaction on the suspended mass. The system thus has a new and larger value of mass—an equivalent mass. This effect can easily be found by filling an instrument with a fluid of low viscosity. The damping may still be so small that free transient oscillations of slow decay can be initiated; but the frequency of oscillation will be found to be markedly lower than that in air—lower, perhaps, by a factor of 2. To term the natural frequency with damping fluid the damped natural frequency is hardly relevant. The addition of fluid creates a new system with new parameters and a new natural frequency, and the damping still has nothing to do with it. This can be demonstrated if a series of liquids with the same density but varying viscosities is employed. Because of the difference of mass between the filled and unfilled instrument, only the natural frequency defined by Eq. (9-7) is unambiguous. Needless to say, the natural frequency may be difficult to determine in a properly damped instrument.

The effect of the additional mass can be approximated by a consideration of the energies in the system. Let the mass be given an initial displacement and then set free to oscillate. The potential energy in the spring is

$$P = \int_0^x kx \, dx = \tfrac{1}{2}kx^2 \tag{9-9}$$

The kinetic energy of the mass is

$$T_M = \tfrac{1}{2}MV^2 = \tfrac{1}{2}M\dot{x}^2 \tag{9-10}$$

The energy loss in damping is

$$E = \int_0^x \zeta\dot{x} \, dx = \int_0^t \zeta(\dot{x})^2 \, dt \tag{9-11}$$

The sum of the potential and kinetic energy plus the damping energy must equal a constant, which is the amount of work which was done to give the mass its initial displacement, or

$$P + T + E = W \tag{9-12}$$

Before substituting into Eq. (9-12), however, it is important to realize that the expression $T_M = \tfrac{1}{2}M(\dot{x})^2$ does not represent all of the kinetic energy in the system.

As the mass M moves downward, the fluid in the annular space between the mass and the case moves upward; and if this annular space is small, the velocity of the fluid is likely to be large. Since kinetic energy is proportional to the square of the velocity, the kinetic energy in the fluid may be many times the kinetic energy in the mass itself, even though the mass of the moving fluid is small. Let the area of the mass be A_1 and the area of the fluid in the annular space be A_2. Then the mean velocity of the fluid is $(A_1/A_2)\dot{x}$; and the approximate kinetic energy of the fluid is $T_f = m/2(A_1/A_2\dot{x})^2$, where m is the mass of the fluid contained in the annular space. As the fluid enters and leaves the annular space there are some end effects that complicate the problem further; but these end effects are not great since the fluid loses velocity rapidly after it leaves the annular space. The kinetic energy of the fluid that moves with the mass may be neglected since the ratio of its mass to M is generally quite small. The total kinetic energy in the system is

$$T = T_M + T_f = \tfrac{1}{2}M(\dot{x})^2 + \tfrac{1}{2}m(A_1/A_2)^2\dot{x}^2$$
$$= \tfrac{1}{2}[M + (A_1/A_2)^2 m]\dot{x}^2 \qquad (9\text{-}13)$$

Substitution into Eq. (9-12) yields the following energy expression:

$$W = \tfrac{1}{2}kx^2 + \tfrac{1}{2}[M + (A_1/A_2)^2 m]\dot{x}^2 + \int_0^t \zeta \dot{x}^2 \, dt \qquad (9\text{-}14)$$

where W is a constant. Differentiation and simplifying gives

$$\ddot{x} + \frac{\zeta}{M + (A_1/A_2)^2 m} \dot{x} + \frac{k}{M + (A_1/A_2)^2 m} x = 0 \qquad (9\text{-}15)$$

The natural frequency of the system now results not as $f_n = 1/2\pi \sqrt{k/M}$ but, instead, as

$$f_n = \frac{1}{2\pi} \sqrt{\frac{k}{M + (A_1/A_2)^2 m}} \qquad (9\text{-}16)$$

If the annular space around the mass is small, A_1/A_2 is likely to be a large number and $(A_1/A_2)^2$ a yet larger number. In this case, the term

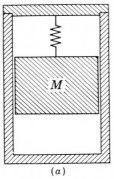
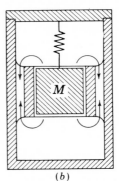

(a)   (b)

Fig. 9-7. Cylindrical accelerometer that exhibits the effect of fluid mass.

$(A_1/A_2)^2 m$ may be so much larger than M as to be the only really significant term.

As an example, consider the accelerometer shown in Fig. 9-7a, which contains a cylindrical inertial mass suspended in a cylindrical case. The case is filled with damping fluid. An annular space of 0.015 in. is provided so that "shear" damping might be achieved. The inertia mass has a diameter of 1 in. Assume the density of the mass to be eight and of the damping fluid to be one. The mass weighs 133 times as much as the fluid filling the annular space around it. However, the area of the mass is 16.7 times the area of the annular space, and the square of the area ratio is approximately 278. With reference to Eq. (9-16), the denominator under the radical becomes approximately $M + 2.1M$ or $3.1M$. The effective dynamic mass of the system has thus been tripled by the manner in which the damping fluid is used, with a resulting loss in natural frequency by the factor $1/\sqrt{3.1}$. By providing an alternate return passage for the damping fluid a design such as shown in Fig. 9.7b avoids this loss in natural frequency.

Accelerometers of this type fit into the category of spring-mass instruments. In these instruments the acceleration to be measured appears as a proportional force (or torque) that acts upon a small mass (or moment of inertia). This force is balanced against a spring and the deflection of this spring then becomes a measure of the force and therefore a measure of the acceleration. For static measurements, only a spring and a mass or inertia are necessary. Under dynamic conditions, however, damping is required to continually dissipate vibrational energy. Accelerometers employ liquid, pneumatic, electric, and other forms of damping. The accuracy of the measurement depends directly upon the accuracy of the spring. Hysteresis, nonlinearities, or nonsymmetrical properties of this spring result in errors in the instrument. For this, and other reasons that are connected with open-loop computations, units of this type are generally less accurate and have a smaller range than those of the force-balance, or "servo," type, which is described in Sec. 9.6. Seismic accelerometers are small and rugged, however, and provide a high output voltage directly from the position pickoff.

9-3. Construction of Seismic Accelerometers. A wide variety of accelerometers are manufactured to satisfy many needs; for example:

1. To measure the acceleration forces that structures, portions of structures, or individual objects undergo under varying conditions of acceleration.

2. To compensate for acceleration effects on missile or aircraft control systems.

3. To feed information into fire-control computers for correction of acceleration effects upon missile trajectory.

4. To actuate telemetering or recording devices directly without amplification.

5. To limit or control acceleration effects where damage could be caused by too great acceleration or deceleration.

Besides the variations of accelerometer construction due to application, there exist numerous variations such as in the type of damping and type of position pickoff. The representative samples that are included in this chapter by no means exhaust the possibilities.

Figure 9-8 shows a photograph of the internal construction of a rugged potentiometer-output accelerometer for the measurement of linear acceleration. The instrument is filled with silicone oil to reduce the effect of vibration, to increase potentiometer life by lubricating and cleansing the coil and wiper, and to allow higher potentiometer wattages due to the improved heat transfer from the coil.

Basically, this instrument consists of a spring-supported (notice the shape of the spring utilized in this instrument) mass that varies the output of one or two precision potentiometers in direct proportion to the g value

Fig. 9-8. A rugged seismic accelerometer with potentiometer output. (*G. M. Giannini and Co., Inc., Pasadena, Calif.*)

of acceleration input. The high-energy-mass system has low natural frequencies of 4.8 to 26.0 cps, depending upon range, and is magnetically damped. Damping is normally set between 0.2 and 0.5 of critical at room temperature. It will not vary more than 0.3 of critical over the temperature range.

Noble-metal alloys are used in the potentiometer coils and brushes, giving long life and positive contact with minimum friction and electrical noise. An automatic spring-loaded caging mechanism is provided to prevent actuation of the potentiometer during periods when operation is not required. Uncaging is accomplished by an electrically operated solenoid. Typical specifications can be summarized as follows:

Range	±1 to ±30 g
Resistance	2,000–20,000 each potentiometer
Resolution	0.25% (400 wires) min
Threshold sensitivity	0.06 g
Natural frequency	4.8–26.0 cps
Damping	0.5 to 0.20 fraction of critical
Linearity	±1%
Hysteresis	0.5%
Friction effect	0.06 g
Repeatability	0.5%
Cross talk	±3% max with 3 g across

Small seismic accelerometers using strain gauges to measure the motion of the seismic mass are designed and built for a wide range of accelerations. A photograph that shows the construction appears in Fig. 9-9, and

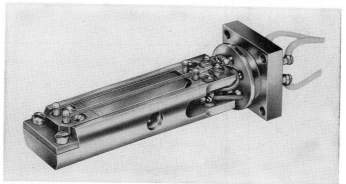

Fig. 9-9. Seismic accelerometer with strain-gauge output. (*Statham Laboratories, Los Angeles.*)

the characteristics are summarized in Table 9-1. Because of the stepless character of a strain gauge, the ultimate resolution of these accelerometers is infinite. The unbonded strain gauge is an electromechanical device that transduces minute displacements to proportional resistance changes.

The transducer is electrically and mechanically symmetrical. In the center of a stationary frame, an armature is supported rigidly in the

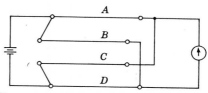

Fig. 9-10. Arrangement of strain-gauge elements.

plane perpendicular to the longitudinal axis. Wound between rigid insulators mounted in the frame and armature are four filaments of strain-sensitive resistance wire. The filaments are of equal length, arranged as shown in Fig. 9-10. As the armature is caused to move longitudinally to the left by an external force, elements A and D increase

TABLE 9-1. CHARACTERISTICS OF A SEISMIC ACCELEROMETER*

Range, g	Approximate natural frequency, cps	Excitation, d-c or a-c, volts	Approximate full-scale open-circuit output, mv	Approximate full-scale excursion, mv
±2	40	11	±25	50
±3	60	11	±25	50
±6	75	11	±25	50
±10	110	11	±25	50
±12	130	11	±23	46
±15	150	11	±23	46
±20	160	11	±24	48
±25	200	11	±24	48
±30	250	12	±25	50
±50	300	12	±26	52
±100	450	12	±26	52

* Courtesy Statham Laboratories, Inc., Los Angeles.

in length while elements B and C decrease in length. Figure 9-10 shows a circuit composed of four resistors, a source of electric current, and a

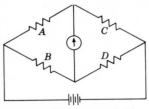

measuring device, disposed in the form of a Wheatstone bridge, as in Fig. 9-11. The change in resistance of the filaments is proportional to their change in length. The resistance change of the filaments alters the electrical balance of the bridge and produces an electric signal at the output. Sufficient

FIG. 9-11. Wheatstone bridge formed from strain-gauge elements.

initial tension is applied to the strain-sensitive resistance wires during assembly to keep them under some residual tension when the armature is in either extreme position. The armature travel is limited mechanically to protect the wires from overload. In order that the bridge will be balanced (zero output current when zero external force is applied to the armature), a trimming resistor is placed in series with one of the bridge elements and is adjusted during assembly to equalize the resistance of the four elements of the bridge. If the bridge is balanced to zero output before the displacement is applied, the unbalance electrical output of the bridge is an exact electrical analog of the displacement.

The outline dimension of the unit of Fig. 9-9 is shown in Fig. 9-12. The instrument weighs approximately 3.5 g.

An ideal accelerometer would be extremely small and have both high output and wide frequency response. In practice a compromise is reached among these three parameters. The accelerometer shown in

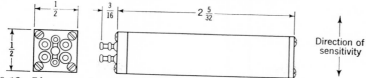

FIG. 9-12. Linear-accelerometer outline dimensions. (*Statham Laboratories, Los Angeles.*)

FIG. 9-13. Seismic accelerometer with variable-reluctance output. (*Wiancko Engineering Co., Pasadena, Calif.*)

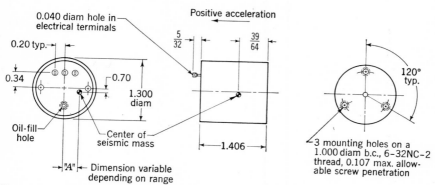

FIG. 9-14. Outline drawing of variable-reluctance-output accelerometer. (*Wiancko Engineering Co., Pasadena, Calif.*)

Figs. 9-13 and 9-14 is reasonably small and has a high output and fairly high frequency response. The seismic system consists of a dihedral spring to which a mass is attached at a short radius. A magnetic armature is part of the system and is caused to rotate as acceleration is applied. The armature is part of a two-arm variable-reluctance bridge. The instrument is used primarily with a 3 kc excitation frequency. Three tapped holes in the cover are used for mounting. Typical specifications can be summarized as follows:

Ranges	± 0.5 to $\pm 500\ g$
Natural frequency	28 to 900 cps
Maximum acceleration	150% of range
Inductance per coil	20 mh (nominal)
Linearity, used with demodulator	1%
Hysteresis	0.1%
Weight	3.5 oz
Resolution	continuous

Figure 9-15 is a photograph of a Micro-G accelerometer used for measuring very low accelerations (as low as $5 \times 10^{-6}\ g$). One application

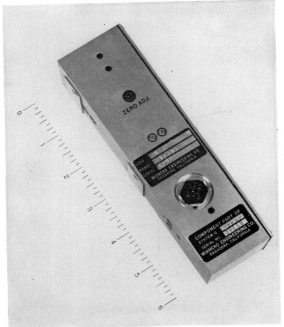

Fig. 9-15. Micro-G accelerometer. (*Wiancko Engineering Co., Pasadena, Calif.*)

is the stabilizing of the platform used in inertial guidance systems for rockets or missiles. To provide a level surface for the platform, two such accelerometers would be mounted at right angles.

The seismic system consists of a spring-mounted pendulum using no knife edges, bearings, or other sources of friction. Hysteresis is negligible (less than 0.01 per cent of full scale) because gravity is the main restoring force on the pendulum. An armature that is part of the system operates in the field of two coils, providing an inductance pickoff of the pendulum motion. The instrument is designed to operate with a special amplitude-modulation system in which a portion of the instrument output is differentiated into an electromagnetic damping circuit in the accelerometer. The current for the damping coil is thus proportional to the velocity of the pendulum.

The body, mounting, and seismic support of the instruments are all machined from one solid aluminum block. Overload stops are built into the instrument to protect it against excessive accelerations or vibrations encountered during flights of missiles or aircraft. The important specifications can be summarized as follows:

Range	$\pm 500\ \mu g$
Natural frequency	1.4 cps
Sensitivity	Approximately 0.1 volt/volt
Linearity	Approximately 2% of range
Excitation	Normally 5 volts at 2–10 kc
Hysteresis	0.01% of acceleration or less
Resolution	continuous
Damping	0.7 critical, within maximum temperature range.

The characteristics of various accelerometers are compared in Table 9-2.

9-4. Accelerometer Design Considerations. The design of an accelerometer depends upon the specification of the range, the natural frequency, the damping ratio, and the sensitivity. Also important to the design of the instrument are the accuracy, linearity, hysteresis, and cross talk. These various design parameters are varied by changing the accelerometer quantities. For example, consider a unit with the following requirements:

Range	$a = \pm 3\ g$
Natural frequency	$= 2$ cps
Damping factor	$= 0.7 \pm 0.1$
Accuracy, including hysteresis and linearity	$\pm 1\%$
A-c output	1 volt rms/g

The maximum excursion of the mass is determined from the natural frequency and the range. When the accelerometer is at the maximum excursion, the following equation must be satisfied:

$$Ma = K\Delta \tag{9-17}$$

where Ma is the maximum force that must be sustained by the mass spring system. $K\Delta$ is the restraining force produced by the spring at its maximum excursion Δ. When Eq. (9-17) is combined with Eq. (9-7), the

Table 9-2. Accelerometer Characteristics

Manufacturer	Type	Acceleration range, g	Sensitivity	Frequency-response range, cps	Type of pickoff	Weight	Linearity, per cent of full scale	Size, in.
Giannini	24132	±1		0–26	Potentiometer	40 oz	±1	3.14 × 2.28 × 3.28
Giannini	24144	±30		0–38.5	Potentiometer	8 oz	1	1.22 diam × 2.5
Consolidated Electrodynamics	4-242-1	0.01–1,000	1.3 mv/g	50–60,000	Porous ceramic disk	8 gm	½	¾ diam × ⅝
Statham Labs	AJ26-0.5-350	±0.5	88 mv/g	0–21	Strain gauge	19 oz	1	3½ × 2¹¹⁄₁₆ × 3¹¹⁄₁₆
Statham Labs	A53-1000-50	±1,000	40 μa/g	0–250	Strain gauge	4 oz	±2	2³⁄₁₆ × 2½ × 1⅛
Statham Labs	A50ITC-50-350	±50	0.4 mv/g	0–500	Strain gauge	6½ oz	1	2³⁄₁₆ × 3⁷⁄₁₆ × 1⁵⁄₁₆
Wiancko	A1101	±0.3	10 v/g	0–24	Variable reluctance	2.3 lb	½	3¹³⁄₃₂ diam × 4
Greenleaf	PCE	±1		0–7	Potentiometer	12 oz	±1	2.3 × 1⅜ × 2.6
Genisco	GLH	±1		0–7	Potentiometer	2 lb	±1	3.4 × 2.4 × 3⅛
Genisco	GMO	±30		0–40	Potentiometer	8 oz	±1	1⅛ × 1⁹⁄₆₄ × 3⅛

natural frequency is written as

$$\omega_n = \sqrt{\frac{K}{M}} = \sqrt{\frac{a}{\Delta}} \qquad (9\text{-}18)$$

For the example, the maximum excursion is

$$\Delta = \frac{a}{\omega_n{}^2} = \frac{3.12}{[(2)(6.28)]^2} = 0.229 \qquad (9\text{-}19)$$

Use of a position pickoff* with an appropriate excitation voltage should produce the required sensitivity (i.e., 1 volt rms per g of acceleration).

The ratio of K/M is determined from the natural frequency [Eq. (9-18)]. The choice of the particular value of M depends upon the threshold sensitivity. The larger the mass, the smaller is the relative effect of striction and hysteresis, but the greater is the sensitivity to cross acceleration (cross talk). The cross talk can be reduced by good mechanical design of the suspension system. In this example, suppose ±0.3 per cent of the accuracy is allocated to threshold sensitivity γ. In terms of acceleration, 0.3 per cent of full scale corresponds to 0.01 g or

$$(0.01)(32.2)(12) = 3.86 \text{ in./sec}^2 \qquad (9\text{-}20)$$

The mass M multiplied by the threshold sensitivity γ should be greater than the maximum friction force $f_{\max}$ or

$$M\gamma \geqslant f_{\max} \qquad (9\text{-}21)$$

If the maximum frictional force is 0.05 oz (for this example), the mass is

$$M = \frac{f_{\max}}{\gamma} = \frac{0.05 \text{ oz-sec}^2}{3.86 \text{ in.}} = 0.0129 \text{ oz-sec}^2/\text{in.} \qquad (9\text{-}22)$$

The weight of this mass is

$$W = (0.0129)(32.2) = 5 \text{ oz} \qquad (9\text{-}23)$$

and the spring constant is

$$K = M\omega_n{}^2 = (0.0129)(12.48)^2 = 2.02 \text{ oz/in.} \qquad (9\text{-}24)$$

Although a seismic accelerometer is perfectly designed and fabricated, it is important to consider several effects that may cause inferior performance. Since the provision of the proper damping ratio is important in obtaining a flat-response spectrum, it is useful to know if the ratio remains constant with ambient conditions. Temperature is the most common offender. In Fig. 9-16 the variation of damping ratio of typical devices using magnetic, silicone-oil, and petroleum-oil damping is plotted. Mag-

* Position pickoffs are discussed in Chap. 3.

netic damping shows the least variation with temperature, although
the temperature coefficients of magnets and the copper alloys in which
eddy currents or back emfs are generated cause some variation.   Silicone
oil is remarkable only by comparison with petroleum or vegetable-base
oils.   Regardless of its poor behavior, there are many situations in which
there is no better substitute.   Magnetic damping is often not practical
in high-natural-frequency devices.   The only practical solution to the
viscosity-variation problem appears to be temperature control or the
incorporation of machine elements that change shape with temperature.

Varying ambient temperature has other undesirable effects.   In an
accelerometer whose response includes static readings, stability of the

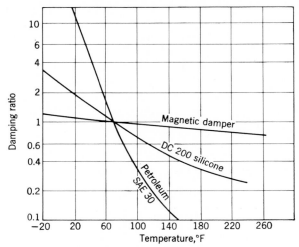

FIG. 9-16. Variation of typical damping devices with temperature.   (*Statham Laboratories, Los Angeles.*)

zero point is often troublesome.   No meter, galvanometer, accelerometer,
or other instrument should be assumed to have a stable zero unless
experimental evidence is available to guarantee it.   In a good instrument
design, large variations are prevented by the method of construction, so
that only small effects, not predictable before trial, are left.   These
residual effects must be individually compensated to achieve minimum
error.   Any individual device that shows appreciable nonrepeatability
of zero change with temperature cannot be closely compensated for zero
errors.   Almost no pure metal or alloy has a constant modulus of elasticity with temperature.   The effect varies with the material and the
temperature, but at laboratory temperatures the steel and bronzelike
alloys become more flexible by 3 to 5 per cent in 100°F.   Any spring element used as a deflection reference requires a correction or compensation
of this magnitude.   Various special alloys sold under trade names such as

Elinvar and Isoelastic are exceptional in that their Young's modulus is nearly constant over the normal experimental temperature range. A measuring instrument usually has a temperature coefficient of output to input ratio, and unless it is stated in suitable fashion by the manufacturer, it should be measured by the user.

Accelerometers are usually considered as responding only to the component of acceleration along the principal axis. This is not necessarily true since the principal axis may not be perpendicular to the base because of manufacturing tolerances. Other types, some in commercial use, have no principal axis. That is, regardless of the direction of a test vibration, some output always results. This is not necessarily harmful; but it is evident that if the vector motion of a test article in space is to be determined, the absence of lateral response is highly desirable.

9-5. Calibration and Testing of Accelerometers. An important consideration in the use of any precision instrument is the setting up of appropriate criteria for evaluating its response characteristics. It is important to devise test methods that will determine instrument response with speed and accuracy. The performance of an accelerometer can be judged in terms of the following parameters: range, sensitivity, linearity, damping, and natural frequency. The simplest method of obtaining the first three is by means of a static test setup, while the latter two must be determined dynamically.

Two practical methods of subjecting the instruments to precise static accelerations are utilized. For the very low ranges, the sensitive axis of the accelerometer may be aligned with the earth's gravitational field. Using a leveled platform or a holding fixture with horizontal bearings and some means of indexing quadrants, the instrument may be inclined through $+1$ g, zero, and -1 g positions and a comparison to a standard thus accomplished. Since a good linear accelerometer is sensitive only along its principal axis, if provision is made to indicate the inclination, fractional increments of less than 1 g are obtained.

Static accelerations higher than 1 g are generated in a centrifuge. The axis of rotation should be vertical so that a ripple of ± 1 g is not superimposed upon the static acceleration. Care should be exercised to align the sensitive axis of the test instrument on a radius of rotation to avoid shortening of the effective radius. Knowledge of the location of the exact center of mass of the seismic system is imperative. If this information is not available, it may be approximated from data of two or more tests made at the same speed with variations in the radius of rotation. Since the acceleration varies as the square of the angular velocity, the speed regulation is important. Effective systems of speed control include the use of a synchronous motor to power the centrifuge, or utilization of the stroboscopic principle as a means of speed indication.

In calibration of a linear accelerometer by the centrifuge method, its linearity is inspected by imposing a change of acceleration on the instrument by varying either the radius of rotation or the speed. The static acceleration experienced in runs of this type is found from

$$a = 2.840 \times 10^{-5} N^2 r \qquad (9\text{-}25)$$

where r is the radius of rotation of the center of gravity of the active mass in inches, N is the speed in revolutions per minute, and a is in standard g units.

Electrical connections are brought out from the spinning accelerometer by brushes and slip rings. Worn-in graphite brushes on silver slip rings have been found to be highly satisfactory, displaying negligible contact resistance throughout widely varying speed ranges. Open-circuit voltages are measured with a precision potentiometer while the input voltage is held constant. With resistance bridge-type linear accelerometers, the sensitivity is expressed as the open-circuit output potential in volts per input volt per g.

A convenient method for finding the dynamic response of an accelerometer whose damping is less than critical is to observe the instrument's response to a step function in acceleration. A linear step function for a linear accelerometer can be approximated by suspending the accelerometer from a string over some padding. The string is cut and the initial fall of the accelerometer results in a step function of 1 g amplitude. In some accelerometers it is impossible to apply a step function by displacing the mass and suddenly releasing it. The value of the damping ratio can be found by measuring the height of the first overshoot. A curve that is useful in determining the damping ratio from the amplitude of the first overshoot is given in the Appendix.

The frequency-response curve of a linear accelerometer can be obtained by calibrating the instrument on a shake table capable of producing an essentially pure sinusoidal force over a large frequency range. While many types of shake table suitable for calibrating an accelerometer are available, one of the simplest and easiest to use is the electromagnetic type of vibration exciter. The force in this type of exciter is generated by an alternating current flowing in a movable coil that is positioned in a region of high magnetic flux density. The magnetic field is derived from a stationary field coil connected to a source of direct current. The shape and strength of the magnetic structure are such as to ensure the generated force being dependent only on the magnitude of the current in the moving coil. Since the force generated is as pure as the current supplied to the moving coil, it is necessary to use an oscillator and power amplifier with low-distortion characteristics.

The exciter is a mechanical system that resonates at certain frequencies; therefore it is not sufficient to monitor the current flowing through the moving coil to ensure that the amplitude of the sinusoidal force produced remains constant as the frequency is varied. To calibrate the exciter, the output of a velocity-type signal generator coil, attached to the shake table and moving in the magnetic field of a permanent magnet rigidly supported in space, can be used. The response of the accelerometer can be measured with a vacuum-tube voltmeter having a flat frequency response over the range of test frequencies.

One convenient method of dynamically testing accelerometers is shown in Fig. 9-17. The accelerometer is rotated at a uniform angular rate about a horizontal axis, so that a sinusoidal forcing function of 1 g peak amplitude is applied. An unusual opportunity is thus afforded to obtain the response of the accelerometer under both static and dynamic conditions in the same test setup without a change of method. As an additional advantage, it becomes possible to apply very low frequency

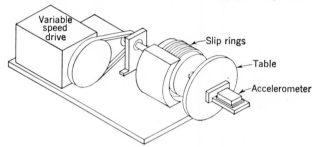

FIG. 9-17. Horizontal-axis test table.

sinusoids in the region where sinusoidal linear translations of large amplitude would otherwise be required to give useful accelerations. However, there are certain important limitations to the method that become apparent when the theory is reviewed.

Assume that an accelerometer is mounted to rotate about a horizontal axis so that the sensitive axis of the accelerometer rotates in a vertical plane. If the center of mass of the accelerometer is mounted off the rotational center by a distance R, a steady reading of $\omega^2 R$ plus the sinusoidal component is obtained. The center for proper mounting is found experimentally; and if the accelerometer is assumed to be linear, no error results if $\omega^2 R$ is held to a small fraction of the range.

There is a certain serious error that must be considered. The source of this error can be seen most simply by writing the differential equation of the system. If M, B, and K have their usual significance of mass, damping coefficient, and spring constant, the equation would normally be written as

$$M\ddot{x} + B\dot{x} + Kx = Mg \sin \omega t \qquad (9\text{-}26)$$

where x is the instantaneous displacement of the mass M. Under conditions of the forces applied during this test, however, the mass experiences a force given by

$$M\omega^2(R + x) \qquad (9\text{-}27)$$

because of the centrifugal force. ω is the angular velocity of rotation of the horizontal shaft. Accordingly the response is governed by the following differential equation,

$$M\ddot{x} + B\dot{x} + (K - M\omega^2)x = Mg \sin \omega t + M\omega^2 R \qquad (9\text{-}28)$$

Thus, in rotating systems, the effective spring constant (i.e., the coefficient of the x term) is decreased by the ratio

$$\frac{(k - M\omega^2)}{k} = 1 - \left(\frac{\omega}{\omega_n}\right)^2$$

where ω_n is the natural frequency.

Hence, the response is too large in the dynamic test described above. The error is parabolic and is less than 1 per cent up to one-tenth of

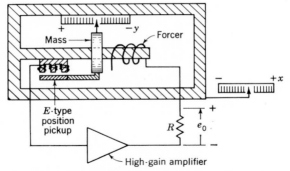

Fig. 9-18. Schematic of force-balance accelerometer.

the natural frequency. If the rotational speed is increased until the natural frequency is reached, the mass is unstable and assumes any position between its limit stops.

9-6. Force-balance Accelerometers; Theory of Operation. Force-balance accelerometers overcome some of the disadvantages of seismic instruments. The basic principle underlying the force-balance accelerometer is shown in Fig. 9-18. In this system a mass is allowed to move along the acceleration-sensitive axis. The position of this mass is measured with a position pickoff, which is generally of the E type, as discussed in Chap. 3. The output voltage from this position transducer is amplified with a high-gain amplifier whose output is a current. The current flows through the windings of a forcer,* which forces the mass

* See Chap. 7 for a discussion of forcers.

back to its original null position.   The forcer current, necessary to zero
the position of this mass, is proportional to acceleration.   This current
is measured as a voltage across a resistor that is in series with the forcer
coil.   In this system, high damping, which is independent of temperature,
and good accuracy are obtained by means of appropriate equalization
in the servo.

The analysis of the force-balance accelerometer of Fig. 9-18 is based
upon the block diagram of Fig. 9-19.   If the mass is free to move along
the rod with essentially zero damping, the force on the mass is related to
displacement as follows:

$$F = Ms^2(Y - X) \tag{9-29}$$

or, rewritten, as

$$Y = \frac{1}{Ms^2}(F + Ms^2X) = \frac{1}{Ms^2}(F + MA) \tag{9-30}$$

$A(s) = s^2X(s)$ and s is the Laplace-transform operator.   Zero initial
conditions have been assumed.   Equation (9-30) is represented by the

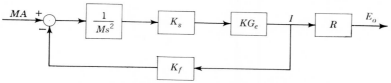

FIG. 9-19. Block diagram of force-balance accelerometer.

first block whose output is Y.   This quantity is converted to a voltage
with a position pickoff, whose transfer function is K_s, and the signal
is amplified with an amplifier and equalizer KG_s.   The current from this
amplifier passes through a forcer, which has a transfer function K_f in
force units per milliampere.   This current forces the mass back to a
null position.   The output voltage is measured at the output of a final
block whose transfer function is R.   The servo force that is fed back
balances the input acceleration force.

With an equalizer of the form

$$G_e(s) = \alpha s + 1 \tag{9-31}$$

i.e., position plus rate compensation, the system is made stable.   The
damping is electrically controllable (as α is varied) so it is independent
of temperature effects.   The closed-loop system is characterized by
the following equation:

$$\frac{E_o}{MA} = \frac{\dfrac{RK_sK(\alpha s + 1)}{Ms^2}}{\dfrac{K_sK(\alpha s + 1)K_f}{Ms^2} + 1} \tag{9-32}$$

which reduces to

$$\frac{E_o}{A} = \frac{RK_sK(\alpha s + 1)}{s^2 + (K_sKK_f\alpha/M)s + (K_sKK_f/M)} \tag{9-33}$$

where $\qquad \omega_n{}^2 = \dfrac{K_sKK_f}{M} \qquad$ and $\qquad \zeta = \dfrac{\alpha}{2}\sqrt{\dfrac{K_sK_fK}{M}} \qquad$ (9-34)

The closed-loop force-balance-accelerometer transfer function is

$$\frac{E_o}{A} = \frac{RK_sK(\alpha s + 1)}{s^2 + 2\zeta\omega_n s + \omega_n{}^2} \tag{9-35}$$

Besides a controlled damping, the resonant frequency is proportional to the square root of the loop gain. Hence, a high resonant frequency is possible with the force-balance accelerometer.

Force-balance instruments, which are applicable to many types of measurement, possess the advantage that the inaccuracies in the mechanical system, such as spring hysteresis, are replaced by fewer electrical inaccuracies, such as forcer errors. The accuracy of the force-balance system depends, to a large extent, on the accuracy with which a forcer can be built. In essence, the feedback system makes possible the use of an electrical standard (forcer) rather than a mechanical standard (spring). An accelerometer of high accuracy and fine resolution can be obtained when temperature compensation (such as a Curie shunt* across the magnetic path of the forcer and appropriate electrical equalization to account for variations of the copper with temperature) is utilized. Instruments of this type are capable of measuring accelerations of the order of 0.001 g. Since the unit is always operating about a null, the linearity can be improved by a factor of 10 over a seismic accelerometer.

9-7. Construction of Force-balance Accelerometers. A practical form for the force-balance accelerometer is shown in Fig. 9-20. The sensor in this accelerometer is basically a d'Arsonval mechanism. Static unbalance of the moving coil is provided by a small weight placed on a transverse arm. A capacitive pickup error detector on the arm measures small excursions of the inertial element; this controls the current delivered by the internal servo system to the moving coil. High closed-loop servo gain is obtained with a level-controlled oscillator followed by a one-tube amplifier. Small position errors are developed. Thus, torques arising from acceleration inputs are precisely opposed by current-generated torques.

The torquing current may be available as the output signal but is usually passed through a precision resistor to develop the output voltage.

* Curie shunt is the name usually given a carpenter-metal magnetic-circuit shunt whose reluctance varies with temperature in the direction opposite from that of iron.

Velocity damping, controlled by circuit components, is independent of temperature. Since the moving assembly has only one degree of freedom, it measures linear accelerations only along its sensitive axis. Since the internal connections make the unit a voltage generator with very low output impedance, an external load will not affect the calibration of the instrument but may cause the instrument to reach saturation at lower acceleration levels.

One plate of the variable capacitance is fixed. The other plate is attached to the moving coil of the torque mechanism. An acceleration input causes a variation in the position of the variable plate of the

(a)   (b)

FIG. 9-20. Force-balance accelerometer. *(Donner Scientific Co., Concord, Calif.)*

capacitor. The capacitor variation produces a variation in plate current according to the curve of Fig. 9-21. This current is used to torque the unit back to a null by means of the d'Arsonval movement.

The specifications of the unit of Fig. 9-20 can be summarized:

Resolution	0.001 % of full scale
Linearity	0.1 % of full scale
D-c reproducibility	0.05 % of full scale
Full-range input	± 01. to $\pm 20\ g$

The unit has zero output with zero input.

9-8. Force-balance Distance Meter. Another practical demonstration of a force-balance accelerometer is considered in this section. The unit provides an output that is proportional to acceleration but is easily converted to distance. A unit that has wide application in inertial-guidance applications is shown in Fig. 9-22. A motor is mounted on an axis perpendicular to the direction of motion. This axis, which is called the output axis, is capable of turning freely. The motor is pendulous about this axis. As an acceleration is applied perpendicular

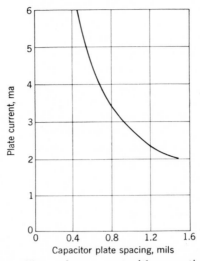

FIG. 9-21. Variation of oscillator plate current with separation of capacitor plates.

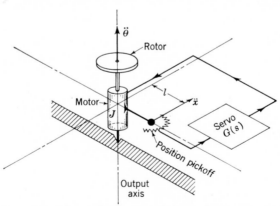

FIG. 9-22. Schematic of a force-balance distance meter.

to the axis of rotation, the pendulous body tends to rotate. The rotation angle is measured, amplified, equalized, and applied to the motor. As the motor armature rotates, a counter torque (or a reaction torque) is applied to cancel the acceleration of the pendulous motor. As a result, the angular acceleration of the motor is proportional to the linear acceleration of the unit. The angular velocity is proportional to the linear velocity, and the angular position of the motor is proportional to the linear position of the accelerometer.

The mathematical description of the unit is facilitated by the following list of quantities:

J' = moment of inertia of motor body and pendulum
I' = moment of inertia of motor rotor
m = unbalanced mass of pendulum
l = length of pendulous arm
β = angular deviation of pickoff
$a = \ddot{x}$ = applied acceleration
T_e = error torque applied to pendulum
T_m = torque output of motor
T_i = input torque due to mass unbalance
B = damping about output axis
K = spring rate about output axis
$G(s)$ = transfer function of servo and equalizer

A functional block diagram of the distance meter is shown in Fig. 9-23. The equations of motion are written from this figure. The torque applied

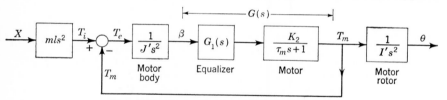

FIG. 9-23. Block diagram of distance meter.

to the motor housing by the pendulous mass is the input torque, which is written

$$T_i = ml\ddot{x} = mla \qquad (9\text{-}36)$$

The error torque available to accelerate the motor housing is

$$T_e = T_i - T_m = J'\ddot{\beta} \qquad (9\text{-}37)$$

In both equations the double dot above the variable corresponds to double differentiation with respect to time. The torque output T_m on the shaft of the motor is

$$T_m = I'\ddot{\theta} + B\dot{\theta} + K\theta \qquad (9\text{-}38)$$

The output of the servo $\bar{T}_m = G(s)$ is the driving function for Eq. (9-38). When this equation is Laplace-transformed,

$$G(s)\beta = (I's^2 + Bs + K)\theta \qquad (9\text{-}39)$$

where all initial conditions are considered zero and s is the Laplace-transform operator. The bars over the variable indicate transformed quantities. From Fig. 9-23 the closed-loop transfer function is

$$\frac{\bar{T}_m(s)}{\bar{T}_i(s)} = \frac{G(s)/J's^2}{1 + G(s)/J's^2} = \frac{G(s)}{J's^2 + G(s)} \tag{9-40}$$

For a first understanding of the problem, take $G(s)$ as a constant. $G(s) \approx K$ where $|G(j\omega)| \gg |J'(j\omega)^2|$ with the result that

$$T_m \approx T_i \tag{9-41}$$

However, $T_i = ml\ddot{x}$, and for small damping and spring rate $T_m \cong I'\ddot{\theta}$. Equating these according to Eq. (9-41),

$$mls^2x \cong I's^2\theta \tag{9-42}$$

or canceling s^2,

$$\theta \cong \frac{ml}{I'}x \tag{9-43}$$

This last expression demonstrates the operation of the distance meter, and is valid if the input function $x(t)$ has reasonably small frequency components. The shaft position of the motor is proportional to the distance moved. The actual design of the unit must, of course, include an account of stability and a more accurate derivation of transfer function.

One of the most important practical features of the distance meter is its low threshold. Since the instrument must sense very small accelerations $(0.001\ g)$ it must be free from coulomb friction, striction, spring rate, etc., about the axis of rotation. To accomplish this the instrument is floated in a lightly viscous silicone oil. A fluid bearing is utilized to further reduce coulomb friction and striction. The fluid viscosity is low enough so that the fluid can be pumped through the bearing at room temperature. A pump, which is conveniently located on each instrument, is simply a double-acting solenoid and is driven with a small pump electrical supply. An expansion device and a fluid filter comprise the remainder of the fluid circuit.

From Eq. (9-43), the scale factor of a distance meter is $ml/2\pi I'$ in number of revolutions per foot. For consistency from unit to unit, the scale factor must be adjustable. This is accomplished by changing the distance meter pendulosity ml, which is easily adjusted with a change in l. The distance of a weight, located on the motor housing and available from the outside of the instrument, is adjusted to change l and hence ml. Because all instruments are manufactured to a close tolerance, this adjustment need only be of second-order.

PROBLEMS

9-1. Compare the seismic and force-balance accelerometers. Consider accuracy, damping, frequency response, and reliability.

9-2. For the seismic accelerometer described by Eq. (9-3), what is the relation among the following frequencies: (a) natural frequency, (b) frequency at which the peak of the amplitude response occurs, and (c) frequency of the transient oscillation.

9-3. Discuss the effect of utilizing fluid to damp an accelerometer. What is the effect on damping ratio and natural frequency?

9-4. Discuss the performance of an accelerometer in which the density of the sensitive mass is less than the density of the damping fluid.

9-5. Derive the equation of motion for the accelerometer of Prob. 9-4. Is the direction of motion of the sensitive mass the same as for an accelerometer in which the density of the sensitive mass is greater than that of the damping fluid?

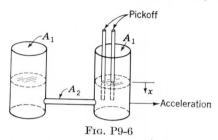

FIG. P9-6

9-6. Derive the equations of motion for the liquid accelerometer shown in Fig. P9-6. The area of each vertical pipe is A_1 and the area of the connecting pipe is A_2. The fluid density is σ and the acceleration of gravity is g. Neglect the viscosity of the fluid and assume that the level of the fluid is indicated by a sensitive resistance bridge whose output voltage E_o is given by the expression

$$E_o = Kx$$

where x is the height of fluid in one of the tubes.

9-7. Derive equations and determine the block diagram for the force-balance distance meter of Fig. 9-22. Find a practical equalizer to stabilize the system.

CHAPTER 10

GYROSCOPES

10-1. Gyroscope Applications. When a body, such as a missile or an aircraft, is moving through space or a ship or a submarine is moving through water, a frame of reference must be established for guidance purposes. Six coordinates, three translations and three rotations, are required to define completely the position of a rigid body. Various coordinate systems exist, but usually the following are used:

1. Longitudinal velocity
2. Rotation about the longitudinal or roll axis
3. Rotation about the pitch axis
4. Rotation about the yaw axis.

These axes are defined in Fig. 10-1. A frame of reference can be established by various methods, such as radio, Doppler radar, celestial (star-tracking), or inertial. The reference system can be established with

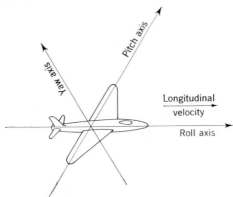

Fig. 10-1. Important aircraft axes.

respect to the fixed reference frame of the earth, to a space coordinate system, or to an arbitrary coordinate system established by the aircraft (guidance-plan reference).

One of the more important methods of establishing a frame of reference utilizes gyros—an inertial reference that is used for inertial-navigation systems. The schematic of Fig. 10-2 shows the use of three gyros and two accelerometers for an inertial navigator. This system has the capability of satisfying the navigational requirement of an airborne body. Either a two-degree-of-freedom gyroscope (double-axis gyroscope) shown in the schematic of Fig. 10-3 or a single-degree-of-freedom

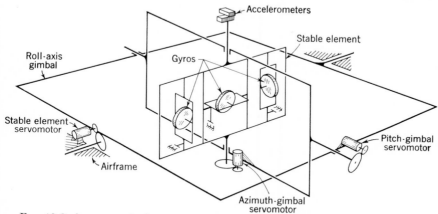

FIG. 10-2. A gyroscopically stabilized platform establishes a reference in space.

gyro (single-axis gyroscope) shown in the schematic of Fig. 10-4 is used for inertial-navigation systems. The schematic shown in Fig. 10-2 utilizes three single-degree-of-freedom gyros. If two axis gyros are utilized, only two are required to stabilize a platform.

The spinning rotor of the double-axis gyro, Fig. 10-3, is mounted in a two-axis gimbal constructed to minimize friction and other sources of torque on both axes. The gimbal permits freedom of motion of the gyro wheel about the two axes other than the spin axis. To the extent that disturbing torques approach zero, the rotor will remain fixed in space and will maintain the direction initially set. The angular displacement is measured with any of the position pickoffs discussed in Chap. 3.

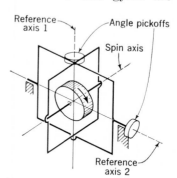

FIG. 10-3. Double-axis gyroscope schematic.

Usually the E transformer is used. To establish a three-axis stabilized platform, two double-axis gyroscopes are required. The spin axes are oriented at right angles to each other. The one redundant axis can be either deactivated or used to improve performance.

In single-axis gyros, two degrees of freedom are provided; but only one axis, usually the outer gimbal, is used for reference. The spin axis is maintained at right angles to this axis by means of a servosystem as shown in Fig. 10-4.

In the usual nomenclature for single-axis gyroscopes, the wheel is spun about the *spin axis*. The support axis of the gyro gimbal, which is at right angles to the spin axis, is called the *output* or precession axis. The *input* or *stabilizing* axis is perpendicular to both the spin and output axes.

Moderately high-precision gyroscopes are utilized in the gyrocompass application. In this application, the gyro errors are less important

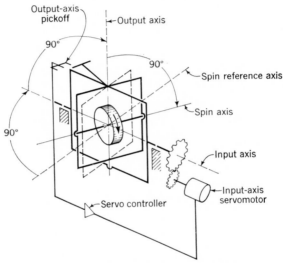

FIG. 10-4. Single-axis gyroscope schematic.

because the system usually is less accurate. Since the environmental conditions, especially acceleration, are less stringent, a gyrocompass is generally used in marine applications.

Gyroscopes are utilized in large numbers for fire- and flight-control applications. The performance of these gyros is usually less demanding than those used for navigation. The limiting factor on accuracy is usually not random drift but rather the degree to which disturbing effects, such as earth rate and accelerations other than gravity, can be minimized. Gyroscopes used in this application are frequently servoed to more accurate gravity references (liquid levels, for example). As can be seen from Fig. 10-5, the automatic-flight-control system for a modern aircraft utilizes at least four gyroscopes and about two dozen other major control components. The "black boxes" shown in Fig. 10-5 are part of the MB-3 automatic-flight-control system designed and manufactured by the

Aeronautical Division of Minneapolis-Honeywell.   The system stabilizes the aircraft and gives the pilot the assistance he needs in flying the jet aircraft through many maneuvers.   The pilot controls the entire system through a "control-stick-steering" transducer and a function-selector panel within the cockpit.   The three rate gyros shown in the control

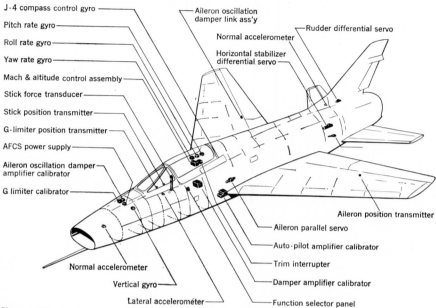

FIG. 10-5. Automatic flight-control system of a modern jet aircraft.   (*Aeronautical Div., Minneapolis-Honeywell Co., Minneapolis.*)

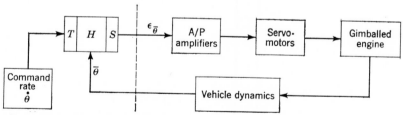

FIG. 10-6. Block diagram of pitch axis of a satellite-rocket guidance system.

system of Fig. 10-5 provide velocity information about the three axes of the aircraft.   In this application the rate information is utilized principally for damping.

Figure 10-6 shows the block diagram for the pitch axis of a satellite-rocket-guidance system.   Changes and corrections needed in pitch axis to guide the rocket to satellite-launching orbit are channeled through the autopilot to the servo system which operates actuators which push and pull on the gimbaled thrust chamber. Resultant changes in the rocket-flight dynamics are sensed by the pitch gyro to complete the closed-loop system. Nomenclature used in this diagram is: H is the angular momentum of gyro wheel; T is the gyro torquer through which the gyro is precessed; and S is the signal pickoff. Other symbols represent the various angles that must be defined: Θ is the actual pitch angle. $E_{\dot{\theta}}$ is the error in the pitch angle measured by the pitch axis gyro. The error

Fig. 10-7. Vertical gyro reference. (*Aeronautical Div., Minneapolis-Honeywell Regulator Co., Minneapolis.*)

is determined by comparing the rate of change of pitch angle $d\theta/dt$ to the reference or command pitch rate $\dot{\theta}_\gamma$.

A single gyro unit that is used to maintain a vertical reference is known as a *vertical gyro*. An example of one such unit is shown in Fig. 10-7. This cageable vertical gyro allows for high accuracy under actual operating conditions. This position- or direction-reference gyro is used in stabilization and flight-control systems for aircraft, special-weapons systems, radar stabilization, and other applications needing accurate angular-position reference. This cageable gyro utilizes a synchro rather than a potentiometer for gimbal-displacement measure. The caging mechanism is in the right of the photograph.

Although the gyroscope takes on many forms, it basically consists of a wheel mounted on a shaft and arranged to be spun at high angular velocity. Frequently, the wheel is mounted in a system of gimbals that permits it freedom to take up any orientation in space. A comparison of the accuracy requirements of gyroscopes is given in Table 10-1.

TABLE 10-1. ACCURACY REQUIREMENTS OF GYROSCOPES

Type of gyro	Application	Gyro drift rate, deg/hr
Rate gyroscope	Fire and flight control	10–100
Directional gyroscope	Flight indication and autopilot	1–10
Vertical gyroscope	Vertical reference	5–50
High-accuracy directional gyro	Navigational reference	0.1–1.0
Restrained gyro	Inertial navigation	0.01–0.1

10-2. Theory of Gyroscope Operation. A simple mathematical model of a gyro is first considered for the purpose of gaining an insight into the operation of the gyroscope. In this example the effects of moments of inertia of the wheel and gimbal system about axes other than the spin axis are neglected. The resulting equation fails to show certain characteristics, but for many purposes the results are adequate. For this derivation the following nomenclature is needed:

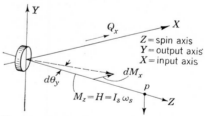

FIG. 10-8. Simplified vector diagram for a gyroscope system.

M_x, M_y, M_z = components of angular momentum about the x, y, and z axes.

I_s = moment of inertia of wheel about the spin axis.

ω_s = angular velocity of the wheel.

$H = I_s\omega_s$ = angular momentum of the wheel.

These quantities are indicated in Fig. 10-8.

At time $t = 0$, a torque Q_x is applied about the x axis. This may be accomplished by pressing down on the gyro housing at point p. Initially, $M_z = I_s\omega_s = H$ and $M_x = M_y = 0$; i.e., the angular momentum of spin lies along OZ and has a magnitude H. Since the rate of change of angular momentum of a system is equal to the applied torque,* the following expression can be written:

$$Q_x = \frac{dM_x}{dt} \qquad (10\text{-}1)$$

which can be expressed in different form:

$$dM_x = Q_x\, dt \qquad (10\text{-}2)$$

If this term is added vectorially to the initial angular momentum (see Fig. 10-8), a new value is obtained. $M_x + dM_x$ is separated from the initial vectory by an angle $d\theta_y$, which from Fig. 10-8 is approximated by the expression

$$d\theta_y = \frac{dM_x}{H} = \frac{Q_x\, dt}{H} \qquad (10\text{-}3)$$

which is rewritten as follows:

$$\omega_y = \frac{d\theta_y}{dt} = \frac{Q_x}{H} \qquad (10\text{-}4)$$

The gyro wheel is precessing about the OY axis with a velocity ω_y. Equation (10-4) demonstrates the fundamental gyroscopic law: a torque about any axis other than the spin axis produces a velocity about the orthogonal axis. Because of this property the gyro is utilized to measure torques ($Q_x = H\omega_y$) by measuring precession velocity.

A large gyroscope can be used to produce a stabilizing counter torque. For applied torques about the x or y axis, the gyro supplies an equal counter torque, which prevents motion in the direction of the applied torque as long as the gyro is able to precess. Once the precession angle θ has reached 90°, the gyroscope is in a state of gimbal lock and ceases to function as a gyroscope. When in the state of gimbal lock, the OZ axis precesses into the OX axis, about which the torque is being applied. With the torque applied about the OX or spin axis, the gyro ceases to produce a counter torque.

To obtain an idea of the order of magnitude of the precession rates and torques involved in a gyro, consider the following example: Assume a wheel has a 3-in. radius, 1-in. thickness, and is made of brass. If the angular velocity is 10,000 rpm and its mass density is 0.3 lb/in.³, then I is equal to 0.098 lb-in. sec² and ω_s is equal to 1,057 radians/sec. The angular momentum H is equal to 103.7 lb-in. sec, and the precession rate is equal to 0.55 radian per minute for a 1 lb-in. applied torque.

The more general gyroscopic equations must be derived to find the

---

* In linear mechanics, the rate of change of linear momentum equals the applied force $F = dmv/dt$.

complete transfer function of a gyroscope. Practical quantities such as spring constant, damping, and moment of inertia about the two axes of interest are included in this derivation. In the subsequent derivation, the following assumptions are made:

1. A small angle is assumed (i.e., $\sin \theta \approx \theta$ and $\cos \theta \approx 1$).

2. Moments of inertia about the x and y axes are constant during the period under consideration.

3. The gimbal system is sufficiently symmetric so that products of inertia can be neglected.

With the gyroscope mounted in a gimbal system and the position of the spin axis displaced from the OZ axis by small angles, θ in azimuth and ϕ in elevation, the following additional nomenclature is needed:

J = moment of inertia of wheel, case, and gimbal system about the x axis. This includes the inertia of the platform or other mounting of the gyroscope.

I = moment of inertia of wheel, case, and gimbal system about the y axis.

L = torque applied about the x axis.

U = disturbing torque applied about the y axis.

The remaining symbols are identical with those given earlier. These quantities are shown in Fig. 10-9. The inertial torques that act in the two directions (x and y) are first obtained. The remaining torques are summed about appropriate axes and application of Newton's law yields the desired differential equations. It is desired to relate the precession angle θ and the gimbal angle ϕ to the applied torques L and U.

The y axis of Fig. 10-9 is called the output axis. The gyro input, which is a torque, appears about the input axis. The applied torque L is the desired input and the precession velocity $\dot\theta$ the desired output.* Undesired torques appearing about the output axis are called disturbing torques since they produce

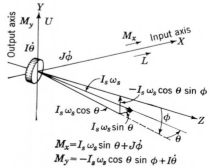

$$M_x = I_s \omega_s \sin \theta + J\dot\phi$$
$$M_y = -I_s \omega_s \cos \theta \sin \phi + I\dot\theta$$

FIG. 10-9. Vector diagram for more complete gyro equations.

drift of the gyroscope. The greatest limitation in the use of gyroscopes is the random disturbing torque U, which causes undesired velocities $\dot\phi$. Such torques as caused by spring constant K and damping D about the y

---

* A dot over the variable means differentiation with respect to time, $\dot\phi = d\phi/dt$.

axis are especially important. A gyro gimbal system is included in Fig. 10-10.

Consider the angular momentum of the spin axis $H = I_s\omega_s$ as shown in Fig. 10-9. For small angular displacements θ and ϕ about the y and x axes, projection of H in the direction of the x and y axes yields (respectively)

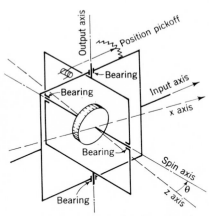

$$H \sin \theta \qquad \text{and} \qquad -H \cos \theta \sin \phi \qquad (10\text{-}5)$$

When combined with the angular momentum due to the precession velocity,

$$M_x = H \sin \theta + J \frac{d\phi}{dt} \qquad (10\text{-}6)$$

$$M_y = -H \cos \theta \sin \phi + I \frac{d\theta}{dt} \qquad (10\text{-}7)$$

FIG. 10-10. A schematic of a gyro gimbal system.

Use of the small-angle approximation, i.e., $\sin \theta$ replaced by θ and $\cos \theta$ by 1, together with the Laplace transformation simplifies Eqs. (10-6) and (10-7) as follows:

$$\bar{M}_x = H\Theta + Js\Phi \qquad (10\text{-}8)$$
$$\bar{M}_y = -H\Phi + Is\Theta \qquad (10\text{-}9)$$

The barred or capitalized variables indicate that the equations are transformed with s as the Laplace-transform operator. Since the time rate of change of momentum is equal to the applied torque,

$$\bar{Q}_x = \mathcal{L}\frac{dM_x}{dt} = s\bar{M}_x = Hs\Theta + Js^2\Phi \qquad (10\text{-}10)$$

$$\bar{Q}_y = \mathcal{L}\frac{dM_y}{dt} = s\bar{M}_y = -Hs\Phi + Is^2\Theta \qquad (10\text{-}11)$$

The damping and spring torques about the input axes are negligibly small compared to the applied torque, so these are neglected with the result that $\bar{Q}_x = \bar{L}$. The damping and spring restoring torques about the output axis are included:

$$\bar{Q}_y = \bar{U} - Ds\Theta - K\Theta \qquad (10\text{-}12)$$

where D is the damping coefficient and K the restoring-torque coefficient, both about the output axis. Upon substituting into Eqs. (10-10) and (10-11),

$$\bar{L} = (Js^2)\Phi + (Hs)\Theta \qquad (10\text{-}13)$$
$$\bar{U} = (-Hs)\Phi + (Is^2 + Ds + K)\Theta \qquad (10\text{-}14)$$

where s is again the Laplace-transform operator (zero initial conditions). Solution by Cramer's rule (a ratio of two determinants) yields the following two equations:

$$\Phi = \frac{\bar{L}/J \ (Is^2 + Ds + K) - \bar{U}(H/J)s}{s^2[Is^2 + Ds + (K + H^2/J)]} \tag{10-15}$$

$$\theta = \frac{\bar{L}\ (H/J) + \bar{U}s}{s[Is^2 + Ds + (K + H^2/J)]} \tag{10-16}$$

Equations (10-15) and (10-16) are the gyro equations. Depending upon the gimbal system and the particular use of the gyro, some of the terms can be neglected.

Since $\bar{U}$ in Eqs. (10-15) and (10-16) is the disturbing torque, the transfer function from torque input to precession-angle output is given by

$$\frac{\theta}{\bar{L}} = \frac{H/J}{s\ [Is^2 + Ds + (K + H^2/J)]} \tag{10-17}$$

when $\bar{U}$ is set equal to zero. Equation (10-17) is the important and useful transfer function for a gyroscope.

From a practical point of view the precession direction of a gyro can be determined as follows: When a torque is applied about a particular axis of the gyro (any axis other than the spin axis), the gyro rotates in such a fashion that the spin axis precesses into the axis about which the torque is applied.

10-3. The Restrained Gyro and Its Construction. If only one axis is free to move with respect to the case, the gyro is called a restrained, single-degree-of-freedom, or single-axis gyro. If K, D, and $\bar{U}$ are set equal to zero in Eq. (10-17) (note that $H^2 - JK$ is much larger than one), the approximate transfer function for a gyro in this mode is

$$\theta \approx \frac{\bar{L}}{sH} \tag{10-18}$$

Because of the form of this transfer function, i.e., the $1/s$ multiplying the torque, this gyro is often called an *integrating gyro*. A more complete transfer function is found by setting K equal to zero in Eq. (10-17) with the result that

$$\frac{\theta}{\bar{L}} = \frac{H/J}{s(Is^2 + Ds + H^2/J)} \tag{10-19}$$

Gyroscopes of this type are the most accurate and usually are utilized to measure angular accelerations. Drift rates on the order of 0.01 to

0.1°/hr are possible.   These gyros are usually used in conjunction with
a platform for inertial-navigation* systems.

Figure 10-11 shows a cutaway sketch of one integrating gyroscope
that is designed to meet the high performance requirements of many
gyro applications.   This unit, like others of its type, is a single-degree-
of-freedom gyro with a floated-gimbal construction.   The gyro element,
a symmetrical wheel, is mounted in a sealed container.   It is powered

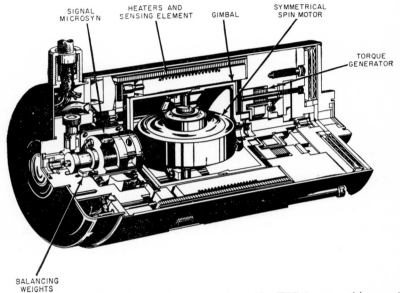

FIG. 10-11. Cutaway view of a single-axis gyroscope, the HIG-6 gyro.   (*Aeronautical
Div., Minneapolis-Honeywell Co., Minneapolis.*)

by a three-phase hysteresis-type motor that is operated from a precisely
controlled frequency source.   A precise frequency source is required to
maintain a constant H $(= I\omega_s)$ and hence induce small error into the
torque equations—Eqs. (10-15) and (10-16).   The frequency of the source
of power for the gyro is chosen so that it will not be identical to any usual
frequency utilized in the system, for example 60 or 400 cps.   Frequently,
an odd value, for example, 389 cps, is chosen; and in this way, interaction
with other a-c quantities is prevented.

The HIG-6, which is shown in Fig. 10-11, is a single-degree-of-freedom
gyro composed chiefly of a gyroscope wheel and inner assembly, a pickoff,
a torque generator, and a viscous fluid.   The gyro may be mounted in any
position that correctly orients the input axis, which is along one diameter

---

* Inertial-navigation systems provide a coordinate reference for automatic navigation systems.   See Ref. 40 for further information.

of the unit and is referenced to a locating pin. The gyro wheel is mounted in a sealed-gimbal assembly, all of which is floated in a viscous fluid of the same density as the average density of the gimbal. The pickoff, or signal generator, is mounted on one end of the gimbal, and the torque generator is mounted on the other end. Constant damping is provided by maintaining constant viscosity of the fluid by means of temperature control.

The Super HIG-6 Gyro has the moving coil pickoff and the torquer on the same side of the unit. One of the outstanding features of this gyro is a low-threshold response to low-input-rate levels, which is due to the reduced gimbal-bearing friction restraints. The reduced friction levels are credited to the nearly perfect neutral flotation of the gimbal in its jeweled bearings. Flotation unloads the bearings, thereby permitting them to be very small. Production units normally display friction levels so low that they are negligible in most practical applications. Another advantage of flotation of the inner gimbal assembly is evident when the unit is subjected to shock. As an example, the Super HIG-6 is so sensitive, yet rugged, that it can measure movements that are 1/3,000 slower than the hour hand on a wrist watch, yet the instrument can be used to hammer a nail.

The HIG-6 is designed for a minimum of drift uncertainty. The motor design is symmetrical about the input axis, and as a result, balance shifts and consequent drift uncertainty are minimized. The gyro is designed for fast response. The low ratio of gimbal inertia to damping coefficient results in a short time constant. Another attractive feature of the HIG-6 is the positional resolution of the signal generator. The minimum detectable displacement as measured by the signal generator is less than 0.01 milliradian.

The command-input capability of the torque generator is also a useful feature. The torque generator may be used to introduce command signals into the control loop of a platform-stabilization system. This gyro is generally intended for precision platform-stabilization applications, although it can be used for precision rate measurement.

The MIG (miniature integrating gyro) gyro, which is shown in Fig. 10-12, is 1.75 in. in diameter and weighs only 0.5 lb. Its performance compares to the larger gyro shown in Fig. 10-11.

The position of the gyro gimbal is usually indicated by an electromagnetic signal generator. Torque is applied to the gimbal by an electromagnetic (permanent-magnet type) torque generator (torquer). The sensitivity of the gimbal pickoff varies with the primary excitation current and frequency. The drift rate is often less than 0.1°/hr.

Single-axis gyros are usually maintained at an elevated temperature by an electric heater. A built-in temperature-sensitive resistance element measures and controls the gyro temperature. Operating temperature is maintained by cycling the heater on and off by means of an external relay or by proportional temperature control.

10-4. Construction of the Free Gyro. If there are no restraining gimbals in any direction on the gyro, the gyro wheel remains fixed in space. The angular position of the body is measured with respect to the gyro wheel, which is the reference. Gyros can be used in this manner to

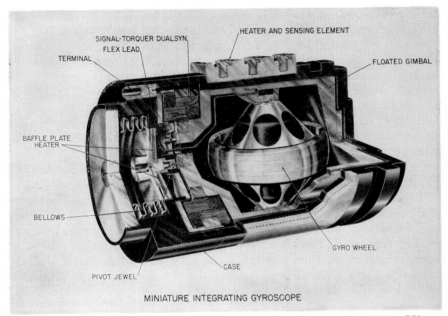

MINIATURE INTEGRATING GYROSCOPE

FIG. 10-12. The MIG gyro (miniature integrating gyro). (*Aeronautical Div., Minneapolis-Honeywell Co., Minneapolis.*)

establish an inertial reference. A cutaway view of a free gyro is shown in Fig. 10-13. The accuracy is usually less than that possible with the single-axis gyros used in an inertial platform. In order to obtain the approximate transfer functions for a gyro in this mode of operation, set $\bar{L}$, I, D, and K equal to zero in Eq. (10-15), with the result that

$$\mathcal{L}^{-1}s\phi = \frac{d\phi}{dt} = \frac{U}{H} \tag{10-20}$$

Similarly, setting $\bar{U}$, I, D, and K equal to zero in Eq. (10-16), a simplified equation results for the other axis:

$$\mathcal{L}^{-1}s\theta = \frac{d\theta}{dt} = \frac{L}{H} \tag{10-21}$$

When the gyro is used in this form, various mechanical members must remain constant with respect to time, temperature, and hysteresis. These gyros are often of lower accuracy; however, with care in design and manufacture, a two-degree-of-freedom gyro can be equally as accurate as a single-degree-of-freedom gyro. Figure 10-14 shows an exploded view of a two-degree-of-freedom gyro that measures the displacement

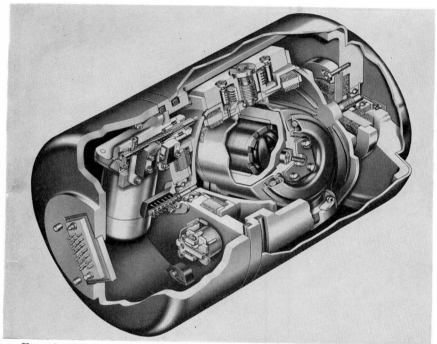

FIG. 10-13. A free gyroscope. (*G. M. Giannini & Co., Inc., Pasadena, Calif.*)

about its two axes by means of a pickoff placed on each gimbal axis. The gyro comprises an isoelastic designed motor (1) sealed in the inner gimbal (2) and its outer gimbal (3) floated in a high-specific-gravity fluid. Both gimbals are positioned by means of a simple and dependable mechanical caging system (4). The position of the outer gimbal is measured with the synchro pickoff (5). The complete symmetry of motor and inner gimbals enables this unit to sustain high vibrational requirements up to 10 g at 5 to 2,000 cps. The drift rate is less than 6°/hr under normal operation. The unit has 360° continuous rotation on the outer gimbal and ±85° on the inner gimbal. A thin, pancakelike synchro is used on the outer gimbal. The gyro fits into a 4.406-in.-diameter and 6.81-in.-long case.

Fig. 10-14. Exploded view of a free gyro.   (*Daystrom Pacific, Los Angeles.*)

FIG. 10-15. A free gyro. (*The Greenleaf Manufacturing Co., St. Louis.*)

A photograph of a free gyro is shown in Fig. 10-15, and the specifications for this unit are summarized as follows:

1. *Gyro motor* (synchronous hysteresis type):
    Excitation: 115 volts, 3 phase, 400 cps
    Power: 25 va max
    Starting time: 5 min to reach 90% of full speed
2. *Pickoffs:*
    Type: synchro on each axis
    Accuracy: 20 minutes max
    Alignment: With the pickoff output signal at null, gimbal axes are orthogonal to each other and to the mounting plane within $\pm\frac{1}{4}°$
    Null voltage: 45 mv max
    Phase shift: Less than 15° with 100 $K\Omega$ load
3. *Gimbal torquer:*
    Precession rate (minimum): 1°/sec
    Fixed-phase excitation: 26 volts, 400 cps, 3 watts max
    Control-phase excitation: 5 watts
    Control-field impedance: $(289 + j353) \pm 10\%$
    Torquers exist on both axes and are capable of driving the gimbals in either direction.
4. *Life:* The gyro is designed for a minimum of 1,000 hours of operation without failure.

5. *Drift:* The drift rate of each axis does not exceed 1° for any 1 min
   when operated at rated conditions on a standard Scorsby test*
   of 5 to 7 rpm at a table deflection of ±15°. The total drift for
   each axis does not exceed 10° at the end of a 10-min test duration
   for each of the six possible attitudes after compensation for the
   earth's rotation.
6. *Physical requirements:* Dimensions, 5½ in. in diam. by 7⅜ in. long
7. *Gimbal freedom:*
   Outer gimbal: 360° rotational freedom
   Inner gimbal: ±85° rotational freedom
8. *Alignment of axes:* The outer gimbal axis will be aligned so as to be
   parallel to the mounting plane.
9. *Warmup:* Maximum gyro warmup time will be 20 min.

10-5. Construction of the Rate Gyro.   In many aircraft maneuvers it
is necessary to measure the rate of roll, pitch, or yaw; and these measurements are used to damp out certain undesirable oscillations of the aircraft
about these axes.   A lower-accuracy gyro, called a *rate gyro,* can usually
be used for this purpose.   In order to understand the operation of a rate
gyro, set $\bar{U}$ equal to zero and equate Eqs. (10-15) and (10-16), eliminating $\bar{L}$.   In so doing, the following expression results:

$$s\Phi = \frac{1}{H}(Is^2 + Ds + K)\theta \tag{10-22}$$

For small I and D, or also with slowly varying time functions, Eq.
(10-22) reduces to

$$\theta = \frac{H}{K}\frac{d\phi}{dt} \tag{10-23}$$

Equation (10-23) indicates that a signal that is proportional to the rate
$d\phi/dt$ is obtained.   Practically, the large value of K is obtained by supporting the output axis with a torsional spring.

A rate gyro produces velocity signals, i.e., yields a voltage proportional
to the time derivative of the input axis angle.   Any low rate drift of this
angle is differentiated and hence of little importance.   Since gyros of this
type are used primarily for damping in systems, high accuracy and low
drift are not as important as in single-axis and double-axis gyros.

An exploded view of a rate gyro is shown in the sketch of Fig. 10-16.
The gyro is hermetically sealed and consists of a spin motor (1) mounted
on a sealed gimbal (2) that is restrained by a torsion spring (3).   The
gyro is floated in liquid, alignment maintained by bearings (4) at both

* This test inserts an angular rotation into each axis of the gyro.   The rates can
be adjusted by varying the speed of rotation and also the angle of the table.

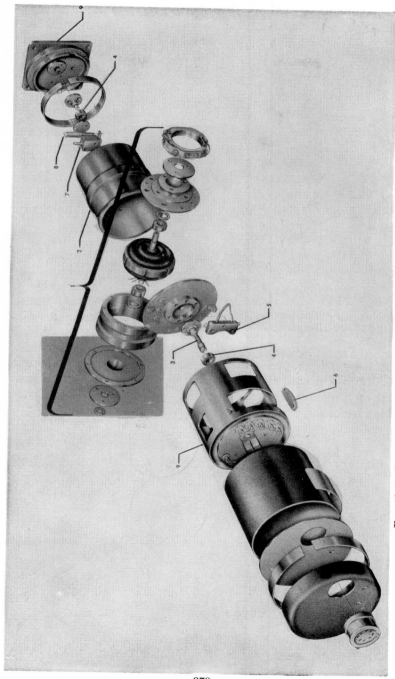

FIG. 10-16. Exploded view of a rate gyro. (*Daystrom Pacific, Los Angeles.*)

379

ends. The angular rate about the axis perpendicular to the axes of the spin motor (1) and gimbal (2) causes a precessional moment about the gimbal axis, resulting in a displacement of a potentiometer wiper (5) mechanically coupled to the gimbal. The damping of the unit is between 0.3 and 0.7 of critical over the temperature range. Two damping assemblies (7) with bimetallic temperature-compensating springs (8) are used. This unit utilizes a potentiometer pickoff with a resolution of 0.6% of maximum rate. The unit is 3.3 in. long with a 2.22-in. diameter.

FIG. 10-17. Rate gyro designed with ultimate simplicity. (*Humphrey, Inc., San Diego, Calif.*)

The rate gyro shown in Fig. 10-17 utilizes a minimum number of precision parts. The unit comprises a simple subassembly with the motor separate from the sensing element. The heart of this rate gyro, which is shown in Fig. 10-18, is the solid-rotor inertial element mounted on precision radial-thrust bearings in a bridgelike gimbal. Two unitized steel flexures provide a pivot and the spring restraint required for the gyro. Use of compatible materials and high-*g* centrifuge balancing adds to superior performance qualities.

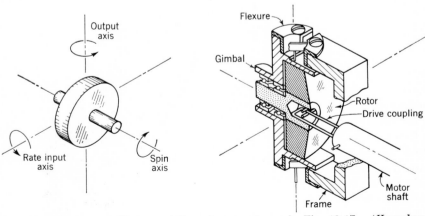

FIG. 10-18. Schematic diagram of the rate gyro shown in Fig. 10-17. (*Humphrey, Inc., San Diego, Calif.*)

10-6. The Vertical Gyro. The vertical gyro is a special class of free gyro that contains a pendulous body. This pendulous body applies torques either electrically, hydraulically, or pneumatically to the appropriate free-gyro axis, so that the gyro is caused to precess in such a manner that one of its axes is aligned with respect to local gravity. The process of aligning the axis with respect to gravity is called *erection*. So

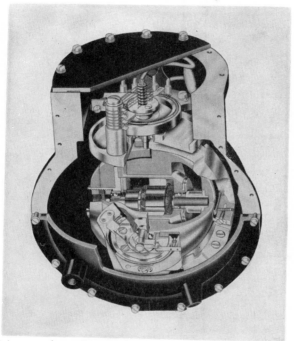

FIG. 10-19. Cutaway view of a vertical gyroscope. (*Summers Gyroscope, Santa Monica, Calif.*)

that the gyro will respond in a negligible fashion to accelerations (other than the earth's gravitation) of the aircraft, various techniques are employed, such as erection cutouts, limiters, and filters. These schemes make the gyro less sensitive to spurious accelerations.

Erection rates may vary from 10 to 20 minutes, and drift in these gyros may be from $\frac{1}{2}$ to $1°/\text{min}$. Vertical gyros are commonly used to detect or control changes in attitude about the pitch and roll axes of an airborne vehicle. Sensitivity is obtained in these two axes by mounting the gyro with its spin axis vertical.

A cutaway view of a roll- and-pitch vertical gyro is shown in Fig. 10-19. This unit is approximately 4 in. in diameter and $5\frac{1}{2}$ in. long and weighs

$3\frac{1}{2}$ lb. Potentiometers on the inner and outer gimbals yield roll and pitch angles with an accuracy of $1\frac{1}{2}°$.

The vertical gyro shown in Fig. 10-20 provides roll-and-pitch displacement signals which can operate remote indicating devices or which can be used wherever attitude information is required. The unit consists of

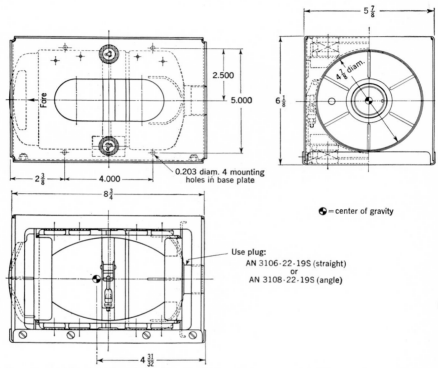

Fig. 10-20. Outline drawing of a vertical gyroscope. (*Eclipse-Pioneer Div., Bendix Aviation Corp., Teterboro, N.J.*)

an electrically erected vertical-seeking gyro. It is enclosed in a hermetically sealed case with separate Autosyn*-transmitter pickoffs on the roll and pitch axes. An outstanding feature of this instrument is the use of the newly developed electrolytic switch, which provides precise erection and has long service life. The unit is rugged, of simple design, and easily serviceable. The transmitter also features a cylindrical-shaped case facilitating sealing and fast initial erection. The gyro is completely self-contained and requires no erection amplifier.

The unit weighs $7\frac{3}{4}$ lb including the shock mount. It has a wheel with a 4×10^6 g-cm²/sec angular momentum. The unit establishes

* This is discussed in Chap. 3.

a vertical within 6 minutes of arc. A 40°/min erection rate can be obtained, and the drift rate is less than $\frac{1}{4}$°/min.

10-7. Gyro Characteristics and Design Considerations. To obtain an idea of the various parameter values for a single-axis gyroscope, typical quantities in Eqs. (10-15) and (10-16) are summarized as follows:

$$\omega_s = 24,000 \text{ rpm} = 2,515 \text{ radians/sec}$$
$$I_s = 1.2 \times 10^3 \text{ g-cm}^2 = 1.2 \times 10^3 \text{ dyne-cm-sec}^2$$
$$H = I_s\omega_s = 3 \times 10^6 \text{ dyne-cm-sec}$$
$$I = 10^4 \text{ g-cm}^2 = 10^4 \text{ dyne-cm-sec}^2$$
$$D = 10^5 \text{ dyne-cm-sec}$$
$$J = 10^6 \text{ g-cm}^2 = 10^6 \text{ dyne-cm-sec}^2$$
$$K = 4 \times 10^4 \text{ dyne-cm/radian}$$

Some of the typical terms in Eqs. (10-15) and (10-16) are computed from the above list of parameters.

$$\frac{H^2}{J} = 9 \times 10^6 \text{ dyne-cm/radian} \tag{10-24}$$

Notice that this term is considerably larger than the output-axis spring rate ($H^2/J = 9 \times 10^6 \gg K = 4 \times 10^4$).

$$\sqrt{\frac{H^2}{JI}} = \text{nutation frequency} = 30 \text{ radians/sec} \tag{10-25}$$

The *nutation frequency* is the undamped natural-resonant frequency of the characteristic equation. With $D = 0$ in the denominator of either Eq. (10-15) or Eq. (10-16), the characteristic equation is

$$Is^2 + \frac{H^2}{J} = 0 \tag{10-26}$$

The roots of this equation are

$$s_i = \pm j\omega_n = \pm j\frac{H}{\sqrt{IJ}} \tag{10-27}$$

ω_n is the frequency at which the undamped gyro oscillates and is termed the nutation frequency. ω_n is also defined as the oscillation of the transient resulting from a step function of applied torque for a lightly damped gyro. The nutation frequency is a figure of merit of the gyroscope.

Several practical gyroscope considerations such as torque generator linearity, gyro balance, and gyro flotation are presented. Because a gyro is expected to maintain high accuracy and sensitivity, considerable care must be exercised in the design and application of these instruments.

Torque-Generator Linearity. Torquers are utilized on gyroscopes to insert computed torques or precession rates into a gyro. Commonly it is necessary to correct for the earth's rotation, i.e., to precess the gyro at precisely the same rate as the earth so that the gyro will appear to remain fixed with respect to an observer located on the earth. Since the earth is rotating at 15°/hr, an untorqued gyro appears to rotate with respect to the earth. In reality, of course, the gyro is fixed and the earth is rotating. By applying proper torques, the gyro can be made to precess so as to cancel the effect of the earth's rotation.

When the gyro is used in conjunction with complete systems (Fig. 10-5) other torques or rates must be inserted. Frequently these torques are computed in a digital or analog computer and are inserted into the gyro with the torquer.

As a third requirement, electrically generated torques are often applied to the gyro through the torquer to cancel the effects of nonrandom but undesirable torques. These torques, which produce drift of the gyro, can often be canceled, at least in part (see Gyroscope Drift, Sec. 10-8), by inserting correction torques through the gyro torquer.

For these three principal reasons the gyro torque generator is an important element in the instrument. The requirements on torquer linearity are especially exacting. Forcers and torquers are considered in Sec. 7-9 of this text.

The linearity of the torque generator is often tested by balancing all the torques acting on the gimbal against the precessional torque due to a component of the earth's turning rate. The test procedure is as follows: With the output axis of the gyro vertical, the input axis is oriented to pick up a known component of the earth's rate. The earth's rate component is adjusted until the total torque on the gimbal is zero, or below some maximum value (for example $\pm 0.035°$/hr equivalent input turning rate). The spin motor supply frequency must hold accurate to ± 0.01 per cent.

Gyro Balance. Because of the high accuracy of these components, considerable care must be exercised in the design of the output axis. Any spring or damping torques that appear about the output axis U of the gyro produce a precession velocity ϕ about the input axis [cf. Eq. (10-15)]. The output-axis spring rate K is especially important, since from Eq. (10-23)

$$\Phi = \frac{K}{H}\frac{1}{s}\Theta = \pounds\frac{K}{H}\int_0^t \theta\, dt \qquad (10\text{-}28)$$

Since the platform angle ϕ is the integral of the gyro angle θ, any errors in the gyro angle, for example due to unbalance, are integrated and result in serious platform errors. For this reason, K must be kept as small and H as large as possible.

The wheel and motor are dynamically balanced as a unit to a high degree of accuracy. Commercial test equipment is available for dynamically balancing gyro wheels.

The entire gyro (wheel, motor, and inner housing) must be statically balanced to a high degree of accuracy (in some cases less than 10 dyne cm) about the output axis for both weight and buoyancy (for floated gyros) unbalance. During the static balance, the wheel is stationary so that

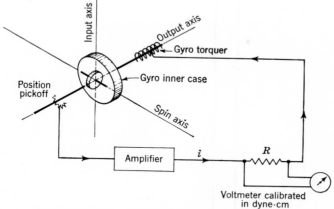

FIG. 10-21. Block diagram of gyro balance system.

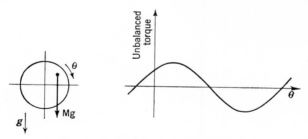

FIG. 10-22. Unbalanced torque curve.

no gyroscopic action is included in the balance. The static balance of the inner case can be accomplished with the automatic control system shown in Fig. 10-21. A caging system amplifies the gyro pickoff angle. This signal is fed to the gyro torquer so that the pickoff signal is nulled. The current necessary to keep the gyro nulled is proportional to the torque unbalance. As the gyro is rotated, a sinusoidal curve, similar to that shown in Fig. 10-22, results. From this curve, the necessary added weights are easily calculated.

Because of the precision with which the gyro must be manufactured, special handling must be provided. The final assembly and test of these components is made in environmentally controlled areas. Exhaustive testing and evaluation of gyros requires thousands of dollars of special mechanical and electronic equipment. One such area is shown in Fig.

10-23. Nylon jackets and caps are worn in the "dust free" room by both engineers and technicians.

Floated Gyros. Single-degree-of-freedom gyros are often supported in a hydraulic or pneumatic bearing. In this case the gyro weight is buoyed up with a flotation fluid. The density of flotation fluid is approximately equal to the mean density of the floated member. The viscosity of the

Fig. 10-23. Environmentally controlled area used to evaluate precision gyroscopes. (*Aeronautical Div., Minneapolis-Honeywell Co., Minneapolis.*)

fluid is stable with temperature and is large enough to produce a high damping. The flotation fluid reduces the gimbal-bearing loading and hence lowers the gimbal-bearing friction. The fluid also provides good shock cushioning for the gimbal during vibration and acceleration conditions. An expansion device is incorporated on the side of the gyro to provide for expansion of the fluid with temperature and altitude. The fluid must be inert so it does not react with any of the exposed wiring or metal within the unit.

The wheel and gyro rotor of many precision gyroscopes are encased in a fluid-tight sphere, which is floated in the fluid. The gas within the sphere is nitrogen or some other inert gas at atmospheric pressure. The case should be fabricated from a magnetic material so that any stray fields produced by the motor are shielded from the sensitive pickoff on the gyro.

10-8. Gyroscope Drift. One of the most important characteristics of a gyro is its drift rate. Inertial-navigation applications require gyros that have a minimum drift rate due to uncertainty torques. In the HIG-6, shown in Fig. 10-11, a drift rate of 1°/hr is equivalent to an unbalance torque of 5.2 dyne-cm. Because of shifts from warmup to warmup and differences in measuring methods, the user cannot generally reproduce the exact values. It is assumed that the gyro has been stabilized at operating temperature for at least 1 hour, and each reading is an average value for a period of not less than 1 min or more than 20 min.

The most important cause of undesirable torques is the reaction torques caused by the signal and the torque generator, which vary as the square of the bias excitation. These torques should not exceed 0.025 dyne-cm per (amp-turn per pole) squared. Thus, as an example, a signal-generator primary excitation of 50 ma corresponds to a maximum allowable reaction torque of 0.9 dyne-cm at the signal-generator null position.

A second source of undesirable torques is caused by the flexible leads or slip rings that carry the signal and power leads into the wheel and inner gimbal assembly.

When the gyro is subjected to acceleration, mass and buoyance unbalance are still other sources of undesirable torque. The change of mass unbalance along the spin reference axis due to a change in spin motor power or temperature can produce an undesirable torque.

The effects of gyroscope parameters can best be understood by reference to the equations. The effect of spin angular momentum H, damping constant D, and spring rate K on the drift of a gyro is considered. The effect of H can be seen by setting the disturbing torque U equal to zero and eliminating the applied torque T between Eqs. (10-15) and (10-16) with the result

$$\Phi = \frac{1}{H}\left(Is + D + \frac{K}{s}\right)\Theta \qquad (10\text{-}29)$$

With a large H, the gyro precession angle Θ causes less gimbal angle Φ. Since ultimately the gimbal angle Φ is to be kept low for zero-input torque, a larger H is desirable. The upper limit of H is fixed by the time required for the gyro to come up to speed. Furthermore, a large H is limited by the physical dimensions of the motor and the centrifugal force on the wheel. Another reason for using a large value of H is indicated from the steady-state error for a step input in torque. The gyro equation [Eq. (10-16)] for $T = 0$ is

$$\Theta = \frac{\bar{U}}{Is^2 + Ds + H^2/J} \qquad (10\text{-}30)$$

For a step input in U ($\bar{U} = U/s$) the steady state value of θ is, from the final value theorem, given by

$$\theta_{ss} = \lim_{s \to o} \frac{Us/s}{Is^2 + Ds + H^2/J} = U \frac{J}{H^2} \qquad (10\text{-}31)$$

Hence, the larger the value of H, the smaller the error θ_{ss} due to an undesirable torque.

The undesirable effect of spring rate K can be understood from Eq. (10-29). For any small constant θ, the spring rate appears as an integration term K/s and as such causes the gimbal angle to increase indefinitely. Because of this integration effect, it is most desirable to keep $K = 0$. Although the spring rate is reduced by proper gyro design, it

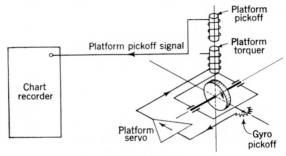

FIG. 10-24. Gyro-drift testing.

can also be reduced by tuning the position pickoff θ with an appropriate capacitor. This capacitor has the effect of introducing an effective negative spring that cancels the positive mechanical spring rate. The resulting effect of the mechanical spring rate is considerably reduced.

The undesirable torques that produce gyroscope drift can be divided into two types—nonrandom and random. The undesirable torques which are consistent and repeatable can be canceled by means of a bias torque that is applied with currents through the precision torquer. The random component of gyro drift cannot be compensated because the undesirable torques that cause this drift cannot be predicted. Although the gyro equations can be analyzed under the conditions of a random torque input, laboratory testing is commonly utilized to determine gyroscope drift.

Before a gyro, especially a restrained gyro, is used in its ultimate application, a considerable amount of laboratory drift testing must be completed. The system of Fig. 10-24 can be used for such testing. A gyro is mounted on a platform that has a single degree of freedom. The gyro stabilizes this axis in space through a single-platform servo. An angular-position pickoff is located between the platform and the stand. The signal from this pickoff is applied to a chart recorder. The recorder measures the angular position of the platform relative to inertial space.

For slowly varying quantities, such as drift, the relation between the gimbal or platform angle ϕ and the gyro precession angle θ is given approximately by

$$\phi = \frac{D}{H}\theta + \frac{K}{H}\int_0^t \theta\,dt \approx \frac{D}{H}\theta \qquad (10\text{-}32)$$

for $K = 0$. The data recorded on the platform angle are easily referred to the gyro angle.

The single-axis platform yields static information concerning gyro-drift performance. To determine the gyro-drift characteristics when the gyro is subjected to disturbing torques, a Scorsby stand is often used. When the platform servo is stabilizing the axis, the Scorsby rotates in such a manner as to apply equal angular velocities about all axes of the platform. In the case of a single gyro an angular velocity is applied about the input axis. Platform angle is measured in this application by optical means.

PROBLEMS

10-1. Discuss the applications of rate gyros, single-degree-of-freedom gyros, and free gyros.

10-2. What is the effect of gyro drift on performance of each gyro in each application of Prob. 10-1?

10-3. The following numerical values represent a single-degree-of-freedom gyro:

$$H = 3 \times 10^6 \text{ dyne-cm-sec}$$
$$I = 10^4 \text{ g-cm}^2$$
$$D = 10^5 \text{ dyne-cm-sec}$$
$$J = 10^6 \text{ g-cm}^2$$
$$k = 4.10^4 \text{ dyne-cm/radian}$$

(a) Find the gyro nutation frequency. (b) Obtain the transfer function θ/T and locate the poles in the complex plane.

10-4. Use the gyro of Prob. 10-3 in the block diagram of Fig. P10-4. (a) Take $G_2(s) = $ constant and determine stability and steady-state errors. (b) Take $G_2(s) = (1 + \alpha s)$ and choose α and A for the optimum system. (c) Take $G_2(s) = 1 + \alpha s + \gamma/s$ and choose α, γ, and A for the optimum system.

Note: An optimum system has zero steady-state error in θ.

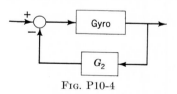

FIG. P10-4

10-5. Discuss the effect of torque-generator linearity and gyro balance upon the performance of a single-degree-of-freedom gyro.

10-6. Under the combined effect of static weight and bouyancy unbalance derive a method of locating the position where the balance weights should be added. Can this be done with only four readings? Use the caging circuit of Fig. 10-21.

10-7. Derive the equation that yields the weight magnitude and position for Prob. 10-6.

CHAPTER 11

HYDRAULIC AND PNEUMATIC SYSTEMS

Hydraulic and pneumatic servos are used extensively in machine tools, in many types of speed-governed systems, in steering boosters, for the positioning of guns and other large power applications in gunfire control, and for the positioning of control surfaces in piloted aircraft and guided missiles where agility, accuracy, and long, rugged life are necessary. Hydraulic and pneumatic components in servomechanisms can deliver large power with relatively small size, and hydraulic servomechanisms find wide application in systems where high static stiffness is required. Since entire books have been written on hydraulic and pneumatic systems, this chapter can do no more than point out the elementary principles of the subject and its application to servomechanisms, together with the problems encountered in servomechanism use.

11-1. Advantages and Disadvantages of Hydraulic Systems. Hydraulic systems offer a number of advantages. In the first place, they have greater power-carrying capacity and are capable of producing many times larger torques than electrical equipment of equivalent size and weight. They are quite durable under rugged use and can easily be adapted for electric control. Hydraulic servomechanisms are used for the largest power servos ranging up to hundreds of horsepower. Where continuous operating is necessary, they give a minimum apparatus-to-horsepower ratio. For intermittent operation, hydraulic systems can provide large amounts of power from an accumulator with a minimum of apparatus and storage volume. Dynamically, hydraulic systems have small time constants and develop a much higher peak torque-squared-to-inertia ratio [cf. Eq. (7-10) for an analysis of T^2/J ratio] than electric motors of the same peak power.

Hydraulic systems operate with an efficiency that is close to that of electric motors; it ranges from about 85 to 95 per cent at full torque and full speed, which is considerably better than electric servomotors. Some units have an efficiency of 92 to 94 per cent at rated load and 85 per cent at about a quarter load. The average horsepower of units is about 45 per cent of peak horsepower; in other words, the peak horsepower obtainable from the hydraulic system can be more than double that

390

of the average rated horsepower. The low compressibility of hydraulic fluids results in smooth and positive operation of actuators and motors. The lubricating properties of oil eliminate the necessity of providing extra lubrication means. Sometimes the high viscosity of oil is advantageous in attenuating spurious high-frequency noise signals.

Among the disadvantages of hydraulic systems, however, is the clumsiness of working with oil lines rather than wires. The leakage of oil from mechanisms or lines is objectionable and can introduce a fire hazard. Variation of viscosity with temperature may produce undesirable changes in control action, and the inertia of the oil gives intense peak pressure (similar to water hammer in pipes) with rapidly varying control signals.

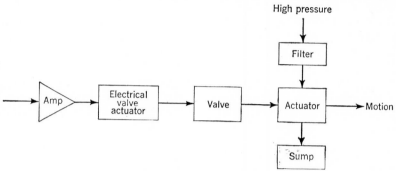

FIG. 11-1. Components in hydraulic servomechanism.

Dash pots and shock absorbers are often used to ease this problem. Sometimes dynamic lags exist in the transmission lines because of the large value of inertia and viscosity and because of pipe expansion. The oil must be kept clean and free from entrained air. Hydraulic systems are usually quite expensive.

As shown in Fig. 11-1, hydraulic systems generally comprise the following components:

1. A source of high-pressure oil and a sump to discharge the used oil, which forms the source of fluid for the high-pressure supply.

2. A valve, which is the means of controlling the flow of high-pressure oil. The valve must be displaced by the actuating signal. This can be done mechanically, but more often the actuating signal is originally in the form of an electrical voltage that is amplified and used to drive some type of electric motor or solenoid device to control the motion of the valve.

3. An actuator, which is the device that actually does the work. This may be a ram type for linear motion or a rotary type for angular motion. In order to reduce the size and weight per horsepower, the rotary type generally operates at high speed and is geared down to the load.

Associated with these major components are such accessories as fittings, gaskets, oil seals, packing rings, various types of on-off valves, pressure valves, and sometimes reducing valves to keep the oil pressure applied to the control valve at a given value. Other important minor components are accumulators to reduce peak pressures and cooling systems for high-power systems.

Filters are commonly used in hydraulic systems to strain out any dirt or chips that might work their way into the oil supply, jam the valves, and wear and score piston and cylinder walls. Some filters exclude particles which have dimensions as small as 1/5,000 in. and which would take 2 days to settle 1 ft in fresh water.

11-2. Properties of Oil. Before discussing the static and dynamic characteristics of hydraulic components and systems, it is well to look at some of the properties of oil. The oil used should be chemically stable, free from acid, and noncorrosive. In a hydraulic system, oil is in constant circulation and is used over and over. Often the oil is churned and agitated and tends to pick up oxygen. Since oils that cannot resist this tendency thicken and become sluggish, a chemically stable oil is needed.

The oil should be viscous enough to give a good seal at pumps, valves, and pistons but not so thick that it offers excessive resistance to flow and thus adds to the load and the excessive wear of parts. Unnecessarily rapid wear of moving parts results when the viscosity is too low.

Unfortunately, the viscosity of oil does not remain constant with variations in temperature. A typical paraffinic petroleum oil changes its viscosity 110-fold with a temperature change from 100 to 0°F. Use of this oil either necessitates automatic temperature controls on the oil or acceptance of a wide-variation component performance. Another type of liquid petroleum product known as univis oil is much better since it changes its viscosity only about 20 times.

Silicone oils, which have been developed more recently, are synthetic high-molecular-weight liquids. A silicone oil increases its viscosity less than fourfold with a temperature change from 100 to 0°F. Another measure of change of viscosity is the temperature at which fluids will pour. The pour point of a typical paraffinic oil is −20°F, whereas a univis oil has a pour point of −50°F. Silicone oils have pour points as low as −130°F.

Silicone oils burn less vigorously than do hydrocarbon oils. They remain free of discoloration, acid formation, sludging, oxidation, and similar phenomena that frequently limit the usefulness of petroleum products. The oil is stable to well over 400°F and has no effect on copper, brass, bronze, aluminum, magnesium, iron, steel, lead, tin, cadmium, or chromium. It is not nearly so good a lubricant as the petroleum products, however. It is a poor lubricant for iron or steel surfaces sliding on iron or steel. It is satisfactory for many other metal combinations such as steel on bronze. Consequently, use of this silicone fluid in piston pumps requires care in the choice of the materials used. For example, an ordinary piston pump using a steel universal link and steel knuckle will fail when silicone fluid is used but will not fail when petroleum products are used. If, however, a bronze knuckle is substituted for a steel knuckle, no appreciable wear takes place. It is somewhat more difficult to seal silicone fluids to prevent them from creeping and leaking.

Another property of all hydraulic fluids is the compressibility of the fluid. This is expressed in terms of the bulk modulus E, whose inverse is a measure of the compressibility. The rate of change of volume with pressure per unit volume is equal to 1 divided by the bulk modulus. This is expressed as an equation,

$$\frac{dv}{dp}\frac{1}{v} = \frac{1}{E} \tag{11-1}$$

The apparent bulk modulus of the oil, however, can be reduced by a factor of $1\frac{1}{2}$ to 3 because of the effect of trapped air in the fluid and the mechanical flexibility of the piping. Hence, it is desirable that the fluid possess low foaming properties. The actual bulk modulus in typical hydraulic circuits is on the order of 100,000 psi, in contrast to a value of 300,000 psi for oil itself.

The bulk modulus influences the gain of servomechanisms since the natural frequency of oscillation is related directly to the square root of the bulk modulus. A high bulk modulus results in a high natural frequency, which in turn permits the use of a higher gain and hence provides a lower error. The natural frequency of the servomechanism is inversely proportional to the square root of the total moving mass; hence, a fluid of low specific gravity permits a higher gain. This is analogous to a spring-mass system whose $\omega_n = \sqrt{K/M}$. The spring is analogous to the bulk modulus, and the mass is related to the specific gravity of this fluid.

As pressure is applied to oil, its viscosity increases in an exponential fashion. At moderate pressure, this increase is relatively slight, but the viscosity increases rapidly with higher pressure.

11-3. Constant-displacement Pumps. There are three types of pump that are used for supplying high-pressure oil to control valves. These are the gear pump, the vane pump, and the piston pump. (Although their application as sources of high-pressure oil for valves and hence as positive-displacement pumps is being discussed here, the latter two may also be designed to be variable-displacement pumps.)

The most common type of hydraulic pump is the simple gear pump, which is illustrated in Fig. 11-2. Its extensive use is primarily due to its low cost, mechanical simplicity, and reliability. Also, oils of practically

all viscosities encountered in hydraulic servos may be used.   Because of
the rather complicated geometry of the tooth forms compared with the
simple piston, as well as the large leakage path between the high- and
low-pressure zones, it is not possible to manufacture these units with the
efficiency ratings found in other types of pump.   Furthermore, by their
inherent geometry, the flat end plates attached to the sides of the unit
distort more under a given pressure load than would an equivalent
cylinder.   For this reason, larger-sized gear pumps are built to generate
only moderate pressures ranging up to about 1,000 psi.   The most common use for gear pumps in servo units is as a supercharger to maintain
pressure on the servomotor.

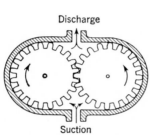

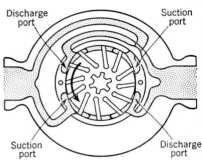

FIG. 11-2. Gear pump.   FIG. 11-3. Vane pump.

A vane pump consists essentially of a regularly slotted rotor turning
inside a stator that either is mounted eccentrically with respect to the
motor or else has a noncircular bore.   This eccentric mounting causes
vanes inserted in the rotor slots to move radially, which creates a variable volume and hence a pumping action between adjacent vanes, as shown
in Fig. 11-3.   The vanes scoop up liquid at each inlet and deliver it at
the next outlet ports.   The vane must be in the extended position to provide pumping action.   A considerable differential pressure exists across
each vane.   This cantilever bending load produces considerable friction
between the side walls of the vane and the slots.   In order to eliminate
movement of the vanes under these conditions, the bore of the stator
over the angular displacement between the inlet and discharge ports is
often designed to be truly circular and centered with respect to the rotor.
This design of bore eliminates the possibility of vane wear and scuffing,
a condition that exists in the conventional eccentric-circle type of stator.
The pump is balanced by virtue of the opposing pairs of inlets and out-
lets.   Vane pumps are capable of operating with rather dirty fluid and
are usually built to operate at about 1,000 to 1,500 psi.   They automatically compensate for wear in the vanes.

Piston-type pumps are used for the highest pressure systems, pressures from about 1,500 to 5,000 psi. The pistons are either radial or axial with respect to the drive shaft. Piston-type pumps are more expensive than the others mentioned and require a very clean oil supply. Piston pumps operate with a high efficiency and low leakage. Vane-type pumps have poorer efficiency, and gear pumps have the lowest efficiency of the three types.

11-4. Variable-displacement Pumps and Motors. In larger power servomechanisms and for those requiring a rotary output motion, a constant-speed electric motor is used to drive a variable-delivery pump whose output fluid is used to drive a hydraulic motor, which in turn

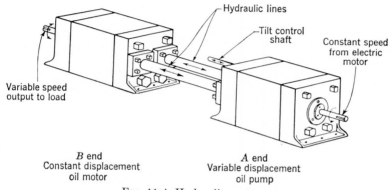

FIG. 11-4. Hydraulic system.

positions the servo controlled shaft. The fluid flow from the pump to the motor is governed in magnitude and direction by the action of a control lever, which is generally positioned by a hydraulic preamplifier in which the hydraulic-ram output positions the control lever. A hydraulic pump and hydraulic motor in combination are known as the *A* and *B* ends, respectively, and are shown schematically in Fig. 11-4. The output-shaft velocity of a hydraulic motor is approximately proportional to the position of the control lever of the *A* end.

A servomechanism utilizing this hydraulic system is shown in Fig. 11-5. The actuating signal is introduced to an electronic amplifier in which an a-c equalizing network has been added for stability. After the signal is amplified, the stroke motor is fed by the amplifier, which in turn controls the position of the control valve. This valve controls the position of the control lever, which meters the fluid flow from the *A* end to the *B* end. The hydraulic motor positions the load. The proper margin of stability is achieved by rate-generator feedback from both the stroke motor and the controlled shaft. High-pressure oil must be supplied continuously to the control valve, which is generally accomplished

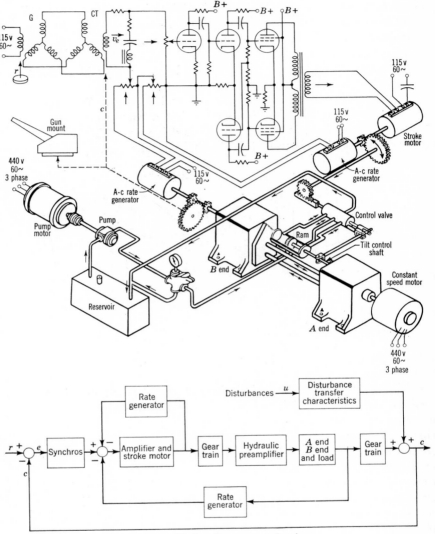

FIG. 11-5. Hydraulic servomechanism.

by means of a hydraulic-power supply consisting of a hydraulic pump, an accumulator, a sump, and various auxiliary devices.

The operation of components of these larger power servomechanisms and some of the dynamic aspects of system performance are now discussed. Variation of the pump displacement (*A* end) controls the amount of liquid that may pass per shaft revolution. Although the displacement of a radial-type piston pump can be varied by changing the eccentricity of the central shaft, by far the most common variable-displacement pump is the axial-piston type, as is shown in Fig. 11-6.

In axial piston pumps, the cylinder block together with its piston is

FIG. 11-6. Variable-displacement pump.   (*Northern Ordnance, Inc., Boston.*)

rotated on the shaft so that the pistons are driven in and out of their respective cylinders in a direction parallel to the shaft.   Liquid is forced into the cylinders by pressure differences while the pistons are moving away from the hydraulic lines and
is driven out by the pistons while
they are moving toward the lines.
As the drive shaft is rotated by means
of an electric motor through reduction gears, the socket ring also rotates
and drives the pistons in and out of
their cylinders.   Holes at the end of
the cylinders commutate with ports
in the valve plate of a fixed structure.

The ports are so arranged that all
cylinders taking in oil are connected

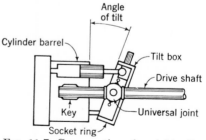

FIG. 11-7. Cross section of variable-displacement pump.

with one port and all cylinders exhausting oil are connected with the opposite port.   Thus, the fluid is permitted to flow through the hydraulic lines.   The stroke length of the piston, and hence the quantity of oil pumped, is governed by the angle of tilt, as shown in Fig. 11-7.   Direction of flow is governed by the direction of tilt.   If the angle is zero, no

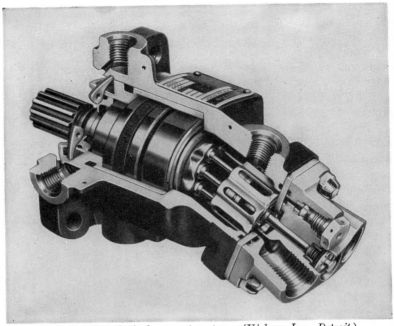

FIG. 11-8. Fixed-displacement motor. (*Vickers, Inc., Detroit.*)

oil flows.   Waterbury and Northern Ordnance control the volume and direction of flow by changing the angle and direction of tilt of the *A*-end tilting box in the manner shown.   Vickers accomplishes the same result by pivoting the entire cylinder block to either side of a neutral position.

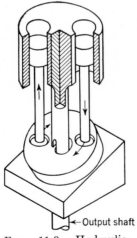

The *B* end, which receives the flow of oil, is similar in construction to the *A* end except that the angle of tilt is fixed.   As shown in Fig. 11-8, the fluid is forced into the *B* end by pressure from the pump.   It exerts a force against the piston that may be resolved into a component normal to the tilt plate and one in the plane of the tilt plate, as shown in Fig. 11-9.   The normal force is opposed by the bearings, but the other force causes a torque around the output shaft of the hydraulic motor; thus, the output-shaft velocity of such a hydraulic motor is approximately proportional to the flow of oil and

FIG.   11-9.   Hydraulic-motor force diagram.

hence the tilt angle of the *A* end.   The pump is constantly putting pressure on one side of the motor while it is constantly receiving liquid from the other side. Liquid is merely circulated from pump to motor and back again.

In order to avoid the deleterious effect of leakage, it is necessary to supply oil at a constant pressure from a replenishing pump to the low-pressure side of the variable-displacement pump. This acts to prevent air entrainment and also to prevent cavitation on the low-pressure inlet side of the variable-displacement pump. Because of the reversing characteristics of the variable-displacement pump, i.e., because it can pump oil in either direction depending upon the direction of the tilt angle, it is necessary to supply this replenishing oil to either of the two sides of the pump through check valves, which are used to prevent high-pressure oil from entering the replenishing system. Oil that leaks around the pistons and through other clearances is collected in either the case of the unit or the sump, and this oil is returned to the replenishing pump by means of hydraulic lines. The replenishing pump is generally a gear pump driven from the same shaft as the main pump and fitted with a relief valve to maintain constant pressure. The hydraulic system usually has a pair of relief valves inserted across the pump connections and arranged to bypass oil from one side to the other whenever the differential pressure exceeds preset limits.

If there is appreciable torque on the motor shaft, the output speed will not vary uniformly with tilt angles, and at very small tilt angles almost no motion will occur. If most of the load is dry friction and hence independent of speed, the pump must be capable of generating high torques even though the speed is low. However, it is under these conditions that internal leakage past the pistons is most effective in reducing the differential pressure. Hence, it is necessary to fine-machine the pistons and cylinders with clearances on the order of a few tenths.

It is also necessary to reduce the effect of the so-called "dead spot" by the application of "dither," in which some member controlling oil flow is caused to vibrate at a frequency well beyond any signal frequencies of interest. Dither is generally applied by means of an auxiliary motor rotating at about 1,700 rpm and consists of an eccentric that vibrates the feedback lever pivot on the stroke-control valve. Dither can improve performance by:

1. Reducing the pilot-valve friction, which reduces the pilot-valve force by as much as a factor of 10.

2. Reducing the effect of backlash in the stroke-control mechanism.

3. Reducing the effect of valve overlap in the pilot system.

4. Reducing the effect of backlash and dead space in gears and in the hydraulic transmission.

In a typical application, a motion of 40/1,000 in. on the dither rod vibrates a feedback pivot and oscillates the control piston ±0.001 in.

The power piston therefore receives pulsating oil flow and pulsates the stroke and hence the A and B ends of the hydraulic system.

In addition to these high-frequency pulsations, which are added for the purpose of reducing the effect of friction and dead spot, the delivery of liquid by the pump fluctuates because the quantity of oil discharged by the cylinders varies with shaft rotation. The amount pumped by each piston is a sinusoidal function of shaft rotation, and a combination of several cylinders is the commutated sum of the separate flows. In appearance, a graph of flow vs. time looks very much like a rectified polyphase voltage. The amount of fluctuation depends upon the angle of the tilt box of the pump and the number of cylinders.

The number of cylinders is always odd, since this fundamentally results in a smaller ripple than if they were even. Furthermore, the magnitude of ripple decreases with increase in the number of pistons. The ripple frequency is determined by multiplying the number of pistons by the shaft speed; a 9-piston pump has a ripple frequency 9 times the shaft speed. Ripple is approximately a linear function of output pressure. For example, a Vickers model PS58-3911-25-ZE gives a pump ripple of about 10 per cent of the output pressure for a flow rate of 4 gal/min. That is, if the average output pressure is 3,000 psi, the actual pump pressure is $3,000 \pm 300$ psi. This ripple is sometimes eliminated by means of a hydraulic filter consisting of the equivalent of electrical resistances, inductances, and capacitances. When the pump is being used as a power supply rather than as a variable-displacement pump, an accumulator can be used as a filter. Just as with an electric commutator, the more pistons used (or, following the analogy, the more commutator bars used), the smaller will be the pulsations. For example, a change from 3 to 13 pistons in a hydraulic pump reduces the fluctuation in flow rate by a factor of 20. Of course, more pistons make a more costly unit.

As an example of the constants that can be expected from a typical hydraulic transmission (Vickers), a combination of pump and motor, consider a 15-hp unit that weighs 8.5 lb without oil and is driven by a 3,300-rpm motor. At its full 30° tilt, it displaces 0.6 in.³ per revolution at 3,000 psi, yields a torque of 286 lb-in., and has an acceleration of 1.2×10^5 radians/sec², a time constant from zero to full speed of about 3 msec, and a torque-squared-to-inertia ratio of 3.4×10^7 lb-in./sec².

There exist several combinations of the application of pumps and motors that provide different types of response.

1. Variable-displacement pumps and constant-displacement motors result in constant-torque variable-horsepower units. At a given loading or hydraulic pressure, horsepower varies as speed, and torque is constant over the entire speed range.

2. Constant-displacement pumps and variable-displacement motors result in a constant-horsepower transmission. At a given hydraulic pressure, horsepower is constant between a minimum speed, determined by the geometric capacity of the motor at full stroke setting, and a maximum speed at reduced-motor-stroke setting dictated by design limits. The torque varies inversely with speed.

3. Variable-displacement pumps and variable-displacement motors may be combined to obtain any desired combination of torque and horsepower.

The following formulas are of use in computing the various important quantities used in hydraulic pumps and motors:

$$\text{Torque} = \frac{\text{in.}^3/\text{rev} \times \text{psi}}{2\pi} \qquad \text{lb-in.}$$

$$\text{Power} = \frac{\text{torque} \times \text{rpm}}{63,025} \qquad \text{hp}$$

$$\text{Acceleration} = \frac{\text{torque}}{\text{inertia}} \times 386 \qquad \text{radians/sec}^2$$

$$\text{Time constant} = \frac{\text{inertia}}{\text{torque}} \times \text{rpm} \times \frac{2\pi}{60 \times 386} \qquad \text{sec}$$

$$\text{Min. rev. to stop} = \text{rpm}^2 \times \frac{\text{inertia}}{\text{torque}} \times \frac{\pi}{60 \times 60 \times 386} \qquad \text{rev.}$$

Inertia is expressed in lb-in.^{2}.

11-5. Accumulators. In conjunction with a pump, a means for storing hydraulic energy is often provided. The device that is used for this purpose is called an accumulator and consists of a chamber in which a quantity of oil under pressure may be stored.

Frequently, the load is characterized by large demands of energy over short intervals of time but with an average demand far below the peaks. In these cases, the accumulator is proportioned to have an energy reserve great enough to supply the peak demand and be recharged by the pump during the intervals when the demand is below average. Thus, a much smaller pump can be used for pressure generation.

Since positive-displacement pumps give a pulsating flow, accumulators are also used as a filtering means. The pulsations send disturbances through the system, causing unsteady action, vibration of parts, water hammer, and metal fatigue, all of which weakens the resistance of the parts to strain. The pulsations can be minimized by building up pressure in the accumulator, which operates in a fashion analogous to a capacitor in an electric circuit. The accumulator also smooths out variations caused by motions of the valve or the sudden opening or closing of the valve and the consequent sudden flow and cessation of flow of hydraulic fluid, which sends shock waves into the oil.

The pressure in the accumulator is developed within the chamber either by means of trapped air or by means of a yielding wall that is opposed by a spring. In the latter type, the reaction of the spring may be thought of as an element that forces the yielding wall in a direction to maintain the required hydraulic pressure. In other types of accumulator, the force generated by the spring is replaced by the chamber of air under pressure. Most accumulators are now of a spherical construction with a flexible diaphragm separating the gas and oil. The sphere is split on the diameter, and the two flange tabs are bolted together with the diaphragm clamped between the flanges.

11-6. Control Valves. Control valves are used to meter the flow of fluid from the high-pressure supply to the actuator or prime mover.

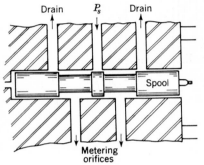

Drain P_s Drain

Spool

Metering orifices

FIG. 11-10. Piston-type valve.

Their input is motion, and they produce large changes in output pressure and flow in response to this input motion. The valve is generally moved by means of a motor which is capable of rotating in both directions or by means of a solenoid type of device which is spring-opposed. The valve can also be controlled by (1) solenoid, (2) mechanical, (3) manual, or (4) hydraulic-pilot methods.

In general there are three types of valve, or hydraulic amplifier, the *piston* type, the *nozzle* type, and the *jet* type. A simple piston-type valve is shown in Fig. 11-10. Two types of piston valves exist, the closed-center and the open-center. They are identical in appearance and differ only in the clearances of some of the parts. The closed-center type is essentially a means of modulating the flow output. The control lands of the piston are adjusted so that they just cut off the flow to the supply exhaust ports when the spool (piston) is in the central position. A change of a few thousandths in input motion can result in a large change in flow output. The valve has zero-pressure output when in its neutral position.

The open-center type of valve, however, can be designed to have any pressure up to almost full supply at both output ports when the valve is at neutral. This pressure is maintained because the valve spool does not quite fully close the input-pressure port, and there is consequently a controlled leakage at all times. The drop across the inlet and outlet ports determines what the pressure will be in the outlet lines. A common operating value is 50 per cent of supply pressure. Sometimes sharp-edged orifices are used in valves in order that the drop across them be independent of the viscosity of the oil and dependent only on its density.

The use of an open-center system results in compressing the trapped air more fully at all times, and therefore there is less change of bulk modulus caused by the fluid compressibility of the entrapped air in the oil. Also, a dead spot or effective backlash cannot exist in an open-center system. This type of valve is quite inefficient, and if the total

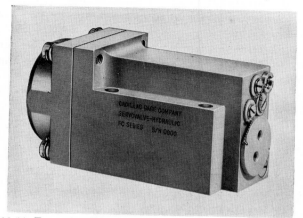

Fig. 11-11. Four-way-slide servo valve. (*Cadillac Gage Co., Detroit.*)

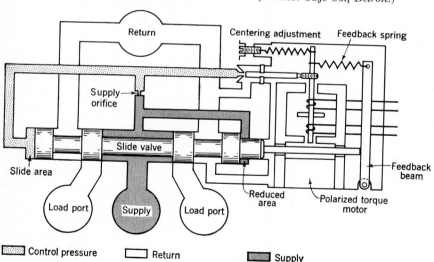

Fig. 11-12. Schematic drawing of a flow-control servo valve.

volume of oil flow must be kept small, as in a guided missile with an accumulator as the only hydraulic supply, an open-center type of system often cannot be used.

Figure 11-11 shows a photograph of a four-way slide valve. A miniature servo is contained in the valve to provide a high force level to provide accurate control of the valve. Figure 11-12 presents a schematic drawing of the valve.   Closing of the loop is accomplished by means of a mechanical force feedback system, which transmits slide-valve deflections to the torque motor armature.

The operation of the servo is based on a balance of forces at the torque motor armature, produced by input current and slide-valve position. The input force to the armature is proportional to the current in the

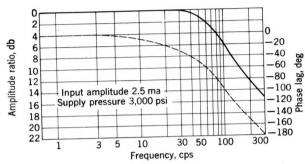

Fig. 11-13. Dynamic response of slide-valve servo valve.

torque motor coils.   The output, or feedback force, is determined by the deflection of the feedback spring, which is directly proportional to the slide-valve position.   Any unbalance between these forces causes an armature deflection that is detected and amplified through the nozzle-orifice system to produce a corrective force at the slide valve.   The resulting deflection of the slide valve, through the force feedback system, restores the force balance at the torque motor armature.   The dynamic response of this valve is shown in the amplitude and phase diagram of Fig. 11-13.

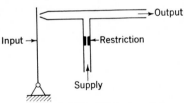

Fig. 11-14. Nozzle-type valve.

The nozzle type of amplifier, which is similar to a pneumatic amplifier, consists of a variable orifice and a fixed orifice, as shown in Fig. 11-14.   Of course, some provision must be made to collect and return the flow of fluid expelled from the nozzle to the sump.   Mechanical simplicity and reliability are virtues of the nozzle amplifier.   The supply tube contains a restriction, as shown in Fig. 11-14. If the nozzle is closed by the baffle, there is no flow of fluid; thus, there is no pressure drop across the nozzle restriction, and the nozzle back pressure is equal to the supply pressure.   If the nozzle is open, fluid passes through the constriction, causing a pressure drop across the nozzle restriction and hence a reduced pressure at the output.   The nozzle-type valve behaves as a calibrated leak whose leak rate is controlled by the baffle. The nozzle valve can be used, however, to produce only small forces, as the maximum volumetric rate of flow from its output is limited.

Sometimes this type of amplifier can be combined with the piston type so that it is a preamplifier for the latter. Such a scheme is shown in Fig. 11-12. Here the actuating signal is fed directly from the vacuum tubes of a d-c amplifier, and the output of the hydraulic preamplifier is a pressure in a chamber. This pressure in turn is responsible for the motion of the spool, which is opposed by a cantilever loading spring. The motion of the spool then permits oil to flow to the hydraulic ram.

The third type of hydraulic amplifier is the jet-pipe relay, which employs a pivoted nozzle so arranged as to discharge fluid into two closely adjacent receiving orifices, as shown in Fig. 11-15. The velocity head in the high-velocity fluid stream is transformed into a static pressure at the throat of the receiving orifices. When the nozzle is directed midway between the two orifices, the pressures within the orifices are low and of equal value. As the nozzle is moved toward one orifice, the pressure in that orifice increases, while the pressure in the other orifice is decreased. This is a "push-pull" type of amplifier as opposed to the

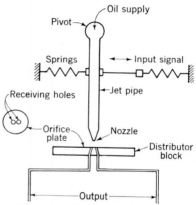

FIG. 11-15. Jet-pipe relay valve.

nozzle type, which is only "single-ended." Despite its somewhat greater mechanical complexity, the jet-type amplifier possesses the advantage of no back pressure on the flapper; i.e., the input force required to move it is somewhat less than for the flapper type of amplifier. Important characteristics of the jet type comprise the following: With a supply pressure of 100 psi and a 1.2-mm nozzle opening, the sensitivity is 5.2 psi/0.001 in., with linearity up to about 50 per cent of supply pressure. The frequency response of this type of valve shows a peak of 8 to 10 db at a frequency on the order of 20 cycles.

Figure 11-16 shows a servo actuator package, which typically includes an actuating cylinder, an electrohydraulic servo valve, and a feedback sensing device. Such integrated units offer the advantages of a comprehensive custom design including reduced over-all complexity and minimum size and weight. To meet the needs of widely varied systems, units can be provided that have either translational or rotary outputs. Additional features such as shutoff or bypass solenoid valves, force-limiting relief valves, piston locks, limit switches, and integral fluid filters can be included.

Fig. 11-16. Servo actuator. (*Moog Valve Co., Inc., East Aurora, N.Y.*)

11-7. Hydraulic Amplifiers. The valve-type hydraulic amplifier is discussed in further detail, since it is the most common of the three types. Two examples of applications are given. The first of these is shown in the schematic diagram of Fig. 11-17a. A pump supplies oil at high pressure to a valve. This oil is ported to the input of a hydraulic ram. Any motion of the valve piston from its central, or neutral, position causes oil to flow into the ram cylinder. This in turn causes the ram piston to attain a velocity proportional to the flow of oil.

The diagram also shows a follow-up link to remove the integration that would result from a valve feeding the ram directly. This link is a mechanical feedback from the ram piston to the sleeve of the valve. If the valve piston is displaced to the left, the hydraulic fluid forces the ram piston to the right, which in turn tends to close the valve port by means of the linkage. When the ram piston finally achieves its new position and the valve is again at neutral, the ports are closed and both the piston and sleeves are at the new position.

This is shown analytically from a consideration of the idealized block diagram of the actuator of Fig. 11-17a and the resulting equations. The position of the hydraulic ram is proportional to the volume of oil that has flowed into the cylinder and therefore to the integral of the rate of oil flow. The rate of oil flow is proportional to the valve displacement. The transfer function of the ram and valve combination, from valve opening e to ram position c, is

$$\frac{C}{E} = \frac{K_1}{s} \qquad (11-2)$$

The feedback link results in a motion b of the valve sleeve, which is proportional to the ram position:

$$\frac{B}{C} = K_2 \tag{11-3}$$

The block diagram of Fig. 11-17b can now be drawn.

The over-all transfer function of the device, from displacement input of the stroke motor to the output position of the ram, is given by

$$\frac{C}{R} = \frac{G}{1 + GH} = \frac{K_1/s}{1 + K_1K_2/s} = \frac{1}{K_2}\frac{1}{1 + (1/K_1K_2)s} \tag{11-4}$$

In the absence of feedback the integration is replaced by a time lag $1/K_1K_2$.

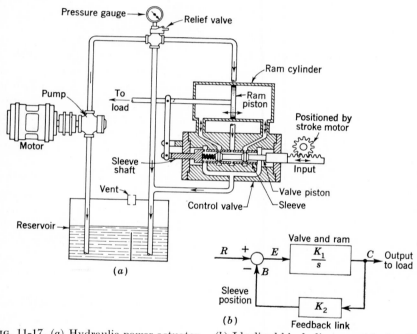

Fig. 11-17. (a) Hydraulic-power actuator. (b) Idealized block diagram of hydraulic-power actuator.

This device can be used as the prime mover or power source of a servomechanism. It can also be used to position a control lever of a hydraulic pump and motor combination for large-power servomechanisms. For these applications, it is known as a preamplifier.

The valve-ram combination shown in Fig. 11-18 is a complete servomechanism. In this application a radar dish is moved through a load angle that is computed by a gun sight. Since the radar dish goes through a limited angle, the linear motion of the ram is no disadvantage. E coils, which must be closely matched to minimize errors, are used to generate the actuating-signal voltage, which is amplified by a conventional electronic amplifier. The motor used to position the control valve is an

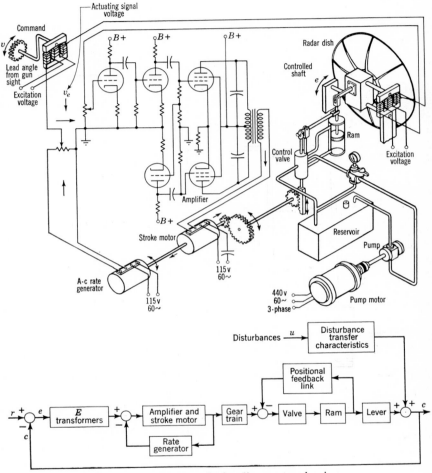

FIG. 11-18. Ram-type hydraulic servomechanism.

a-c servomotor, and a rate generator is used to provide stability to the system.

Servomechanisms employing rams and control valves enjoy popular usage in aircraft and guided missiles to position the control surfaces. Because of the incompressibility of the oil, such a servo can withstand enormous torque loads applied to the controlled shaft. For many types of control valve, a rotary motor geared to a rack is not used, but solenoids or torque motors with D'Arsonval* movements are employed.

In the second example a flapper-type amplifier is utilized to actuate the spool and hence control the flow of high-pressure oil to a ram-type

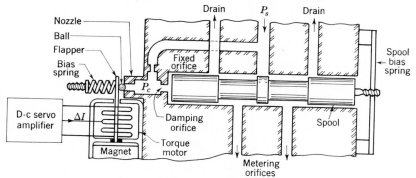

FIG. 11-19. Hydraulic preamplifier.

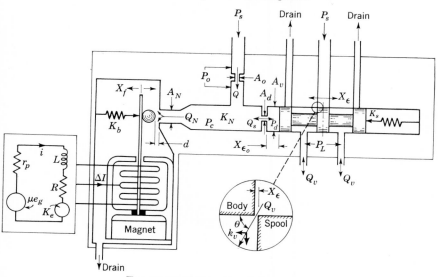

FIG. 11-20. Schematic of Fig. 11-19.

motor. The particular type of valve shown in Fig. 11-19 controls an output flow of 16 in.³/sec to the load, and the supply pressure to the valve is 1,500 psi. The schematic diagram given in Fig. 11-20 and the photograph of Fig. 11-21 show the construction of its parts.

* A D'Arsonval movement utilizes the torque produced by the interaction of two fluxes. One flux is obtained from a permanent magnet and the other, which is variable, is obtained from a coil carrying current.

The operation of the valve can be described as follows: The signal for actuating the valve is an electrical voltage that is amplified in a d-c servoamplifier. Two currents that oppose each other are developed in the control coils of a d-c force motor. The absolute difference between the two currents is proportional to the magnitude of the input signal. The relative magnitudes are determined by the sign of the input signal. The resultant magnetic fields of the d-c force-motor windings produce a force and a force gradient on the flapper armature whose movement is opposed by a bias spring. The position of the flapper at the nozzle of

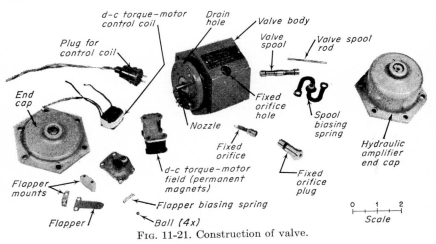

Fig. 11-21. Construction of valve.

the pressure chamber determines the pressure within the chamber. The pressure in the chamber, which is many times that required to position the flapper at the nozzle of the chamber, acts on a valve spool opposed by a loading spring. Through the porting action of the valve spool, hydraulic fluid is permitted to flow to the load. Thus, the complete valve contains two levels of power amplification—the electrical signal controls the power flow to the pressure chamber, and the valve spool controls the power delivered to the load.

The following are the physical properties of the valve. The coils of the motor consist of 2,500 turns each, with a resistance of 600 ohms and 250 mh measured at 1,000 cycles. The orifice of the preamplifier is 0.0008 in. The diameter of the valve spool is $\frac{1}{4}$ in., and the diametrical clearance is about 0.0002 in. The weight of the entire valve is 1.1 lb.

From an operational point of view, the valve performance can be analyzed in terms of the block diagram of Fig. 11-22. This is the open-loop diagram for the valve operation independent of load effects. All sources of disturbances operating on the system are indicated. A complete discussion of the dynamics of the system is beyond the scope of this book, but a few of the more significant test results, both static and dynamic, are described.

The chamber pressure varies about 600 psi for 0.0007-in. change of nozzle position for the most sensitive position of the flapper. After the flapper has moved about 0.0015 in., the gain falls off rapidly with position owing to the nonlinearity of the device. However, most of the operation of the valve is in the linear region, where the chamber pressure changes uniformly with motor current. Tests on the valve show a flow

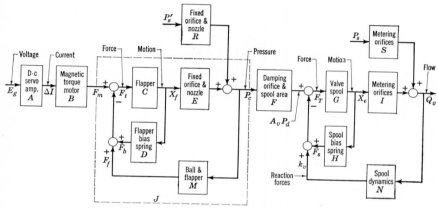

FIG. 11-22. Block diagram of Fig. 11-19.

rate of 2 in.³/sec per thousandths of spool displacement from its neutral position. The valve is linear on both sides of zero, with practically no dead space, although various valves of the same manufacturer produce dead space due to overlap of the flange and ports. Another significant static characteristic is the output flow of the valve as a function of differential coil current. The rate of flow is about 4 in.³/sec/ma differential current in the force motor for a supply pressure of 1,500 psi.

One interesting aspect of the operation of this type of valve is the reaction forces that tend to move the valve. These are dependent not upon the actuating signal but upon flow and are therefore spurious forces. They are of two types:

1. A momentum force, which is caused by the influx of oil momentum into the chamber immediately above the valve metering orifice.

2. A Bernoulli force, which is caused by the flow of oil past the valve spool, tending to lower the pressure where the velocity is highest.

The combination of these two forces constitutes the total reaction forces, which are on the order of $\frac{1}{10}$ lb/in.³ per sec of flow. One objective of the valve design is to make the control force applied to the spool large compared with these reaction forces. It is accomplished in this valve, since the maximum reaction force is about 2 lb, whereas the control force on the spool changes 15 lb to produce this flow, thus making the net force on the spool 13 lb for full flow.

An important dynamic property of the valve is the transfer function from amplifier input voltage to chamber pressure P_c. It is desirable that this be a constant, invariant with frequency. Figure 11-23 indicates

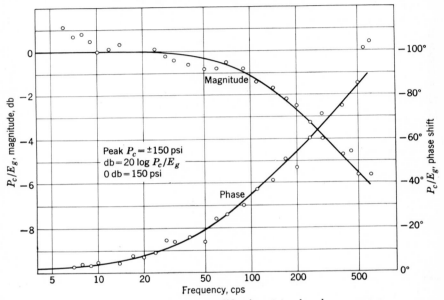

FIG. 11-23. Transfer locus; amplifier input to chamber pressure.

that the magnitude of the transfer function starts to fall off at signal frequencies above 100 cycles. Of interest also is the over-all dynamic response of valve-spool displacement from voltage input of the d-c amplifier to displacement of the valve. This is given in Fig. 11-24, which shows a corner frequency on the order of 18 cycles and hence a linear single-order time constant on the order of 9 msec. A second-order time constant is calculated from the curve to be about 0.5 msec. Valves have been built that are flat out to about 100 cycles. These are generally linear if the power output stays within 50 per cent of the power rating.

One of the difficulties with a valve such as that just described is the problem of manufacture to the extremely close tolerances necessary to ensure that it will have no dead space. The valve must be relatively friction-free yet have no leakage around the valve spool in the zero-flow position. The position of the valve corresponding to zero actuating signal must also be capable of simple adjustment, preferably in the field.

11-8. A Hydraulic-power Servomechanism. As a final example of hydraulic servomechanisms, a system consisting of the units outlined in the block diagram of Fig. 11-25 is discussed. The hydraulic transmission of the block diagram is a Vickers model AA-16801-A, which at rated

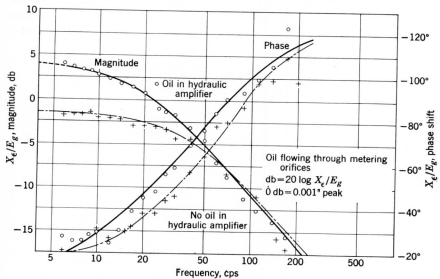

FIG. 11-24. Transfer locus; amplifier input to valve spool displacement.

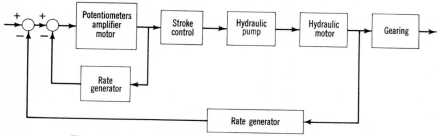

FIG. 11-25. Block diagram of a hydraulic servomechanism.

speed of 1,200 rpm yields 8.8 lb-ft of torque. This unit is driven by a 1.5-hp 3,540-rpm three-phase motor with double-shaft extension, the other shaft of which is used for powering another hydraulic pump. This is common practice when two systems are necessary, as in, say, the train and elevation of a gun control. A Diehl 20-volt two-phase a-c servomotor with a 240:1 gear ratio to the stroke control is driven with a three-stage amplifier. The a-c rate generator has a transmission that is flat to 30 cycles, and therefore its dynamics can be ignored in considering the dynamics of the rest of the system.

The stroke control is shown in Fig. 11-26. This normally operates at an oil pressure of about 80 psi. The dynamic response of the stroke control alone is given in Fig. 11-27.

The steady-state characteristics of the hydraulic transmission, given in terms of torque vs. speed for various stroke angles, is shown in Fig. 11-28. The dynamic response of the entire system, from the input to the amplifier to the output of the rate generator geared to the controlled shaft,

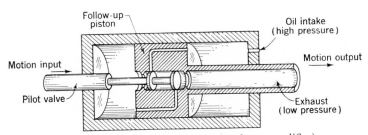

FIG. 11-26. Stroke control (motion-force amplifier).

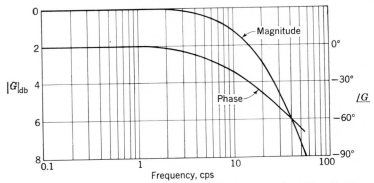

FIG. 11-27. Frequency response of the stroke control of Fig. 11-26.

is given in the open-loop frequency-response data of Fig. 11-29. The transmission is fundamentally nonlinear, and the output is not sinusoidal for a sinusoidal input. The phase and magnitude vary with input amplitude as well as with frequency. Entrained air makes the elasticity of the transmission quite nonlinear at low pressures and hence provides low torques. The step response, from amplifier input to rate-generator output, is given in Fig. 11-30.

It must be emphasized that the tests given are for the unloaded condition; a typical load might consist of the number of inertias elastically coupled to the servomotor with various amounts of backlash and friction. Other types of load torque, dynamic and otherwise, are not considered.

Dynamically, the hydraulic transmission can be expressed in terms of

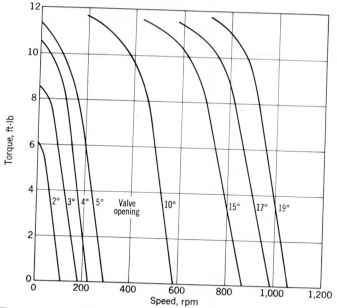

FIG. 11-28. Steady-state characteristics of hydraulic transmission.

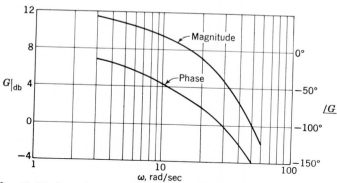

FIG. 11-29. Open-loop frequency response of the servo of Fig. 11-25.

two parameters, the undamped natural period τ_1 and the damping ratio ζ, as shown in the following transfer function:

$$G_1 = \frac{K}{s(\tau_1^2 s^2 + 2\tau_1 s + 1)} \tag{11-5}$$

This system has a measured natural period of oscillation of 9 cycles. τ_1 is 0.0178 sec, and ζ is 0.35.

As an experiment, the 15-in. lines of 0.062-in. wall thickness that connected the pump and motor were replaced by 5-ft lines of 0.032-in. wall thickness, and this caused oscillations during tracking. It is interesting to note that although the system was designed to have a slewing rate in excess of 40°/sec using 95°F oil, when the oil temperature was reduced to 10°F, the slewing rate decreased to 25°/sec. This occurred despite the fact that a high grade of hydraulic paraffinic oil was used.

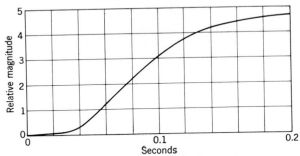

Fɪɢ. 11-30. Rate-generator output for step amplifier input for the system of Fig. 11-25.

11-9. Advantages and Disadvantages of Pneumatic Systems. Pneumatic servos find wide application in many medium-powered control systems. The gap that exists between the lower-powered electrical control systems and the relatively higher-powered hydraulic control systems can be filled with pneumatic servos. Advantages of the pneumatic servo are (1) no high-pressure oil-leakage problems, (2) relatively simple systems, (3) low weight with high power, and (4) no need for reservoirs.

Pneumatic circuits are extremely simple for obtaining such favorable dynamics for the amplifier as proportional plus integral or proportional plus integral plus derivative in controllers used in industry. This, coupled with the fact that extremely long time constants can be obtained in a very small space, results in over 90 per cent of the industrial control systems employing pneumatics. The discussion that follows, however, is confined only to servomechanisms, i.e., positioning systems, rather than the more general industrial-process control systems, for which pneumatics has such a wide application.*

One of the disadvantages of pneumatic servos is the difficulty of lubricating the moving parts. Also because of the compressibility of air, additional time lags can be introduced into the system, and without careful design, this compressibility can also be a disadvantage.

The compressibility of the gas is based upon the ideal gas law, which for a perfect gas gives the relationship

$$pV = WRT \tag{11-6}$$

* See Chap. 10 of Ref. 1 for a discussion of the application of pneumatics to industrial control systems.

where p is the pressure, V the volume, W the weight, T the temperature, and R the gas constant. A consistent set of units is used in Eq. (11-6) to make it dimensionally correct.

11-10. Pneumatic Components. The appearance of pneumatic components is quite similar to that of hydraulic components, and for this reason they are treated in less detail.

Pneumatic Amplifiers. The simplest type of pneumatic amplifier is called the *baffle-nozzle* system and is shown in the schematic of Fig. 11-31. The system comprises a small hole which is at the end of a tube (nozzle) which contains a restriction. The small hole can be closed by a plate

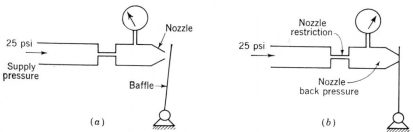

FIG. 11-31. The baffle-nozzle system.

(baffle). With the tube connected to a pressure supply of 25 psi (pounds per square inch), for example, the air passes through the constriction and the nozzle if the baffle is not closing off the nozzle, as shown in Fig. 11-31a. Because the nozzle opens to atmospheric pressure (0 psi), a pressure drop exists across the restriction that equals the supply pressure (25 psi above atmospheric pressure). If the nozzle is closed by the baffle, there is no flow of air; thus, there is no pressure drop over the nozzle restriction, and the nozzle-back pressure equals the supply pressure.

As the baffle position is varied through a short distance in front of the nozzle, the nozzle-back pressure is caused to vary between supply and atmospheric pressure. A typical nozzle has a diameter of 0.050 in., and a 0.010 motion of the baffle can result in a complete change of nozzle-back pressure. Hence the baffle-nozzle system constitutes a highly sensitive amplifier that requires little force to operate the baffle. In normal operation, the baffle is attached to the measuring element, and the nozzle-back pressure is the output that is available to position a control valve. Because of the limited amount of air available through the restriction, a piston actuator cannot be driven by this amplifier.

The back pressure is a linear function of the position of the baffle for only a limited motion of the baffle. Outside this region, the curve becomes quite nonlinear, as shown by the curve of Fig. 11-32. By restricting the motion of the baffle, the system is made relatively linear in a region about an operating point.

Control Valves. Both electrically operated and pneumatically operated control valves are used in servomechanisms. Electrically operated valves are similar to the hydraulic valves shown in Fig. 11-12. Both rotary and linear (cf. Fig. 11-12) motion valves are widely used for controlling double-acting piston actuators.

Numerous process control systems depend upon the control of a flow to or from the process. Pneumatically controlled valves are frequently utilized for this purpose. These valves can be driven directly from the baffle-nozzle system (cf. Fig. 11-31).
A schematic drawing of such a valve is shown in Fig. 11-33. The principle of operation of the valve is indicated in this figure. The pressure is applied against a rubber diaphragm, which acts against the force of a spring. The displacement of

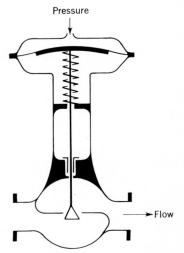

FIG. 11-33. Pneumatic control valve.

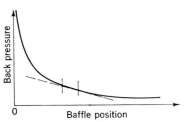

FIG. 11-32. Back pressure vs. baffle position for a typical baffle nozzle system.

the diaphragm is thus proportional to the pressure. The plug of the valve is positioned by the motion of the control valve, and the flow is thus controlled. The valve can be either normally open, which means that it closes as pressure is applied, or normally closed, which means that it opens as pressure is applied. A typical valve is designed to travel through its complete stroke for a pressure variation of 3 to 15 psi.

The baffle-nozzle system can be coupled directly to a pilot valve through which a considerable flow can pass. Hence the pilot valve, which resembles the hydraulic valve of Fig. 11-12, can be pneumatically operated. The small power necessary to operate the valve is delivered by a small bellows or diaphragm connected to the nozzle-back pressure. One such system is shown in Fig. 11-34. The pilot valve comprises a steel ball that can move between two seats. When one valve port is closed, the other port is opened. Supply pressure is applied to one of the valves, and hence the air flows around the ball and out through the exhaust port. As the air flows through the valve, there is a pressure drop over each port since each port forms a restriction. The pressure in the chamber around the ball depends upon the position of the ball. This pressure varies between supply pressure (exhaust port closed) and atmospheric pressure (supply port closed). The ball is connected to the bellows

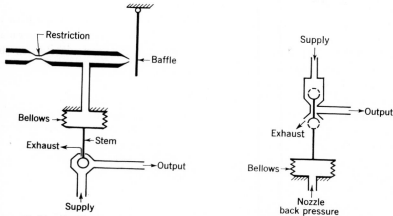

FIG. 11-34. Baffle-nozzle system and pilot valve.

FIG. 11-35. Pilot valve.

by means of a stem. The bellows is actuated with the back pressure from the baffle-nozzle system.

Another type of pilot valve is shown in Fig. 11-35. This valve utilizes two balls in a direct-acting pilot valve. As the nozzle-back pressure increases in a direct-acting valve, the output pressure increases. The

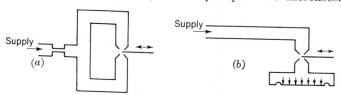

FIG. 11-36. Baffle-nozzle system designs.

pilot valve of Fig. 11-34 is reverse-acting in that the output pressure decreases as the nozzle-back pressure increases.

Two other types of pneumatic valve are shown in Fig. 11-36. These units operate in a manner similar to the valve shown in Fig. 11-31. In Fig. 11-36a, a free vane is moved between two opposite nozzles. This creates a controllable flow and hence a controllable back pressure. This valve operates as two nozzle-baffle valves; however, it has the advantage of requiring much less force to move the baffle. The breakaway force required on a single baffle is usually quite large.

The vane used in Fig. 11-36b controls the amount of the air jet that is directed against the diaphragm. As the vane is inserted into the jet, less air is caught by the lower nozzle, hence decreasing the pressure on the diaphragm.

Actuators. For large power applications a pneumatic actuator, similar to that shown in Fig. 11-37, is capable of delivering a tremendous thrust. Pneumatic actuators of this type find wide use in both industrial and

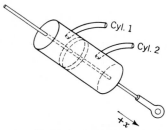

military applications. The actuator comprises a piston that moves within a cylinder. Two connecting rods, which are on each side of the piston, transmit the piston force and motion to the output. The connecting rods are sealed at each end of the cylinder so that the rod can move relative to the piston with minimum air leak. The air is applied to the cylinders through a manifold system. For positive x mo-

FIG. 11-37. Double-acting actuator.

tion (cf. Fig. 11-37), a transfer or pilot valve applies line pressure to cylinder 1 and exhausts cylinder 2. For negative x motion, cylinder 1 is exhausted and pressure is applied to cylinder 2. The actuator must be manufactured with a high degree of accuracy, and seals must be used on the piston and on each connecting rod to prevent excessive air leak.

11-11. A Pneumatic-power Servomechanism. Figure 11-38 shows a pneumatic autopilot that positions a missile control surface as a function of the applied voltage. The error signal, formed by subtracting a func-

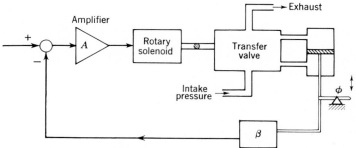

FIG. 11-38. Block diagram for pneumatic autopilot.

tion of output angle ϕ from the input, is amplified with a linear d-c amplifier of gain K. The amplifier, which uses an a-c preamplifier stage, a demodulator, and a d-c power-amplifier output stage, has no appreciable time delays in the frequency range of interest. The output of the amplifier drives a rotary solenoid, which, in turn, positions a pneumatic valve. The position of this transfer valve directs the air into one of two cylinders of a double-acting actuator. The actuator is similar to that shown in Fig. 11-37.

The details of the mechanical arrangement are shown in Fig. 11-39. The actuator is connected through a series of mechanical linkages to one of the control surfaces of the missile. Identical systems drive the other control surfaces. Feedback from the output position of the control

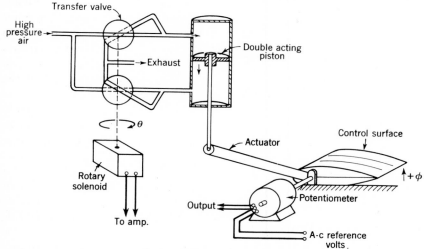

FIG. 11-39. Mechanical arrangement for pneumatic autopilot.

surface is provided with a potentiometer. Although aerodynamic considerations dictate the over-all feedback through the airframe, an electrical feedback is employed to improve response of the autopilot. Since aerodynamic forces operate on the control surfaces while it is in flight, it is important that these aerodynamic loads be considered during analysis and design of the autopilot. As a first approximation, these restoring forces can be written

$$F_R = aT_k\phi + bT_b\dot{\phi} = K_1\phi + K_2\dot{\phi} \qquad (11\text{-}7)$$

where a, b, K_1, and K_2 are constants. This corresponds to a spring restoring force plus a damping term. Position feedback is required to return the control surface to its zero position with zero input signal.

With 600 psi air supplied and a 2-in.-diameter actuator, an 1,800-lb thrust (subtracting the area of the connecting rod) is applied to move the control surface. The load on the control surface is simulated by an inertia (4 lb-in./sec^2 magnitude) and two restoring springs (800 lb-in. total for both springs). The amplitude frequency response for the system is shown in the sketch of Fig. 11-40. Because of the compressibility of the air and because of the nonlinearities of the transfer valve and actuator, the over-all system is quite nonlinear.   The feedback improves linearity and the dynamic response.

The phase response that is shown in Fig. 11-40 does not follow a linear second-order system (see Appendix).   Also, as the amplitude of the exciting signal is increased, the amplitude and phase response change.

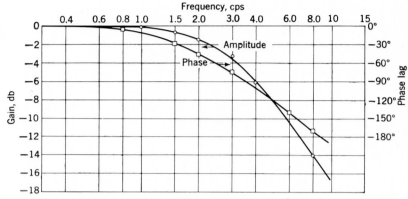

FIG. 11-40. Dynamic-response pneumatic servo.

For large signals the response is quite nonlinear, and the output wave-form deviates considerably from a sinusoid.

PROBLEMS

11-1. Explain how the vane pump can be used as a variable-displacement pump.

11-2. Accumulators have been used as the sole source of power of hydraulic servomechanisms.   State an application where such a use is practical.

11-3. Compare the advantages and disadvantages of three types of constant-displacement pumps used for obtaining a high-pressure source of oil.

11-4. Compare the advantages and disadvantages of the piston, nozzle, and jet types of hydraulic amplifier.

11-5. What are the advantages and disadvantages of open-center and closed-center piston valves?

11-6. What are the consequences of the existence of momentum and Bernoulli forces in a piston-type valve?

11-7. Show graphically the effect of the number of cylinders on the ripple output of a variable-displacement piston pump.

11-8. Compare the advantages and disadvantages of hydraulic and Amplidyne servos.

11-9. Explain how the compressibility of air can cause additional time lags in a pneumatic system.

11-10. When a gas is used instead of a liquid, are the effects of momentum forces increased or decreased?   Why?   Are the effects of Bernoulli forces increased or decreased?

11-11. Draw a mathematical block diagram for the pneumatic autopilot of Fig. 11-39.

11-12. Compare the advantages and disadvantages of pneumatic, hydraulic, and electronic servos.

CHAPTER 12

MANUFACTURE OF SERVOMECHANISMS

12-1. Introduction. The performance of servomechanisms depends upon the manufacturing process by which they are made as much as the design itself. As a matter of fact, the most difficult problems concerning servomechanisms are often not those of making the servomechanism stable or designing it to have tolerable accuracy but rather those of making it small enough, light enough, or easy enough to manufacture or service. It is the purpose of this chapter to discuss the process by which servomechanisms are made. This description is not meant to be a complete treatise on the subject of manufacturing or even on the subject of manufacturing the components mentioned. It is rather a discussion of the subject as it applies to servomechanisms, stressing those points which are important in their design and manufacture. It is felt that by giving the servomechanism designer an appreciation of the problems of manufacture, the design can be approached with greater understanding.

The mechanical parts of servomechanisms are manufactured to tolerances on the order of 1/10,000 in., and their manufacture involves skill and knowledge not common to other types of manufacture. Because of the many different types of servomechanism, ranging from flea-power devices for positioning dials to several hundred horsepower electro-hydraulic devices for positioning 16-in. guns, it would be impossible to describe the manufacturing processes associated with each. Instead, the manufacturing problems associated with the manufacture of small instrument servomechanisms of the electromechanical type are discussed. Much of the information given is applicable to larger types of servomechanism. The chapter is divided into two principal parts: (1) the various mechanical components and how they affect servo performance and (2) both mechanical- and electrical-assembly practices.

Mechanically, an instrument servomechanism may comprise gears, shafts, bearings, electromechanical components, limit stops, cams, brakes, clutches, linkages, and other mechanical devices. The tolerances to which these parts are manufactured are extremely important to the ease with which the device can be assembled and the ability of the finished unit to meet performance specifications. Some auxiliary types of mechanical components that are used in servomechanisms, such as differentials, couplings, and limit stops, are discussed first. Then gearing, hole location for the components, electromechanical components, bearings, and shafting are treated.

12-2. Auxiliary Mechanical Components. Differentials are used for mechanically adding and subtracting the angular position of two shafts. They are generally made according to one of two types, either the planetary type or, more commonly, the beveled-gear differential. The beveled

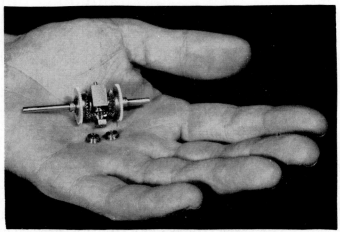

Fig. 12-1. Mechanical differential. (*Ford Instrument Co., Long Island City, N.Y.*)

gears may be straight bevel gears, spiral bevel gears, or zerol gears. Figure 12-1 shows a miniature mechanical differential that operates with low friction, smooth transmission of torque, low breakaway torque ($\frac{1}{100}$ oz-in.), and small backlash (less than 5 minutes of arc).

Cams are used for eccentric motion of output relative to input. They have some kind of curved surface, such as a groove or contour. The curved surface is positioned by the input, and each point on the curved surface represents a different output value. They can be used for computing (ballistic cams) or merely for causing electrical switches to open or close at particular shaft positions. A variety of cams, which are shown in Fig. 12-2, provide a wide degree of versatility. These cams can be produced to an accuracy of ± 0.0005 in. Two-dimensional designs are used to obtain a motion or function that bears a nonlinear relation to another single motion or function: $y = f(x)$. They can also be cut with constant lead curves for linear relationships. Besides the many analytical functions that can be cut—including square roots, reciprocals, trigonometric functions, logs, reciprocals of square roots, combined trigonometric functions—many empirical functions, such as ballistic data, can be cut on a cam. Figure 12-3 shows three types of two-dimensional cams that are commonly utilized in servomechanisms.

3-D cams make available to the user a compact unit that continuously and accurately satisfies an arbitrary function: $z = f(x,y)$, where x and y are independent variables (inputs), and z is the dependent variable or

Fig. 12-2. Two- and three-dimensional cams. (*Ford Instrument Co., Long Island City, N.Y.*)

output. Some typical functions, which have been cut into these cams, are:

1. Jet fuel supply as a function of rpm and temperature
2. Ballistic corrections as a function of elevation angle and range or time of flight
3. Bomb characteristics as a function of air speed and altitude or dive angle
4. Magnetic variation as a function of latitude and longitude

Figure 12-4 shows a three-dimensional cam. The cam itself is barrel-shaped and rotates on its axis. A ball follower slides along the surface of the barrel, held against it by spring pressure. Its output movement z is determined by its lateral position along the surface of the cam and by the angular (rotational) position of the cam.

Dials are used in servomechanisms for indicating the positions of shafts. They are sometimes placed on shafts that are geared together so that a

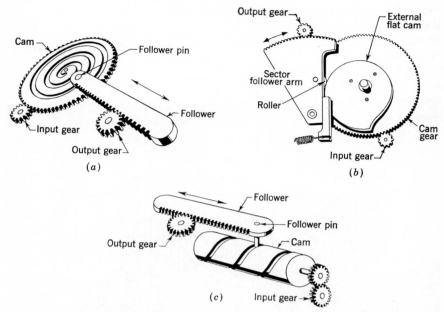

FIG. 12-3. Three types of two-dimensional cams. (a) Grooved flat cam with radial follower; (b) external flat cam with angular follower; (c) grooved cylindrical cam with typical follower.

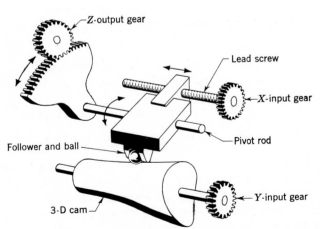

FIG. 12-4. 3-D cam with angular follower. Follower is positioned by lead screw (x input) and by cam rotation (y input). Follower movement rotates pivot rod, which, in turn, causes sector gear to rotate output gear (z).

vernier effect is obtained. Several types are shown in Fig. 12-5. When the gearing between shafts is accurate, the position of the coarse shaft can be read more accurately. Counters are also used to indicate the positions of shafts.

There are also many types of mechanical computing mechanisms such as multipliers, component solvers, integrators of the ball-disk type, sine and cosine generators, and linkages. One type of ball-disk integrator is shown in the schematic of Fig. 12-6. In this integrator, a disk mounted

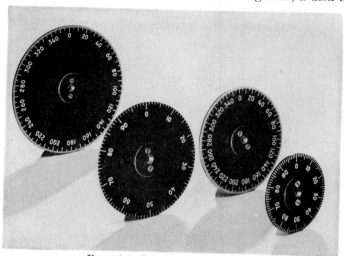

Fig. 12-5. Servomechanism dials.

on a gear is turned directly by an input gear. Two steel balls, one on top of the other, are held in position by a carriage that moves across the face of the disk. The disk turns the bottom ball, which rotates the upper ball, which in turn drives a roller having an output gear at one end. The balls can be positioned by the carriage anywhere along a line from the edge of the disk across the center to the other side. Their speed of rotation increases with distance from the center of the disk; rotation is in the opposite direction on each side. The pressure needed to hold the balls against each other and against the disk and roller comes from two springs.

Couplings are often used to connect the ends of two shafts together so that they rotate at the same speed with the same angular position. There are a number of types commonly employed, all of which compensate for slight misalignment of shaft. They are the bellows, the disk, and the Oldham types. The bellow-type coupling consists of two hubs connected by a flexible metal bellows. Because any misalignment of the shaft results in flexing of the bellows with a possibility of metal fatigue, this is suitable only for low-torque and low-speed applications. The disk consists of a flexible disk that is secured by pins to a pair of hubs. Like the bellows type, it is free of backlash, but it is capable of somewhat higher speed and heavier loads than the bellows coupling. The Oldham-type coupling is shown on Fig. 12-7 and is used for the highest speeds and heaviest loads. It consists of two hubs that have surfaces machined across them to receive a double, female, floating member. The floating

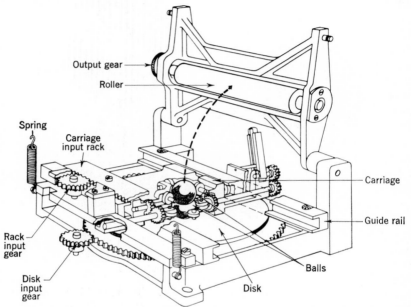

Fig. 12-6. Schematic of a ball-and-disk integrator. (*Ford Instrument Co., Long Island City, N.Y.*)

member is held in place between the hubs. The coupling compensates for lateral misalignment of shaft and also for slight angular misalignment. However, if the parts are not machined accurately, some backlash can result. It must also be recognized in using any of these couplings that, if there is any misalignment of the shafts, the angular position of the shaft on one side of the coupling will not be precisely the same as the angular position on the other side.

Limit stops are mechanical safety devices that prevent shafts from rotating farther than they should. When low torques are involved and small inertias are to be stopped, the limit stop can consist of metal-to-metal contact with no cushioning. If cushioning is necessary, pieces of rubber or springs can be used to absorb the shock. One type of limit stop that is capable of a great many revolutions before stopping consists of a traveling nut on a screw thread. A guide nut is used to prevent the traveling nut from rotating, and two adjusting nuts limit the travel. The threaded shaft is stopped from turning when the stop plate on one end of the traveling nut hits the stop plate on the adjusting nut. This type is illustrated in Fig. 12-8.

Another type of mechanical limit stop consists of a series of washers, each of which has a projection for a small angle on its outer periphery. The number of turns of the shaft is adjusted by the number of washers used and the setting of a mechanical stop.

Sometimes both electrical and mechanical limit stops are used. Electrical limit stops operate first, i.e., the driving motor is deenergized by means of electrical switches such as microswitches actuated by cams. Then motion is positively stopped by mechanical limit stops. This protects the mechanical limit stops from the severe shock that might result from full-speed and full-torque application of the motor.

Fig. 12-7. Oldham-type shaft coupling. (*Ford Instrument Co., Long Island City, N.Y.*)

Clutches disconnect electrically two shafts that are coupled together; brakes are used to stop the motion of shafts electrically. Either can be designed to operate or to release with the application of current.

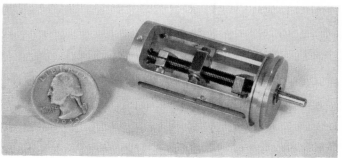

Fig. 12-8. Limit stop. (*Ford Instrument Co., Long Island City, N.Y.*)

Hand cranks are used to rotate shafts by hand. Usually the hand crank is decoupled from the shaft that it is to rotate. Hence the hand crank does not rotate when the shaft rotates automatically.

12-3. Servomechanism Gears.   Gearing is used in servomechanisms to convert the high-speed low-torque power available at the motor to a low-speed high-torque power at the controlled shaft.   Many types of gear are used, including spur, helical, internal, bevel, spiral, worm, and worm-wheel; of these, spur gears are by far the most common.   Worm gears are not often used because of their high friction, particularly if there is a load on the controlled shaft.   In addition, if the shaft must be rapidly reversed, the presence of any appreciable inertia on the controlled shaft can cause damage.   Bevel gears, spiral bevel gears, zerol gears, and hypoids are used if the shafts do not all lie in the same plane.   Internal

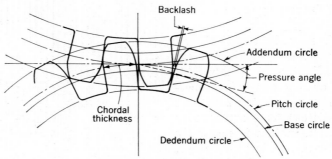

FIG. 12-9. Spur-gear nomenclature.

gears are sometimes used on differentials.   Planetary gears and large ring gears are frequently found in power servomechanisms.   Considerable emphasis is placed here on spur gears not only because they are the most commonly used but also because their study can serve as an introduction to the manufacture of the other types of gears.   The calculation of gear stresses and selection of the proper tooth width and diametrical pitch is not discussed, since this information can be found in the mechanical-engineering literature.

Figure 12-9 is a diagram of a spur gear showing the nomenclature pertaining to various portions of the gear.   Most spur gears are of the involute form.   The involute is a curve which is described by the end of a line which is unwound from the circumference of a circle called the *base circle*.   The involute tooth form is chosen because the relative rate of motion of two mating gears is independent of the distance between the centers of the base circles and is dependent only upon their relative size. The angle between the common tangent to the two base circles and a line perpendicular to their common-center line is called the *pressure angle*. The pressure angle is also the angle between the common tangent to the pitch circles and a straight line normal to both the mating profiles of the teeth at the point of contact.   With an involute tooth form, this pressure angle remains constant as the gear rotates. Most gears are cut with either a 14.5° pressure angle or a 20° pressure angle. The common diametrical pitches used in instrument servomechanisms are 32, 48, 64, 96, and 120. Good practice is the guide in the selection of diametrical pitches. Strength is rarely an important consideration in instrument

Fig. 12-10. Typical fine-pitch servomechanism gears. (*Western Gear Corp., Lynwood, Calif.*)

servos since gears are principally used for the transmission of motion. Figure 12-10 shows some typical instrument gears.

To reduce wear, mating gears are often made from different materials. Similar materials seize and pick up metal from each other and thus further aggravate the condition of wear. Tests that have been conducted indicate that the combination of steel against brass has one-tenth the wear of steel against steel and one-fiftieth the wear of brass against brass. The smaller gears should, of course, be made of the harder material. If the equipment must be subjected to wide temperature variations, caution must be exercised in the use of dissimilar metals for mating gears or for gears and the mounting plates. Corrosion is also a greater threat when dissimilar metals are used.

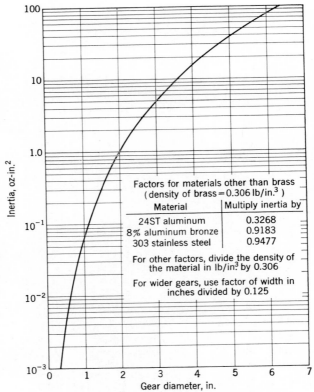

Fig. 12-11. Moment of inertia of brass gears.

Characteristics of gears important to their application to servomechanisms are inertia and the error of the gear itself. Such properties of gear trains as friction, backlash, and error are discussed later in the chapter.

The moment of inertia of a solid gear can easily be calculated from the formula

$$J = \tfrac{1}{2}Mr^2$$

where J = inertia, slug-ft^2

M = mass, slugs

r = radius of gear, ft

Figure 12-11 gives the moment of inertia of brass gears having a $\frac{1}{8}$-in. face. For different thicknesses, inertia is directly proportional to the thickness.   If a different material is used, the table indicates multiplying factors.   Because the inertia of a body, including the gear itself, is reflected as the square of the gear ratio, the significant inertia of the gear train in instrument servomechanisms is often contained in the first gear. Since the inertia of the motor pinion adds directly to that of the motor rotor, some manufacturers cut the motor pinion as an integral part of the motor shaft.

To minimize the inertia of the gearing, the maximum reduction should not be obtained in the first mesh.   Formulas are available for minimizing

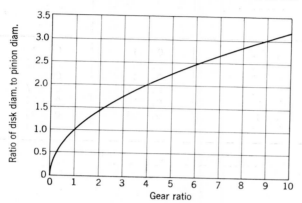

FIG. 12-12. Importance of reflected inertia.

the gearing inertia for any total desired gear ratio.*   Some measure of the importance of the inertia of a gear meshing with a pinion can be obtained from Fig. 12-12, which plots the diameter of a disk whose inertia is equal to the inertia of the gear reflected to the pinion.   For example, if a gear ratio of 10:1 is used on the first mesh of the gear train whose pinion is cut into a $\frac{1}{8}$-in. shaft of the motor, the reflected inertia of the mating gear is equivalent to that of a disk whose diameter is $3 \times \frac{1}{8} = \frac{3}{8}$ in.   A quick appraisal of the importance of the inertia of the larger gear can be made.

Although error in gearing can exist only when two or more gears are used in a gear train, it is common to speak of the error of a single gear. This can result from improper tooth spacing, tooth-thickness variation, and eccentricity of the pitch line.   The absence of these effects is a measure of the quality of a gear.   Tolerances have been set up by the American Gear Manufacturers' Association (AGMA) and grouped into seven classes, which are given in Table 12-1.   While these tolerances are a measure of the quality of the gear, they do not establish the actual angular error of the output of a gear train whose center distances are

* See Sec. 12-5 for design information on gear trains.

immobile.   The class of the gear is determined by measuring the variation in center distance between the gear and a master gear of zero error
as the gear is rotated in intimate contact with the master gear.   Typically, the record of the variation in center distance resembles the graph
of Fig. 12-13.   The total composite error is computed as the difference
between the largest and smallest value of the distance between the

TABLE 12-1. GEAR TOLERANCES

AGMA class	Total composite error, in.	Tooth-to-tooth composite error, in.
Commercial 1	0.006	0.002
Commercial 2	0.004	0.0015
Commercial 3	0.002	0.001
Commercial 4	0.0015	0.0007
Precision 1	0.001	0.0004
Precision 2	0.0005	0.0003
Precision 3	0.00025	0.0002

centers of the gear and master in the course of one complete revolution of
the gear being tested.   The tooth-to-tooth composite error is the maximum variation of the center distance encountered anywhere on the gear
when rotating from one tooth to the next.

Gear errors not only cause errors in the servomechanism but also cause
stresses that can reduce gear life by as much as 25 per cent.   Satisfactory
tolerance for instrument gearing in servomechanisms depends upon the

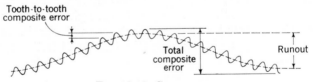

FIG. 12-13. Gear errors.

application.   The eccentricity of the pitch line (runout) for most servomechanisms can be on the order of 1/1,000 in.   For fine computing
mechanisms and very accurate servos, tolerances on the order of half
that are specified.   Lateral runout, i.e., wobble, in itself does not contribute directly to gearing errors.   The presence of lateral runout may
indicate a condition of the blank that would make it difficult to cut an
accurate gear.   The presence of lateral runout also may indicate poor
workmanship, so that in precision gears its value is generally limited to
1/1,000 in./in. of gear diameter.

The accuracy of gears can be checked in a number of different ways.

The pitch diameter of a gear can be checked by inserting wires of the proper diameter between the gear teeth and measuring over the wires across the diameter. This measurement can be taken at several points around the gear. It indicates, however, only the variation in diameter of the pitch line and not the eccentricity between the bore and the pitch line. One way of determining this eccentricity is by a rolling fixture

FIG. 12-14. Instrument used for checking fine-pitch gears. (*Fellows Gear Shaper Company, Springfield, Vt.*)

that rotates a master gear with the gear under test. During this test, the gears are kept in close contact by means of a spring. A dial indicator is used to measure the variation in center distance as the two gears are rotated together. Typical fixtures that accomplish this are manufactured by Michigan Tool Co. of Detroit and Parkson of England. If desired, recorders can be connected to the device to record directly the variation in center distance. Figure 12-14 is a photograph of a Fellows Red Liner, which makes this record directly. The principle of operation is that variations in center distance between master and work are measured and recorded on a constantly moving paper chart as the two rotate in contact. This type of measurement is designated by the AGMA as a "composite" check.   The instrument has a capacity of 4 in. pitch diameter of work and the diameter of the master-gear arbor is ½ in.

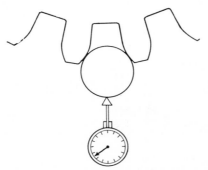

A device using a rack master gear instead of the circular master gear is the Kodak Konju-gage, which has certain advantages with regard to accuracy, wear, and cost of masters. Rolling fixtures all rely upon the accuracy of a master gear, and the reading of the dial indicator of the chart is actually a composite of the error of the master and the gear under test.   The sum of the errors in round master gears normally supplied is

Fig. 12-15. Absolute measurement of gear eccentricity.

about 0.0003 in. TIR (total indicator reading, i.e., the total variation of the pitch line from the gear center).   The difficulty of measuring gears of class 2 precision or better using this type of master can be appreciated.

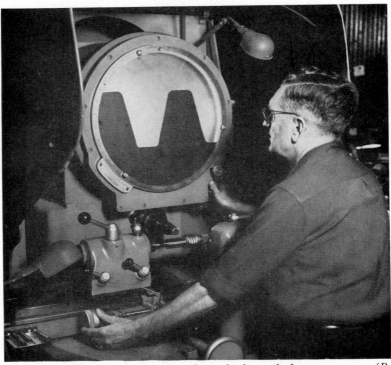

Fig. 12-16. An optical comparator used to check tooth form on gear. (*Barber-Coleman Co., Rockford, Ill.*)

An absolute method of measuring the runout of gears can be utilized. The gear is turned on an arbor and rotated with a dial indicator used to read the variation in height from the arbor of a wire placed between successive teeth, as illustrated in Fig. 12-15. For production testing, it is usually necessary to make this measurement at only four 90° points on

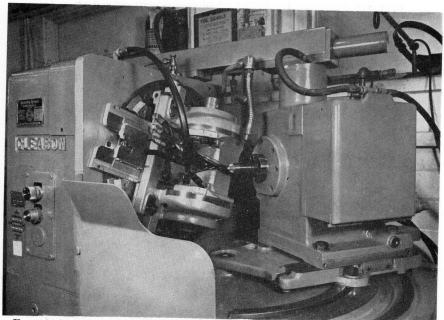

FIG. 12-17. Straight bevel-gear generator. (*Western Gear Corp., Lynwood, Calif.*)

the gear, after first finding a high point. In-between measurements are made only if something unusual appears in the readings.

The accuracy of tooth shape, which is another check on the gear manufacture, can be learned by projection of the tooth form by means of a contour projector. Such inaccuracies of manufacture as tooth-thickness variation and profile error or departure of tooth profile from the form mathematically required can be discovered by projecting the gear teeth onto a screen and comparing the projected shape with a drawing of the correct mathematical form of tooth. An optical comparator, which is one such machine, is shown in Fig. 12-16. It can also be used to disclose base-pitch error, which is the maximum difference between any two successive tooth measurements, i.e., the physical displacement of a tooth from its correct mathematical position.

12-4. Gear Manufacture. Spur gears can be manufactured by milling, hobbing, or shaping. Milling of production gears is virtually obsolete because of the slowness of the process. It consists in milling the teeth individually with a forming cutter, which is in the shape of the groove between adjacent gear teeth. The gear is successively indexed from tooth to tooth. Because of the accuracy that can be held by this method, master gears are often cut on these machines. Figure 12-17 shows a

Fig. 12-18. Gear hobbing. (*Barber-Coleman Co., Rockford, Ill.*)

Gleason Conaflex straight-bevel-gear generator. This machine is capable of cutting gears in all of the usual kinds of gear material and can hold accuracies in the range of tolerances that is required for master gears.

Hobbing of gears consists in generating the teeth by means of rotating the blank in contact with a wormlike cutter. This process is illustrated by the photograph of Fig. 12-18. The third method, shaping, is fastest, although not quite so accurate as hobbing. It consists of passing a cutter shaped like another spur gear rapidly up and down across the face of the blank. During this process both the cutter and the gear are rotating slowly in mesh, thus generating teeth. This is illustrated in Fig. 12-19.

Any of these methods can yield gears whose pitch line has an eccentricity within a thousandth of an inch and often within a few ten-thousandths if conditions are right. To produce these conditions, however, the machines must be in top shape, the cutters must be sharp and properly

FIG. 12-19. Gear shaping. (*Fellows Gear Shaper Co., Springfield, Vt.*)

ground, a proper balance must be made between roughing and finishing cuts, the holding fixtures must be properly made with precision locating faces, care must be given to setup and to mounting of blanks, the blanks must be machined with precision holes and faces held true with the bore, homogeneous material must be used for the blanks, and gear blanks must be designed to have sufficient rigidity.

After the gears are cut, a number of operations can be employed for finishing them. These are burnishing, shot peening, grinding, lapping, and shaving. Burnishing consists in meshing the gear pressed against hardened gears in an effort to cold-work the surface of the gear tooth. This is also accomplished to some extent by "running in" the finished gear train. Shot peening is a means of cold-working the surface of the teeth to add to their strength by bombardment with little balls. Grinding is a means of abrasively removing the distortion caused by heat-treating processes. Lapping is a means of reducing small surface irregularities by rotating the gear to be finished with another gear, using a grinding compound on the teeth.

These finishing methods are rarely used on instrument servo gears. Shaving, however, is frequently used to reduce eccentricity in precision gears and can do so by a factor of about 2 over the original manufactured eccentricity. Shaving consists in meshing a cutter shaped like a helical

FIG. 12-20. Speed-reducer concentric shaft with slip clutch. (*Bowmar Instrument Corp., Fort Wayne, Ind.*)

gear with the gear being shaved. As the two rotate, minute amounts of metal are scraped off the gear, thus improving the tooth form and reducing eccentricity and tooth-space error.

Any burrs on the gear teeth resulting from manufacturing operations should be carefully removed by filing, scraping, or cleaning with a wire brush. In addition, the bore of the gear must be manufactured to close tolerances, so that it will fit concentrically on its shaft.

12-5. Gear Trains. Feedback control systems make wide use of high-quality gear trains for the following reasons:

1. Mechanically matching the motor to the load. Since a servo motor often operates at high speed but low torque, a gear train is required to drive the load with a greater torque but less speed.

2. Adding and subtracting mechanical signals.

3. Reversing direction of rotation.

4. Gain adjustment in the closed loop.

5. Scale changing, for example, a two-speed system.

For many systems which use a potentiometer for transducing the position of the shaft the motor must run at a reasonable velocity while the potentiometer can turn only 1 to 10 turns. A precision miniature speed reducer is shown in Fig. 12-20. The dimensions are 1.062 in. in diameter and 1.312 in. in length. The unit drives a load torque of 8 to 12 oz-in. with a starting torque of 0.010 at the input shaft. The backlash of this unit is 30 min maximum at the output shaft. Various gear ratios are available. The unit has a concentric input and output shaft with a slip clutch.

Figure 12-21 shows a sketch of a gear head which is designed to operate with standard servomotors. The output shaft is concentric to the mounting diameters. The dimensions and tolerances of the servo-type mounting are identical to those specified for the respective-size BuOrd motors. The units are designed so that the gearing is supported in a cantilever-type construction. The design maintains higher accuracies between bearing centers

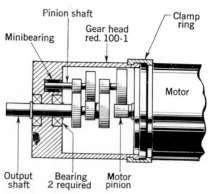

Fig. 12-21. Sketch of a gear head attached to a servomotor. (*Sterling Precision Corp., Flushing, N.Y.*)

as well as concentricity of shaft to gear pitch line. The use of 303 stainless steel for intermediate pinions, aluminum bronze for intermediate gears, and hardened stainless steel for output pinion and gear results in smooth and quiet operation, long wear, and high output torques. Utilizing a ring clamp for attaching the gear head to the motor eliminates space loss in over-all length. The ring clamp also permits the rotation of the motor relative to the gear head, thus making it possible to compensate for eccentricity between the motor pinion and motor mounting pilot diameter for optimum adjustment of the initial gear mesh. The clamp ring is designed to provide a secure lock on mating surfaces and to ensure accurate alignment.

The unit shown in the photograph of Fig. 12-22 is available in any desired ratio up to 1,267:1. All gears are precision cut and are aluminum bronze except the output gear, which is hardened stainless steel. Shafts and pinions are stainless steel. Pinion design precludes undercutting, which results in a smooth-running, low-backlash unit. The output shaft is concentric with the mounting diameter. Attaching this gear head to a servomotor creates a clean, fully enclosed, self-contained unit.

Friction in the gearing of instrument servomechanisms is a serious problem, since most of the static error, aside from the inaccuracy of the error detector, results from gear friction. Such friction may be caused by too tight a gear mesh, variation of tooth form or spacing, or such surface conditions as pits, nicks, and dirt.   The type of material from which the gears are made is an important factor.   Gears made with nylon teeth have much less friction than metal, for example.   If the surface condition is good and the gears are precisely made, friction can be reduced by loosening the mesh.   Backlash (Fig. 12-9), which is the amount by which tooth space exceeds the thickness of an engaging tooth, may be the result of such action.

GEAR HEAD ATTACHED TO SERVO MOTOR

FIG. 12-22. Photograph of a gear head suitable to be attached to standard servomotor. (*Sterling Precision Corp., Flushing, N.Y.*)

A fraction of a degree of backlash introduced in an otherwise stable mechanism can cause the system to be unstable.   For example, Fig. 12-23 shows the experimental transient response to a step-function command of an instrument servomechanism using an a-c resonant filter for an equalizing network.   As the backlash is increased, the system becomes more and more oscillatory until finally a backlash of about 15 minutes at the controlled shaft causes instability.   If, instead of an equalizing network, a rate generator is used, this particular servo will not become unstable no matter how much backlash is introduced, although the system will become more oscillatory.   The use of a rate generator rather than cascaded equalizing networks permits the use of poorer gearing in a servomechanism without deterioration of performance.

Although friction and backlash appear to be quite different problems, they can occur in the same gear mesh if the pitch line of the meshing gears is not concentric with their supporting shafts.   As the gears are rotated, the eccentricities combine to produce excessive friction at one portion of the revolution and backlash at another portion. An eccentricity of 0.001 in. on each of two 1-in. 14.5°-pressure-angle gears can result in a maximum backlash angle of about $\frac{1}{10}°$.

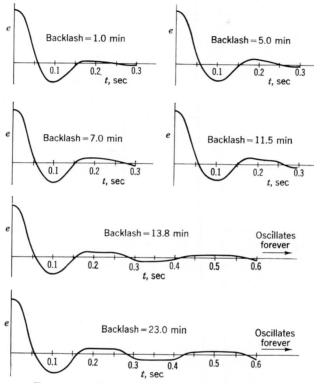

Fig. 12-23. Effect of backlash on servo stability.

Since backlash in gearing may have to be specified to prevent its causing instability, a set of standards has been established. Table 12-2 gives the AGMA tolerances on backlash for the various classes. In class D, for which there is no backlash for any pitch, adjustable meshes must be used. Some companies have set up finer divisions on classes of backlash between the C and D range. Backlash can be measured with a dial indicator by holding one gear fixed and gently rocking the other. Backlash is the total movement attainable between meshing teeth measured at a tangent to the pitch circle.

Split gears are sometimes used to keep backlash to a minimum. A split gear is actually a combination of two gears whose faces are adjacent and whose relative positions are controlled by means of a spring. The two portions of the gear are rotated with respect to one another against the action of the spring and are meshed with the mating gear. The action of the spring tends to spread the two portions of the gear apart. The gear tooth width is therefore variable, depending upon the tooth-to-tooth spacing of the mating gear. Such a gear is used only for the transmission of position and is used at the end of the gear train, with no load driven by the split gear.

Error in gearing is the result of errors in the individual gears and backlash. If the error detector is coupled directly to the controlled shaft, any

TABLE 12-2. GEAR-TRAIN BACKLASH

Backlash class	Diametral-pitch range	Backlash in mating gears, in.	Approx. change in center distance for 20° pressure angle	Approx. change in center distance for 14½° pressure angle
A	20–45	0.004–0.006	0.0055–0.0082	0.0077–0.0116
	46–70	0.003–0.005	0.0042–0.0068	0.0058–0.0097
	71–90	0.002–0.0035	0.0028–0.0046	0.0039–0.0068
B	20–60	0.002–0.004	0.0028–0.0055	0.0039–0.0077
	61–120	0.0015–0.003	0.002–0.0042	0.0029–0.0058
	121 and finer	0.001–0.002	0.0014–0.0028	0.0019–0.0039
C	20–60	0.001–0.002	0.0014–0.0028	0.0019–0.0039
	61–120	0.0007–0.0015	0.001–0.002	0.00135–0.0029
	121 and finer	0.0005–0.001	0.0008–0.0014	0.00097–0.0019
D	No measurable backlash at any pitch			

error in gearing between the servomotor and the controlled shaft is not of great importance. If, however, the controlled shaft is geared to the error-detecting means, errors in gearing will reflect directly into the servo error. For example, in a 1- and 36-speed synchro system, the actuating signal normally comes from the 36-speed synchro, and any inaccuracy in gearing between the 36-speed synchro and the controlled shaft results in servo error between the command and the ultimately controlled shaft even if the synchro error and the actuating signal are zero.

The error caused by backlash can be computed separately from the errors of the gears themselves. If two gears are perfectly meshed and their centers are then separated an additional distance d, the resulting backlash is given by the following equation:

$$\text{Backlash} = 2d \tan \phi \qquad (12\text{-}1)$$

where ϕ is the pressure angle. If d is expressed in thousandths of an inch, the backlash at the pitch circle is also given in thousandths. The angular backlash, in radians, is given by the following formula:

$$\beta = \frac{2d}{r} \sin \phi \tag{12-2}$$

where r is the radius of the gear whose backlash angle β is being determined. In the event that one of two mating gears is eccentric, the two pitch circles of the mating gears are no longer tangent. The maximum backlash can be found from the above formulas if the gears have no backlash when the high point of the eccentric gear is meshing and the total eccentricity is d. For example, if a 1-in. gear has an eccentricity and hence a change of center distance of 0.0005 in., a backlash of 0.0004 in. results, which represents an angular error of about 2.4 minutes.

Even when a pair of mating gears are rotating in the same direction and backlash is therefore not a factor, eccentricity in one of them causes an angular error in the output. If the output gear is perfect and the

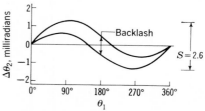

FIG. 12-24. Gearing error caused by eccentricity.

input gear has an eccentricity d_1, then the error $\Delta\theta_2$ in radians for an angular position θ_1 of the input gear is given* by

$$\theta = -\frac{d_1}{r_2} \sin \phi + \frac{d_1}{r_2} \sin (\theta_1 + \phi) \tag{12-3}$$

This equation is valid if there is zero backlash when the high point of gear 1 is meshing with gear 2. The value of $\Delta\theta_2$ is obtained for clockwise rotation by considering ϕ positive and for counterclockwise rotation by considering ϕ negative. Equation (12-3) is plotted in Fig. 12-24 for a gear in which $r_2 = 0.153$ in., $\phi = 20°$, and the eccentricity $d_1 = 0.00015$ in.

The allowable eccentricity for a total error spread $S = 2\,\Delta\theta_{2\,\text{max}}$ is given by

$$d_1 = \frac{r_2}{2(1 + \sin \phi)} S \tag{12-4}$$

The counterparts of Eqs. (12-3) and (12-4) for an eccentric output gear and a concentric input gear, under the condition of zero backlash when the high point of gear 2 is meshing with gear 1, are

$$\theta_2 = -\frac{d_2}{r_2} \sin \phi - \frac{d_2}{r_2} \sin (\theta_2 + \phi) \tag{12-5}$$

$$d_2 = \frac{r_2}{2(1 + \sin \phi)} S \tag{12-6}$$

* R. L. Thoen, Gear Eccentricity, *Machine Design*, vol. 23, no. 9, pp. 155–158, 1951.

The additional backlash caused by nontangent pitch circles can be included by the application of Eq. (12-2).

12-6. Bearings. Precision in the manufacture of bearings is of critical importance in servomechanisms. Because of their inherently low-friction and low-wearing characteristics over long periods of time, most bearings used in servomechanism manufacture are ball bearings. Commonly, either the normal inch series or the flange type is used in servomecha-

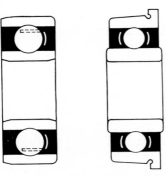

nisms. Both of these are shown in Fig. 12-25. The latter type has become popular because the flange and taper of the outer race permit the bearing to be snapped into place without the necessity of a counterbore operation in the plate in which the bearing is mounted.

Eccentricity in bearings is just as important as in gears since the shafts that support the gears are mounted in the bearings. The Anti-friction Bearing Manufacturers' Association has established classes that define the tolerances to which bearings are manufactured or selected. Table 12-3

FIG. 12-25. Inch series and flange-type ball bearings.

gives the tolerance on the smaller bearings that might be used in instrument-servo manufacture, from ¼-in. bore, ⅝-in. OD to ½-in. bore, 1⅛-in. OD. The class 1 is a standard SAE tolerance, so that, if bearings are ordered without specifying a class, this is the class which is normally supplied. Fine-instrument servomechanisms, however, utilize bearings

TABLE 12-3. BEARING TOLERANCES*

ABEC class	Bore, +0.0000 in. to minus	OD, +0.0000 in. to minus	Eccentricity, TIR	
			Inner race	Outer race
1	0.0003	0.0004	0.0004	0.0006
3	0.0002	0.0003	0.0003	0.0004
5	0.0002	0.0002	0.0002	0.0002
7	0.00015	0.0002	0.0001	0.0002

* Anti-friction Bearing Manufacturers' Association (ABMC).

of class 5 or 7. In addition to radial play, which is partly responsible for the eccentricity, bearings have a type of play that will permit the inner race of the bearing to be rotated slightly with respect to the outer race in a direction at right angles to the bore axis of the bearing. If the mechanical unit is properly designed, however, the bearings are far enough apart so that this type of play is not important. The radial play of a bearing can be reduced by preloading it, i.e., by means of the spring displacing the inner race along the bore axis with respect to the outer race. While this reduces the radial play, it also tends to increase the friction of the bearing.

Friction, which is usually of most importance in bearings, results from errors in the balls or races and also from surface roughness of these parts.

FIG. 12-26. Automatic bearing-torque tester. (*Sunshine Scientific Inst., Philadelphia.*)

It can likewise be produced by dirt or chips in the bearing. Another type of friction trouble is windup, which produces varying friction or torque peaks caused by conventional-type separators that do not prevent the ball from "climbing" on the separators and hence increasing the friction. The use of spring-type separators, which employ small coil springs interposed between the balls so that the balls and springs are independent of each other, materially reduces this problem at the expense of somewhat constant friction. (Variation of friction torque is usually more important than the level of the torque itself, if it is fairly low.) Windup, however, is only a problem when bearings are rotated in one direction for long periods of time.

Figure 12-26 is a photograph of an automatic tester used to record the torque of ball bearings, and Fig. 12-27 shows typical records of bearing tests. For such tests, the bearings are tested under a thrust of between 330 and 400 g even though the bearings normally operate under a radial load. This is a precaution lest the servo parts be required to operate momentarily under thrust conditions.

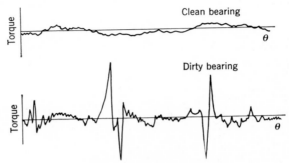

FIG. 12-27. Recording of bearing torque.

If a servomechanism is to be made under the conditions of interchangeable manufacture, the tolerances on size and location of the holes in which bearings and electromechanical components are mounted are most important. Consider first the size of these holes. A typical small 400-cycle synchro, which might have to be mounted in a gear train, has the following tolerances:

Mounting-flange diameter	+0.0000 in.
	−0.0005 in.
Shaft diameter	+0.0000 in.
	−0.0002 in.
Eccentricity of shaft to mounting flange	0.0008 TIR

If the mounting hole is made to the upper limit of the synchro mounting diameter and the synchro gear bore is made to the upper limit of the synchro shaft diameter, the possible variation of the gear position is 0.0007 in. To this must be added the eccentricity of the shaft to the pilot, yielding a total possible variation of the gear position of 0.0011 in. In addition, tolerances on the mounting hole of the synchro and the bore of the gear result in an appreciable variation of the gear position, thus permitting the possibility of binding or backlash. A typical potentiometer has the following tolerances:

Mounting diameter	+0.0000 in.
	−0.0005 in.
Shaft diameter	+0.0000 in.
	−0.0005 in.
Eccentricity of shaft to mounting flange	0.0025 TIR

A problem similar to that described for synchros is seen to exist.

Holes for mounting components can be bored in a lathe, milling machine, or jig borer or can be drilled by using drill presses and radial drills with suitable drill fixtures.   Holes in plates, casting, or gears for instrument servomechanisms can be bored to a diametral accuracy of a few tenths over the entire length of the hole.   They can also be drilled and reamed or honed to this accuracy.   Of course, it is important that the

FIG. 12-28. Skilled operator using Swiss jig borer.   (*The Ahrendt Instrument Co., College Park, Md.*)

axis of the hole be perpendicular to the mounting surface for the bearing or other component.

The location of the holes relative to one another determines the center distances of the gears in the gear train and hence affects backlash and friction of the gearing.   In the production of servomechanisms, these holes can be located accurately by means of drill jigs and other fixtures or production boring machines.   Individual plates or castings can be bored on a lathe or a milling machine by the use of machinists' buttons or by taking trial cuts and repetitively measuring the distance between the hole centers.

Another device for locating holes accurately is the jig borer.   The normal accuracy of a jig borer is such as to permit the location of any two widely spaced holes to within 0.0002 in. of their correct location and, for holes separated by an inch or two, within 0.0001 in. Figure 12-28 shows a Swiss jig borer in operation.

For such dimensions to have any meaning, the castings or plates must be free of warpage, but often the very process of boring the hole causes the plates to warp. If this is the case, a hole of almost the proper diameter should be rough-bored first, then the plate or casting surfaces finished, and then the final hole bored. For example, aluminum plate as it comes from the rolling mill must first be straightened by means of a press, holes of almost the proper size bored, then either ground or milled on both sides, and the final hole bored.

12-7. Mechanical Assembly. The assembly of servomechanisms is also of crucial importance. No matter how accurately the parts are made, if they are not properly assembled, the performance of the servomechanism may be impaired. Use of adjustable gear centers avoids some of the problems of accurate hole location at the expense of a greater number of manufactured parts and a more costly assembly process. This method also permits a very fine adjustment of gearing backlash and friction. It consists in mounting some of the bearings and electromechanical components in movable plates so that the positions of the shafts can be shifted relative to the fixed structure. After they are shifted and the gear meshes properly made, the plates can be doweled into place. Strategic choices of movable shafts might result in a gear train in which every mesh is adjustable but only a few of the shafts are movable. The unit can be so designed that the positioning of one shaft will adjust the meshes of two sets of mating gears. Devices such as potentiometers and synchros that might be replaced or rotated for zeroing should fit snugly into their own mounting holes even if these holes are in movable mountings. In other words, the meshes should not be adjusted by means of the relative motion of the synchro in its mounting hole since the replacement of the synchro might change the amount of backlash.

Sometimes parts that can be shifted relative to one another, such as adjustable gear meshes, are doweled together—i.e., a dowel or pin is driven into matched holes in two parts of the assembly to hold them in position after they have been adjusted. This makes it possible to disassemble the units and reassemble them in exactly their original position without further adjustment. The dowels should be fastened only into the parts that have been correctly aligned. Doweling holes are drilled at right angles to the surface of the parts, with a drive fit in the larger of the parts to be doweled and a push fit in the smaller part.

If gears are on fixed center, they cannot be moved; but the gears themselves can be removed and shaved if they are too tight. Sometimes gears are "run in" after assembly to reduce the tightness. When they are run in, they can be rotated by means of the servomotor or an auxiliary motor, and for the most careful work only a light oil is used on the teeth. Another "compound," which is somewhat more degrading to tooth form, is the use of a mixture consisting of Bon Ami and water. Even when such a compound is used on aluminum gears, it will not load them, and they can be washed after they have been satisfactorily run in.

The frictional torque at the motor shaft of an instrument servomechanism is on the order of a few tenths or even hundredths of an ounce-inch for a properly constructed gear train. The backlash, if completely taken up at the motor shaft, is on the order of a few degrees and can sometimes be kept to within a fraction of a degree. Of course, backlash at the synchro shaft or the controlled shaft is of most importance to stability and accuracy.

The end play of gears can be controlled by means of collars pressed against the bearings. Spur gears should be positioned for proper alignment of the gear faces, and if they are the same thickness, their faces should be flush within 1/10,000 in. after they have been adjusted for correct end play. If they are not the same thickness, the thinner one should be approximately centered on the other, although often the pinion is made thicker just to minimize the alignment problem. The shafts should have less than 0.003 in. end play. Gears should fit the shaft with a sliding-push fit. If they can be made to spin on the shaft, they are too loose and should not be used. If a gear is too tight, the hole can be enlarged with a machine reamer or expansion reamer the same size as the shaft, only minute amounts of metal being scraped out at each operation before retrying. The gears themselves can be used dry to minimize the collection of dirt in the teeth or can be lubricated with a thin film of instrument grease, such as Aero-Shell Grease 11, Ordnance Specification 14-G-S, or molybdenum disulfide and oil. A thin coat should be applied to the gear teeth and excess wiped off with a clean, lint-free cloth.

The shafting used in instrument-servomechanism manufacture is generally of precision-ground stock. It should run within 0.002 to 0.0005 in. TIR at all points. If a shaft is too big for correct fit on a bearing, it must be polished down with a fine emery or crocus cloth. A motor-driven chuck or lathe can be used for this and the shaft polished evenly for the full length of the bearing fit. It can be polished undersize at other positions to make it easier for the bearings to be assembled. During this operation, frequent checks should be made with micrometer calipers to ensure evenness and proper fit on the bearing. Before trying a bearing on a shaft, the shaft end should be checked for burrs and removed with a smooth file. The shaft should be wiped with an oiled rag to prevent sticking in the bearings. A properly fitted shaft will allow the bear-

ings to be pushed over its entire length by hand but will not slip from the
position to which it is fitted when the shaft is held in a vertical position.

The bearings should have a light-finger-press fit on the shafts and a
light-force fit to place them in holes. The flange type is snapped lightly
into holes. Bearings should never be forced into a seat or onto a shaft,
because this results in distortion, injury to the bearing and consequent
increase in friction load. When being pressed on or off a shaft, the bearings should be pressed on the inner race; when being pressed into or out
of a hole or seat, the bearings should be pressed on the outer race. They
should not be assembled into units until absolutely necessary and should
be protected with paper and masking tape after assembly. They should
be protected with dust covers when not being worked on.

Ball bearings are washed by direct immersion in a solvent. They may
be strung on wire and lightly agitated in the solvent to speed the cleaning
process. Varsol, carbon tetrachloride, or an equivalent solvent may be
used. If carbon tetrachloride is used, care must be taken to remove, dry,
and oil the bearings a few minutes after immersion. In no case should
the bearings be left in the solvent any longer than necessary to loosen and
remove the protective grease. Bearings can be dried by blowing with
compressed air at moderate pressure. During this operation, the bearings should not be spun in the air, as this might cause damage to the balls
and races. After drying, the bearings are immediately oiled with a few
drops of instrument oil, such as Lehigh Chemical Co. Ordnance Specification 14-0-20. Bearings are then slowly turned and inspected.

Plates and castings, when used to mount bearings, shafts, and components, should be accurately aligned so that they are parallel to one
another. After all the components are in place, the gears and collars are
fastened firmly to the shafts by pinning. The parts of the gear train or
shaft assembly are correctly positioned in the instrument, and setscrews
are used to hold the gears, collars, and other components in place. The
hubs of the gears and the collars are drilled perpendicular to the adjoining
surfaces when the mating parts are in the exact relative position. (Usually the hub is provided with a pilot hole spotted about halfway through
one side to guide the drill.) While the holes are being drilled, care should
be taken that chips do not get in the bearings or meshes. After the holes
have been drilled, the pins can be seated and then staked. A taper pin is
set with the large end about 1/5,000 to 1/10,000 in. below the surface of
the hub to provide room for staking. The small end is set flush or a little
below the surface of the hub. Every taper pin is driven in tightly and
staked at the large end only. Instead of taper pins, roll pins can also be
used.

Sometimes split hubs are used on gears, in which case the clamp is
fitted snugly on the hub and the hub turns freely on the shaft. After the

screw is tightened, the clamp holds the hub firmly on the shaft without closing completely.

12-8. Electrical Components and Assembly. The selection of electrical components and the assembly of electronic chassis have been more extensively treated in the literature than have the manufacture and assembly of mechanical portions of servomechanisms. As a consequence, this subject is treated in less detail in this book.

The first step in the assembly of an electronic chassis is to have the proper circuit design. It is assumed that the circuits themselves have been properly designed for reliable operation of the servo within the performance specifications. The use of electrical breadboards made up of a universal chassis and tube or transistor sockets with screw-terminal connections facilitates experimental work in the early stages of component selection.

The actual layout of the chassis should be accomplished to avoid the use of long leads in order that pickup and distributed capacitance and inductance will be minimized. Shielded leads can also be used in order to minimize pickup. Test points should be made accessible for servicing. The unit should be so manufactured that proper protection against moisture and dust is obtained. Wire markers and color coding facilitate servicing of the instrument. The components should be laid out to avoid the necessity of removing wires or parts to obtain access to terminals and mounting screws. Fuses should be designed into all primary power circuits, and all points, components, terminals, and wires should be adequately labeled. For safety of operating and maintenance personnel, adequate protection in the form of covers and electrical interlocks should be provided to avoid the possibility of any contact with potentials in excess of 50 volts. Capacitors should have bleed resistors to permit discharge of dangerous voltages. All external metal parts should be at ground potential and adequate caution signs used to remind the operator or maintenance man of potential danger.

Electrical and electronic components should be chosen for quality, ease of mounting, and reliability. In general, nonflammable materials are preferred. Thermoplastics or materials that are water-absorptive or capable of supporting fungus should be avoided and such materials as glass-filled melamine used in preference. Metallic materials and their treatment should be carefully chosen to avoid oxidation or corrosion. For minimizing the effect of atmospheric conditions, hermetically sealed components, such as transformers and chokes, should be used. The components should be chosen with due care that voltage and current and power ratings are not exceeded and that temperature variations do not cause drift or faulty operation of the servo. Where suitable substitutes are available, the use of proprietary items should be avoided.

In the actual assembly of the wired electrical components, lock washers, self-locking nuts, or staked nuts should be used to avoid loosening by vibration. The component should be so mounted as to avoid strains that might impair the operation of the circuit. All rivets should be properly seated and headed over, and nuts should be carefully tightened. Soft solder should not be relied upon for mechanical connections. Wire from which the insulation has been stripped should have the ends of the insulation painted with varnish or covered with a plastic sleeve to avoid the possibility of unraveling. Terminal connectors should be chosen to clamp to both the insulation and the wire. Strong terminals capable of soldering and resoldering should be used. Good mechanical connections should be made before soldering, particularly when there is a possibility of the heat of a soldering iron on one side of a terminal loosening a wire soldered on the other side (especially bad when the other side is inside a hermetically sealed can or in some other inaccessible place). Acid-core solder should not be used, and the connection should be made carefully to avoid use of excess solder and to avoid a cold-solder joint. Due care should be taken to make good ground contact with the chassis, particularly when dealing with painted or anodized surfaces.

The wiring should be done in a neat fashion and laced in a professional manner. Care must be exercised in deciding which leads should be laced together, i.e., avoid lacing power leads and signal leads together. Grommets should be used in going through holes in metal partitions. In the manufacture of the unit, too much flexing of the wires may cause some of the strands to break, especially at the point where solderless lugs are attached. Lacing should be knotted in such a manner that it cannot come loose. Cables should be held rigidly so that there is no possibility of moving parts such as gears rubbing against the wires. Similarly, the wires should be tied down to avoid wearing due to vibration, but enough slack must be left in the leads for ease in servicing.

Modern techniques of electronic manufacture include the liberal use of subassemblies, such as boards upon which resistors and capacitors can be assembled. Such construction provides ease of manufacture and of inspection and permits the simultaneous manufacture of various parts independently. In mass production of such boards or electronic chassis, a single wire is put across two points in every chassis rather than wiring each one completely; thus the wiring personnel have to concentrate on putting a component or wire between two points in a large number of units rather than constantly referring to circuit schematics and different portions of the electronic chassis. Printed circuits are also extensively used so that many connections are made rapidly without the use of individual wiring. The use of wafers and module construction, which can be used both for breadboards and for high production, is a further development along these lines. In both this case and that of printed circuits, soldering by dipping rather than the usual hand operation can be accomplished.

Encapsulation of the completed electronic circuit provides mechanical rigidity, which is necessary for servos that operate in a high-g-vibration atmosphere. An epoxy resin is commonly used in applications where weight is of less importance. Besides the added weight, units that are encapsulated cannot be repaired in case of failure of component. Use of transistors permits a totally enclosed package.

A saving of weight can be achieved by dipping the electronic circuit in the epoxy resin rather than complete encapsulation. This provides the necessary mechanical rigidity and in certain cases permits the removal of a component part. Great strides have been made in the use of foaming plastics for encapsulating electronic components. These plastics are light in weight, permit the removal of a component part, and yet provide the required mechanical support.

PROBLEMS

12-1. Explain the operation of a ball-disk integrator.

12-2. Derive the angular error resulting from angular misalignment of shafts using the Oldham-type coupling. Derive the error caused by the shafts being parallel but not directly in line.

12-3. Sketch an electrical-type limit stop.

12-4. Show how the master-gear errors (assuming simple eccentricity) can be measured and subtracted from a Fellows Red Linear chart by repeating tests on the gear being inspected.

12-5. Why is it usually necessary to take measurements at only four 90° points on a gear to measure its eccentricity?

12-6. Why is it poor practice to drive a load using a split gear?

12-7. Derive Eq. (12-2).

12-8. Why is it unwise to use proprietary items when suitable substitutes are available?

CHAPTER 13

SERVOMECHANISM ADJUSTMENT AND
TROUBLE SHOOTING

13-1. Introduction. It is necessary to adjust a servomechanism for proper operation both in breadboard form and after production manufacture. The position transducers, such as potentiometers and synchros, must be aligned to a given reference. This is called *zeroing*. The phase of the voltages in the system must be adjusted for proper operation. Other adjustments include such factors as scale and gain setting.

It is sometimes necessary to "trouble-shoot" and service a servo that has been in service for a while. It is the purpose of this chapter to set forth logical procedures and guiding principles for adjustment and servicing.

13-2. Motor and Synchro Connections. Correct connection of the motors and synchros is one of the most important steps in adjusting a servomechanism. If either pair of terminals on the control motor are reversed, the motor rotates in the opposite direction with respect to the error signal. Frequently a 180° phase reversal occurs during the assembly of the servomechanism. Reversal of either pair of motor leads corrects the error in connection.

It is important in connecting the synchros together that the synchros coupled to the command shaft and those coupled to the controlled shaft be properly connected electrically to one another. That is, the S_1 lead of the transmitter should be connected to the S_1 lead of the control transformer and so on. Interchange of the S_1 and the S_3 leads causes the controlled shaft to rotate in the opposite direction from the command shaft. That is, when the command shaft is rotating clockwise, the servo causes the controlled shaft to rotate counterclockwise. Similarly, interchange of the stator leads of the synchro transmitter and the control transformer can cause the controlled shaft to be in error from its proper zero by multiples of 120°. An error in connection of the terminals can also cause the synchro to rotate in the wrong direction. If either the excitation leads or the actuating-signal leads from the synchros are reversed, the servo will be unstable and will drive away from null. If no limit stops are encountered, the servo will drive toward a null that is located 180°

456

away from a stable null.   Open leads, caused either by a disconnection outside the synchro or by faulty operation of the brushes and slip rings inside the synchro, also result in faulty operation of the servo.

13-3. Aligning to an Established Reference.   To establish a reference for the purpose of identifying the positions of the command shaft and the controlled shaft, a certain position of the command shaft is arbitrarily defined as zero position.   In the case of a servo transmitting a ship's course with respect to north, for example, zero position of the course transmitter is normally considered to be due north.   For a servo transmitting the position of a target with respect to the observer's ship, the azimuth position of the target is considered to be zero if it is ahead. Similarly, zero elevation is considered to be horizontal.   The zero position of a machine-tool servomechanism might be either the farthest travel of the table or the mid-point of its travel.   Sea level is usually taken as the zero reference for an altitude indicator.

After the zero position of the command shaft, and, hence, the zero position of the controlled shaft, is defined, other positions can be indicated. If the command enters the system in the form of a shaft position, properly set dials can be used to indicate intermediate positions.   The procedure of setting a dial on a linear system is simple: The shaft is held in its zero position and the dial fastened to the shaft so that it reads zero at this position.   If the dial is securely fastened, all other positions of the shaft are defined on the dial.

Most servomechanisms must have the proper relative positions between the servo shafts and the shafts of the error detector.   This is most important when potentiometers are used as error detectors because of their limited angular travel.   Proper adjustment should be made so that the desired angular travel of the servo is within the range of travel of the potentiometers.   For example, if potentiometers are used in servos that, in conjunction with a gyroscope, indicate the roll of a ship, and if the potentiometers are limited to 180° rotation, it is desirable that the brush of the potentiometer be midway between the two limit stops when the ship is at the center of its roll.   This position of the brush travel is defined as its zero position.   The potentiometers are properly zeroed when the zero position of the command shaft and the zero positions of the potentiometer shafts coincide.

The zero adjustment is normally made as follows: The command shaft is placed in its zero position and the shaft of the first potentiometer is coupled to it.   (Sometimes the command shaft is the shaft of the potentiometer itself.)   The case of the potentiometer is then loosened in its mounting until the brush is at the mid-point of its travel.   The potentiometer case is next clamped in this position.   One of the two potentiometers constituting the error detector is thus zeroed.

The controlled shaft is put in its zero position. For example, when a director is used to position a gun, the gun must be bore-sighted with the director to be certain both are pointing in the same direction. The shaft of the other potentiometer is coupled to the controlled shaft and voltage is applied across the potentiometer windings. The case of the potentiometer is then rotated until the actuating signal is zero. This defines a position of zero error in the error detector. When the case is clamped in this position, the entire servo is thus zeroed. Both the cases and the dials should be fastened securely to avoid loss of synchronism due to slippage.

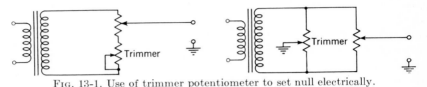

Fig. 13-1. Use of trimmer potentiometer to set null electrically.

The location of a potentiometer null can be varied over a small range by the addition of a trimmer potentiometer. Figure 13-1 indicates two methods of achieving this vernier adjustment. Fine adjustment of the null is achieved with the trimmer potentiometers only after an approximate null has been obtained.

13-4. Zeroing Synchros. It is somewhat more difficult to zero a servomechanism that employs synchros. The zeroing of synchros having only a single-speed transmission system is discussed first.

Synchros have a built-in reference, which is an electrical zero. This offers the advantage that two units can be zeroed at a remote location from one another and still be accurately aligned. As in the case of potentiometers, the problem of establishing a zero position for the command shaft exists. When this position is established, a synchro transmitter coupled to the command shaft can be set to electrical zero by rotating the body of the synchro with respect to its mounting. The controlled shaft can be set to the same zero and the control transformer zeroed at this position. With this accomplished, the servo can be electrically connected, a pair of synchros being used as error detectors, so that the servo will position the controlled shaft with respect to the command shaft. When the command shaft is at the zero position, the controlled shaft will also be at zero under the condition of no error in the servomechanism.

The zeroing of a synchro transmitter, a synchro differential transmitter (if one happens to be in the transmission system), and a synchro control transformer is considered in the next sections.

13-5. Zeroing a Transmitter. With the proper voltage connected to $R_1 R_2$ of a synchro transmitter, the voltage across $S_1 S_3$ is zero when the synchro is at electrical zero.   These terminals are indicated on the sketch of Fig. 13-2.   The voltage across S_1S_3 is also zero, however, when the synchro is 180° away from electrical zero.   When the command shaft is put at zero position and the synchro transmitter shaft is coupled to the command shaft, the synchro is zeroed by rotating the stator of the transmitter until the voltage from S_1 to S_3 is zero.   In this position the null is established; however, it is not known whether a stable or unstable null exists.   These two nulls are 180° apart.

There are several methods of discovering whether the electrical corresponds to a stable or unstable null.   If it is the latter, the stator of the transmitter must be rotated 180° until the voltage from S_1 to S_3 is again zero.   In Fig. 13-2 the rotor is shown in the zero position. If the polarity of the voltage from S_2 to S_3 (or S_2 to S_1) is the same as the polarity of the voltage from R_1 to R_2, then the transmitter is properly zeroed.   Another method can be described as follows: If, upon looking down the rotor shaft from the front of the transmitter, the rotor shaft is rotated clockwise a small angle, the polarity of the voltage now developed from S_1 to S_3 will be the same as the voltage from R_1 to R_2 if the synchro is in the vicinity of the stable electrical zero.   The polarity can be checked

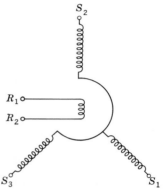

Fig. 13-2. Synchro transmitter at electrical zero.

by means of an oscilloscope or by means of a voltmeter.   Use of a voltmeter requires the connecting of various voltages in series, the principle being used that two voltages connected in series add when they are of the same polarity and subtract when they are of opposite polarity.

There is another method of zeroing a transmitter, which does not involve the measurement of polarities.   (In all the discussion that follows, the voltage values given are for synchros having a 1 volt/deg sensitivity and a maximum secondary voltage of 90 volts.   For other types of synchro, the voltage magnitudes should be appropriately scaled.) Connect the leads R_1 and S_2 together.   When the voltage S_1S_3 is approximately zero, connect a voltmeter from S_1 to R_2.   If the meter reads about 37 volts for a synchro having 1 volt/deg sensitivity, then the synchro generator is near the stable null.   If, however, the meter reads about 193 volts, the generator is 180° out and should be rotated until this voltage is about 37 volts, with the voltage S_1S_3 zero.   If desired, the voltage S_1S_3 can again be checked to be sure that it is a minimum.   During all the foregoing procedure, the synchro shaft is rigidly connected to the command shaft, which is at its zero position.

13-6. Zeroing a Differential Transmitter. A differential transmitter
is zeroed in much the same manner as a transmitter. Figure 13-3 is
drawn to aid in understanding the polarities. In this case, 90 volts
excitation is applied to S_1S_2, although 115 volts can be applied for a short
period without undue heating of the instrument. R_2 is connected to S_2
and a voltmeter connected across the S_1R_1 leads. The maximum voltage
that can exist is twice the excitation voltage; so caution must be exercised
in the choice of meter scales. The synchro stator is rotated until that
voltage is a minimum. The synchro is now only approximately zeroed,

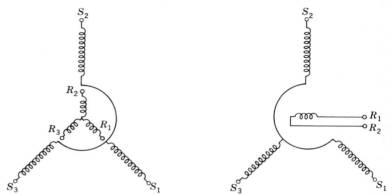

FIG. 13-3. Synchro differential trans-   FIG. 13-4. Synchro control transformer
mitter at electrical zero.   at electrical zero.

because only part of the windings are energized during this procedure and
any dissymmetry in the windings can result in some inaccuracy. To correct this condition, the differential transmitter is reconnected and 78 volts
are applied between S_2 and S_1S_3 tied together. The synchro stator is
rotated whatever small amount is necessary to make the voltage from R_1
to R_3 a minimum.

13-7. Zeroing a Control Transformer. A synchro control transformer
is zeroed by applying 78 volts between S_2 and S_1S_3 tied together. Figure
13-4 shows the control transformer in its zero position. The synchro is
zeroed when the voltage from R_1 to R_2 is approximately zero; but again
this occurs at both zero and 180° out. Rotating the shaft clockwise
through a small angle aids in discovering in which of the two positions the
rotor is. The resulting voltage from R_1 to R_2 should be of the same
polarity as the voltage from S_1S_3 to S_2.

Another method consists of applying a voltage from S_1 to S_3. The
polarity of the voltage from R_1 to R_2 should be the same as the voltage
from S_1 to S_3 for the electrical-zero position.

A control transformer can also be zeroed without measuring phase.
Connect R_2 and S_3 together, put a voltmeter between R_1 and S_1, and

apply 90 volts between S_1 and S_3. The stator of the control transformer can be unclamped and rotated until the voltage from S_1 to R_1 is a minimum (about half the excitation voltage). Then, with 78 volts applied between S_2 and S_1S_3 tied together, the voltage from R_1 to R_2 should be approximately zero. The synchro stator should be rotated whatever slight amount is necessary to effect this minimum. The synchro is then at its stable electrical zero.

13-8. Zeroing a Double-speed System. When double-speed synchro transmission systems are used, the problem of zeroing is somewhat more complicated. Both the fine and the coarse synchro transmitters are zeroed independently with respect to the command shaft and set at electrical zero. The synchro control transformers are also independently zeroed, but if there is a stick-off* voltage to be used in the zero, it must be energized and added to the coarse rotor voltage before zeroing the synchro. The synchro is then zeroed with respect to the output of the synchro plus the stick-off voltage.

An alternate method of zeroing a double-speed system employing stick-off voltage consists of zeroing the fine control transmitter exactly and the coarse control transmitter approximately, with the stick-off voltage source disconnected. Then the stick-off voltage source is reconnected and the servo, which is operating on the fine synchro output, is allowed to drive the servo to null. At this point, the stator of the coarse control transmitter is rotated until its output voltage is zero.

It is important that synchros be properly zeroed, since otherwise certain kinds of synchronizing circuits cause inaccuracy in the servo. Oscillations and instability may also result.

13-9. Aligning Gyros and Accelerometers. When inertial elements provide the input to a servomechanism, the problem of setting the nulls becomes more complex. There are two steps in the setting of the null. One consists of bringing the electrical null of the pickoff into correspondence with the null of the mechanical system. This part of the problem is solved in much the same way as that for zeroing synchros and potentiometers. When the mechanical system of the instrument is at null, the output from the electrical pickoff must also be zero. The mechanical null of an accelerometer is found by applying zero (0) acceleration along the sensitive axis and permitting the system to come to rest. The accelerometer can be placed upon a level table to remove acceleration from the sensitive axis.

A gyro mechanical null occurs when the axes are mutually perpendicular. In a rate gyro† the wheel is restrained with a spring system. The

---

* Stick-off voltage is described in Chap. 3.

† Chapter 10 is devoted to a discussion of gyroscopes, and Chap. 9 presents a discussion of accelerometers.

mechanical null of the free and restrained gyros is determined by the mechanical design; i.e., the pickoff is mounted at 90° with respect to the other axes.

With the instrument resting in its mechanical-null position, the voltage output from the electrical pickoff is reduced to zero. In the case of a resistance pickoff, this is achieved by varying a trimmer resistor (cf. Fig. 13-1). When an electromagnetic pickoff is utilized, a small a-c bias voltage is added.

An accelerometer and a gyro must also be oriented properly in space. The instrument mounting must be designed so that it can be pointed in the correct direction. Usually locating pins are sufficient to provide this mechanical null. The sensitive axis is located with respect to the guide pins by careful design and fabrication of the instrument at the factory.

In some applications, adjustment is designed into the mounting that accepts the instrument. In this manner the instrument is aligned in its mounting. Both optical and electrical means are utilized to align the instrument. When the electrical pickoff from the instrument is used as an error indicator, the nulling of the instrument by an external mechanical adjustment tends to compensate for other errors and usually produces the best results. For example, when a properly nulled accelerometer is slowly rotated about its sensitive axis, no signal output will exist provided the alignment is correct.

13-10. Voltage Phase Adjustment. One of the most important adjustments that must be made on a completed servomechanism is that of phase shift. If the system is to operate satisfactorily, error detectors, motors, detectors, etc., must be supplied with voltages of the proper phase.

If potentiometers are used for error detectors, the phases of the voltages applied to the two potentiometers must be the same, so that the actuating-signal voltage contains no quadrature component. If double-speed synchros are used, the stick-off voltage must be in phase with the output of the coarse synchro, again so that no quadrature voltage is introduced. A simple device for measuring the phase of a test voltage with respect to a standard is described in Chap. 14.

The output of any a-c rate generator should be checked with the voltage output of the synchros to be certain that it is in phase with the synchro voltages. If it is not, phase adjustments should be made on the excitation voltage that is applied to the rate generator. Since the phase angle of the voltage output of the rate generator varies with the speed of its shaft, adjustment should be made at the speed that minimizes the change in phase angle over the most important operating range of the servo.

If a phase-sensitive detector is used in the servomechanism, care must be taken that the phase of the supply voltage is precisely the same as the phase of the signal voltage.   Adjustments can be made on the phase angle of the supply voltage in order to bring the two voltages into the proper phase relationship.   If a modulator is used in the servomechanism, the output signal of the modulator must also have the proper phase, particularly if it is to be added to another signal.

A two-phase motor is frequently excited from the output of an amplifier.   The other winding of the motor is constantly excited with a supply. These two voltages must be at right angles.   The phase of the voltage can be adjusted on the supply winding by means of a capacitor in series with the fixed-voltage winding.   It is normal to hold the motor stalled away from its correspondence position and adjust the capacitor until the voltage across the control winding and the fixed-voltage winding are 90° out of phase.

The phases of all the signals should be checked as they pass through the amplifier and through various components and elements of the system to be certain that they bear the proper phase relationship with one another.

The polarity of the motor field voltage and the amplifier voltage must be such that the servo does not run away.   Similarly, the voltage output from the rate generator must be in the proper polarity to increase its stability rather than decrease it.   Any feedback voltages that are used within the system must be of such a direction as to improve the performance of the servo rather than to detract from it.   These polarities should therefore be checked.

13-11. Scale Factor, Gain, and Other Adjustments.   There are various other adjustments that must be made, such as magnitude adjustments on the synchronizing network, the amplitude of the feedback signals, and the magnitude of the gain of the servomechanism.   The synchronizing network must operate at the proper error between the controlled shaft and the command shaft.   The relative gains of the feedback networks and the forward amplifier must be so adjusted as to be optimum.   If the servo is being manufactured in quantity, the proper adjusting procedure or proper values of these settings should be set forth in the instruction. If, however, it is an experimental unit, the proper settings must be obtained experimentally by gradually adjusting each in turn.

Voltage-magnitude and waveshape measurements are invaluable aids to making field checks and adjustments to be certain that the system is in proper operating condition.   Since the phases of the various voltages affect the servo gain, it is desirable to check the phase shift first and then make the gain adjustments on the servo.   Some simple dynamic measure of performance can also be used to check the gain setting, such as the transient response to a step reference input or, with small servos, the number of overshoots in response to a step function in position. Methods of testing the servomechanisms are considered in Chap. 14.

13-12. Trouble Shooting. Trouble shooting a servomechanism requires a combination of a clear understanding of the principles of servomechanisms, a thorough knowledge of the operating characteristics of the components, a familiarity with the system being studied, and an ability to reason. Some of the aids to familiarity with the servo include a clear schematic diagram and actual circuit diagrams, including mechanical schematics. Circuit diagrams are most useful in checking voltages for proper magnitude and phase.

The engineer or technician, when trouble shooting, operates like a detective putting together clues. Each symptom suggests possible faults in the servo and therefore suggests tests to narrow the possibilities. If the servo is completely out of adjustment, the process of reasoning is temporarily abandoned while a thorough check is made on the entire system. The steps that should be taken before beginning the trouble shooting can be summarized as follows:

1. Test the operation of each component in the system. Be certain that each building block of the system is operating according to the specifications originally established.

2. Check the nulls throughout the system and re-zero any that exhibit an excessive null.

3. Check and adjust the phase shift at all points in the system.

4. Check and set the voltage gains of all active parts of the system.

If the system is still malfunctioning after completion of the above procedure, further trouble shooting is required. The major manifestations of faulty performance usually can be grouped under the headings of no operation at all, sluggishness, instability, and inaccuracy. Of course, these faults occur in combination as well; and, what is worse, they may be intermittent. A few of the possible causes of each of these types of problem are suggested in Table 13-1, but the great variety of servos precludes a discussion of each possible cause.

Failure of the servo to operate at all may be caused by such obvious faults as power off, fuse blown, wiring open, short circuit, loose or jammed gearing, or by a failure in such components as tubes, resistors, capacitors, transformers, and motor. Checks with meters or an oscilloscope should result in localizing the difficulty.

Sluggish operation of the servo may be caused by incorrect gain settings, improper phasing, low amplifier gain caused by faulty wiring or components, excessive mechanical friction in the gearing or components, amplifier saturation by noise, or malfunctioning of other components in the system. Again, reason out the possible causes and make simple checks to reveal the source of the trouble.

Instability can be caused by improper gain settings, improper gain or phase, or operation of such stabilizing means as rate generators, networks, or feedback circuits, faulty performance of mechanical stabilizers, excessive ripple or pickup, improper zeroing of synchros, or excessive mechanical backlash. As in the case of all trouble shooting, it is easier to discover the cause of the difficulty when the engineer is familiar with the

TABLE 13-1. GUIDE TO SERVOMECHANISM TROUBLE SHOOTING

Malfunction	Power off	Blown fuse	Open wire	Component failure	Incorrect gain setting	Improper phasing	Excessive friction	Sticking gear train	Loose gear train	Improper reference voltage	Faulty equalizer network	Improper rate-generator setting
Failure to operate	X	X	X	X								
Sluggish operation					X	X	X	X		X	X	X
Instability					X				X	X	X	X
Excessive error					X	X	X	X	X	X		

operation of the servo and each of the components when the system is functioning properly. Any aid, such as a chart of proper voltage magnitudes in various portions of the circuit or a circuit diagram, will reduce the effort necessary to find the difficulty, especially for the person who is encountering the system for the first time.

Excessive error in the servo may be caused by sluggish operation of the servo itself or inaccuracies in some of its parts. If the actuating signal is small but the error is large, the difficulty is in the latter category. It can be caused by excessive error in the error detector itself, by dial, gear, or coupling slippage on a shaft, by wrong gear ratio between the controlled shaft and the ultimately controlled shaft (as between the fine and coarse shafts of a double-speed system or between the controlled shaft and a dial or counter indication), or by inaccuracy in linkages, couplings, or gearing. The difficulty can often be localized by plotting the error as a function of the rotation angle of the controlled shaft. By this means, the space frequency of the error can be determined and the error localized to a certain gear mesh or to a component that rotates at a certain speed relative to the controlled shaft. If the error is constant but excessive, it is probably caused by improper zeroing.

PROBLEMS

13-1. Prove the validity of each of the methods of zeroing a synchro transmitter.

13-2. Prove the validity of the methods of zeroing a synchro control transformer.

13-3. What would be the effect of an open S_3 lead in a synchro transmission system?

13-4. Show how servo oscillation can be caused by improper zeroing of synchros in a double-speed transmission system.

13-5. Why is phase adjustment important in servomechanisms?

13-6. For a sluggishly operating servo, explain how each of the faults listed can cause this operation.

13-7. Show how instability can be caused by any of the faults listed in the text.

13-8. Show how a wrong gear ratio can cause a servo to have excessive error.

CHAPTER 14

TESTS OF SERVOMECHANISMS

14-1. Introduction. The purpose of this chapter is to discuss the various servo characteristics that must be verified by test and to describe some of the techniques and equipments by which these tests are performed. Considered here are the types of tests that are used either for the evaluation of the performance of a servomechanism or for the purpose of development. Excluded is a discussion of evaluations not peculiar to the subject of servomechanisms, such as environmental tests and life tests. It is assumed, however, that the tests are performed under conditions approximating those existing in actual operation or required by the general specifications. Hence, the effects of such external conditions as variation of voltage and frequency and environmental conditions are properly taken into account.

It is assumed in making the measurements described in this chapter that the servomechanism has been properly adjusted before making the performance test. It is also important to recognize that the measurements described in this chapter often cannot be made exactly because the servo performance extends beyond the fringes of nonlinearities. This necessitates the combination of interpretation with test observations, and the experience of the tester is of no small value in this regard. Proper laboratory techniques should be employed, the limitations of accuracy of the tools must be known, and appropriate checks of the results, such as making on-the-spot plots of the data obtained, should be made.

This chapter is divided into two major portions: (1) the quantities that are to be measured and (2) the signal sources. In the first of these, the measurement of such quantities as phase, angular position, and torque is discussed since they are typical quantities of interest in servomechanisms. The second portion covers the generation of typical command signals. The best performance evaluation of a servomechanism is to use it in its actual application. In lieu of this, however, typical test signals can be generated in order to evaluate the performance of the servomechanism. These signals include constant-velocity command, constant-acceleration command, step-function-angle command, sinusoidal-signal sources, and specialized commands.

14-2. Suppressed Carrier Modulation. The form of the signal that is present in most a-c servos is shown in Fig. 14-1 for a sinusoidal modulating signal. This signal is called *suppressed carrier*. The equation for a suppressed carrier signal is

$$e = \sin \omega_s t \sin \omega_c t = \cos (\omega_c - \omega_s)t - \cos (\omega_c + \omega_s)t \qquad (14\text{-}1)$$

where ω_s = signal frequency and ω_c = carrier or modulating frequency. Typical carrier frequencies are 60, 400, 1,000 cps, etc. Signal frequencies

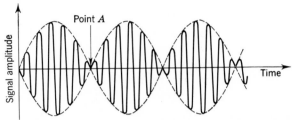

FIG. 14-1. Suppressed carrier signal that is modulated with a sinusoid.

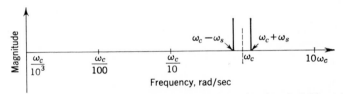

FIG. 14-2. Frequency spectrum for suppressed carrier signal of Fig. 14-1.

are usually small—0 to 10 cps. The name for this type of modulation arises from the second part of Eq. (14-1). Notice that only the frequencies $\omega_c + \omega_s$ and $\omega_c - \omega_s$ exist in this expression. Since there is no component at the carrier frequency, this type of modulation is called suppressed carrier. A frequency spectrum (i.e., a plot of harmonic magnitudes plotted against frequency) is plotted in Fig. 14-2 to a log scale.

Of more importance than the name of the signal is how it arises in servo systems. The special transformer that is shown in Fig. 14-3 has a secondary that can be rotated mechanically with respect to the primary. When the mechanical angle θ is 90°, full voltage e_1 is developed across the secondary. As θ is varied, a voltage is developed across the output. For small θ, this voltage can be written as

$$e_o = e_1 \sin \omega_c t \sin \theta \approx (e_1 \sin \omega_c t)\theta \qquad (14\text{-}2)$$

It is this type of signal which is developed at the output of a-c position pickoffs, which are discussed in Chap. 3. A pickoff, which is described by Eq. (14-2), produces a linear voltage with respect to shaft position for small angular rotations.

The sign of the signal is contained in the phase of the carrier signal. In the region where the signal amplitude approaches the origin (point A in Fig. 14-1), the carrier signal shifts phase by 180°. This is also shown by Eq. (14-2). The carrier signal changes sign as θ changes sign. If a complete a-c system is employed, the torque output from the motor is

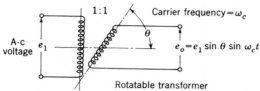

FIG. 14-3. Rotatable transformer that is capable of generating a suppressed carrier signal.

proportional to the magnitude of the signal. The direction of the torque applied depends upon the phase of the carrier. If a zero-frequency carrier is required, a phase-sensitive demodulator* must be used to restore correct polarity information to the output.

14-3. Carrier Phase Measurement. Two types of phase measurement may be necessary in the adjustment or testing of servomechanisms. These are the measurement of the phase of the carrier voltages and the measurement of the phase of suppressed carrier signals, each with respect to some established reference. Measurement of the phase of carrier voltages is normally a static test to ensure that the various alternating voltages appearing in the system, such as the actuating-signal voltage,

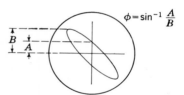

FIG. 14-4. Measurement of phase with an oscilloscope.

rate-generator voltages, motor voltages, phase-sensitive-detector voltages, and modulator voltages, have the proper phase relationship with respect to one another. Measurement of the phase of suppressed carrier signals is a dynamic measurement normally required in obtaining the frequency response of the entire system or of components.

The phase relationship of two voltages can be measured in a number of ways, all of which require the use of an oscilloscope. A direct method is shown in Fig. 14-4. The voltages whose phases are to be compared are applied to the horizontal- and vertical-axis terminals of an oscilloscope. The gains of the oscilloscope amplifiers are set at any arbitrary values that make the figure a reasonable size. A typical figure is shown. From

* See Chap. 4 for a discussion of phase-sensitive demodulators.

the measurement of the proportions of the figure, the phase between the two voltages can be calculated from the formula. If, as is common, it is necessary to learn only whether or not two voltages are in phase, the presence of a straight line indicates that phase relationship. The presence of a circle or an untilted ellipse indicates a phase difference of 90° between the two voltages.

Familiarization with the ellipses shown in Fig. 14-5 permits rapid estimation of phase shift directly from the oscilloscope. The ellipses are

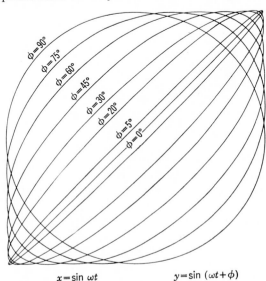

$$x = \sin \omega t \qquad\qquad y = \sin (\omega t + \phi)$$

Fig. 14-5. Family of elipses with various phase shifts between x and y axes.

shown for several common angles. Frequently an estimate of the phase shift is valuable in development testing.

A more accurate method of measuring the phase of carrier voltages uses the null method and requires the use of a phase-shifting network. In this method, the phase of some voltage such as the line voltage is chosen as a standard. Some sort of phase-shifting network is used to shift the phase of the output of the network a measured amount. To measure the phase of any arbitrary test voltage, therefore, this voltage is applied to two of the terminals of the oscilloscope. To the other two is applied the standard voltage, whose phase is varied until a straight line appears on the oscilloscope screen. Since the phase of this reference voltage is known, the phase of the test voltage is also known.

One method of shifting phase a known amount is by means of a transformer and an RC network, as shown in Fig. 14-6. The locus of the output voltage of this network is the circle shown, and the phase of the reference voltage can be varied from near 0 to almost 180°. By knowing the values of resistance and capacitance and the frequency applied, the phase of the reference voltage can be calculated. A more convenient and often more accurate method is to measure the voltage drops across the resistance and capacitance and from these calculate the phase of the reference voltage E_2.

A more convenient phase shifter, however, can be made from a synchro with a dial attached to its shaft. A closely balanced three-phase voltage

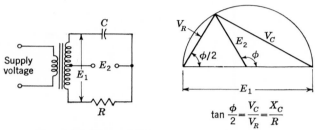

$$\tan \frac{\phi}{2} = \frac{V_C}{V_R} = \frac{X_C}{R}$$

Fig. 14-6. Phase-shifting network and relations.

is applied to the stator winding of the synchro, as shown in Fig. 14-7. The output of the rotor is a voltage that is constant in magnitude and variable in phase through 360° with one-to-one correspondence to the shaft angular position. The phase of the output voltage can thus be read from the dial. The synchro employed should be a control transformer, since synchro receivers and transmitters tend to rotate at synchronous speed when excited with three-phase voltage. When balanced

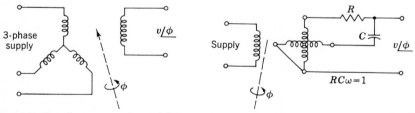

Fig. 14-7. Synchro as a phase-shifting network.

Fig. 14-8. Resolver as a phase-shifting network.

two-phase voltage is available, a resolver* can be used. The use of an unbalanced (i.e., with unequal magnitudes or improper phase angles) multiphase source results in an error between the phase of the output voltage and the synchro shaft position.

Provided that the frequency of the source voltage is fairly constant, a single-phase voltage can be used with a resolver-type phase shifter, as illustrated in Fig. 14-8. The dial is attached to the shaft as before, and

* See Chap. 3 for a discussion of resolvers.

the resistor and capacitor are connected across two of the terminals, care being taken that the capacitor has a very high leakage resistance. The values of R and C are so chosen that $RC\omega = 1$ for ω equal to the carrier frequency (in radians per second). After approximate values are chosen, they can be adjusted by spinning the rotor of the resolver and observing the magnitude of the output voltage on an oscilloscope. When the RC values are properly chosen, the magnitude of the output voltage is constant. Care must be taken in using this method that the output not be loaded, since the accuracy would be impaired.

The amount of quadrature present in the carrier voltage can be measured instead of its phase. This is accomplished by applying this voltage to a phase-sensitive rectifier whose reference voltage is in phase with the quadrature voltage. Any quadrature voltage in the signal will appear in the output of the phase-sensitive detector as a direct voltage, whereas the in-phase voltage will be eliminated. The resulting voltage can be measured by a meter or a recorder.

14-4. Suppressed-carrier-signal Measurement. It is often desirable to measure the relative phase angles of the envelopes of two suppressed carrier signals. An example of this need exists when the reference input

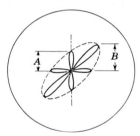

FIG. 14-9. Suppressed-carrier-phase measurement.

and actuating signal of the servo are converted to suppressed carrier voltages and it is necessary to measure the phase angle between the two signals. One method is to apply the two signals to a dual-channel recording oscillograph, such as is manufactured by Brush or Sanborn. If the recorder will respond to carrier-frequency plus and minus sidebands, the voltages are applied directly to the recorder amplifier inputs. The signal envelopes can then be recorded in their relative time position and the phase angle easily computed, although often not as accurately as by another method to be described. If a "d-c" recorder is used and the carrier frequency is beyond the range of the recorder, a phase-sensitive demodulator must be used for both voltages. As long as identical demodulators and filters are used for each of the two signals, the phase of each will shift the same amount and their relative phase will be unchanged.

A second method of measuring the phase angles between two signals does not require a recording oscillograph. The two suppressed carrier signals are applied to the horizontal and vertical terminals of the oscilloscope. The result is a Lissajous figure, just as in the case of measuring the phase of carrier voltages. A typical oscilloscope presentation is shown in Fig. 14-9, and the phase angle ϕ between the two envelopes is given by

$$\phi = \sin^{-1} \frac{A}{B} \qquad (14\text{-}3)$$

A variation of this method applies the suppressed carrier signal to one of the two pairs of terminals and applies to the other a suppressed carrier signal that can be shifted through a known phase angle. When a straight line is obtained on the oscilloscope, the voltage being measured is of the same phase as the reference voltage. The principal disadvantage of this general method is that the waveforms are not always pure sinusoids, and the resulting figure is difficult to interpret.

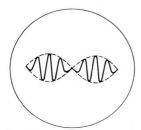

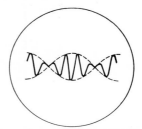

Fig. 14-10. Suppressed carrier signal, zero phase with respect to reference (sweep).

Fig. 14-11. Suppressed carrier signal, 90° phase with respect to reference (sweep).

A more desirable method consists in presenting the voltage on the y axis of the oscilloscope and impressing a sweep voltage of signal frequency to the x axis. The instant of initiation of this sweep voltage can be varied to occur at any time on the signal cycle, and by this means the phase of the signal can be measured relative to a standard. The sweep voltage is synchronized to the signal source that is used to measure the performance of the servomechanism. By means of this synchronized sweep, one cycle of the signal can be presented on the oscilloscope. The sweep circuit is so designed that the point of initiation of the sweep in the cycle can be advanced or retarded. If it has been adjusted to coincide with the start of the cycle, a typical suppressed carrier signal appears as in Fig. 14-10. If, however, the sweep is retarded 90° (calculated at signal frequency), the figure appearing on the screen is as shown in Fig. 14-11.

The phase of the sweep is always adjusted until the nodal point of the suppressed carrier envelope coincides with the initiation point of the sweep, and the phase angle is read on a dial. The amount of advancement of the sweep is measured by means of a calibrated dial, and the phase difference between any two signals under study can easily be measured. Since the accuracy of phase determination is dependent to a great extent on the shape of the suppressed carrier envelope, signals with broad nodal points are not easy to measure accurately. If this is a difficult problem, a sharply defined nodal point can be obtained for this signal by modulation of the z axis of the oscilloscope to brighten that component of the carrier which has the proper carrier phase. A sharp nodal point is thus presented. This technique, however, is often an unnecessary refinement.

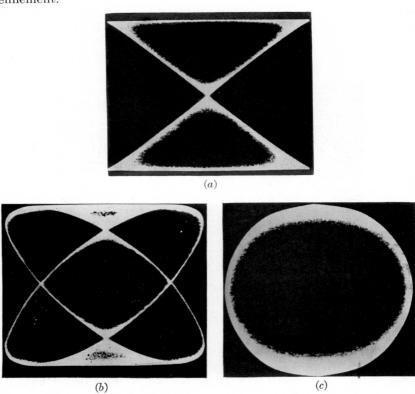

(a)

(b)   (c)

FIG. 14-12. Oscillograph Lissajous figures.   (a) Zero phase shift; (b) 45° phase shift; (c) 90° phase shift.   (*Servo Corporation of America, New Hyde Park, N.Y.*)

Frequently a demodulated signal is available for comparison with the suppressed carrier signal. For example, with a suppressed carrier signal applied to the input of a motor, the shaft output follows the amplitude of the modulated wave. The phase shift between the input suppressed carrier signal and the output shaft position can easily be determined from an oscilloscope. The sinusoidally modulated signal is applied to the input to the system (motor terminals in this example) and also to the x axis of the oscilloscope. A potentiometer excited with a unidirectional voltage is used to measure the output position. This signal is applied to the y axis of the oscilloscope. Lissajous figures such as shown in Fig. 14-12 result. The phase shift is measured from the ellipses as indicated in Fig. 14-4 or 14-5.

A commercial instrument that is convenient for measuring phase shift and other quantities is shown in the photograph of Fig. 14-13. The phase-measurement portion of the instrument operates in a manner that is similar to that shown in Fig. 14-7. A block diagram for the instrument is included in Fig. 14-14.

Fig. 14-13. Photograph of a servoscope. (*Servo Corporation of America, New Hyde Park, N.Y.*)

The instrument contains two synchros with their stator windings connected in the conventional manner. The rotor of one synchro is driven by a variable-speed drive, consisting of a servoamplifier, servomotor, and tachometer generator. The rotor of the driven synchro is excited externally from the servo power line for use with testing a-c control systems and from an internal 3,900-cycle oscillator for generating low-frequency signals for testing d-c control systems. Attached to the shaft of the rotating synchro is a synchronizing switch used to trigger a saw-tooth signal generator.

The modulation signal frequency may be varied over a 200 to 1 range (0.1 to 20 cps or 0.15 to 39 cps) by controlling the speed of the velocity servo through an input potentiometer. Another potentiometer on the same shaft is used to control the time constant of the electronic sweep circuits.

Thus the instrument synchronously generates two signals, a sinusoidally modulated suppressed carrier signal and a saw-tooth signal. The amplitude is constant, and the period is equal to 1 cycle of the modulated signal. The signal may be made to lag or lead the saw-tooth signal in phase or time.

If the sinusoidally modulated suppressed carrier signal is applied to the vertical plates and the sweep signal is applied to the horizontal plates of

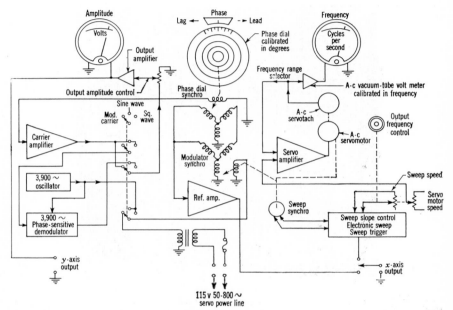

FIG. 14-14. Simplified block diagram of servo analyzer.   (*Servo Corporation of America, New Hyde Park, N.Y.*)

a cathode-ray oscilloscope, the result is a pattern on the cathode-ray oscilloscope that is shown in Fig. 14-15a. However, when the system response (servoscope input) is applied to the vertical axis in place of the signal, any difference in phase appears as a shift along the x axis (see Fig. 14-15b). The phase dial is turned so that the response pattern matches the reference pattern. Since the phase dial actually shifts the signal an amount equal and opposite to the phase shift in the system under test, the phase lead or lag is obtained directly by reading the calibrated dial.

As an alternate method, the engineer may make use of the Lissajous pattern. This is obtained by applying the sinusoidal reference signal, in place of the sweep, to the oscilloscope horizontal x axis. When the phase shift is zero, the pattern takes the form of a straight line displayed at an angle as in Fig. 14-15c. As the control system under test introduces a phase shift, the pattern assumes an expanding elliptical shape until it shows a circle pattern of 90° shift as in Fig. 14-15d. From 90° to 180° phase shift, the pattern collapses into an ellipse and finally into a straight line at an angle.

The sine-wave signal is generally utilized to test d-c servo systems. The system response is applied to the oscilloscope vertical y axis. The

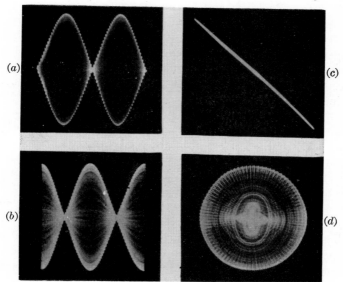

Fig. 14-15. Oscillograph patterns for various types of systems.

sweep may be applied to the oscilloscope horizontal x axis. The resulting pattern is a sine wave. However, it is difficult to measure phase shift accurately with this pattern. Therefore, the sinusoidal reference signal is usually applied to the x axis instead. Figure 14-12a shows the resulting pattern at zero phase shift. As the phase shift is increased, the crossover point separates until, at 45° phase shift, it shows the pattern in Fig. 14-12b. Figure 14-12c shows the pattern at 90° phase shift. In order to determine the phase lead or lag, the phase dial is rotated until the response pattern duplicates zero phase shift. Since the phase dial actually shifts the signal an amount equal and opposite to the phase shift in the system, the phase lead or lag is obtained by reading the calibrated dial directly.

14-5. Measurement of Angular Position. The most obvious method of measuring the angular position of a shaft is by means of dials or a dial and a pointer. Dials with vernier scales that are engraved in minutes and have a guaranteed accuracy of approximately 6 seconds can be commercially obtained.   The use of a magnifying glass or microscope aids in reading the scales.

To obtain additional accuracy, it is sometimes possible to make angular measurements at a higher-speed shaft.   For example, when the position of the controlled variable is desired and a 1- and 36-speed synchro transmission system is being employed, it is often possible to measure the angular position of the controlled shaft by measuring the position of the 36-speed shaft.   Backlash and gearing inaccuracies between the shafts result in inaccuracies by this method.   In some cases, however, it is only necessary to know the angular position of the controlled shaft relative to the 36-speed command-shaft position.   In so far as its effect on the position of the controlled shaft is concerned, it is not necessary to position the high-speed command synchro to a very great accuracy, since the error in positioning this shaft is divided by 36.

While the use of dials is generally limited to cases where static measurements are being made, the dials can be photographed under dynamic conditions if desired.   For example, the relative angular positions of two shafts can be determined by attaching dials and pointers and taking a high-speed photograph during their motion.   The use of a strobotron will ensure a brilliant flash of light at the precise instant desired.

There are also various optical means of measuring angles, as by the reflection of a beam of light on a surface a number of feet distant from the shaft whose position is being measured.   On the other hand, if the shaft whose position is to be measured can be placed on a rotary table and have its axis coincident with that of the rotary table, a mirror can be mounted on the shaft to be measured.   Any increments of angle can be measured as the angle through which the table must be rotated in order to bring the mirror back to the original position.   This original position can be established as that which gives a coincident reflection of cross hairs or other references.   A rotary table such as a dividing head, which is used in a machine shop, can be employed.   These can be obtained with accuracies of 2 seconds.

Angular position can often be measured by converting to an electrical voltage and then using the conventional instruments for measuring or recording this voltage.   (Sometimes combinations of measuring means are used, as in the use of dials for a low-frequency oscillation and an electrical signal for higher-frequency oscillations.)   For example, the size of the actuating-signal voltage can be measured, and if the error in the detector is small, this voltage is a measure of the servo error.   It is desirable to eliminate from the measurement the effect of inaccuracies of the error detector.

Because of inaccuracy in the conversion means, these conversion methods are of a much cruder sort than those depending on the use of dials. Their most striking advantage, however, is in obtaining dynamic measurements, in which the exact accuracy of the position of a shaft is not of primary concern. When frequency-response tests are being made on a servomechanism the magnitude of shaft-angle displacements can be measured by the size of oscilloscope or oscillograph traces. For example, suppose it is desired to measure the amplitude and phase (which is the frequency response) of the servomechanism. The shaft position can be measured with any of the position indicators discussed in Chap. 3. Either alternating or direct current can be used for the measurement.

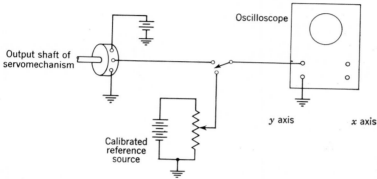

Fig. 14-16. Measurement of amplitude by comparison with a calibrated source.

To plot the dynamic response the amplitude and phase-angle variation must be measured at a number of discrete values of frequency. Measurement of phase is discussed in the previous sections. The amplitude, or angle, is measured by displaying it on the y axis of the oscilloscope. A calibrated reference voltage can then be switched onto the face of the screen and compared with the magnitude of the suppressed carrier that was previously present. (The use of a long-persistence screen facilitates a comparison of their relative magnitudes.) The angular-position voltage and the calibration signal are alternately switched onto the y axis as indicated in Fig. 14-16. Many commercially available oscilloscopes have calibration signals built into the instrument. The magnitude of the reference voltage is varied until it is exactly equal to that of the suppressed carrier voltage. Thus, the size of the suppressed carrier voltage is determined. If a permanent record of the signal is recorded, the oscilloscope screen can be photographed.

Such measurements are often made easier by the fact that most servomechanisms already have some means of converting voltages to electrical signals, such as synchros or potentiometers. The servo actuating signal can therefore usually be obtained directly. The position of either the controlled shaft or the command shaft can be indicated with a potentiometer or synchro, thus enabling positions to be measured electrically. If the servomechanism has a rate generator, it can be used to measure shaft velocity. During sinusoidal tests, the magnitude and phase of the controlled-shaft position can be obtained by means of integration. In testing a servomotor, for example, the position of the shaft is difficult to measure during high-frequency oscillation. Also, the magnitude response is falling off at the rate of 6 db/octave or more, thus causing an ever-diminishing magnitude of oscillation as frequency is increased. It may be desirable to couple a rate generator directly to the motor shaft. Of course, the characteristics of the rate generator must be taken into account and corrections made for its transfer function, inertia, and friction loading.

14-6. Measurement of Torque. The typical method of measuring the static torque in a servomechanism is by means of a torque arm, the force

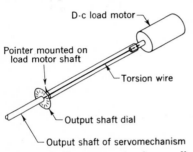

D-c load motor

Pointer mounted on load motor shaft

Torsion wire

Output shaft dial

Output shaft of servomechanism

FIG. 14-17. Dynamometer for small servomechanisms.

being measured at some distance from the axis of rotation. For small servomechanisms, this is easily accomplished. For large servomechanisms, it is often an insuperable problem. However, even for the latter it is often possible to place a torque arm on a higher-speed shaft than the controlled shaft and appropriately scale down the values. The servo response to applied load torque can be measured by applying various loads and measuring the error.

If the servo exhibits a large amount of coulomb friction, it may be preferable to measure the error due to load changes with the command shaft rotated at various constant velocities. Some means of applying the load changes to the rotating shaft, such as a friction clutch, must be used. A cork plate rubbing against a polished disk or a fluid magnetic clutch can be used to apply accurate and constant loads.

Dynamic torque measurements, i.e., measurements of torque delivered by the output shaft of the servomechanism at various velocities, are frequently required. These measurements are usually made with a dynamometer. A dynamometer is a device that is capable of applying a load to the shaft and of providing a means to measure the torque that is developed. A convenient form of dynamometer for small servomechanisms is shown in Fig. 14-17. A torsion wire is connected between the output shaft of the servomechanism and the shaft of a load motor. A disk is attached to one shaft (the output shaft of the servomechanism in this case). A pointer is mounted on the load motor shaft by means of a cylinder that brings the pointer into close proximity to the disk. The torsion wire and disk are calibrated in units of ounce inches per degree. When the system is operating with a constant-velocity input to the servomechanism, the load can be varied by adjusting the conditions of the d-c load motor. Both positive and negative load torques can be generated depending upon whether the d-c unit is operated as a generator or as a motor. The torque is read and the speed is measured by means of a strobotac. This is an instrument that flashes a light at precise and variable frequencies. At any setting of the system under test, the strobotac frequency is adjusted until it is synchronized with the speed of the system. This condition is evidenced by observing the motion of the pointer with respect to the disk. When the strobotac is flashing at the same frequency as the system is rotating, the pointer and disk appear to stand still. In this condition the torque is easily read from the disk, and the velocity is read from the strobotac. Care must be exercised in making this measurement to be certain that the strobotac is flashing at the fundamental and not at a harmonic of the shaft speed.

14-7. Measurement of Hysteresis, Threshold, and Linearity. The servo specifications frequently require the measurement of hysteresis, threshold, and linearity. These quantities are measured under static conditions and are usually based upon the measurement of angular position, which is discussed in Sec. 14-5.

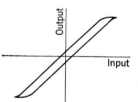

Hysteresis is a phenomenon of electromechanical systems that causes the input-output relation to behave similarly to that shown in the sketch of Fig. 14-18 (the effect is exaggerated in this figure). The system follows a different curve when the shaft is rotated in a clockwise direction than

FIG. 14-18. Sketch of hysteresis curve.

when rotated in a counterclockwise direction. One of the greatest causes of hysteresis is gear-train backlash, which is discussed in Chap. 12. Determination of hysteresis is based upon an angle measurement. The input is moved in the positive direction, and the output shaft angle is measured by any of the methods in Sec. 14-5. From the maximum positive value the input is reduced to the maximum negative value; the input is then returned to zero. In making this measurement it is important to continue in the same direction, without making any readings out of order.

A dial indicator can be used on any gear mesh to make the measurement for the purpose of determining backlash. The tangential displacement at the pitch radius of the gear in question is a measure of backlash. This can be expressed as an angular error if desired. The effect of several cascaded backlashes can be measured.

Threshold is usually caused by coulomb friction in the motor and gear train. Since a finite signal is required before the motor will move, the input-output curve does not remain linear through the origin but rather has a form similar to that shown in the exaggerated sketch of Fig. 14-19. The width of the dead band is found by determining the largest positive signal input that can be applied without output shaft motion, then repeating for the largest negative signal. Because of the frequent combined occurrence of backlash and threshold, it is important to observe the motor shaft and not the output shaft. Indication of motion can usually be made visually.

The measurement of linearity is based upon knowledge of the angular displacement as a function of the input signal. Since amplifiers and motors do not maintain a linear input-output relation over the entire

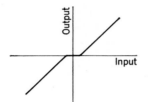

FIG. 14-19. Sketch of threshold curve.   FIG. 14-20. Sketch of saturation curve.

range, the linearity of the over-all system must be determined. This is accomplished by applying signals and measuring the angular position for the entire range (negative to positive). A typical characteristic is shown in Fig. 14-20.

14-8. Signal Sources. The signal sources to be described are those for introducing constant-velocity, constant-acceleration, and step-function-angle commands, sinusoidal signals, and specialized command signals. Most equipment utilized for generating signal sources needed for servo measurement is tailor-made for the application.

A simple source for constant-velocity signals can be obtained from any variable-speed drive capable of accurate setting to the constant velocities desired. This drive can be used to rotate the command shaft. One particularly convenient method of obtaining a constant-velocity drive is the electronic governor shown in Fig. 8-4. Care must be exercised in the use of all devices for generating test signals to see that they do not generate other, spurious signals. Minute variations in the velocity of the variable-speed drive may not be apparent but may cause jitter on the command signal. For this reason it may be necessary to apply mechanical smoothing, for example, by coupling a large-inertia disk to the constant-speed drive.

The velocity error, measured at various command velocities, is the relative position of the command shaft and the controlled shaft. For the degree of accuracy necessary for this type of test, the dynamic error can be measured with a recording of the calibrated actuating-signal voltage.

Unless test apparatus is constructed for this special purpose, it is usually difficult to obtain a constantly accelerating command-shaft position signal. The method commonly used, however, employs a sinusoidal input of relatively large magnitude and long period, and the actuating signal is recorded or measured. The resulting servo error is a combination of the velocity and acceleration errors. At the point of the command cycle where the velocity is zero, the acceleration is a maximum and the error can be assumed to be almost entirely due to the acceleration. Similarly, a measure of the velocity error is obtained at the peak velocity of the sinusoid.

The introduction of a step-function change of signal can be accomplished in a number of ways. A field test that can easily be employed, particularly for instrument servos, comprises the forcing of the motor shaft away from its controlled position and releasing it. The motion of the motor shaft can be observed to determine whether it overshoots several times before coming to rest or whether it sluggishly approaches its final position.

A more sophisticated and quantitative method of introducing step-function changes employs a cam and a switch on a constant-velocity shaft. The cam is cut so that the switch is closed for half a revolution and is opened for the remainder. By means of a switch a step input voltage is inserted into and removed from (square-wave) the error circuit of the servo. The switch can be used to provide on-off operation of any electrical device, such as a solenoid-operated valve.

If this method is used to test the servomechanism transient response, a voltage is added to the actuating-signal voltage and the controlled shaft moves away from its original position. This added voltage is then short-circuited, thus restoring the electrical circuit to its original condition. The controlled shaft, however, is away from its desired position, and the transient response for an initial error is determined under these conditions. The response thus obtained is very close to the response that would be obtained if the command shaft were suddenly rotated to a new position. The speed of the constant-velocity drive can be set at such a value that the transient is repetitively introduced. The same cam, or at least the same constant-velocity drive, can be used to trigger a sweep; and the signal representing the actuating signal or the controlled-shaft position can be applied to the oscilloscope. Because of noise voltages normally present in the actuating signal, it is desirable to measure the controlled-shaft position, even if it is necessary to couple an additional synchro to the controlled shaft for this purpose. The oscilloscope can be blanked out during the transient resulting from the introduction of the added voltage. The use of a controlled sweep therefore allows the complete transient response of the servo to be repetitively presented. A long-persistence screen yields a picture of the transient response. If desired, a pen-type oscillograph can be used to record the transient response.

For particularly careful measurements, the step function can be introduced at a precise point of the carrier phase. This may be of significance, since the transient response of a servomechanism is slightly different if the step function is introduced at the instant when the carrier is going

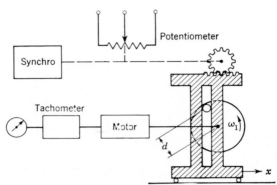

FIG. 14-21. Sketch of scotch-yoke mechanism.

through zero voltage or at the instant when the carrier signal is passing through a maximum voltage.

It is often desirable to generate sinusoidal signals, both of angular position and of suppressed carrier voltages. Cams, linkages, scotch yokes, and wobble plates can be used for mechanical position. Often however, harmonic signals, are generated with the fundamental. A sketch of a scotch-yoke mechanism is included in Fig. 14-21. An inertia disk is rotated through a gear train with a variable speed motor. A d-c motor is frequently utilized. A tachometer is mounted on the same shaft with the motor and is used to measure the shaft velocity ω_1. The yoke mechanism, which is shown shaded in Fig. 14-21, is driven with a pin that is offset a distance d from the center of the inertia disk. As the disk is rotated, the yoke oscillates in a sinusoidal motion defined by the equation

$$x = d \sin \omega_1 t \tag{14-4}$$

A rack on the yoke engages a pinion gear, which in turn drives a potentiometer, synchro, or some other shaft.

The frequency is adjusted by varying the speed of the motor. The amplitude of the motion is adjusted by varying the distance d. The amplitude of the output voltage is easily changed by varying the reference voltage applied to the potentiometer or synchro.

It is desirable that the magnitude of oscillation be capable of adjustment while the device is running.   The output of a mechanical oscillator can be coupled directly to the command shaft of the servo.   This type of signal source should be used for the most accurate frequency-response tests of complete servomechanisms under actual circuit conditions.   A photograph of a device that produces an adjustable sinusoidal angular shaft position is shown in Fig. 14-22.

If desired, a suppressed carrier voltage can be generated by coupling the mechanically oscillating shaft to a synchro or a rate generator.   A

Fig. 14-22. Mechanical oscillator.   (*The Ahrendt Instrument Co., College Park, Md.*)

suppressed carrier signal with less harmonics can be obtained by other methods, for example, a synchro transmitter rotated at a constant velocity.   When a small excitation voltage is applied to the rotor leads, the output across any two of its stator leads is a suppressed carrier signal. The magnitude of the voltage output of the synchro varies with the sine of the angle of its shaft position.   This is also true if a resolver is used. The output of a control transformer can be used to generate a suppressed carrier signal.   For this application, its rotor is locked and the rotor of the transmitter that excites it is rotated at a constant velocity.

A flexible method of generating suppressed carrier signals, however, is the adding together of two voltages of slightly different frequencies. Two oscillators with their outputs in series produce a 1-cycle suppressed carrier signal of 60-cycle carrier if one oscillator is set at 59 cycles and the other at 61 cycles.   Instead of using oscillators with their attendant drift problems, however, two synchros can be used by exciting their stator leads with balanced three-phase voltages and connecting their rotor outputs in series. If the rotors are driven at a constant velocity and the electrical connections are so made that one transmitter's rotor is driven in the same direction as the rotating field and the other in the opposite direction, the output is a suppressed carrier voltage. The carrier frequency is determined by the excitation of the synchro transmitter, and the signal frequency is dependent upon the number of revolutions per second of the rotor shafts. The phase of the suppressed carrier signals can be varied by rotating the stators of the synchros relative to each

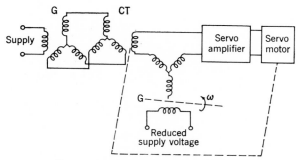

Fig. 14-23. Introducing a test signal.

other. A means should be provided for separately adjusting the magnitudes of the outputs and separately phasing the two voltages. Such a suppressed carrier generator can be used for accurate tests of any components or networks or for open-loop tests of the entire servo.

This suppressed carrier signal can be added to the synchro actuating signal, and closed-loop tests can be made on the servomechanism. If the signals introduced are within the linear range of the error-detecting synchros, the servo will respond to these signals in an effort to null the input voltage to the amplifier. The relationship of the various signals under these latter conditions is shown in Fig. 14-23. Care must be exercised to ensure that the signal introduced is in phase with the actuating signal from the control transformer.

It may also be desirable to introduce other types of command signals, for example, the inverse-tangent function. One convenient source of an inverse-tangent function is an engine lathe. The synchro generator, with its shaft vertical, can be attached to the bed of the lathe. An arm is placed on the synchro shaft and is rested in the U on the tool post. When the constant feed of the lathe is turned on, the saddle, in traveling along the bed of the lathe, generates an inverse-tangent curve. Similarly, other types of command signal can be obtained, as by the use of cams specially cut for the signal desired.

14-9. Consolidated Test Equipment. Figure 14-24 shows a typical setup used for testing servomechanisms. The constant-velocity drive provides a shaft rotation at a constant and measurable velocity. Coupled to the constant-velocity drive are two synchros for generation of suppressed carrier voltages, a cam and a switch device for the insertion of step-function transients, a mechanical oscillator (scotch yoke) for oscillating a mechanical shaft sinusoidally, and an adjustable phase sweep. The sweep can be phased with respect to the mechanical oscillator and other signal-generating equipment by a differential or other method of

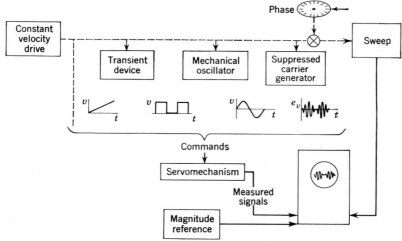

FIG. 14-24. Servo test apparatus.

changing the point of initiation with respect to the constant-velocity drive shaft. The phases are measured by means of the attached dial.

One type of sweep circuit that can be used is a conventional RC network, and it can be triggered by a contact or cam-operated switch. The use of such a circuit, however, often makes it difficult to maintain linearity at low frequencies, but unless waveform is being studied, this is not a serious limitation. Another method employs a potentiometer whose winding covers about 355° but which is capable of rotation through 360°. It is energized with a direct voltage, and its shaft is attached to the constant-velocity drive. Another method utilizes a suitably shaped cam, a light source, and a photocell in which the cam is positioned to mask part of the light falling on the cell. The photocell current can be made almost any function of shaft rotation. In each case, a magnitude reference voltage is used as a means of measuring the magnitude of the oscilloscope traces.

Of course, not all the devices shown need be connected to the constant-velocity drive at the same time. If, for example, the transient response of the servomechanism is being investigated, the mechanical oscillator and the suppressed carrier generator can be disconnected. Similarly, the transient device can be disconnected and the mechanical oscillator reconnected if the sinusoidal response of the servomechanism or its components is required.

The *servoscope*, which is shown in Fig. 14-9, can be used to provide a variety of electrical input signals. The instrument provides a sine wave for frequency response tests of d-c systems, a square wave for transient tests of d-c systems, and a suppressed carrier modulated with a sine wave for frequency-response tests of a-c systems.

It is frequently necessary, however, to devise special test equipment and test methods. A typical example occurs in the testing of gyro systems. Frequently the gyro must be mounted in a special fixture that is capable of providing the necessary input signals.

PROBLEMS

14-1. What are the advantages and disadvantages of different methods of measuring carrier phase?

14-2. Derive the equations given in Figs. 14-4 and 14-6.

14-3. Explain mathematically how the circuit of Fig. 14-8 operates.

14-4. Explain the advantages and disadvantages of various methods of measuring the phase of suppressed carrier signals.

14-5. Derive the exact expressions for the output of a bell crank and a scotch yoke, and give an expression for the most important harmonic error.

14-6. What are the advantages and disadvantages of each of the methods of generating a suppressed carrier signal?

CHAPTER 15

A TYPICAL SERVOMECHANISM AND
ITS OPERATION

In this chapter, much of the information offered in previous chapters is applied to a complete description of an instrument servomechanism. The many requirements aside from those which bear directly upon the performance of the servo are not discussed.

15-1. Specifications of a Typical Servomechanism. The servomechanism is required to operate from a 400-cycle single-phase a-c power source using 1- and 36-speed synchros yielding 1 volt/deg actuating signal. The controlled shaft positions a mirror at half speed over a total angle of 52.5°, against an antibacklash torsion spring of 90 oz-in., whose

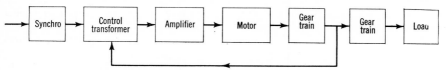

FIG. 15-1. Functional diagram of servomechanism.

variation over the travel of the mirror shaft is less than 5 oz-in. When the mirror rotates at half speed, the sum of the angle of incidence and the angle of reflection results in a reflected image that rotates at 1-speed, which is the same speed as the command shaft.

A functional diagram of the system is shown in Fig. 15-1. Although a double-speed synchro system is employed, the analysis is based upon the sensitive (36×) synchro. The desired mirror position is inserted into the system by means of a synchro. The actual position of the mirror is measured with a control transformer, and the voltages are subtracted within the control transformer. This error signal is amplified and used to drive a motor that powers the mirror load through an appropriate gear train. The static accuracy requirement is ±1 minute of arc at the mirror shaft. The servo must have a frequency response that exhibits no resonance below 6 cycles and does not produce a control ratio (M_p) with magnitude greater than 1.3. The phase shift of the servo is to be less than 10° under 3 cycles and less than 30° under 6 cycles.

The maximum velocity required is 60°/sec at 1-speed and the velocity-error coefficient more than 1,000 sec^{-1}. The acceleration must be at least 120°/sec^2 at 1-speed, and the acceleration-error coefficient must be greater than 200 sec^{-2}. The jitter at the mirror shaft under any constant-velocity conditions has to be so damped as not to exceed $\frac{1}{4}$ minute of arc. The voltage of the supply is 115 volts ± 10 per cent and the frequency, 400 cycles ± 5 per cent. The only appreciable servo load results from gearing, the torsion spring, and a shaft seal, which is employed to prevent the entry of moisture.

The simplified block diagram for a possible system is shown in Fig. 15-2.

For a first approximation, the motor is assumed to have a single time constant; and the amplifier, synchro, and control transformer are represented by a constant transfer function. The product of all the constants is K_v, the velocity-error constant for the type 1 system.

15-2. Steady-state Requirements. The steady-state requirements are first obtained. The required velocity and acceleration of the controlled shaft, together

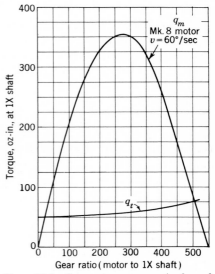

FIG. 15-3. Servo torque required and motor torque available.

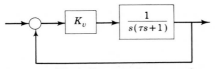

FIG. 15-2. Block diagram of servomechanism.

with the measured load of the seal, result in the graph of Fig. 15-3, in which the required torque at the controlled shaft q_t is plotted against gear ratio between prime mover and the controlled shaft. Also plotted is the available torque q_m from the motor chosen, which is a function of the motor power and torque curves as discussed in Sec. 7-7. The q_t curve is based on the following torque equation:

$$q_t = q + a(J + N^2 J_m) \tag{15-1}$$

where q = load torque (assumed constant)
a = load acceleration required
J = load inertia
J_m = motor inertia

Figure 15-3 is discussed further in Sec. 2-9.

Because of the range of power required, the servo is placed in the small-instrument-servo classification.   A 115-volt 400-cycle motor of 5 watts is chosen.   This motor admittedly overpowers the servo, but it presents little difficulty in procurement.   Catalogue data on the motor show its

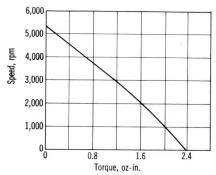

FIG. 15-4. Torque-speed curve of motor.

rotor inertia to be 3.5 g-cm² and its torque-speed curve as given in Fig. 15-4.   Based upon the equations of Sec. 7-4, the parameters of the motor are computed as follows:

$$m = \frac{1}{2} \frac{2.35 \text{ oz-in.}}{(5,300)(2\pi)/(60)(\text{radians/sec})} = 0.212 \times 10^{-2} \text{ oz-in.-sec} \quad (15\text{-}2)$$

$$k = \frac{2.35 \text{ oz-in.}}{115 \text{ volts}} = 2.04 \times 10^{-2} \text{ oz-in./volt} \quad (15\text{-}3)$$

The total inertia load reflected to the motor shaft is 2.5 g-cm².   The quantity is easily checked from the synchro and gear-train data.   The total inertia is

$$3.5 + 2.5 = 6.0 \text{ g-cm}^2 = \frac{6.0}{980} (0.0137) = 8.38 \times 10^{-5} \text{ oz-in. sec}^2$$

The time constant of the motor is

$$\tau = \frac{J}{m} = \frac{8.38 \times 10^{-5}}{0.212 \times 10^{-2}} = 0.0396 \text{ sec} \quad (15\text{-}4)$$

and the first-corner frequency of the motor is

$$\omega_1 = \frac{1}{0.0396} = 25.2 \text{ radians/sec} \ (= 4 \text{ cps}) \quad (15\text{-}5)$$

and its experimentally measured second corner occurs at about 20 cps.

The motor constant is

$$K_m = \frac{k}{m} = \frac{2.04 \times 10^{-2}}{0.212 \times 10^{-2}} = 9.62 \frac{\text{radians/sec}}{\text{volt}} \qquad (15\text{-}6)$$

A total gear ratio of 470 is chosen, resulting in the mechanical-gearing schematic shown in Fig. 15-5. In this figure T corresponds to the

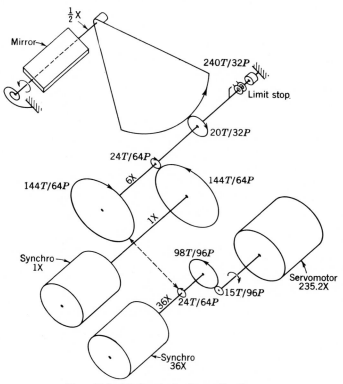

Fig. 15-5. Mechanical schematic of servo.

number of teeth and P to the pitch of the gear. Hence $20T/32P$ indicates that the gear has 20 teeth of 32-pitch. Gears with 14.5° of pressure angle are to be used.

At this point an appraisal of the servo static error can be made. The synchro pair contributes $\frac{10}{36}$ minutes of error referred to the 1-speed shaft, or $\frac{5}{36}$ minutes at the mirror shaft. Other sources of static error come from the servo static error and from the error in the gearing between the 36-speed shaft and the $\frac{1}{2}$-speed mirror shaft. The principal error in the gearing is in the final mesh. Errors in the other meshes are reduced by a factor of the gear ratio to the mirror shaft. The principal error

occurs in either the pinion or the controlled-shaft gear.   These gears are
32-pitch, the pinion diameter is 0.625 in., and the sector-gear diameter is
7.5 in.   An eccentricity of either the pinion or the sector gear of 0.001
would result in a static error of $\frac{1}{4}$ minute at the mirror shaft.   Tooth-to-
tooth error of 0.0002 would result in a static error of 0.2 minute.   If class
2 precision gears, which have an eccentricity of 0.0005 in., and a tooth-to-
tooth error of 0.0003 in. are used, the total error in the gearing can be held
to less than 0.86 minute (see Tables 12-1 and 12-2 for information on gear
tolerances).

Because of the requirement on jitter, necessitating a very smooth-
running gear train, the gears for this servo are all precision-made and
shaved.   The torque required at the motor shaft to turn the motor, the
gearing, and the two synchros is 0.032 oz-in.   Because of the windup
action of the spring, it is not necessary to have very small backlash in the
gear train.

15-3. Dynamic Requirements.   The dynamic requirements of this
servomechanism are set forth by the specification on control ratio M_p and
velocity- and acceleration-error co-
efficients.   As a rough check to
determine the difficulty of the
problem involved, consider the root-
locus plot of the simple system
shown in Fig. 15-2, where the open-
loop transfer function is

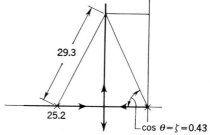

$$KG(s) = \frac{K_v/\tau}{s(s + 1/\tau)} \quad (15\text{-}7)$$

FIG. 15-6. Root locus for servomechanism.

where $1/\tau = 25.2$.   This   plot   is
shown in Fig. 15-6.   From the specifications for the system (Sec. 15-1),

$$\text{velocity constant } K_v = 1{,}000 \text{ sec}^{-1}$$
$$\text{control ratio } M_p = 1.3$$

Reference to the Appendix, page 555, shows that an M_p of 1.3 corresponds
to a damping ratio of 0.43.   The gain of the system corresponding to a
damping ratio of $\zeta = 0.43$ is

$$\frac{K_v}{\tau} = (29.3)^2 = 858$$

and the velocity constant is $K_v = 858 \times 0.0396 = 34 \text{ sec}^{-1}$.   From the
specification, the desired K_v is 1,000 sec^{-1}.   Hence, with an unequalized
system the K_v is approximately 30 times too small.

The same information can be found from the servo of 6–12 slope (i.e., a servo whose G locus has asymptotes of -6 db/octave and -12 db/octave) as shown in Fig. 15-7.

The control-ratio requirement means that the phase margin ϕ must be on the order of 45° (see the Appendix, page 555), and the corner frequency calculates out to 113 cycles in the following manner:

$$\frac{1}{K_v} = \frac{\sin \phi}{\omega} = \frac{0.707}{\omega} = \frac{1}{1,000} \tag{15-8}$$

At gain crossover,

$$\omega = 707 \text{ radians/sec} = 113 \text{ cycles} \tag{15-9}$$

The open-loop frequency response of a servomechanism using a 6–12 slope and complying with the requirements as set forth is shown in Fig.

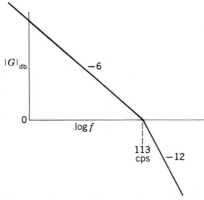

FIG. 15-7. Required open-loop frequency response, 6–12 servo.

15-7. To achieve such a frequency response requires that the corner frequency of the servomotor be equalized almost 5 octaves from its original value of 4 cycles. It is apparent from this analysis that a servomechanism having the open-loop frequency response of Fig. 15-7 is impractical. In searching for a type of servo whose dynamic response is capable of practical realization and yet will comply with the specified requirements, similar calculations are performed on other types of servos. The open-loop response of a servo that will meet the requirement is shown in Fig. 15-8. The original system must be modified to introduce some equalization means.

15-4. Methods of Equalization. Various methods of equalization can be used to achieve the required system dynamics. Those considered are listed as follows:

1. The use of a d-c generator, or a-c rate generator and rectifier, with a capacitor-resistor feedback network.

2. The use of a straight a-c amplifier with a combination lead and lag network of the types shown as Nos. 11 and 12 in Table 5-1.

3. The addition of inertia to the motor and a lead network (No. 3 or 11), either d-c or a-c type, cascaded in the amplifier.

4. The use of a combination lead and lag network such as No. 5 of Table 5-1, thus equalizing at signal frequency by using a modulator and demodulator.

5. The use of a lead network (No. 3 or 11) in conjunction with a friction damper on the motor.

6. The use of output-voltage feedback through a network to the input of the amplifier.

The first method is a feasible way of accomplishing the design aim, but it was not considered desirable to add the complexity and expense of a rate generator, in part because of procurement problems. The second

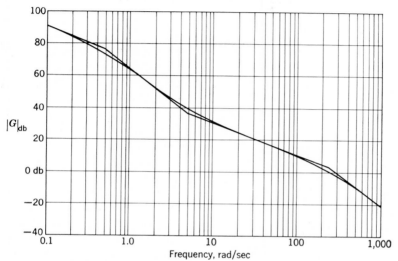

Fig. 15-8. Required open-loop frequency response, 6–12–6–12 servo.

method was discarded immediately because of the variation of power-supply frequency, which prohibits the use of any a-c equalizing network. The third method could have been used with a demodulated signal and the d-c lead network, and an inertia equal to 40 times that of the motor could have been added and the servo would still obtain the desired acceleration. The added inertia would also help to smooth any jitter in the gear train. However, because of the fact that a network is necessary in addition to the added inertia, the method was discarded. Furthermore, the added inertia compromised the mechanical design of the system.

The fourth method, the use of d-c equalizing networks, was one of three systems breadboarded. Usually, only one system is assembled, but circumstances were such in this particular problem that three systems were built. This resulted in useful information being obtained on each of three methods of accomplishing the same end. The test data are presented and compared on all three.

15-5. Use of Demodulator Network Modulator (Fourth Method). The dynamic characteristics of the d-c network used to equalize the servo

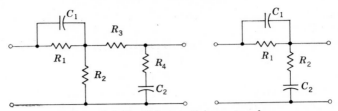

FIG. 15-9. Possible equalizing networks.

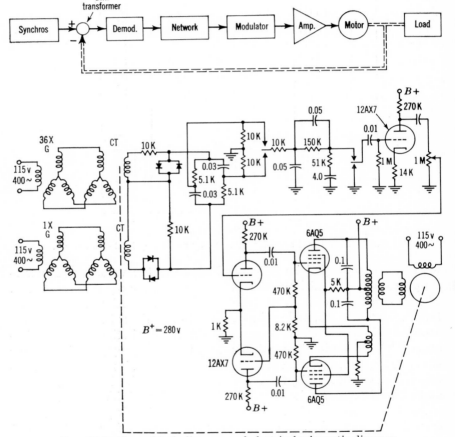

FIG. 15-10. Servo block diagram and electrical schematic diagram.

can be obtained in either of the two ways shown in Fig. 15-9. The first of these shows the simple cascade of a lead network and a lag network. The second of these is a combination network that accomplishes the same end. The difficulty with the first network is an impedance problem, so that, in order to prevent the first network from being loaded by the second, it is necessary that the second network have a high impedance input.   A slight disadvantage with the combination network is the rigid relationship between the corner frequencies, but this can be eliminated by placing resistors in parallel with C_2 or in series with C_1 (network 6 or 7, Table 5-1).   It was decided to use the combination type.   A block diagram and complete electrical schematic diagram are shown in Fig. 15-10.

The resulting servomechanism had a velocity-error constant of 2,000 sec^{-1}, an acceleration-error constant of 500 sec^{-2}, and a static error including gearing of less than 1 minute as measured by very accurate dials placed on the mirror shaft.   The use of this equalizing network, however, always introduces poor transient response if there is any variation of friction in the load.   This is caused by the charging up of the large capacitor in the network if the gear train momentarily pauses because of the friction load.   When the friction is overcome, a transient results.   The response

FIG. 15-11. Oscillograph trace of actuating signal.

FIG. 15-12. Actuating signal of improved system.

of this system, therefore, to a smooth constant-velocity reference input is a jitter at the mirror shaft on the order of $\frac{1}{4}$ minute.   An oscillograph trace of the actuating-signal voltage under conditions of a constant velocity of 15° per sec input velocity is shown in Fig. 15-11.

This jitter can be eliminated by the use of a drag-cup or solid-rotor motor instead of a squirrel-cage type.   Either of these motors has a smooth torque vs. position characteristic.   The problem of cogging can be reduced by increasing the gear ratio between the motor and the 36-speed synchro.   This also reduces the effect on the servo static error of any friction at any mesh other than the motor mesh.   If the friction is in the motor gear mesh, however, increasing the gear ratio will not help.

15-6. Use of a Lead Network plus Motor-friction Damper (Fifth Method).   The fifth method can be used with a d-c network plus a friction damper, which provides the additional lag required.   The amplifier used in this case is the same as that of Fig. 15-10 except that the lag network has been changed to a lead network by removing the large capacitor.   The use of this method of obtaining the dynamics results in a considerable improvement of the jitter characteristic, and a recording of the actuating signal when the servo is following a constant reference-input velocity of 15°/sec is shown in Fig. 15-12.   The use of choppers for demodulators and modulators in the servo, however, makes the system somewhat sensitive to variations in chopper performance.

15-7. Use of Voltage Feedback through a Network (Sixth Method).   The remaining method used to achieve the desired accuracy of the servo is the sixth listed.   The block diagram and amplifier circuit diagram are

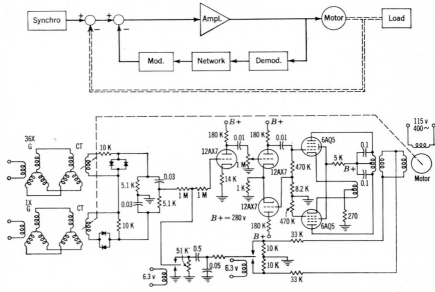

FIG. 15-13. Block diagram and electrical schematic of the sixth method.

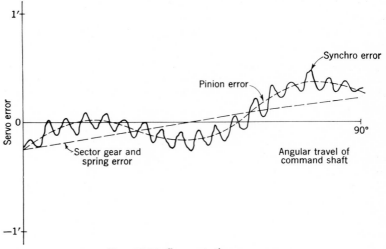

FIG. 15-14. Servo static accuracy.

shown in Fig. 15-13. The amplifier consists of a conventional amplifying channel with inverse feedback around the last stage and a feedback path from the motor voltage, through a pair of choppers, to the input of the amplifier. The coarse and fine synchro signals are introduced to a synchronizing network consisting of resistors and selenium rectifiers, and the resulting signal is shifted in phase so that the control voltage applied to the motor is 90° out of phase with the constant-voltage excitation applied to the other winding from the line. The motor feedback voltage is applied to the first chopper to rectify the signal. It then passes through a combination RC and CR network. If the amplifier gain is high enough, the over-all transfer function of the amplifier is the reciprocal of the transfer function of the network in the feedback path. This combination network, therefore, produces the necessary high-gain, low-frequency characteristic and the extension of the motor corner frequency.

The use of this circuit no longer results in any erratic performance due to normal variation of chopper characteristics. The jitter characteristics are about the same as those of Fig. 15-12. The velocity-following-error constant of the servo is 8,000 sec^{-1}, and the acceleration-error coefficient is 750 sec^{-2}. The static error is less than 1 minute. Figure 15-14, which shows the results of the static test, is a plot of static error vs. the angular position of the controlled shaft.

A study of this error plot is helpful in locating the sources of the errors. For example, the component of error, which is constant in slope from one end of the curve to the other, is caused by either the variation in torque of the spring as it unwinds or the eccentricity of the sector gear. The larger portion is caused by the latter. The sixth-space harmonic error is the result of pinion eccentricity, and synchro error accounts for the 72nd harmonic.

The characteristics of the resulting servomechanism are summarized as follows:

Torque sensitivity at motor shaft	1.56 oz-in./min
Torque sensitivity at controlled shaft	735 oz-in./min = 13,150 lb-ft/radian
Static error	Less than ± 1 min at the mirror shaft
Servo electrical error (measured as actuating signal)	Less than 0.05 minute (this is in addition to a constant 0.2-minute error necessary to overcome the spring load, which can be calibrated out in zeroing)
Velocity-error coefficient	$K_v = 8{,}000$ sec^{-1}
Acceleration-error coefficient	$K_a = 750$ sec^{-2}
Amplifier gain	150 volts/volt (control-transformer output to motor)
Amplifier power output	12.5 watts
Maximum constant-velocity jitter of mirror shaft at 30° per sec reference input	0.15 minute
Maximum velocity	100°/sec
Maximum acceleration	5,000°/sec^2

BIBLIOGRAPHY

1. Ahrendt, W. R., and J. F. Taplin: "Automatic Feedback Control," McGraw-Hill Book Company, Inc., New York, 1951.
2. Arguimbau, L. B.: "Vacuum-tube Circuits," John Wiley & Sons, Inc., New York, 1948.

3. Bibliography on Feedback Control, pt. I, *AIEE Tech. Paper* 53-250, April, 1953.
4. Bibliography on Feedback Control, pt. II, *AIEE Tech. Paper* 53-251, April, 1953.
5. Bibliography on Feedback Control, pt. III, *AIEE Tech. Paper* 53-393, August, 1953.
6. Bibliography of the Frequency-response Method as Applied to Automatic Feedback-control Systems, *ASME Paper* 53-A-13, by A. M. Fuchs.
7. Bibliography of Magnetic Amplifier Devices and the Saturable Reactor Art, *Trans. AIEE*, vol. 70, 1951, by J. G. Miles.
8. Bode, H. W.: "Network Analysis and Feedback Amplifier Design," D. Van Nostrand Company, Inc., Princeton, N.J., 1945.
9. Bronwell, A.: "Advanced Mathematics in Physics and Engineering," McGraw-Hill Book Company, Inc., New York, 1953.
10. Brown, G. S., and D. P. Campbell: "Principles of Servomechanisms," John Wiley & Sons, Inc., New York, 1948.
11. Chesnut, H., and R. W. Mayer: "Servomechanisms and Regulating Systems Design," John Wiley & Sons, Inc., New York, 1951.
12. Churchill, R. V.: "Introduction to Complex Variable and Applications," McGraw-Hill Book Company, Inc., New York, 1948.
13. Churchill, R. V.: "Modern Operational Mathematics in Engineering," McGraw-Hill Book Company, Inc., New York, 1944.
14. Coblenz, A., and H. L. Ownes: "Transistors: Theory and Application," McGraw-Hill Book Company, Inc., New York, 1955.
15. Davis, S. A.: Mechanical Components for Automatic Control, *Product Engineering*, September, 1954.
16. Davis, S. A.: Rotating Components for Automatic Control, *Product Engineering*, November, 1953.
17. Evans, W. R.: "Control System Dynamics," McGraw-Hill Book Company, Inc., New York, 1954.
18. Evans, W. R.: Control System Synthesis by Root Locus Method, *Trans. AIEE*, 1950.
19. Gardner, M. F., and J. L. Barnes: "Transients in Linear Systems," John Wiley & Sons, Inc., New York, 1948.
20. Guillemin, E. A.: A Note on the Ladder Development of *RC* Networks, *Proc. I.R.E.*, vol. 40, no. 4, pp. 482–485, 1952.
21. Guillemin, E. A.: "A Summary of Modern Methods of Network Synthesis," vol. 3, "Advances in Electronics," Academic Press, New York, 1951.
22. Guillemin, E. A.: "Communication Networks," vol. 2, John Wiley & Sons, Inc., New York, 1942.
23. Guillemin, E. A.: "Introductory Circuit Theory," John Wiley & Sons, Inc., New York, 1953.
24. Houdyshell, H. H.: "Precision Potentiometer Life and Reliability," presented at the Electronic Components Conference, Atlantic City, N.J., May, 1955.
25. I.R.E. Standards on Terminology for Feedback Control Systems, *Proc. I.R.E.*, vol. 44, no. 1, 1956.
26. James, H. M., N. B. Nichols, and R. S. Phillips: "Theory of Servomechanisms," vol. 25, M.I.T. Radiation Laboratory Series, McGraw-Hill Book Company, Inc., New York, 1947.
27. Jasper, N., J. C. Taylor, and W. T. White: Transistor-magnetic Amplifiers, *Elec. Mfg.*, vol. 60, no. 3, 1957.
28. Lo, A. W., R. O. Endres, J. Zawels, F. D. Waldhauer, and C. C. Cheng: "Transistor Electronics," Prentice-Hall, Inc., Englewood Cliffs, N.J., 1955.

29. MacColl, L. A.: "Fundamental Theory of Servomechanisms," D. Van Nostrand Company, Inc., Princeton, N.J., 1945.

30. MacMillan, R. H.: "An Introduction to the Theory of Control," Cambridge University Press, London, 1951.

31. Martin, T. L.: "Electronic Circuits," Prentice-Hall, Inc., Englewood Cliffs, N.J., 1955.

32. Masher, D. P.: Modulation and Demodulation with Semiconductors, *Tech. Rept.* 2, Electronic Nuclear Instrumentation Group, Massachusetts Institute of Technology, 1953.

33. Middlebrook, R. D.: "An Introduction to Junction Transistor Theory," John Wiley & Sons, Inc., New York, 1957.

34. Nixon, F. E.: "Principles of Automatic Controls," Prentice-Hall, Inc., Englewood Cliffs, N.J., 1953.

35. Reddick, H. W., and F. H. Miller: "Advanced Mathematics for Engineers," John Wiley & Sons, Inc., New York, 1947.

36. Routh, E. J.: "Dynamics of a System of Rigid Bodies," 3d ed., Macmillan & Co., Ltd., London, 1877.

37. Ryder, R. M., and R. J. Kirchner: Some Circuit Aspects of the Transistor, *Bell System Tech. J.*, vol. 28, no. 3, 1949.

38. Savant, C. J.: "Basic Feedback Control System Design," McGraw-Hill Book Company, Inc., New York, 1958.

39. Savant, C. J.: "How to Design Notch Networks," Electronics Engineering Manual, McGraw-Hill Book Company, Inc., vol. 7, pp. 242-245, New York, 1953.

40. Savant, C. J., R. C. Howard, C. B. Solloway, and C. A. Savant: "Principles of Inertial Navigation," McGraw-Hill Book Company, Inc., New York, 1960.

41. Savant, C. J., and C. A. Savant: Notch Network Design, *Electronics*, vol. 28, no. 9, p. 172, 1955.

42. Schmidt, H. A.: The Precision Potentiometer as Voltage Divider, *Prod. Eng.*, Annual Handbook of Product Design, McGraw-Hill Book Company, Inc., New York, 1954.

43. Seely, S.: "Electron Tube Circuits," McGraw-Hill Book Company, Inc., New York, 1950.

44. Shea, R. F.: "Transistor Circuits," John Wiley & Sons, Inc., New York, 1953.

45. Slater, J. M.: Gyroscopes for Inertial Navigators, *Mech. Eng.*, vol. 79, no. 9, pp. 832–835, 1957.

46. Soroka, W. W.: "Analog Methods in Computation and Simulation," McGraw-Hill Book Company, Inc., New York, 1954.

47. Thaler, G. J., and R. G. Brown: "Servomechanisms Analysis," McGraw-Hill Book Company, Inc., New York, 1953.

48. Truxal, J. G.: "Automatic Feedback Control System Synthesis," McGraw-Hill Book Company, Inc., New York, 1955.

49. Truxal, J. G.: "Control Engineers' Handbook," McGraw-Hill Book Company, Inc., New York, 1958.

50. Von Kármán, T., and M. A. Biot: "Mathematical Methods in Engineering," McGraw-Hill Book Company, Inc., New York, 1955.

51. Van Valkenburg, M. E.: "Network Analysis," Prentice-Hall, Inc., Englewood Cliffs, N.J., 1955.

52. *Westinghouse Tech. Data Bull.* 52-600, October, 1954.

53. Winston, J.: "Design and Application of Hysteresis Clutches," *Elec. Mfg.*, vol. 60, no. 6, pp. 114–127, 1957.

APPENDIXES

THEORY OF SERVOMECHANISMS

A-1. Block Diagrams. In order to analyze typical servomechanisms without confusion of a variety of electric-circuit elements and wires, hydraulic components, and other miscellaneous servo components, it is desirable to represent a complex system by means of a much simplified diagram. The block diagram of a servomechanism is a graphical representation of the flow of information and the functions performed by parts of the equipment. Lines represent the flow of information, with arrowheads to indicate the direction of flow.

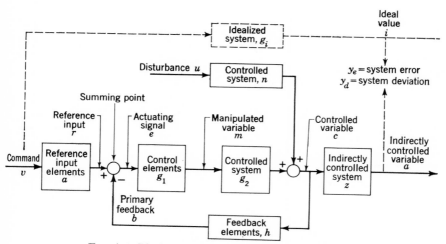

FIG. A-1. Block diagram of feedback control system.

A single-loop feedback control system is shown in the block diagram of Fig. A-1. Definitions of the elements and signals in the system are given in the Glossary, page 539. The variable at the output of the box is the input variable operated upon by the function within the box; in the linear case the output of the box is equal to the product of the function within the box and the input variable. Block diagrams of a given system are obtained by studying the operation of each element in order to determine its transfer function. By studying the relationship of the various ele-

TABLE A-1

Parameter	Equation	Description
Translational systems: Mass	$f_1 - f_2 = M \dfrac{d^2x}{dt^2};$ $\dfrac{dx}{dt} = \dfrac{1}{M} \int (f_1 - f_2)dt$	The net force acting on a body is equal to its mass times its acceleration with respect to an arbitrary fixed reference
Spring	$f = Kx; \quad \dfrac{dx}{dt} = \dfrac{1}{K} \dfrac{df}{dt}$	The force which must be applied to each end of a spring to deflect it a distance x is equal to the spring constant K times x
Dashpot	$f = D\left(\dfrac{dx_1}{dt} - \dfrac{dx_2}{dt}\right)$	The force which must be applied to each end of a dashpot to produce a relative motion of its two ends is equal to the viscous damping coefficient D times the relative velocity
Rotational systems: Inertia	$q_1 - q_2 = J \dfrac{d^2\theta}{dt^2};$ $\dfrac{d\theta}{dt} = \dfrac{1}{J} \int (q_1 - q_2)dt$	The net torque acting on a body is equal to its inertia times its angular acceleration with respect to an arbitrary fixed reference
Torsional spring	$q = G(\theta_1 - \theta_2)$	The torque which must be applied to each end of a torsional spring to produce a relative angular deformation $\theta_1 - \theta_2$ of its two ends is equal to the rotational spring constant times the angular deformation
Rotational dashpot	$q = B \dfrac{d\theta}{dt}$	The torque which must be applied to a rotational dashpot to cause it to rotate with an angular velocity is equal to the rotational viscous damping coefficient times the angular velocity
Electrical systems: Inductance	$v_1 - v_2 = L \dfrac{di}{dt};$ $i = \dfrac{1}{L} \int (v_1 - v_2)dt$	The voltage drop caused by current flowing in an inductance is equal to the inductance times the rate of change of the net current flowing in in the direction of the drop
Capacitance	$v_1 - v_2 = \dfrac{1}{C} \int i\,dt;$ $i = C \dfrac{d}{dt}(v_1 - v_2)$	The voltage drop caused by current flowing through a capacitance is equal to the integral of the net current flowing through the capacitance divided by its capacitance
Resistance	$v_1 - v_2 = Ri;$ $i = \dfrac{1}{R}(v_1 - v_2)$	The voltage drop caused by current flowing through a resistance is equal to the net current flowing through the resistance multiplied by the resistance

English gravitational units

t = time, sec
x = distance, ft
M = mass, slugs
K = spring constant, lb/ft
D = damping coefficient, lb/ft/sec

q = torque, lb-ft
J = inertia, slug-ft^2
θ = angle, rad
G = torsional spring constant, lb-ft/rad
B = rotational damping coefficient, lb-ft/rad/sec

Electrical units

t = time, sec
v = voltage, volts
i = current, amp
L = inductance, henrys
C = capacitance, farads
R = resistance, ohms

TABLE A-2. ELEMENTARY $\mathcal{L}$ TRANSFORMATION PAIRS

$F(s) = \displaystyle\int_0^\infty f(t)\, \epsilon^{-st}\, dt$	$f(t) \qquad \text{for } t > 0*$
1. $\dfrac{A}{s}$	A
2. $\dfrac{1}{s + A}$	ϵ^{-At}
3. $\dfrac{B}{s^2 + B^2}$	$\sin Bt$
4. $\dfrac{s}{s^2 + B^2}$	$\cos Bt$
5. $\dfrac{Cs + D}{s^2 + B^2}$	$A \cos (Bt + \psi)$ $A = \sqrt{C^2 + \left(\dfrac{D}{B}\right)^2}$ $\psi = \tan^{-1} \dfrac{C}{D/B}$
6. $\dfrac{B}{(s + A)^2 + B^2}$	$\epsilon^{-At} \sin Bt$
7. $\dfrac{s + A}{(s + A)^2 + B^2}$	$\epsilon^{-At} \cos Bt$
8. $\dfrac{1}{s^2}$	t
9. $\dfrac{n!}{s^{n+1}}$	t^n
10. $\dfrac{1}{(s + A)^2}$	$t\, \epsilon^{-At}$
11. $\dfrac{1}{(s + A)^n}$	$\dfrac{1}{(n - 1)!}\, t^{n-1}\, \epsilon^{-At}$
12. $sF(s) - f_0$	$f'(t)$
13. $s^2 F(s) - f_0 s - f_0{}'$	$f''(t)$
14. $\dfrac{F(s)}{s} + \dfrac{f_0^{-1}}{s}$	$\displaystyle\int_0^t f(t)\, dt$
15. $\epsilon^{-sT} F(s)$	$f(t - T)u(t - T)\dagger$

* $f(t) = 0$ for $t < 0$.

$\dagger f(t - T) = 0$ for $0 < t < T$.

ments, the interconnection of the blocks is determined. The results of this analysis are utilized to coordinate the blocks into one diagram, which shows the operation of the entire system.

A number of analytical methods are used to study the performance of servomechanisms. Those commonly used in the analysis of linear servo-mechanism are operational techniques, root-locus methods, and frequency-response techniques. Simultaneous differential equations are written relating various signals and solved by using any of the standard techniques (see Refs. 3, 23, 37) for solving linear differential equations with constant coefficients. Table A-1 is presented as an aid to the writing of such equations.

A-2. The Laplace Transform Method. The most popular of the operational techniques used for the solution of differential equations is the Laplace transformation. The independent variable is changed from time to a complex variable s, so chosen that derivatives, integrals, and trigonometric functions can be expressed algebraically. The use of this method involves the following steps:

1. Transform the differential equation, inserting initial conditions.
2. Solve for the transform of the desired unknown.
3. Perform the inverse transformation.

The first step is accomplished by the use of the Laplace integral:

$$F(s) = \int_0^\infty f(t)e^{-st}\, dt \tag{A-1}$$

The quantity $F(s)$ is capitalized to indicate that it is a function of s and not time t. A symbolic representation of this transform is given as follows:

$$F(s) = \mathcal{L}[f(t)] \tag{A-2}$$

This step is accomplished by using Table A-2, so that no integration, as implied in Eq. (A-1), is actually involved in solving the problem.

The second step is an algebraic one, in which the transform of the function of time is found as a ratio of polynomials. When this has been accomplished, the equation reduces to a proper fraction:

$$F(s) = \frac{A(s)}{B(s)} = \frac{A(s)}{s^n + as^{n-1} + bs^{n-2} + \cdots} \tag{A-3}$$

The denominator is factored and written in the form

$$F(s) = \frac{A(s)}{(s - s_1)^k(s - s_2)^l \cdots (s - s_m)(s - s_{m+1}) \cdots (s - s_n)} \tag{A-4}$$

This may be rewritten by partial fractions in the following form:

$$F(s) = \frac{K_1}{(s - s_1)^k} + \frac{K_2}{(s - s_1)^{k-1}} + \cdots + \frac{K_{k+1}}{(s - s_2)^l} \frac{K_{k+2}}{(s - s_2)^{l-1}}$$

$$+ \cdots + \frac{K_{k+l+1}}{s - s_m} + \frac{K_{k+l+2}}{s - s_{m+1}} + \cdots + \frac{K_n}{s - s_n} \quad \text{(A-5)}$$

For single roots,

$$K_{k+l+1} = \left[\frac{(s - s_m) A(s)}{B(s)} \right]_{s=s_m} \quad \text{(A-6)}$$

For multiple roots, the K corresponding to the rth among n equal roots is

$$K_r = \frac{1}{(r - 1)!} \left[\frac{d^{r-1}}{ds^{r-1}} \frac{A(s)}{B(s)} (s - s_1)^n \right] \quad \text{(A-7)}$$

Instead of using these equations, the addition represented by Eq. (A-5) can be performed and the coefficients of like powers of s equated, thus obtaining a number of simultaneous equations from which the various K's can be solved.

The inverse transform is then written, using Table A-2, as follows:

$$f(t) = K_1 \frac{1}{(k - 1)!} t^{k-1} e^{s_1 t} + K_2 \frac{1}{(k - 2)!} t^{k-2} e^{s_1 t} + \cdots$$

$$+ K_{k+1} \frac{1}{(l - 1)!} t^{l-1} e^{s_2 t} + K_{k+2} \frac{1}{(l - 2)!} t^{l-2} e^{s_2 t} + \cdots$$

$$+ K_{k+l+1} e^{s_m t} + K_{k+l+2} e^{s_{m+1} t} + \cdots K_n e^{s_n t} \quad \text{(A-8)}$$

The final and initial values of the function of time can be obtained directly from the transform equation by the use of the following equations:

$$\lim_{t \to 0} f(t) = \lim_{s \to \infty} sF(s) \quad \text{(A-9)}$$

provided the limit exists, and

$$\lim_{t \to \infty} f(t) = \lim_{s \to 0} sF(s) \quad \text{(A-10)}$$

provided $f(t)$ is stable (i.e., all poles of $F(s)$ are in the left half plane).

A-3. Transfer Functions. One of the principal values of the use of the Laplace transformation is that it reduces the difficulty of describing the dynamics of an element or an entire system. This method consists in the use of transfer functions. The *transfer function* of a linear system is the ratio of the transform of its output to the transform of its input when the initial values of both the input and output quantities and their time derivatives and integrals are zero. By following the rules of algebra, the transformed differential equation can be solved for the quotient of the output variable divided by the input variable. By the use of transfer functions, signal lines on a block diagram can be labeled with the transform of the variable they represent and the blocks described by the transfer function. Thus, the simple electrical network of Fig. A-2 is described by the following equation:

$$\frac{v_1 - v_2}{R} = C\frac{dv_2}{dt} \tag{A-11}$$

which is transformed as follows:

$$\frac{V_1(s) - V_2(s)}{R} = CsV_2(s) \tag{A-12}$$

yielding the transfer function

$$\frac{V_2(s)}{V_1(s)} = \frac{1}{1 + RCs} = \frac{1}{1 + \tau_1 s} = \frac{\omega_1}{s + \omega_1} \tag{A-13}$$

The block-diagram representation of the network, therefore, is given as in Fig. A-3. If the exact form of the transfer function is not known but

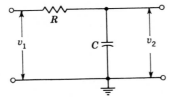

FIG. A-2. RC network.

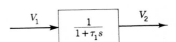

FIG. A-3. Block diagram of the RC network.

it is known that the dynamics of the system described by the block could be represented by a transfer function, a single letter that represents the transfer function is used. The transfer function of two systems connected in cascade is the product of the two transfer functions, for the important condition that the addition of the second system does not load the first. For electrical networks, this criterion reduces to the necessity of having a high input impedance for the second network relative to the impedance of the first network.

The block diagram of an entire servomechanism can be drawn in terms of transfer functions. Thus Fig. A-1 can be redrawn and each of the letters representing signals or functions capitalized. The resulting block diagram is shown in Fig. A-4. If any of the transfer functions of the blocks are known, they are substituted for the single capital letter. In discussing the theory of servomechanisms, it is common to simplify this block diagram further by eliminating the reference-input elements, the indirectly controlled system, and the idealized system. The effect of these portions of the servo can be taken into account later. Thus, the command becomes the reference input, and any inaccuracy in the error-measuring means is assumed zero. Simplification of the block diagram in this manner emphasizes the analysis of the dynamic performance of the system. The resulting block diagram is shown in Fig. A-4.

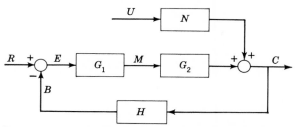

FIG. A-4. Simplified block diagram of a servomechanism.

From the block diagram of Fig. A-4, the fundamental equations relating the variables can be obtained. The actuating signal is found from the following equation (where $G = G_1G_2$):

$$E = \frac{1}{1 + GH} R - \frac{H}{1 + GH} UN \qquad \text{(A-14)}$$

The expression for the controlled variable is

$$C = \frac{G}{1 + GH} R + \frac{1}{1 + GH} UN \qquad \text{(A-15)}$$

In a number of systems the feedback element H has a value of unity, and the equations then reduce to

$$E = \frac{1}{1 + G} R - \frac{1}{1 + G} UN \qquad \text{(A-16)}$$

and

$$C = \frac{G}{1 + G} R + \frac{1}{1 + G} UN \qquad \text{(A-17)}$$

If there are no disturbances on the system or it is desired, through the use of the superposition theorem, to determine the effect of reference-input variations independent of load disturbances, Eqs. (A-16) and (A-17) reduce to

$$E = \frac{1}{1 + G} R \qquad \text{(A-18)}$$

and

$$C = \frac{G}{1 + G} \qquad \text{(A-19)}$$

By the use of the above equation, the transient response of the servomechanism can be found if the transfer functions of the various portions of the system are known. For example, consider a system that consists of a reference-input shaft, a controlled shaft having inertia J and viscous-damping coefficient B, and a controller that supplies a restoring torque

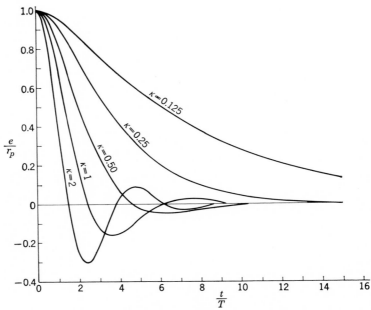

Fig. A-5. Response to step-function reference-input angle.

proportional to the actuating signal. The equation relating restoring torque and the motion of the shaft c is

$$J \frac{d^2c}{dt^2} + B \frac{dc}{dt} = Ke \tag{A-20}$$

This yields for the transfer function G

$$G = \frac{K}{Js^2 + Bs} \tag{A-21}$$

Equation (A-21) can be rewritten in the form

$$G = \frac{\omega_0 \omega_1}{s(s + \omega_1)} \tag{A-22}$$

in which

$$\omega_0 = \frac{K}{B} \tag{A-23}$$

$$\omega_1 = \frac{B}{J} \tag{A-24}$$

The actuating signal is solved (the same as the error in this simple system) in the absence of disturbances as follows:

$$E = \frac{s(s + \omega_1)}{s^2 + \omega_1 s + \omega_0 \omega_1} R \qquad\qquad \text{(A-25)}$$

For a step-function reference input of magnitude r_p,

$$R = \frac{r_p}{s} \qquad\qquad \text{(A-26)}$$

or, for a step-function velocity reference input of magnitude r_v,

$$R = \frac{r_v}{s^2} \qquad\qquad \text{(A-27)}$$

Equation (A-25), when solved for these two forms of reference input, yields the transient responses shown in Figs. A-5 and A-6, in which

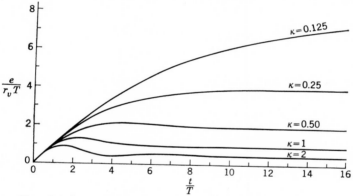

Fig. A-6. Response to step-function reference-input velocity.

$\kappa = \omega_0/\omega_1$ and $T = 1/\omega_1$. These curves indicate the effect of changing system torque sensitivity (e.g., amplifier gain) or controlled-shaft inertia and damping. The constant-velocity following error shown in Fig. A-6 is easily obtained from Eqs. (A-25) and (A-27) by using the final-value theorem of Eq. (A-10):

$$e = \frac{1}{\omega_0} r_v = \frac{B\omega_0}{K} \qquad\qquad \text{(A-28)}$$

This result is corroborated by inspection of the block diagram.

If this system had an additional time lag τ_1, so that the expression for G would be the product of G of Eq. (A-22), and a transfer function of the form of Eq. (A-13), its response to a step-function reference-input angle of magnitude r_p would be as given in Fig. A-7 for $\kappa = 1$ and various values of $\tau_1 = T_1/T = T_1\omega_1$.

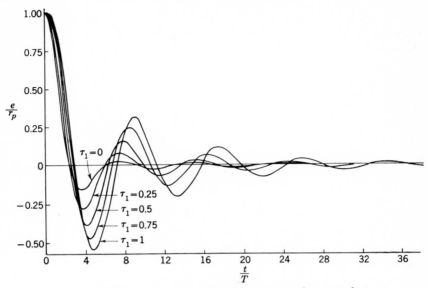

Fig. A-7. Response to step-function reference-input angle.

A-4. Stability: The Routh Criterion. The stability of the system can be determined without solving for the inverse transformation, or even solving for the roots of Eq. (A-14), by the use of Routh's criterion. This consists of arranging the terms of the denominator of $1/(1 + GH)$ (after multiplying out the various transfer functions so that both numerator and denominator are simple algebraic expressions) in the following manner:

$$As^n + Bs^{n-1} + Cs^{n-2} + \cdots \qquad (A-29)$$

The coefficients are arranged in the following array:

$$
\begin{array}{cccccc}
A & C & E & G & \cdot & \cdot \\
B & D & F & H & \cdot & \cdot \\
X_1 & X_2 & X_3 & X_4 & \cdot & \cdot \\
Y_1 & Y_2 & Y_3 & Y_4 & \cdot & \cdot \\
\cdot & \cdot & \cdot & \cdot & \cdot \\
\cdot & \cdot & \cdot & \cdot & \cdot & \cdot \\
\cdot & \cdot & \cdot & \cdot & \cdot & \cdot
\end{array}
$$

where $\qquad X_1 = \dfrac{BC - AD}{B} \qquad X_2 = \dfrac{BE - AF}{B} \qquad$ etc.

$\qquad\qquad Y_1 = \dfrac{X_1 D - BX_2}{X_1} \qquad Y_2 = \dfrac{X_1 F - BX_3}{X_1} \qquad$ etc.

This procedure is effected to yield $n + 1$ rows.

The system will be stable if all the terms in the first column are of the same sign. If the signs of the terms in the first column are not identical, the number of changes of signs in reading successive values of this column will equal the number of roots with positive real parts.

If in the course of computation a zero occurs in an element of the first column or a row of zeros occurs, a more complicated calculation must be effected; but this is outside the scope of the present work.

A-5. Stability with the Root-locus Method. The root-locus method is based upon knowledge of the location of the roots of the system with zero gain, i.e., with the feedback loop opened. In most cases these are easily determined from the open-loop transfer function, which for the root-locus method is written KGH. K is the constant portion of the loop gain, $G(s)$ is the forward-loop transfer function, and $H(s)$ is the feedback loop transfer function. These

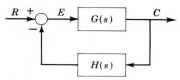

FIG. A-8. Generalized block diagram.

quantities are defined in the block diagram of Fig. A-8. For a first example, let

$$K = \frac{AK_mK_s}{\tau} \qquad G(s) = \frac{1}{s\left(s + \dfrac{1}{\tau}\right)} \qquad H(s) = 1 \qquad \text{(A-30)}$$

In subsequent expressions, the "function of s" is understood, i.e., G is written for $G(s)$ and H for $H(s)$.

Consider the transformed expression that relates output to input and is derived from the block diagram of Fig. A-8.

$$\frac{C}{R} = \frac{KG}{1 + KGH} \qquad \text{(A-31)}$$

where $1 + KGH$ is the characteristic equation. The location of the roots of $1 + KGH$ determines system stability.

The open-loop transfer function KGH is a ratio of factored polynomials

$$KGH = \frac{K_1(s\tau_1 + 1)(s\tau_3 + 1)}{s^n(s\tau_2 + 1)(s\tau_4 + 1)} \qquad \text{(A-32)}$$

where s is a root of $1 + KGH = 0$ for a particular value of K. Equation (A-32) may be rewritten in the following form (this form should always be used for root-locus analysis):

$$KGH = \frac{K_1\tau_1\tau_3}{\tau_2\tau_4} \frac{(s + 1/\tau_1)(s + 1/\tau_3)}{s^n(s + 1/\tau_2)(s + 1/\tau_4)} \qquad \text{(A-33)}$$

Each term in the KGH function is a complex number and is written in polar form as

$$s + \frac{1}{\tau_1} = A_1 e^{j\phi} \tag{A-34}$$

Hence the entire KGH function is a complex quantity and is written in polar form

$$KGH = \frac{K(A_1 e^{j\phi_1})(A_3 e^{j\phi_3})}{(A_0^n e^{jn\phi_0})(A_2 e^{j\phi_2})(A_4 e^{j\phi_4})} \tag{A-35}$$

$$= \frac{KA_1 A_3}{A_0^n A_2 A_4} e^{j[(\phi_1 + \phi_3) - (n\phi_0 + \phi_2 + \phi_4)]} = A e^{j\phi} \tag{A-36}$$

where $K = K_1 \tau_1 \tau_3 / \tau_2 \tau_4$. The algebraic equation from which the roots are determined is

$$1 + KGH = 1 + A e^{j\phi} = 0 \tag{A-37}$$

This equation furnishes the two expressions

$$\text{Angle of } KGH = \arg KGH = \phi = (2k + 1)180° \tag{A-38}$$

where $k = 0, 1, 2, 3, \ldots$ and

$$\text{Magnitude of } KGH = |KGH| = A = 1 \tag{A-39}$$

Equations (A-38) and (A-39) are the result of setting $1 + KGH = 0$. The root locus is plotted by finding all points s_i that satisfy Eq. (A-38). With the locus plotted, Eq. (A-39) is used to determine the gain at points along the locus.

A-6. Rules for Rapid Construction of Root-locus Diagrams. The rules that are stated and demonstrated in this section enable the engineer to sketch rapidly the locus diagrams. The following open-loop transfer function is used to demonstrate the method:

$$KGH = \frac{K(s + 10)}{s(s + 5)(s + 2 + j15)(s + 2 - j15)} \tag{A-40}$$

The zeros, indicated by O, and poles, indicated by X, are shown in Fig. A-9.

Rule 1: *Continuous curves, which comprise the locus, start at each pole of KGH for K = 0. The branches of the locus, which are single valued functions of gain, terminate on the zeros of KGH for K = ∞.* The zeros and poles of KGH are first located on the s plane, an X for each pole and a O for each zero. According to rule 1, the locus starts at the poles and terminates at the zeros. Each branch of the locus is a continuous curve between a pole and a zero and is a single-valued function of gain along the curve. For the example [Eq. (A-40)] shown in Fig. A-9, there exist four branches, starting from the poles located at $s = 0$, $s = -5$, $s = -2 + j15$, $s = -2 - j15$. Since there is only one finite zero, located at $s = -10$, three of the roots must terminate at infinity. The rule can be expanded to read: The locus starts at the poles and terminates on either finite zeros or ($\#P - \#Z$) zeros located at infinite s. $\#P$ is the number of poles and $\#Z$ is the number of zeros of KGH. The number of separate branches equals the number of poles.

The gain K is usually positive and varies from zero to infinity.

Rule 2: *The locus exists at any point along the real axis where an odd number of poles plus zeros is found to the right of the point.* To determine whether the locus exists in a given region along the real axis, count the number of zeros plus poles that lie to the right of the trial point. If there is an odd number of these, the locus does exist.

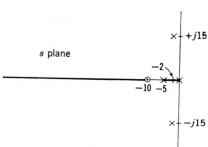

FIG. A-9. Example of rules 1 and 2 applied to the systems:

$$KGH = \frac{K(s + 10)}{s(s + 5)[(s + 2)^2 + 15^2]}$$

For the example of Fig. A-9, the locus exists along the real axis from the origin to the point $s = -5$ and from $s = -10$ to minus infinity. These regions along the real axis are shown darkened in Fig. A-9. Any complex zeros or poles, such as $s = -2 + j15$, are ignored in applying this rule.

Rule 3: *For large values of gain the branches of the locus are asymptotic to the angles*

$$\frac{(2k + 1)180°}{\#P - \#Z} \quad \text{for } k = 0, 1, 2, \dots \qquad (A-41)$$

where $\#P$ is the number of poles and $\#Z$ is the number of zeros.

If the number of poles exceeds the number of zeros, some of the branches will terminate on zeros that are located at infinity. Rule 1 states that the number of branches that terminate at infinity is the number of poles minus the number of zeros. As the gain becomes large, these branches are asymptotic to straight lines whose angles are given by Eq. (A-41).

For the example of Fig. A-9, $\#P = 4$ and $\#Z = 1$, and the asymptotic angles are computed as follows:

$$\theta_k = \frac{(2k + 1)180°}{+3}$$

$$k = 0 \qquad k = 1 \qquad k = 2$$
$$\theta_0 = +60° \qquad \theta_1 = +180° \qquad \theta_2 = +300° \qquad (A-42)$$

Since only three branches extend to infinity, all the angles are computed, and these are plotted in Fig. A-10.

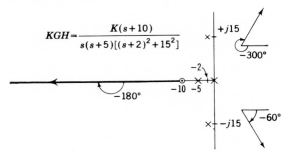

$$KGH = \frac{K(s+10)}{s(s+5)[(s+2)^2 + 15^2]}$$

FIG. A-10. Asymptotic directions determined by rule 3.

Rule 4: *The starting point for the asymptotic lines is given by*

$$CG = \frac{\Sigma \text{ poles } - \Sigma \text{ zeros}}{\#P - \#Z} \tag{A-43}$$

which is called the center of gravity of the roots. The angular directions to which the loci are asymptotic are given by rule 3. The asymptotic lines start at the center of gravity of the zero-pole configuration. This point is found from Eq. (A-43). For the example of Fig. A-9, the CG (center of gravity) is found as follows:

$$\Sigma\text{Poles } (-5) + (-2 + j15) + (-2 - j15) + 0 = -9$$
$$\Sigma\text{Zeros} = -10$$
$$\#P = 4$$
$$\#Z = 1$$

and
$$CG = \frac{(-9)(-10)}{4-1} = \frac{1}{3}$$

The asymptotic lines, found in Eq. (A-42), start from the center of gravity. These lines are placed on the s plane as shown in Fig. A-11.

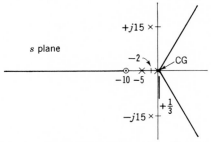

FIG. A-11. Location of center of gravity of roots (rule 4).

Since the complex zeros and poles always appear in conjugate pairs, i.e., equal vertical distances from the real axis, the center of gravity always lies along the real axis.

Rule 5: *The breakaway point s_b is found from the equation*

$$\frac{-1}{|s_b - 1/\tau_2|} + \frac{-1}{|s_b - 1/\tau_4|} + \frac{+1}{|s_b - 1/\tau_1|} = \frac{-1}{|s_b - 1/\tau_6|} + \frac{1}{|s_b - 1/\tau_3|} \quad \text{(A-44)}$$

where $|s_b - 1/\tau_i|$ is the magnitude of the distance from the assumed breakaway point s_b and the corresponding real-axis zeros and poles. The distances are read graphically. The regions along the real axis where the locus exists are determined from rule 2. If the acceptable region on the real axis lies between a single-order zero and a single-order pole (single-order means one zero or one pole located at a point), the locus moves from the pole to the zero along the real axis. If the acceptable region along the real axis lies between two single-order poles, the two roots that start from these poles approach each other along the axis on the loci. As the gain is increased, these roots form a double-order root at the point at which they coalesce (come together). As the gain is further increased, the loci break away from the real axis and form a complex conjugate pair of roots.

The point s_b at which the roots come together and break away is found as follows:

1. Guess a point, s_b.

2. Measure the distances between the guessed point and the real-axis zeros and poles.

3. Equate the sum of the reciprocals of the distances from s_b to the zeros and poles to the left of s_b to the sum of the reciprocals of the distances to the right of s_b. These are added with a negative sign for the poles and a positive sign for the zeros.

4. If the sum to the left does not equal the sum to the right, guess another value of s_b and repeat.

Rule 6: *Two roots leave or strike the axis at the breakaway point at an angle of $\pm 90°$.* The two roots of Fig. A-9 approach each other along the real axis, coalesce, and break away. The angle that the locus makes with the real axis is $\pm 90°$.

Rule 7: *The angle of departure from complex poles and the angle of arrival to complex zeros is found by summing the angles to all the singularities. The angle is found by subtracting 180° from this sum.* The initial angle of departure of the roots from complex poles is helpful in sketching root-locus diagrams. The zero-pole configuration of Fig. A-9 is redrawn in Fig. A-12 for the purpose of finding the angle of departure from the complex poles at $s = -2 + j15$. The angles subtended by the poles and zeros to the pole in question are added (positive for zeros and negative for poles):

$$-(\theta_0 + \theta_2 + \theta_4) + \theta_1 \tag{A-45}$$

A protractor is used to measure these angles.

$$-(97.6° + 90° + 78.7°) + 62° = -204.3°$$

When 180° is subtracted, an angle of departure of

$$-204.3° - 180° = -384.3°$$

is found and is shown in Fig. A-12.

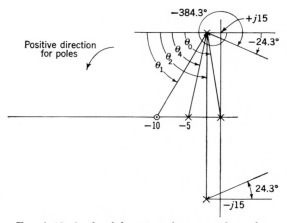

Fig. A-12. Angle of departure from complex poles.

The root-locus procedure is based upon the location of the poles and zeros of KGH in the s plane. These points do not move. They are merely the terminal points for the loci of the roots of $1 + KGH$. If the locus crosses the imaginary axis for some gain K, the system becomes unstable at this value of K. The degree of stability is determined largely by the roots near the imaginary axis. The root-locus sketch provides the engineer with the form of the locus and is helpful in making a more accurate plot.

A-7. Measurement of Gain. The rules of Sec. A-6 center about the angle criterion of Eq. (A-38), which is repeated:

$$\arg KGH = (2k + 1)180° \tag{A-46}$$

After the locus is sketched and certain points located more accurately, the values of gain that occur at certain points along the locus must be found. This gain K is evaluated from the criterion of Eq. (A-39) as follows:

$$|KGH| = 1 \quad \text{or} \quad K = \frac{1}{|GH|} \tag{A-47}$$

where $|GH|$ is the product of the magnitudes of the distances from the point at which the gain is to be evaluated to the zeros, divided by the product of the distances to the poles as follows:

$$K = \frac{\text{product of pole distances}}{\text{product of zero distances}} \tag{A-48}$$

The magnitudes are measured directly from the root-locus plot. If no zeros are present in the transfer function, the product of the zero distances is taken equal to unity.

A-8. Stability: Frequency-response Method. In the stability analysis of a servomechanism, the frequency response is often employed because of the simplicity with which the responses of various functions can be combined, whether the data be experimental or analytical. It is a characteristic of any stable linear system that if the input is excited with a sinusoidal function, the system undergoes a transient state, which usually dies out, and the output ultimately becomes sinusoidal at the same frequency. In general, however, the magnitude is different from the input, and the zero point on the cycle starts at a different point in time with respect to the corresponding zero of the input cycle, therefore indicating a phase shift. The analytical expression for any servomechanism whose transfer functions are known analytically can be converted from the function of the complex variable s to the function of angular frequency ω by the substitution $s = j\omega$, where $j = \sqrt{-1}$. Thus, the steady-state system response to sinusoidal stimuli can easily be determined. If the reference input of the servomechanism is oscillated sinusoidally and the steady-state performance obtained, the ratio of the transform of the actuating signal to the transform of the reference input is known as the *actuating ratio* or, in the case of a simple servomechanism (when the error is equal to the actuating signal), as the *error ratio* and is equal to the factor $1/(1 + G)$. Similarly, the ratio of the complex number that characterizes the magnitude and phase of the controlled-shaft output $C(j\omega)$ to the complex number that characterizes the sinusoidal reference input $(R(j\omega)$ is given by

$$\frac{C(j\omega)}{R(j\omega)} = \frac{G(j\omega)}{1 + G(j\omega)} \tag{A-49}$$

where H is taken as unity. For the simple second-order system the closed-loop transfer function is

$$\frac{C(j\omega)}{R(j\omega)} = \frac{\kappa}{(\kappa - \lambda^2) + j\lambda} \tag{A-50}$$

where $\lambda = \omega/\omega_n$. This is plotted on Figs. A-13 and A-14.

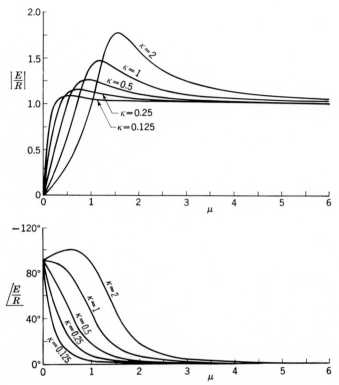

Fig. A-13. Error ratio of an idealized servomechanism.

The size of the peak magnitudes is a measure of how oscillatory the servo is, as can be seen by comparing these response curves with those of Fig. A-5 for the same value of κ. A servomechanism that is perfect has zero-magnitude error ratio for all frequencies, and the magnitude and phase of $C(j\omega)/R(j\omega)$ are unity and zero degrees, respectively, for all frequencies.

It is also of interest to find the frequency response of various elements of the system. This can be obtained by substituting $s = j\omega$ into the transfer function of the element. One method of representing the data obtained is by plotting the magnitude and phase of the frequency transfer function on a polar plot. The resulting curve is known as a *frequency*

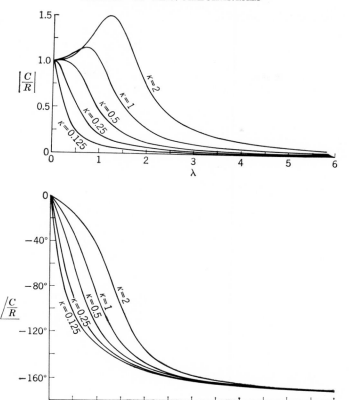

FIG. A-14. Control ratio of an idealized servomechanism.

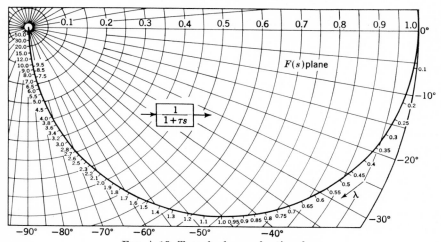

FIG. A-15. Transfer locus of a time lag.

transfer locus. The frequency transfer locus of the network of Fig. A-2 is given in Fig. A-15 where $\lambda = \omega/\omega_1 = \omega\tau$.

If it is desired, the transfer function of the entire servomechanism can be investigated by this means. The transfer locus of G of the idealized servomechanism is shown in Fig. A-16. Changes in gain can be effected merely by changing the magnitude scale of the graph.

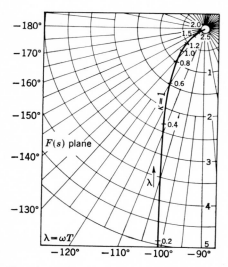

FIG. A-16. G locus of an idealized servo-mechanism.

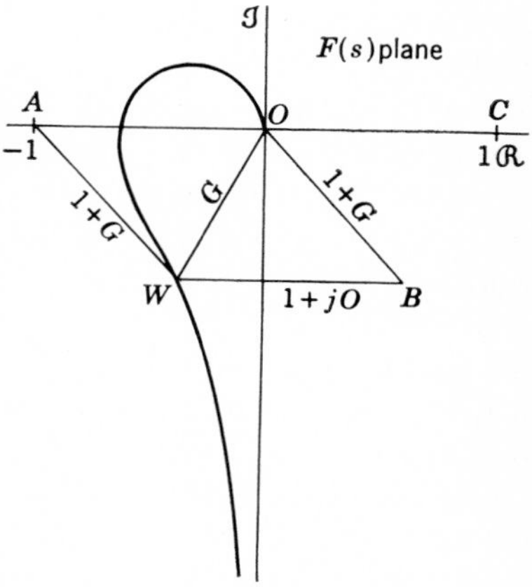

FIG. A-17. Construction of ratios.

The magnitude and phase of either the control ratio or the error ratio can be obtained from the open-loop transfer locus of the servomechanism by means of the geometrical construction shown in Fig. A-17. From this figure the following equations result:

$$\frac{E}{R} = \frac{1}{1 + G} = \frac{1}{AW} = \left|\frac{1}{AW}\right| \underline{/-OAW} \tag{A-51}$$

$$\frac{C}{R} = \frac{G}{1 + G} = \frac{OW}{AW} = \left|\frac{OW}{AW}\right| \underline{/WOC - OAW} \tag{A-52}$$

One of the most important uses of the G locus is in the determination of system stability. It is possible to predict whether or not a system will be stable when it is connected closed-loop, even though the data used are a combination of experimental data for physical equipment and calculated design values for the remainder of the components. A fundamental theorem of Cauchy, applied by Nyquist to the analysis of feedback amplifiers, enables the stability to be determined graphically. For single-loop systems the stability criterion is as follows: Plot the G locus for all frequencies from minus infinity to plus infinity. If the point $-1 + j0$ is enclosed, the system is unstable; otherwise it is stable. If it is not clear from the locus whether or not the -1 point is enclosed, draw a vector from $-1 + j0$ to the locus for any given frequency; if the net angle through which the vector sweeps as the frequency is increased from minus infinity to plus infinity is zero, the -1 point is not enclosed and the system is stable. If the net angle is other than zero, it is unstable.

To apply this criterion, G must be zero at infinite frequency. The only reason why the graph would not show it as zero is that the response was not considered at high enough frequencies or that the experimental or analytical data did not take into account distributed parameters that would make the transmission zero at infinite frequency. G can be plotted for positive frequencies as before, and for negative frequencies all that is necessary is to substitute $-j\omega$ for s. (The G locus for negative frequencies, however, is the mirror image about the real axis of the positive-frequency locus. If there are any poles of G at the origin of the s plane, it is necessary in using this stability criterion to map the contour of Fig. A-18 onto the

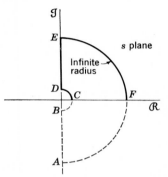

Fig. A-18. Contour enclosing right half s plane.

$F(s)$ plane, the function G being employed, and to shrink the inner radius and expand the outer radius until they approach zero and infinite radius, respectively. This will avoid the pole of G at the origin, as found in most servomechanisms.

An important characteristic of the servo that the transfer locus discloses, in addition to the stability itself, is the margin of stability. The *phase margin*, for example, indicates in terms of phase how close the transfer locus of a servomechanism comes to looping the -1 point. It is determined by finding the phase of G at the frequency at which G has unity magnitude. Add $180°$ to this angle, and the result is the phase margin. The phase margin also can be determined as the angle between the negative real axis and the angle of the locus of the frequency where G has unity magnitude. The value of approximately $45°$ is often used in the adjustment of servomechanisms. *Gain margin* is a measure of how much the gain of the servo can be increased or decreased before the servo becomes unstable.

A-9. Plotting Transfer Functions by Means of the Asymptotic Approximation. Another method of representing a transfer locus of an element or of the open-loop transfer function of the servomechanism utilizes logarithmic frequency and logarithmic-magnitude scales. Magnitude spectra are often asymptotic to straight lines by virtue of the physical relations involved, and errors in experimental data are thus easily spotted. The use of logarithmic scales generally employs decibels as a measure of magnitude, so that the semilogarithmic graph paper may be used. If a quantity has a magnitude k, its magnitude expressed in decibels is 20 log k, logarithms to the base 10 being used. Ratios of frequencies are often expressed in terms of octaves, and, by definition, the number n of octaves between two frequencies f_1 and f_2 is given by

$$n = \frac{\log\ (f_2/f_1)}{\log 2} \tag{A-53}$$

The most commonly encountered functions in servo systems are (1) frequency invariant factors, (2) simple* zeros and poles at the origin, (3) simple zeros, (4) simple poles, and (5) quadratic zeros and poles.

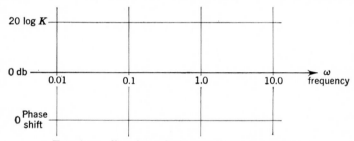

Fig. A-19. db gain and phase shift for a constant.

Each of these functions can be plotted point by point. Because of the nature of the plot, however, a linear asymptotic approximation of the decibel-magnitude curves permits a rapid method of plotting these factors. In all cases, these curves are plotted on semilog paper. The linear scale is the gain plotted against frequency ω, the latter being plotted on a logarithmic scale. Phase shift is plotted on a linear scale against logarithmic frequency.

Frequency Invariant Factors. The products of the gains, which are constants independent of frequency, are plotted from the function

$$20 \log_{10} K \qquad \text{in db} \tag{A-54}$$

where K represents the product of all the frequency invariant terms in the GH function. Equation (A-54) is plotted, in Fig. A-19, as a constant with zero phase shift.

Zeros or Poles at the Origin. For zeros or poles at the origin of the form

$$(j\omega)^n \qquad \text{or} \qquad \frac{1}{(j\omega)^n}$$

* Simple means there is only a first-order zero or pole at a point.

the amplitude and phase curves are found by taking the logarithm of these functions:

$$\log_e j\omega^{+n} = \pm n \log_e \omega + jn90° \qquad (A\text{-}55)$$

For simple zeros or poles the integer n is unity. The amplitude in decibels is $\pm n20 \log_{10} \omega$, and the phase shift in degrees is $\pm n90°$. The $\pm n$ accounts for either zeros or poles; $+n$ corresponds to zeros and $-n$ corresponds to poles.

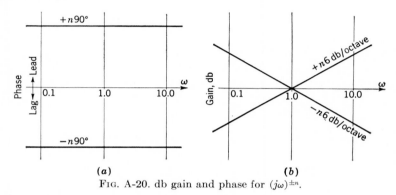

(a) (b)

Fig. A-20. db gain and phase for $(j\omega)^{\pm n}$.

The phase-shift curve for a term of this type is constant $\pm n90°$. For a single zero at the origin, the phase shift is a constant $+90°$; and for a single pole at the origin, the phase shift is a constant $-90°$, as shown in Fig. A-20a.

The amplitude is a straight line with a slope approximately equal to $\pm n6$ db/octave, where n is the number of zeros or poles at the origin. An increase of frequency by 1 octave corresponds to a doubling of the frequency. For a single zero, the straight line is of slope $+6$ db/octave and intersects the zero decibel axis at the point $\omega = 1$. The curve for a single pole, which is shown in Fig. A-20b, is a straight line with slope -6 db/octave passing through the zero-decibel axis at the point $\omega = 1$. These straight lines, which are shown in Figs. A-20a and b, are not asymptotic approximations but, rather, are the actual curves.

The slope of the amplitude curves (straight lines at $\pm n6$ db/octave) can be verified by considering the change in decibel amplitude for a change in frequency of 1 octave.

$$\Delta \text{ db} = 20(\log \omega_2\tau - \log \omega_1\tau) = 20 \log \frac{\omega_2}{\omega_1} \qquad (A\text{-}56)$$

But ω_2 is equal to $2\omega_1$, hence

$$\Delta \text{ db} = 20 \log_{10} 2 = 20(0.30103) \cong 6 \text{ db/octave} \qquad (A\text{-}57)$$

For ease in plotting, the constant portion of the transfer function K can be combined with the $\pm (j\omega)^n$ term. Usually only a single or double pole exists at the origin. Take as an example a single pole at the origin. The constant and this pole are combined as follows:

$$\frac{K(\omega\tau_1 + 1) \cdots}{j\omega(\omega\tau_2 + 1) \cdots} = \frac{(\omega\tau_1 + 1)}{j(\omega/K)(\omega\tau_2 + 1) \cdots} \qquad (A\text{-}58)$$

The term to be plotted is

$$\frac{1}{j(\omega/K)} \qquad (A\text{-}59)$$

The term of Eq. A-59) has the same slope as the single pole at the origin

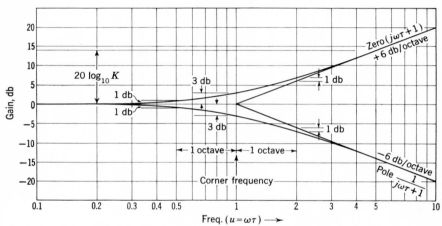

Fig. A-21. Amplitude response of $K(j\omega\tau + 1)$ and $1/(j\omega\tau + 1)$.

$1/j\omega$, but the amplitude curve intersects the zero-decibel line at the frequency $\omega = K$. The phase shift remains a constant at $-90°$.

Simple Zeros. For simple zeros of the form

$$j\omega\tau_1 + 1 \qquad (A\text{-}60)$$

the linear asymptotic approximation is used. For $\omega\tau_1 \ll 1$,

$$20 \log_{10} |j\omega\tau_1 + 1| \cong 20 \log_{10} 1 = 0 \text{ db}$$

For small values of ω the magnitude remains at zero decibels. When ω becomes much greater than $1(\omega\tau_1 \gg 1)$,

$$20 \log_{10} |j\omega\tau_1 + 1| \cong 20 \log_{10} \omega\tau_1$$

For large values of ω, the amplitude and phase response of a simple zero $(j\omega\tau_1 + 1)$ resemble those for a simple zero at the origin $j\omega\tau_1$. The slope, for large ω, is $+6$ db/octave. The 6-db/octave straight-line asymptote intersects the zero-decibel line when $\omega\tau_1 = 1$, or when $\omega = 1/\tau$. The point of intersection at $\omega = 1/\tau_1$ is termed the *corner frequency*. The two straight lines, one along the zero-db axis and the other at $+6$ db/octave, intersecting at the point $\omega = 1/\tau_1$, are asymptotic approximations for a simple zero of the form $(j\omega\tau_1 + 1)$. This straight-line asymptote is

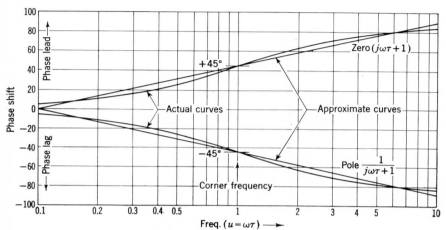

FIG. A-22. Phase response of $(j\omega\tau + 1)$ and $1/(j\omega\tau + 1)$.

shown in Fig. A-21. The procedure to follow when plotting the amplitude curve for $(j\omega\tau_1 + 1)$ is outlined as follows:

1. Locate the corner frequency, i.e., $\omega = 1/\tau_1$.
2. Plot a line with a slope of 6 db/octave passing through this point to the right (increasing frequency) and a straight line along zero decibels to the left.

The actual curve for the amplitude rises $+3$ db above the asymptote at the corner frequency and approximately $+1$ db, respectively, at 1 octave above and 1 octave below the corner frequency. These deviations from the asymptotic approximation are computed by evaluating the magnitude of the zero $(j\omega\tau_1 + 1)$ at the corner frequency and at one-half and twice the corner frequency.

The phase shift for a simple zero is obtained from the expression

$$\phi = \tan^{-1}\omega\tau_1 \qquad (A\text{-}61)$$

The frequency ω is plotted on a logarithmic scale. The arctan curve has a value of $45°$ when $\omega\tau_1 = 1$, which is at the corner frequency. The phase curve starts at $0°$ and increases to a maximum of $90°$ and is symmetric about the $45°$ point. The complete frequency-response curve for the zero comprises the amplitude curve shown in Fig. A-21 and the phase-shift curve shown in Fig. A-22.

Since the phase curve is a familiar arctan curve, it too is often sketched. An approximate straight-line phase curve can be used to aid in sketching the phase response.   The straight line passes through 0° at $\frac{1}{10} \times$ corner frequency, $+45°$ at the corner frequency, and 90° at 10 × corner frequency.   If a line is drawn, as shown in Fig. A-22, the maximum deviation from the actual curve is 6°.

Simple Poles.   Simple poles of the form $1/(j\omega\tau_2 + 1)$ can be treated similarly to simple zeros.   Since the logarithm of the reciprocal is equal to the negative of the logarithm,

$$20 \log \frac{1}{j\omega\tau_2 + 1} = -20 \log (j\omega\tau_2 + 1)$$

the curve for a simple pole is identical to that for a simple zero with the exception of a minus sign.   For small frequencies, $\omega < 1/\tau_2$, the amplitude remains at zero decibels.   For large frequencies, $\omega > 1/\tau_2$, the asymptote is a straight line at -6 db/octave.   This asymptote, which is shown in Fig. A-21, intersects the zero-decibel axis at $\omega = 1/\tau_2$.   The actual amplitude curve deviates from the straight-line approximation by -3 db at the corner frequency and by -1 db at both $1/2\tau_2$ and $2/\tau_2$. The phase-shift curve is identical to that for the case of the zero; but since the pole is in the denominator of GH, the sign is changed when the angle is brought into the numerator:

$$\phi = -\tan^{-1} \omega\tau_2 \qquad (A\text{-}62)$$

The curve defined by this equation is an arctan curve that starts from zero phase shift and approaches $-90°$ phase lag for large frequencies. The $-45°$ phase shift occurs at the corner frequency.

If the transfer function has a repeated zero or pole—for example, if there are two equal poles or two equal zeros—the amplitude curve resembles the case for a single zero or pole; however, the slope changes from 6 to 12 db/octave and the phase shift is at $\pm 90°$ at the corner frequency for a zero or pole rather than at $\pm 45°$ for a single zero or pole. The phase shift varies from zero to $\pm 180°$ rather than from zero to $\pm 90°$.

Quadratic Zeros and Poles.   Occasionally, quadratic poles of the form

$$G(j\omega) = \frac{\omega_n{}^2}{(\omega_n{}^2 - \omega^2) + j2\zeta\omega\omega_n} \qquad (A\text{-}63)$$

occur in the GH function.   Equation (A-63) can be put in dimensionless form by replacing ω/ω_n by the frequency ratio λ with the result:

$$G(j\lambda) = \frac{1}{(1 - \lambda^2) + j2\zeta\lambda} \qquad (A\text{-}64)$$

The magnitude and phase of Eq. A-64 are plotted in Figs. A-23 and A-24. Because the amplitude and phase response for quadratic poles depend not only upon the corner frequency but also upon the damping ratio ζ, these dimensionless charts are used to make the plot. The amplitude and phase response are plotted by locating the corner frequency and damping ratio for the particular frequency factor. The damping

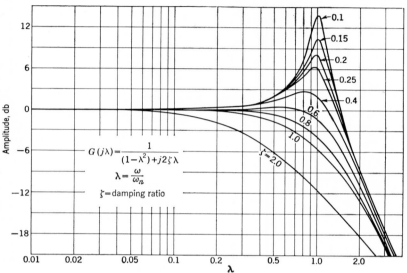

Fig. A-23. Magnitude of quadratic function.

ratio and corner frequency are found by comparison of the given expression with Eq. (A-63). For example, suppose it is required to plot the function

$$\frac{1}{s^2 + 3s + 10} \qquad (A\text{-}65)$$

Equation (A-65) is put into the form of Eq. (A-64) by comparison.

$$\left[\frac{\frac{1}{10}}{\frac{s^2}{10} + \frac{3s}{10} + 1} \right]_{s=j\omega} = \left[\frac{1}{(s/\omega_n)^2 + 2\zeta(s/\omega_n) + 1} \right]_{s=j\omega} \qquad (A\text{-}66)$$

Equating like terms,

$$\omega_n = \sqrt{10} \qquad \text{and} \qquad \zeta = \frac{\omega_n}{2} \frac{3}{10} = 0.475$$

The transfer loci of a number of useful functions are given, with the

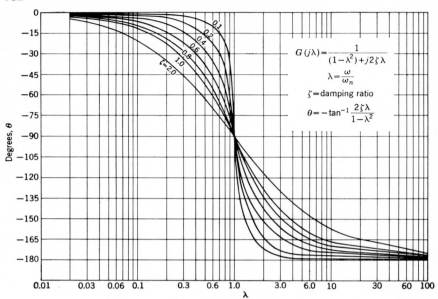

FIG. A-24. Phase of quadratic function.

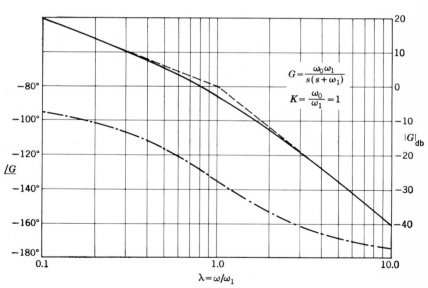

FIG. A-25. Simple idealized servomechanism.

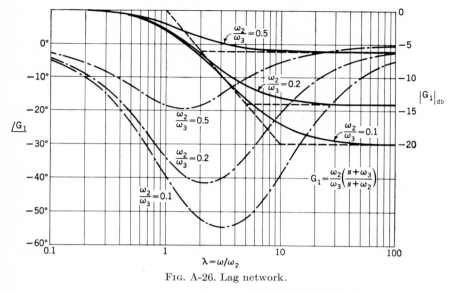

Fig. A-26. Lag network.

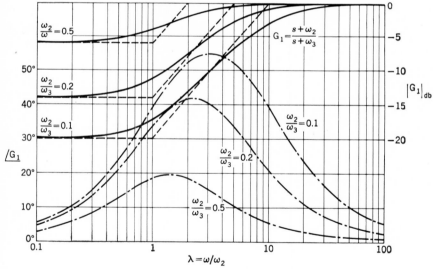

Fig. A-27. Lead network.

asymptotes dotted to show corner frequencies clearly. Figure A-25 is the locus of a simple idealized servomechanism and is known by the magnitude of the downward slopes of the asymptotes as a 6–12 servo. Figures A-26 and A-27 show the responses of lag and lead networks, respectively. To find the response of two systems in cascade, the respective magnitudes and phases given in the logarithmic plots of their loci are added. To change gain or multiplying factors, add the same number of decibels to every point on the G locus, as by changing the ordinate scale.

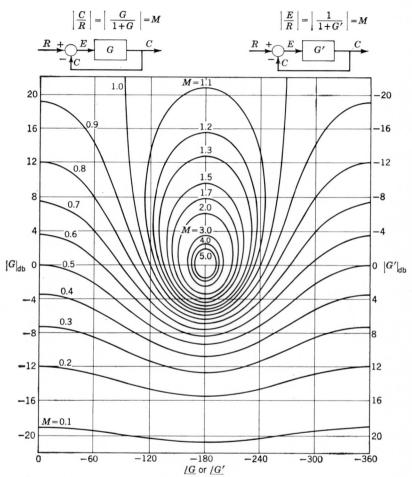

FIG. A-28. Loci of constant magnitudes of control ratio and error ratio.

If the magnitude of the error ratio or the control ratio is desired, combine the magnitude and phase responses and replot on Fig. A-28, reading off the intersections of the G locus with the locus given. The effect of changes in gain can be seen by mentally sliding the G locus in the direction parallel to the magnitude axis.

A-10. Multiple-loop Servos. Multiple-loop servomechanisms are used for the purpose of aiding the performance of servomechanisms, improving their linearity, and reducing noise, for stabilization, for increasing the power level of a signal, for synthesizing functions, and for a variety of related reasons. After a system has been determined to be stable, its performance can be expressed in terms of the error ratio and control ratio, as with any other system.

To determine the stability of a multiple-loop system, there are four methods that can be used. They are as follows:

1. Examine the stability of each minor loop. If a loop is stable, it may be replaced by a single block having an equivalent transfer function in determining the stability of the entire system.

2. Reduce the multiple-loop system to an equivalent single loop by recognizing the presence of parallel transfer functions.

3. Write an equation involving all the elementary transfer functions of this system and linking the actuating signal E with the reference input R. Examine the denominator of the error ratio E/R for the location of its zeros, after clearing fractions (ratios of transfer functions) from both numerator and denominator.

4. Write a set of simultaneous equations, and solve for the determinant.

The first of these is self-explanatory. The second method is merely a recognition that block diagrams may be drawn so that the system appears to be a multiple-loop system, although it actually consists of only a single loop. The third and fourth methods are basically the same, but the use of determinants is a more systematic way of accomplishing the result. The use of determinants involves writing a set of simultaneous equations, by writing an equation for each output variable in terms of the inputs. The performance characteristics may be found by solving the simultaneous equations in terms of the various stimuli. The location of the zeros of the delta of the determinant must be in the left-half s plane for stability. Stability can be determined by using Routh's criterion or graphically by seeing whether or not the -1 point is looped by the sums of the various loci constituting the delta.

A-11. Error Coefficients. Another method of determining the effectiveness of a servomechanism employs the time components of error. In this method, the servo characteristics must be represented analytically, but the reference-input function can be graphically presented. The only requirement of the reference-input function is that its frequency spectrum have a characteristic of falling off rapidly with increased frequency. This implies that the reference input has no sudden motions. The method consists in graphically or analytically determining the derivatives of the reference-input motion, determining the servo error contribution for each of the derivatives of the reference-input motion, and adding these component errors together to yield the total error.

The actuating signal of a linear servomechanism can be expressed in terms of the following series:

$$e = K_0 r + K_1 \frac{dr}{dt} + K_2 \frac{d^2 r}{dt^2} + \cdots \tag{A-67}$$

This expression consists of a sum of terms, each of which is composed of one of the derivatives of the reference-input motion and a constant whose value depends upon the characteristics of the servomechanism. Various constants, different for each different servomechanism, can be computed in accordance with the following expressions:

$$\begin{aligned}
K_0 &= \left[\frac{1}{1+G} \right]_{s=0} \\
K_1 &= \left[\frac{d}{ds} \left(\frac{1}{1+G} \right) \right]_{s=0} \\
K_2 &= \left[\frac{1}{2} \frac{d^2}{ds^2} \left(\frac{1}{1+G} \right) \right]_{s=0} \\
K_n &= \left[\frac{1}{n!} \frac{d^n}{ds^n} \left(\frac{1}{1+G} \right) \right]_{s=0}
\end{aligned} \tag{A-68}$$

The constants have been calculated for various types of servos and are shown in Table 2-2. Servomechanisms whose loci have an initial slope of -6 db have zero position error ($K_0 = 0$) but have velocity, acceleration, and higher derivative errors. Servomechanisms whose loci have an initial slope of -12 db/octave have zero position or velocity error ($K_0 = K_1 = 0$). Zero acceleration error is obtained if the initial slope is -18 db/octave or more.

The components of Table 2-2 can be computed from Eq. (A-68) but frequently can be found more easily by a series expansion. To illustrate this approach, K_1 and K_2 for the 6–12 system are found. The transfer function is

$$G(s) = \frac{\omega_0 \omega_1}{s(s + \omega_1)} \tag{A-69}$$

The E/R ratio is written

$$\frac{E}{R} = \frac{1}{1 + G(s)} = K_0 + K_1 s + K_2 s^2 + \cdots \tag{A-70}$$

Equation (A-69) is inserted into (A-70) and expanded:

$$\frac{E}{R} = \frac{s(s + \omega_1)}{s^2 + \omega_1 s + \omega_0 \omega_1} = \frac{\omega_1 s + s^2}{\omega_0 \omega_1 \left(1 + \frac{s}{\omega_1} + \frac{s^2}{\omega_0 \omega_1} \right)} \tag{A-71}$$

The term in the denominator is expanded with the series

$$\frac{1}{1+x} = 1 - x + x^2 \cdots$$

yielding the result

$$\frac{E}{R} = \frac{\omega_1 s + s^2}{\omega_0 \omega_1}\left[1 - \frac{s}{\omega_0} - \frac{s^2}{\omega_0 \omega_1} + \left(\frac{s}{\omega_0} + \frac{s^2}{\omega_0 \omega_1}\right)^2 + \cdots\right] \quad \text{(A-72)}$$

The indicated multiplication is carried out and terms are collected

$$\frac{E}{R} = \left(\frac{1}{\omega_0}\right)s + \left[\frac{1}{\omega_0 \omega_1}\left(1 - \frac{\omega_1}{\omega_0}\right)\right]s^2 + \cdots$$

$$= \left(\frac{1}{\omega_0}\right)s + \left(\frac{\omega_0 - \omega_1}{\omega_0^2 \omega_1}\right)s^2 + \cdots \quad \text{(A-73)}$$

Comparison of Eq. (A-73) with (A-70) yields

$$K_1 = \frac{1}{\omega_0} \quad \text{and} \quad K_2 = \frac{\omega_0 - \omega_1}{\omega_0^2 \omega_1} \quad \text{(A-74)}$$

which checks with the terms in Table 2-2.

A-12. A-C Servos. The form of the signal information in a servo-mechanism is often electrical, and if it is an alternating voltage, the direction of the signal is determined from the instantaneous polarity of the

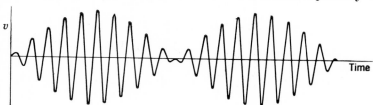

Fig. A-29. Suppressed carrier voltage.

voltage with respect to some reference and the magnitude of the envelope is a measure of the size of the signal. If the signal is also sinusoidal, the form of the signal voltage is

$$v = \sin \omega_s t \sin \omega_c t \quad \text{(A-75)}$$

where ω_s is the angular frequency of oscillation of the signal and ω_c is the carrier frequency. If a potentiometer winding were excited with an alternating supply and its shaft oscillated sinusoidally about the position of zero output voltage, a modulated wave of the form of Eq. (A-75) would be obtained, the frequency of supply would be the carrier frequency, and the signal frequency would be the frequency of shaft oscillations. The form of the voltage is shown in Fig. A-29 for one value of ω_s and one value of ω_c.

Employing elementary trigonometric relations, the product of the two sine terms of Eq. (A-75) can be written as a sum:

$$v = \tfrac{1}{2} \cos [(\omega_c - \omega_s)t] - \tfrac{1}{2} \cos [(\omega_c + \omega_s)t] \qquad \text{(A-76)}$$

The voltage v is identically equal to the sum of two sinusoidal voltages, neither of which has the frequency ω_c of the supply and neither of which has the frequency ω_s of the signal. It is termed a *suppressed carrier* voltage, since the carrier frequency is not present. When a voltage given by either Eq. (A-75) or (A-76) is introduced to a network, the network modifies this voltage and produces an output. The form of the output voltage can be found by determining how each sideband frequency is modified by the network and using the superposition theorem, the two separate components of the signal being added to achieve the output voltage.

The output voltage is given by the following expression:

$$v_0 = \frac{B}{2} \sin \omega_c t \cos (\omega_s t + \alpha) + \frac{C}{2} \cos \omega_c t \cos (\omega_s t + \beta) \qquad \text{(A-77)}$$

where

$$B^2 = A_u{}^2 + A_l{}^2 + 2 A_u A_l \cos (\phi_u + \phi_l)$$

$$\alpha = \tan^{-1} \frac{A_u \cos \phi_u + A_l \cos \phi_l}{A_u \sin \phi_u - A_l \sin \phi_l}$$

$$C^2 = A_u{}^2 + A_l{}^2 - 2 A_u A_l \cos (\phi_u + \phi_l)$$

$$\beta = \tan^{-1} \frac{-A_u \cos \phi_u + A_l \cos \phi_l}{A_u \sin \phi_u + A_l \sin \phi_l}$$

where A_u is the magnitude of the transfer function of the network at the upper sideband frequency, A_l is the magnitude of the transfer function of the network at the lower sideband frequency, ϕ_u is the phase of the transfer function of the network at the upper sideband frequency, and ϕ_l is the phase of the transfer function of the network at the lower sideband frequency. If the characteristics of the network are symmetrical about the carrier frequency, such that the gain for the upper sideband frequency $\omega_c + \omega_s$ equals the gain for the lower sideband frequency $\omega_c - \omega_s$ and the phases are the negative of one another, then a pure suppressed-carrier-voltage output results which is

$$v_0 = A_u \sin (\omega_s t + \phi_u) \sin \omega_c t \qquad \text{(A-78)}$$

Networks designed to have a minimum transmission at carrier frequency, such that their magnitude characteristics show a notch at this frequency, produce a lead phase angle to advance the phase of the envelope of the signal. The process of cascading such networks in the servoamplifier is known as *equalization at carrier frequency.*

GLOSSARY OF TERMS
(Based on Preliminary AIEE Reports)

Actuating ratio is the frequency response of the actuating signal to the reference input. Under linear conditions this ratio is expressed $E/R = 1/(1 + GH)$.

Actuating signal (e) is the reference input minus the primary feedback.

Command (v) is the input that is established or varied by some means external to and independent of the feedback control system under consideration.

Control accuracy is the degree of correspondence between the ultimately controlled variable and the ideal value.

Control area of a feedback control system is the time integral of the absolute value of the difference between the controlled variable and its final value following a specified step input or disturbance. The step input or disturbance must be specified in location and magnitude.

Control elements (g_1) comprise the portion of the feedback control system that is required to produce the manipulated variable from the actuating signal.

Control precision is the degree of reproducibility of the ultimately controlled variable for several independent applications of the same reference input under the same operating conditions.

Control ratio is the frequency response of the controlled variable to the reference input. Under linear conditions, this ratio is expressed mathematically as $C/R = G/(1 + GH)$.

Controlled system (g_2) is the body, process, or machine a particular quantity or condition of which is to be controlled.

Controlled variable (c) is that quantity or condition of the controlled system which is directly measured and controlled.

Corner frequency of a factor of a transfer function is the frequency at which lines asymptotic to its log-magnitude curve intersect.

Dead time is a fixed interval of time between the impression of an input on an element or system and the undistorted response to the input.

Disturbance (u) is a signal (other than the reference input) that tends to affect the value of the controlled variable.

Error ratio is the frequency response of the system error with respect to the reference input. Under linear conditions the ratio is expressed mathematically as Ye/R. In simple systems where the system error is equal to the actuating signal, the actuating ratio becomes the error ratio, i.e., $Ye/R = E/R = 1/(1 + G)$.

Feedback control system is a control system that tends to maintain a prescribed relationship of one system variable to another by comparing functions of these variables and using the difference as a means of control.

Feedback controller is a mechanism that measures the value of the controlled variable, accepts the value of the command, and, as the result of a comparison, manipulates the controlled system in order to maintain an established relationship between the controlled variable and the command.

Feedback elements (h) comprise the portion of the feedback control system that establishes the relationship between the primary feedback and the controlled variable.

Frequency response of a system or element is the steady-state ratio of magnitude and the difference in phase of the output with respect to a sinusoidal input. The range of frequency and conditions of operation and measurement must be specified.

Gain of a system or element is the ratio of magnitude of the output with respect to the magnitude of sinusoidal input. The frequency and conditions of operation and measurement must be specified.

Gain crossover is a point in the plot of loop ratio at which the magnitude of the loop ratio is unity.

Gain margin is the amount by which the magnitude of the loop ratio of a stable system is different from unity at phase crossover. It is frequently expressed in decibels.

Ideal value (i) is the value of the ultimately controlled variable that would result from an idealized system operating from the same command as the actual system under consideration.

Idealized system (g_i) is one whose performance is agreed upon to define the relationship between the ideal value and the command.

Indirectly controlled system (z) is the body, process, or machine that determines the relationship between the indirectly controlled variable and the controlled variable.

Indirectly controlled variable (q) is that quantity or condition which is controlled by virtue of its relation to the controlled variable and which is not directly measured for control.

Input resolution between two variables of a system or element is the maximum change in the variable considered as the input that can be made without causing a change in the variable considered as the output. Resolution may be dependent upon conditions of operation and the operating point. If these are not specified the maximum value of the resolution over the entire operating range and for all conditions of operation is implied.

Log-magnitude–angle diagram is a plot of the log magnitude vs. angle of a transfer function with frequency as a parameter.

Log-magnitude and phase diagram is a plot of the log magnitude and phase angle of a transfer function vs. log frequency. Log magnitude and frequency may be multiplied by constants.

Loop gain is the magnitude of the loop ratio.

Loop input resolution at a specific variable is the input resolution when the loop is opened at the specified variable.

Loop output resolution at a specific variable is the output resolution when the loop is opened at the specified variable.

Loop ratio is the frequency response of the primary feedback to the actuating signal. Under linear conditions the ratio is expressed mathematically as $B/E = GH$.

Manipulated variable (m) is that quantity or condition which the controller applies to the controlled system.

Normal time response is the time response with zero initial-energy storage.

Nyquist diagram is a closed polar plot of a loop transfer function from which stability may be determined. For a single-loop system it is a map on the $F(s)$ plane of an s-plane contour that encloses the entire right half of the s plane excluding poles of the loop transfer function.

Output resolution between two variables of a system or element is the minimum change in the variable considered as the output that can be made by changing the variable considered as the input. Resolution may be dependent upon conditions of operation and the operating point. If these are not specified, the maximum value of the resolution over the entire operating range and for all conditions of operation is implied.

Parabolic, when used to describe a function of time, means that the function is zero for zero and negative values of time and has a constant second derivative for positive time.

Parametric variation is a change in system properties not caused by the actuating signal that may affect the performance or operation of the feedback control system.

Phase crossover is a point on the plot of loop ratio at which its phase angle is 180°.

Phase margin is the angle by which the phase of the loop ratio of a stable system differs from 180° at gain crossover.

Primary feedback (b) is a signal which is a function of the controlled variable and which is compared with the reference input to obtain the actuating signal.

Primary-feedback ratio is the frequency response of the primary feedback to the reference input. Under linear conditions this ratio is expressed mathematically as $B/R = GH/(1 + GH)$.

Ramp, when used to describe a function of time, means that the function is zero for zero and negative time and has a constant first derivative for positive time.

Reference input (r) is a signal established as a standard of comparison for a feedback control system by virtue of its relation to the command.

Reference-input elements (a) comprise the portion of the feedback control system that establishes the relationship between the reference input and the command.

Response time of a system or element is the time required for the output to first reach a specified value after the application of a step input or disturbance.

Rise time of a system or element is the time required for the output to increase from one specified percentage of the final value to another, following the application of a step input. Usually the specified percentages are 10 and 90 per cent.

Servomechanism is a feedback control system in which the controlled variable is mechanical position.

Settling time of a system or element is the time required for the absolute value of the difference between the output and its final value to become and remain less than a specified amount, following the application of a step input or disturbance. The specified amount is often expressed in terms of per cent of the final value.

Spurious command is an undesired component of the command.

Spurious reference input is an undesired component of the reference input.

Stability is the property of a system or element whose response to a stimulus dies down if the stimulus is removed.

A statement that a system is stable means that the system is stable under all normal operating conditions and for all types of stimuli normally encountered. A system may be referred to as being stable in one region of operation and not in another. If this is the case, the region of stability should be specified.

A system is normally regarded as unstable if its output is oscillating in the absence of stimuli but may be specified as being stable if the oscillations are constrained to less than a prescribed magnitude.

Steady-state error is the error that remains after the transient has expired.

Step, when used to describe a function of time, means that the function is zero for zero and negative time and has a constant finite value for positive time.

Stimulus is any type of signal that affects the controlled variable, for example, reference input and disturbance.

Summing point is a descriptive symbol used in block diagrams to denote the algebraic summation of two or more signals. The direction of information flow is indicated by arrows and the algebraic nature of the summation by plus and minus signs.

System deviation (y_d) is the value of the ultimately controlled variable minus the ideal value. The system deviation is the negative of the system error. (See *Ideal value.*)

System error (y_e) is the ideal value minus the value of the ultimately controlled variable. (See *Ideal value.*)

Time constant of an exponential component of a transient response is the time required for the component to decay from one value to $1/e$ of that value.

In an element or system whose response to a step input is a first-order exponential, the time constant is the output change to be completed, divided by the rate of change of the output. If the response to a step input is not a first-order exponential, this ratio is not constant with time. In such a case, the definition in the first paragraph still applies to each exponential component of the response.

Mathematically, the time constant is equal to τ in the transform factor $(1 + \tau s)^{-1}$ and in the exponential $e^{-t/\tau}$.

Time response of a system or element is the output as a function of time following the application of a prescribed input under specified operating conditions.

Total overshoot is the maximum negative value of the system error for a specified positive stimulus.

Transfer function of a linear system or element is the ratio of the transform of the output to the transform of its input under the conditions of zero initial-energy storage. It is a complete description of the dynamic properties of a system and may be represented as a mathematical expression, the frequency response, or the time response to a specified input.

Transfer locus of a system or element is a complex plot of its frequency response.

Transient error is the difference between the system error at any time and the steady-state system error for a specified positive stimulus.

Transient overshoot is the maximum negative value of the transient error.

LETTER SYMBOLS*

Recommended terms	Symbol	Obsolete terms from the literature
Actuating signal	e	Error, unbalance, actuating error, correction, deviation
Command	v	Input, desired value, set point, control point
Control elements	g_1	Amplifier, controller, servoamplifier, relay plant, load
Controlled system	g_2	Process, plant, load
Controlled variable	c	Output, regulated variable, measured variable
Disturbance	u	Load, disturbance, upset, noise, drift
Feedback elements	h	Conversion elements
Ideal value	i	Desired value
Idealized system	g_i	Ideal system, desired system, preferred system, reference system
Indirectly controlled system	z	Process, plant, load
Indirectly controlled variable	q	Output, regulated variable
Manipulated variable	m	Monitoring feedback
Reference input	r	Input, reference standard, desired value, set point
Reference-input elements	a	Conversion elements, primary elements, sensing elements
System error	y_e	Error, deviation

* A block diagram that further defines these symbols is included in Fig. A-1.

SERVOMECHANISM CONVERSION FACTORS

Multiply:	By:	To Obtain:
Angular measure:		
degrees	17.45	mils
degrees	60	minutes
degrees	1.745×10^{-2}	radians
mils	5.730×10^{-2}	degrees
mils	3.438	minutes
mils	1.000×10^{-3}	radians
minutes	1.667×10^{-2}	degrees
minutes	0.2909	mils
minutes	2.909×10^{-4}	radians
radians	57.30	degrees
radians	1.000×10^{3}	mils
radians	3.438×10^{3}	minutes
Army mil	$\frac{1}{6,400}$	revolutions
Angular velocity:		
deg/sec	1.745×10^{-2}	radians/sec
deg/sec	0.1667	rpm
deg/sec	2.778×10^{-3}	rps
radians/sec	57.30	deg/sec
radians/sec	9.549	rpm
radians/sec	0.1592	rps
rpm	6.0	deg/sec
rpm	0.1047	radians/sec
rpm	1.667×10^{-2}	rps
rps	360	deg/sec
rps	6.283	radians/sec
rps	60	rpm
Damping:		
$\dfrac{\text{ft-lb}}{\text{radians/sec}}$	20.11	$\dfrac{\text{oz-in.}}{\text{rpm}}$
$\dfrac{\text{oz-in.}}{\text{rpm}}$	4.974×10^{-2}	$\dfrac{\text{ft-lb}}{\text{radians/sec}}$
$\dfrac{\text{oz-in.}}{\text{rpm}}$	6.75×10^{-3}	$\dfrac{\text{newton-m}}{\text{radians/sec}}$
Inertia:		
g-cm^2	10^{-7}	kg-m^2
g-cm^2	5.468×10^{-3}	oz-in.^{2}
g-cm^2	7.372×10^{-8}	slug-ft^2
oz-in.^{2}	1.829×10^{2}	g-cm^2

Multiply:	By:	To Obtain:
oz-in.^{2}	1.348×10^{-5}	slug-ft^2
slug-ft^2	1.357×10^7	g-cm^2
(lb-ft-sec^2)	7.419×10^4	oz-in.^{2}
slug-ft^2	1.357	kg-m^2
lb-in.^{2}	2.925×10^{-4}	kg-m^2
oz-in.^{2}	1.829×10^{-5}	kg-m^2
Torque:		
ft-lb	1.383×10^4	g-cm
ft-lb	192	oz-in.
g-cm	7.235×10^{-5}	ft-lb
g-cm	1.389×10^{-2}	oz-in.
oz-in.	5.208×10^{-3}	ft-lb
oz-in.	72.01	g-cm
oz-in.	7.0612×10^{-3}	newton-m (joules)
Distance:		
cm	10^{-2}	m
in.	2.5400×10^{-2}	m
ft	0.30480	m
yd	0.91440	m
km	10^3	m
miles	1609.4	m
Velocity:		
ft/sec	0.30480	m/sec
miles/hr	0.44704	m/sec
knots	1.152	miles/hr
Mass:		
g	10^{-3}	kg
slug	14.594	kg
Force and weight:		
dynes	10^{-5}	newtons
poundals	0.13826	newtons
lb (force)	4.4482	newtons
Energy:		
ergs	10^{-7}	joules
kwhr	3.6×10^6	joules
calories	4.182	joules
ft-lb	1.356	joules
Btu	1055	
Power:		
ergs/sec	10^{-7}	watts
cal/sec	4.182	watts
Btu/hr	0.2930	watts
joules/sec	1.00	watts
hp	746	watts
ft-lb/sec	1.356	watts
Pressure:		
dynes/cm^2	10^{-1}	newton/m^2
psi	6.895×10^3	newton/m^2
atm	1.013×10^5	newton/m^2
cm Hg	1333	newton/m^2

Multiply:	By:	To Obtain:
Density:		
g/cm^3	10^3	kg/m^3
lb/ft^3	16.018	kg/m^3
$\dfrac{Torque}{Error}$:		
$\dfrac{oz\text{-}in.}{minute}$	0.0558	$\dfrac{lb\text{-}ft}{radian}$
$\dfrac{lb\text{-}ft}{radian}$	17.9	$\dfrac{oz\text{-}in.}{minute}$

NATURAL TRIGONOMETRIC FUNCTIONS*

Angle †	Sin ‡	Cos	Tan	Cot	Angle
0	0.0000	1.0000	0.0000	∞	90°
0° 30′	.0087	1.0000	.0087	114.59	89° 30′
1°	.0175	.9998	.0175	57.290	89°
1° 30′	.0262	.9997	.0262	38.188	88° 30′
2°	0.0349	0.9994	0.0349	28.636	88°
2° 30′	.0436	.9990	.0437	22.904	87° 30′
3°	.0523	.9986	.0524	19.081	87°
3° 30′	.0610	.9981	.0612	16.350	86° 30′
4°	0.0698	0.9976	0.0699	14.301	86°
4° 30′	.0785	.9969	.0787	12.706	85° 30′
5°	.0872	.9962	.0875	11.430	85°
5° 30′	.0958	.9954	.0963	10.385	84° 30′
6°	0.1045	0.9945	0.1051	9.5144	84°
6° 30′	.1132	.9936	.1139	8.7769	83° 30′
7°	.1219	.9925	.1228	8.1443	83°
7° 30′	.1305	.9914	.1317	7.5958	82° 30′
8°	0.1392	0.9903	0.1405	7.1154	82°
8° 30′	.1478	.9890	.1495	6.6912	81° 30′
9°	.1564	.9877	.1584	6.3138	81°
9° 30′	.1650	.9863	.1673	5.9758	80° 30′
10°	0.1736	0.9848	0.1763	5.6713	80°
10° 30′	.1822	.9833	.1853	5.3955	79° 30′
11°	.1908	.9816	.1944	5.1446	79°
11° 30′	.1994	.9799	.2035	4.9152	78° 30′
12°	0.2079	0.9781	0.2126	4.7046	78°
12° 30′	.2164	.9763	.2217	4.5107	77° 30′
13°	.2250	.9744	.2309	4.3315	77°
13° 30′	.2334	.9724	.2401	4.1653	76° 30′
14°	0.2419	0.9703	0.2493	4.0108	76°
14° 30′	.2504	.9681	.2586	3.8667	75° 30′
15°	.2588	.9659	.2679	3.7321	75°
15° 30′	.2672	.9636	.2773	3.6059	74° 30′
16°	0.2756	0.9613	0.2867	3.4874	74°
16° 30′	.2840	.9588	.2962	3.3759	73° 30′
17°	.2924	.9563	.3057	3.2709	73°
17° 30′	.3007	.9537	.3153	3.1716	72° 30′
18°	0.3090	0.9511	0.3249	3.0777	72°
18° 30′	.3173	.9483	.3346	2.9887	71° 30′
19°	.3256	.9455	.3443	2.9042	71°
19° 30′	.3338	.9426	.3541	2.8239	70° 30′
20°	0.3420	0.9397	0.3640	2.7475	70°
20° 30′	.3502	.9367	.3739	2.6746	69° 30′
21°	.3584	.9336	.3839	2.6051	69°
21° 30′	.3665	.9304	.3939	2.5386	68° 30′
Angle	Cos	Sin	Cot	Tan	Angle

* Read up for titles at bottom of table.
† Read up in last right-hand column for angles greater than 45°.
‡ Sine (90° − A) = cos A.

NATURAL TRIGONOMETRIC FUNCTIONS. (Continued)

Angle	Sin	Cos	Tan	Cot	Angle
22°	0.3746	0.9272	0.4040	2.4751	68°
22° 30'	.3827	.9239	.4142	2.4142	67° 30'
23°	.3907	.9205	.4245	2.3559	67°
23° 30'	.3987	.9171	.4348	2.2998	66° 30'
24°	0.4067	0.9135	0.4452	2.2460	66°
24° 30'	.4147	.9100	.4557	2.1943	65° 30'
25°	.4226	.9063	.4663	2.1445	65°
25° 30'	.4305	.9026	.4770	2.0965	64° 30'
26°	0.4384	0.8988	0.4877	2.0503	64°
26° 30'	.4462	.8949	.4986	2.0057	63° 30'
27°	.4540	.8910	.5095	1.9626	63°
27° 30'	.4617	.8870	.5206	1.9210	62° 30'
28°	0.4695	0.8829	0.5317	1.8807	62°
28° 30'	.4772	.8788	.5430	1.8418	61° 30'
29°	.4848	.8746	.5543	1.8040	61°
29° 30'	.4924	.8704	.5658	1.7675	60° 30'
30°	0.5000	0.8660	0.5774	1.7321	60°
30° 30'	.5075	.8616	.5890	1.6977	59° 30'
31°	.5150	.8572	.6009	1.6643	59°
31° 30'	.5225	.8526	.6128	1.6319	58° 30'
32°	0.5299	0.8480	0.6249	1.6003	58°
32° 30'	.5373	.8434	.6371	1.5697	57° 30'
33°	.5446	.8387	.6494	1.5399	57°
33° 30'	.5519	.8339	.6619	1.5108	56° 30'
34°	0.5592	0.8290	0.6745	1.4826	56°
34° 30'	.5664	.8241	.6873	1.4550	55° 30'
35°	.5736	.8192	.7002	1.4281	55°
35° 30'	.5807	.8141	.7133	1.4019	54° 30'
36°	0.5878	0.8090	0.7265	1.3764	54°
36° 30'	.5948	.8039	.7400	1.3514	53° 30'
37°	.6018	.7986	.7536	1.3270	53°
37° 30'	.6088	.7934	.7673	1.3032	52° 30'
38°	0.6157	0.7880	0.7813	1.2799	52°
38° 30'	.6225	.7826	.7954	1.2572	51° 30'
39°	.6293	.7771	.8098	1.2349	51°
39° 30'	.6361	.7716	.8243	1.2131	50° 30'
40°	0.6428	0.7660	0.8391	1.1918	50°
40° 30'	.6494	.7604	.8541	1.1708	49° 30'
41°	.6561	.7547	.8693	1.1504	49°
41° 30'	.6626	.7490	.8847	1.1303	48° 30'
42°	0.6691	0.7431	0.9004	1.1106	48°
42° 30'	.6756	.7373	.9163	1.0913	47° 30'
43°	.6820	.7314	.9325	1.0724	47°
43° 30'	.6884	.7254	.9490	1.0538	46° 30'
44°	0.6947	0.7193	0.9657	1.0355	46°
44° 30'	.7009	.7133	.9827	1.0176	45° 30'
45°	.7071	.7071	1.0000	1.0000	45°
Angle	Cos	Sin	Cot	Tan	Angle

MOMENT OF INERTIA NOMOGRAPH

(Moment of Inertia of Cylindrical Bodies in Weight Units of oz-in.^{2}
Reeves Instrument Corp., New York.)

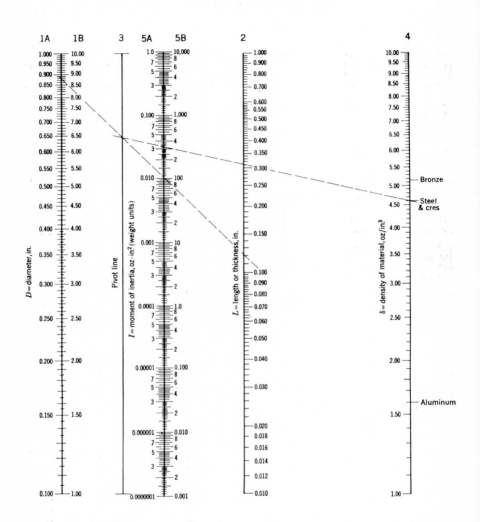

This nomograph can be used to compute the moment of inertia I of cylindrical bodies (gears, shafts, etc.) about their center of rotation. The moment of inertia I of a body is, by definition, that property of a body which for a given torque T determines its angular acceleration α, or $T = I\alpha$. I must be in mass units of oz-in.-sec^2. The relationship between I_{weight} and I_{mass} is $I_w = I_m \times G$, so that

$$I_w \text{ oz-in.}^2 = I_m \text{ oz-in.-sec}^2 \times 386 \text{ in./sec}^2$$

MOMENT OF INERTIA CONVERSION NOMOGRAPH

(Conversion Chart for Moment-of-inertia Units. *Reeves Instrument Corp., New York.*)

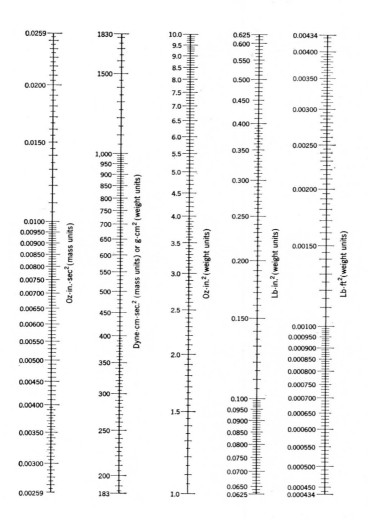

This chart can be used to convert units of moment of inertia as applicable. Values given in the scales above are the equivalent of each other. Care should be exercised to move the decimal point the same number of places and in the proper direction for values of both the input scale and the output scale. Example: 0.0325 oz-in.² = 5.94 g-cm².

S PLANE AND LOCATION OF ROOTS

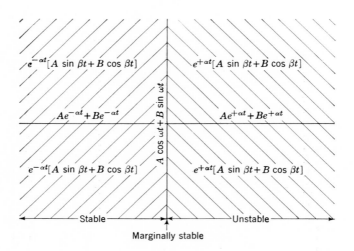

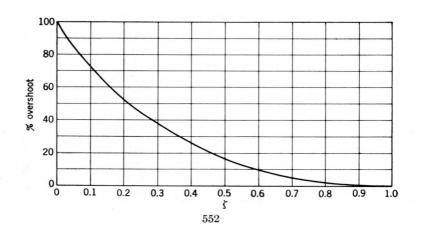

PERCENT OVERSHOOT VERSUS ζ FOR A
SECOND-ORDER SYSTEM

DECIBEL CHART

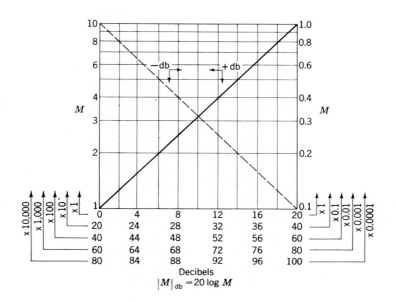

Decibels

$$|M|_{db} = 20 \log M$$

OCTAVE CHART

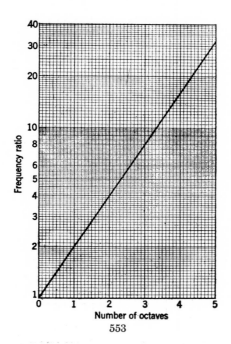

Number of octaves

AMPLITUDE DEVIATION FOR THE QUADRATIC FUNCTION*

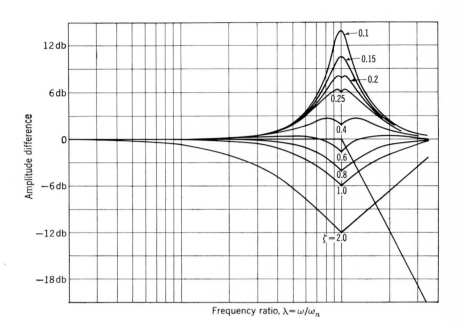

Frequency ratio, $\lambda = \omega/\omega_n$

PHASE-SHIFT DEVIATION FROM A STRAIGHT-LINE APPROXIMATION FOR A SECOND-ORDER SYSTEM†

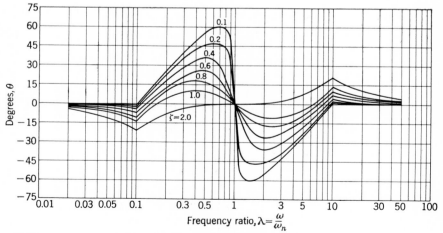

Frequency ratio, $\lambda = \dfrac{\omega}{\omega_n}$

* These curves represent the deviations from the 12 db asymptote, shown on the figure, as a function of the damping ratio.

† The straight-line approximation to the phase curve starts at zero degrees at $\lambda = 0.1$ and ends at -180 degrees at $\lambda = 10$. These curves give the deviations from this straight line as a function of ζ.

DAMPING RATIO ζ vs. PHASE MARGIN φ_m

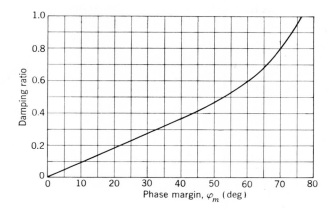

DAMPING RATIO ζ vs. MAXIMUM $M(M_p)$

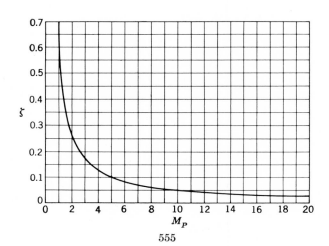

INDEX